Fire
Services Safety Officer
Second Edition

**Clint
Clausing**
Lead Senior Editor

**Alex Abrams
Jeff Fortney**
Senior Editors

Lynn Wojcik
Contract Writer

Brad McLelland
Lead Instructional Developer

INTERNATIONAL FIRE SERVICE TRAINING ASSOCIATION

Validated by the International Fire Service Training Association

Published by
Fire Protection Publications • Oklahoma State University

The International Fire Service Training Association (IFSTA) was established in 1934 as a *nonprofit educational association of fire fighting personnel who are dedicated to upgrading fire fighting techniques and safety through training*. To carry out the mission of IFSTA, Fire Protection Publications was established as an entity of Oklahoma State University. Fire Protection Publications' primary function is to publish and distribute training materials as proposed, developed, and validated by IFSTA. As a secondary function, Fire Protection Publications researches, acquires, produces, and markets high-quality learning and teaching aids consistent with IFSTA's mission.

IFSTA holds two meetings each year: the Winter Meeting in January and the Annual Validation Conference in July. During these meetings, committees of technical experts review draft materials and ensure that the professional qualifications of the National Fire Protection Association® standards are met. These conferences bring together individuals from several related and allied fields, such as:

- Key fire department executives, training officers, and personnel

- Educators from colleges and universities

- Representatives from governmental agencies

- Delegates of firefighter associations and industrial organizations

Committee members are not paid nor are they reimbursed for their expenses by IFSTA or Fire Protection Publications. They participate because of a commitment to the fire service and its future through training. Being on a committee is prestigious in the fire service community, and committee members are acknowledged leaders in their fields. This unique feature provides a close relationship between IFSTA and the fire service community.

IFSTA manuals have been adopted as the official teaching texts of many states and provinces of North America as well as numerous U.S. and Canadian government agencies. Besides the NFPA® requirements, IFSTA manuals are also written to meet the Fire and Emergency Services Higher Education (FESHE) course requirements. A number of the manuals have been translated into other languages to provide training for fire and emergency service personnel in Canada, Mexico, and outside of North America.

Copyright © 2015 by the Board of Regents, Oklahoma State University

All rights reserved. No part of this publication may be reproduced in any form without prior written permission from the publisher.

ISBN 978-0-87939-590-2   Library of Congress Control Number: 2015953576

Second Edition, First Printing, December 2015   *Printed in the United States of America*

10   9   8   7   6   5   4   3   2   1

If you need additional information concerning the International Fire Service Training Association (IFSTA) or Fire Protection Publications, contact:

Customer Service, Fire Protection Publications, Oklahoma State University
930 North Willis, Stillwater, OK 74078-8045
800-654-4055   Fax: 405-744-8204

For assistance with training materials, to recommend material for inclusion in an IFSTA manual, or to ask questions or comment on manual content, contact:

Editorial Department, Fire Protection Publications, Oklahoma State University
930 North Willis, Stillwater, OK 74078-8045
405-744-4111   Fax: 405-744-4112   E-mail: editors@osufpp.org

Chapter Summary

Table of Contents

List of Tables

Acknowledgements

The 2nd edition of **Fire and Emergency Services Safety Officer** is designed to train firefighters to certify as either a health safety officer (HSO) or incident safety officer (ISO) according to the professional qualifications included in NFPA® 1521.

Acknowledgement and special thanks are extended to the members of the IFSTA validating committee who contributed their time, wisdom, and knowledge to the development of this manual.

IFSTA Fire and Emergency Services Safety Officer, Second Edition Validation Committee

Chair

Jeff Morrissette
State Fire Administrator
State of Connecticut Commission
on Fire Prevention and Control
Windsor Locks, Connecticut

Vice Chair

Christopher Garrett
Fire Chief
Owasso Fire Department
Owasso, Oklahoma

Secretary

Paul Boecker, III
Former Captain
Sugar Grove Fire District
Yorkville, Illinois

Committee Members

John Barker
Captain
Champaign Fire Department
Champaign, Illinois

Scott Bryant
Captain/Safety Officer
Linden-Peters Fire District
Linden, California

Robert Chatton
Assistant Fire Chief
Pitt Meadows Fire Rescue Service
Pitt Meadows, British Columbia (Canada)

Nicholas Eschner
Fire Protection Specialist/Fire Inspector/Plans Examiner
McHenry Township Fire Protection District
Skokie, Illinois

Michael Gorsuch
Captain
Columbia River Fire and Rescue
St. Helens, Oregon

Daniel Gray
Battalion Fire Chief
Fairfax County Fire and Rescue Department
Fairfax, Virginia

Jeff Griffin
Executive Director
Oregon Fire Chiefs Association
Eugene, Oregon

Joseph Guarnera
Massachusetts Fire Service Professional Development Coordinator
Massachusetts Firefighting Academy
North Chelmsford, Massachusetts

IFSTA Fire and Emergency Services Safety Officer, Second Edition Validation Committee

Committee Members (cont.)

Greg Hickey
Captain
City of Hartsville Fire Department
Hartsville, South Carolina

Mark Keough
Battalion Chief
City of Mesa Fire Department
Mesa, Arizona

Patrick Mahoney
Lieutenant
Baytown Fire Department
Houston, Texas

Michael McGreal Jr.
Deputy Fire Chief
Wilmette Fire Department
Wilmette, Illinois

Brian Morrow
Assistant Chief
Orange County Fire Rescue
Winter Park, Florida

Richard Rodewald
Drill Master/Safety Officer
Council Bluffs Fire Department
Council Bluffs, Iowa

Demond Simmons
Captain
City of Oakland Fire Department
Oakland, California

Gregory Willis
Chief
Wetumpka Fire Department
Wetumpka, Alabama

Much appreciation is given to the following individuals and organizations for contributing information, photographs, and technical assistance instrumental in the development of this manual:

Action Training

Bob Esposito

Brian White

California Office of Emergency Services

Chicago (IL) Fire Department

Chris Mickal, District Chief, New Orleans (LA) Fire Department

City of Pitt Meadows (British Columbia, Canada) Fire Rescue

Dan Madrzykowski

Dick Giles

Ed Prendergast

Emergency Services Training Institute, Texas A&M Engineering Extension Service

Fred Teryn, Air Force Civil Engineering Center (AFCEC)

The Intergovernemental Risk Management Agency

The International Association of Fire Chiefs (IAFC)

Iowa Fire Service Training Bureau

James F. Ritter, Director, Connecticut Department of Transportation — Division of Occupational Safety and Health

Jan C. Doddy/Doddy Photography

Jason Decremer, Program Manager, Connecticut Fire Academy

John Lewis

L.A. City Fire Department

Marty Clinton and Ron Prettyman, United States Air Force Academy Fire Department

Michael Callan

The National Institute of Standards and Technology (NIST)

National Oceanic and Atmospheric Administration

Neal Moore, Stillwater (OK) Fire Department

Oklahoma State University Colvin Recreation Center and University Health Clinic

Peter Susca

Ron Jeffers

Ron Moore, McKinney (TX) Fire Department

Scott R. Adams, Safety Compliance Officer, Connecticut Occupational Safety and Health Administration (OSHA)

Stephen A. Coulon, Instructor, Connecticut Fire Academy

Steve Baker

Stillwater (OK) Fire Department

Tarrant County College, Tarrant County, TX

United States Air Force

United States Environmental Protection Agency

Village of Wilmette (IL) Fire Department

Yates and Associates

Last, but certainly not least, gratitude is extended to the following members of the Fire Protection Publications staff whose contributions made the final publication of this manual possible.

Fire and Emergency Services Safety Officer, Second Edition, Project Team

Lead Senior Editor
Clint Clausing, Editorial Manager

Contract Writer
Lynn Wojcik
Department Head
Bachelor of Technology
Emergency Responder Administration
Oklahoma State University – Oklahoma City
Oklahoma City, Oklahoma

Director of Fire Protection Publications
Craig Hannan

IFSTA/Curriculum Manager
Leslie Miller (current)
Lori Raborg (previous)

Coordinator, Publications Production
Ann Moffat

Editors
Alex Abrams, Senior Editor
Jeff Fortney, Senior Editor

Illustrators and Layout Designers
Clint Parker, Senior Graphic Designer
Errick Braggs, Senior Graphic Designer
Missy Hannan, Senior Graphic Designer

Lead Curriculum Developer
Brad McLelland, Instructional Developer

Curriculum Developers
David Schaap, Instructional Developer
Simone Rowe, Instructional Developer
Whitney Ray, Instructional Developer

Tara Roberson-Moore, Instructional Developer
Brittany Cook, Curriculum Research Assistant
Joel Billings, Curriculum Graduate Assistant

Photographers
Alex Abrams, Senior Editor
Brad McLelland, Instructional Developer
Clint Clausing, Editorial Manager
Clint Parker, Senior Graphic Designer
Fred Stowell, Senior Editor (retired)
Jeff Fortney, Senior Editor
Leslie Miller, Curriculum Manager
Mike Sturzenbecker, National Sales and Marketing Manager
Missy Hannan, Senior Graphic Designer
Veronica Smith, Senior Editor

Technical Reviewers

Darin White
Battalion Chief of Special Operations/Safety Officer
Oakland Fire Department
Oakland, California

John H. Oates
Fire Chief
East Hartford Fire Department
East Hartford, Connecticut

Editorial Staff

Clint Clausing, Editorial Manager
Tara Gladden, Editorial Administrative Support Specialist

Indexer
Nancy Kopper

The IFSTA Executive Board at the time of validation of the **Fire and Emergency Services Safety Office**r, 2nd Edition was as follows:

Dedication

This manual is dedicated to the men and women who hold devotion to duty above personal risk, who count on sincerity of service above personal comfort and convenience, who strive unceasingly to find better and safer ways of protecting lives, homes, and property of their fellow citizens from the ravages of fire, medical emergencies, and other disasters

...The Firefighters of All Nations.

Introduction

Introduction Contents

Introduction

Safety is of primary importance to firefighters both at an incident scene and as a part of their daily duties. The safety officer is a key line-of-defense against injury, illness, and casualties. Safety officers are categorized as either health safety officer (HSO) whose primary duties are to protect the wellness of firefighters or incident safety officers (ISO) who are responsible for monitoring activities at incident scenes and ensuring that firefighters safely perform their duties when on response. Health safety officers are appointed members of the fire department administration and may be firefighters. Incident safety officers must meet the qualifications included in NFPA® 1021 for Officer Level II and must be firefighters.

Health safety officers create, implement, and maintain the risk management plan for their organizations. HSOs are responsible for implementing, administering, and managing health and wellness programs. They are also the record keepers for all health, injury, fatality, illness, exposure, and fitness-for-duty records and reports. HSOs investigate accidents and finalize postincident analysis reports following every incident. Finally, and most importantly, the health safety officer has the opportunity and responsibility to change the safety culture in his or her jurisdiction through work with chiefs and committees to make recommendations for improvements to health and safety programs, training programs, and apparatus and equipment specifications.

Incident safety officers (ISO) play a more immediate role in a fire service organization. The ISO is at the incident scene, monitoring hazards and firefighter activities throughout the response so that fire fighting operations can be amended or halted if any safety concerns arise. The ISO is also tasked with identifying hazards before incident operations begin and briefing firefighters on these hazards. According to NFPA® standards, an ISO should be appointed at every incident and live-training evolution.

Purpose and Scope

This 2nd edition of **Fire and Emergency Services Safety Officer** is written for individuals and firefighters who are seeking certification as either a health safety officer or incident safety officer. The purpose is to provide all of the accurate and necessary information a firefighter needs to become a certified HSO or ISO according to the 2015 edition of NFPA® 1521 *Fire Department Safety Officer Professional Qualifications*.

The scope of this manual is the job performance requirements of NFPA® 1521 for HSO (Chapter 4) and ISO (Chapter 5). The information in this manual is intended to meet the minimum requirements for certification to the standard. State/provincial or jurisdictional variations to safety officer job requirements are beyond the scope of this manual. Students and instructors are advised to research their state/provincial and local laws, codes, and regulations to learn about their jurisdiction's specific requirements.

Book Organization

This manual is organized according to the job function. Chapters 1 through 12 focus almost exclusively on the job performance requirements for health safety officer (HSO). Chapters 13 through 16 focus on the job performance requirements for incident safety officer (ISO).

Terminology

This manual is written with a global, international audience in mind. For this reason, it often uses general descriptive language in place of regional- or agency-specific terminology (often referred to as *jargon*). Additionally, in order to keep sentences uncluttered and easy to read, the word *state* is used to represent both state and provincial level governments (or their equivalent). This usage is applied to this manual for the purposes of brevity and is not intended to address or show preference for only one nation's method of identifying regional governments within its borders.

The glossary at the end of the manual will assist the reader in understanding words that may not have their roots in the fire and emergency services. The sources for the definitions of fire-and-emergency-services-related terms will be the *NFPA® Dictionary of Terms* and the IFSTA **Fire Service Orientation and Terminology** manual.

In addition to these terms, this manual is following language changes being made at NFPA®. The term *personal protective equipment (PPE)* is replaced by the new term *protective clothing and equipment*. Similarly, *rapid intervention team (RIT)* is replaced by *rapid intervention crew (RIC)*.

Resources

To help you increase your knowledge of occupational safety and health issues, this manual contains references to additional materials where appropriate. These materials were used in the development of this manual and are recommended by the members of the validation committee for your use.

Key Information

Various types of information in this book are given in shaded boxes marked by symbols or icons (case histories, safety alerts, and information boxes). See the following definitions:

Case History

A case history analyzes an event. It can describe its development, action taken, investigation results, and lessons learned.

Safety Alert

Safety alert boxes are used to highlight information that is important for safety reasons. (In the text, the title of safety alerts will change to reflect the content.)

Carabiner Safety

If a carabiner has been dropped from waist height (or higher) onto a hard surface, it should not be used in a life safety application until it has been lab tested. There is no practical way to field test a carabiner after an impact event.

Information

Information boxes give facts that are complete in themselves but belong with the text discussion. It is information that needs more emphasis or separation. (In the text, the title of information boxes will change to reflect the content.)

Thermal Imager Terminology

When first introduced to the fire service, the tool used to detect thermal radiation was frequently referred to as a *thermal imaging camera* or TIC. While this name is still in common usage, the NFPA® has adopted the term *thermal imager* (TI) to describe this type of equipment in NFPA® 1801, *Standard on Thermal Imagers for The Fire Service*. While these names should be considered interchangeable, this book will use *thermal imager* when discussing this tool and its requirements for use.

What This Means to You

What This Means to You

These boxes take information presented in the text and synthesize it into an example of how the information is relevant to (or will be applied by) the intended audience, essentially answering the question, "What does this mean to you?"

Cost/Benefit Analysis — Examination of the proposed expense of an effort and deciding if the overall benefit is worth the investment of money and/or time.

A **key term** is designed to emphasize key concepts, technical terms, or ideas that safety officers need to know. They are listed at the beginning of each chapter and the definition is placed in the margin for easy reference. An example of a key term is:

Three key signal words are found in the book: **WARNING, CAUTION**, and **NOTE**. Definitions and examples of each are as follows:

- **WARNING** indicates information that could result in death or serious injury to safety officers or other emergency personnel. See the following example:

WARNING!
Ill or injured responders should never be allowed to transport themselves to a medical facility for treatment, regardless of the apparent severity of their condition.

- **CAUTION** indicates important information or data that safety officers need to be aware of in order to perform their duties safely. See the following example:

CAUTION
HIPAA prohibits responders from making comments concerning patients to anyone outside the continuity of care.

- **NOTE** indicates important operational information that helps explain why a particular recommendation is given or describes optional methods for certain procedures. See the following example:

NOTE: FEMA's *Developing Effective Standard Operating Procedures for Fire and EMS Departments* is a resource that can assist the HSO with developing SOP/Gs as a part of the fire department team.

Chapter Learning Activities and Review Questions

Each chapter ends with a set of review questions. Chapters may also include learning activities following the review questions. These two sections are included for those individuals who are using this manual for independent study and are not using this manual as part of a course. The learning activity is designed to be completed if the reader so desires and can be completed independently. The review questions provide review and may be used as part of classroom work as well. **Appendix B** provides possible responses to all the learning activities in the manual.

Metric Conversions

Throughout this manual, U.S. units of measure are converted to metric units for the convenience of our international readers. Be advised that we use the Canadian metric system. It is similar to the Standard International system, but may have some variation.

We adhere to the following guidelines for metric conversions in this manual:

- Metric conversions are approximated unless the number is used in mathematical equations.
- Centimeters are not used because they are not part of the Canadian metric standard.
- Exact conversions are used when an exact number is necessary, such as in construction measurements or hydraulic calculations.
- Set values, such as hose diameter, ladder length, and nozzle size, use their Canadian counterpart naming conventions and are not mathematically calculated. For example, 1½ inch hose is referred to as 38 mm hose.

The following two tables provide detailed information on IFSTA's conversion conventions. The first table includes examples of our conversion factors for a number of measurements used in the fire service. The second shows examples of exact conversions beside the approximated measurements you will see in this manual.

U.S. to Canadian Measurement Conversion

Measurements	Customary (U.S.)	Metric (Canada)	Conversion Factor
Length/Distance	Inch (in) Foot (ft) [3 or less feet] Foot (ft) [3 or more feet] Mile (mi)	Millimeter (mm) Millimeter (mm) Meter (m) Kilometer (km)	1 in = 25 mm 1 ft = 300 mm 1 ft = 0.3 m 1 mi = 1.6 km
Area	Square Foot (ft^2) Square Mile (mi^2)	Square Meter (m^2) Square Kilometer (km^2)	1 ft^2 = 0.09 m^2 1 mi^2 = 2.6 km^2
Mass/Weight	Dry Ounce (oz) Pound (lb) Ton (T)	gram Kilogram (kg) Ton (T)	1 oz = 28 g 1 lb = 0.5 kg 1 T = 0.9 T
Volume	Cubic Foot (ft^3) Fluid Ounce (fl oz) Quart (qt) Gallon (gal)	Cubic Meter (m^3) Milliliter (mL) Liter (L) Liter (L)	1 ft^3 = 0.03 m^3 1 fl oz = 30 mL 1 qt = 1 L 1 gal = 4 L
Flow	Gallons per Minute (gpm) Cubic Foot per Minute (ft^3/min)	Liters per Minute (L/min) Cubic Meter per Minute (m^3/min)	1 gpm = 4 L/min 1 ft^3/min = 0.03 m^3/min
Flow per Area	Gallons per Minute per Square Foot (gpm/ft^2)	Liters per Square Meters Minute (L/(m^2.min))	1 gpm/ft^2 = 40 L/(m^2.min)
Pressure	Pounds per Square Inch (psi) Pounds per Square Foot (psf) Inches of Mercury (in Hg)	Kilopascal (kPa) Kilopascal (kPa) Kilopascal (kPa)	1 psi = 7 kPa 1 psf = .05 kPa 1 in Hg = 3.4 kPa
Speed/Velocity	Miles per Hour (mph) Feet per Second (ft/sec)	Kilometers per Hour (km/h) Meter per Second (m/s)	1 mph = 1.6 km/h 1 ft/sec = 0.3 m/s
Heat	British Thermal Unit (Btu)	Kilojoule (kJ)	1 Btu = 1 kJ
Heat Flow	British Thermal Unit per Minute (BTU/min)	watt (W)	1 Btu/min = 18 W
Density	Pound per Cubic Foot (lb/ft^3)	Kilogram per Cubic Meter (kg/m^3)	1 lb/ft^3 = 16 kg/m^3
Force	Pound-Force (lbf)	Newton (N)	1 lbf = 0.5 N
Torque	Pound-Force Foot (lbf ft)	Newton Meter (N.m)	1 lbf ft = 1.4 N.m
Dynamic Viscosity	Pound per Foot-Second (lb/ft.s)	Pascal Second (Pa.s)	1 lb/ft.s = 1.5 Pa.s
Surface Tension	Pound per Foot (lb/ft)	Newton per Meter (N/m)	1 lb/ft = 15 N/m

Conversion and Approximation Examples

Measurement	U.S. Unit	Conversion Factor	Exact S.I. Unit	Rounded S.I. Unit
Length/Distance	10 in	1 in = 25 mm	250 mm	250 mm
	25 in	1 in = 25 mm	625 mm	625 mm
	2 ft	1 in = 25 mm	600 mm	600 mm
	17 ft	1 ft = 0.3 m	5.1 m	5 m
	3 mi	1 mi = 1.6 km	4.8 km	5 km
	10 mi	1 mi = 1.6 km	16 km	16 km
Area	36 ft²	1 ft² = 0.09 m²	3.24 m²	3 m²
	300 ft²	1 ft² = 0.09 m²	27 m²	30 m²
	5 mi²	1 mi² = 2.6 km²	13 km²	13 km²
	14 mi²	1 mi² = 2.6 km²	36.4 km²	35 km²
Mass/Weight	16 oz	1 oz = 28 g	448 g	450 g
	20 oz	1 oz = 28 g	560 g	560 g
	3.75 lb	1 lb = 0.5 kg	1.875 kg	2 kg
	2,000 lb	1 lb = 0.5 kg	1 000 kg	1 000 kg
	1 T	1 T = 0.9 T	900 kg	900 kg
	2.5 T	1 T = 0.9 T	2.25 T	2 T
Volume	55 ft³	1 ft³ = 0.03 m³	1.65 m³	1.5 m³
	2,000 ft³	1 ft³ = 0.03 m³	60 m³	60 m³
	8 fl oz	1 fl oz = 30 mL	240 mL	240 mL
	20 fl oz	1 fl oz = 30 mL	600 mL	600 mL
	10 qt	1 qt = 1 L	10 L	10 L
	22 gal	1 gal = 4 L	88 L	90 L
	500 gal	1 gal = 4 L	2 000 L	2 000 L
Flow	100 gpm	1 gpm = 4 L/min	400 L/min	400 L/min
	500 gpm	1 gpm = 4 L/min	2 000 L/min	2 000 L/min
	16 ft³/min	1 ft³/min = 0.03 m³/min	0.48 m³/min	0.5 m³/min
	200 ft³/min	1 ft³/min = 0.03 m³/min	6 m³/min	6 m³/min
Flow per Area	50 gpm/ft²	1 gpm/ft² = 40 L/(m².min)	2 000 L/(m².min)	2 000 L/(m².min)
	326 gpm/ft²	1 gpm/ft² = 40 L/(m².min)	13 040 L/(m².min)	13 000L/(m².min)
Pressure	100 psi	1 psi = 7 kPa	700 kPa	700 kPa
	175 psi	1 psi = 7 kPa	1225 kPa	1 200 kPa
	526 psf	1 psf = 0.05 kPa	26.3 kPa	25 kPa
	12,000 psf	1 psf = 0.05 kPa	600 kPa	600 kPa
	5 psi in Hg	1 psi = 3.4 kPa	17 kPa	17 kPa
	20 psi in Hg	1 psi = 3.4 kPa	68 kPa	70 kPa
Speed/Velocity	20 mph	1 mph = 1.6 km/h	32 km/h	30 km/h
	35 mph	1 mph = 1.6 km/h	56 km/h	55 km/h
	10 ft/sec	1 ft/sec = 0.3 m/s	3 m/s	3 m/s
	50 ft/sec	1 ft/sec = 0.3 m/s	15 m/s	15 m/s
Heat	1200 Btu	1 Btu = 1 kJ	1 200 kJ	1 200 kJ
Heat Flow	5 BTU/min	1 Btu/min = 18 W	90 W	90 W
	400 BTU/min	1 Btu/min = 18 W	7 200 W	7 200 W
Density	5 lb/ft³	1 lb/ft³ = 16 kg/m³	80 kg/m³	80 kg/m³
	48 lb/ft³	1 lb/ft³ = 16 kg/m³	768 kg/m³	770 kg/m³
Force	10 lbf	1 lbf = 0.5 N	5 N	5 N
	1,500 lbf	1 lbf = 0.5 N	750 N	750 N
Torque	100	1 lbf ft = 1.4 N.m	140 N.m	140 N.m
	500	1 lbf ft = 1.4 N.m	700 N.m	700 N.m
Dynamic Viscosity	20 lb/ft.s	1 lb/ft.s = 1.5 Pa.s	30 Pa.s	30 Pa.s
	35 lb/ft.s	1 lb/ft.s = 1.5 Pa.s	52.5 Pa.s	50 Pa.s
Surface Tension	6.5 lb/ft	1 lb/ft = 15 N/m	97.5 N/m	100 N/m
	10 lb/ft	1 lb/ft = 15 N/m	150 N/m	150 N/m

Health Safety Officer Responsibilities

Chapter Contents

Key Terms

NFPA® Job Performance Requirements

This chapter provides information that addresses the following job performance requirements of NFPA® 1521, *Standard for Fire Department Safety Officer Professional Qualifications (2015)*.

4.1.1

4.11.1

Learning Objectives

After reading this chapter, students will be able to:

1. Explain the health safety officer's role as safety advocate for the fire department. (4.1.1)

2. Describe the functions of a health safety officer. (4.1.1)

3. Describe the functions of an occupational safety and health committee. (4.11.1)

Chapter 1
Health Safety Officer Responsibilities

Case History

Suburban Metro Fire Department (SMFD) is a mid-sized, combination department with 40 career and 35 paid on-call firefighter/medics. In May of 2013, at a house fire, SMFD experienced both a line of duty death (LODD) of a probationary firefighter and a civilian fatality. In addition to the LODD, a 20-year veteran of the dept. was severely burned. The National Institute for Occupational Safety and Health (NIOSH) conducted a firefighter fatality investigation. The NIOSH report listed several contributing factors:

- Lack of crew integrity
- Inadequate fireground communications
- Lack of personnel accountability
- Lack of annual medical evaluations
- Lack of a safety officer

NIOSH made several recommendations as a result of its investigation, one of which was that the SMFD provide a health and safety officer. The chief developed the following job description for the position of health and safety officer.

The Health and Safety Officer (HSO) shall perform the following functions as part of his or her responsibilities:

- *Plan and coordinate safety activities*
- *Work closely with the safety committee*
- *Ensure accidents are investigated*
- *Devise corrective measures to prevent accidents*
- *Ensure safety training for all employees*
- *Ensure compliance with safety directives*
- *Ensure that, at a minimum, records of all the following are kept:*
  - *Accidents*
  - *Injuries*
  - *Inspections: facilities, apparatus, equipment, and protective clothing*
  - *Exposures*
  - *Medical monitoring*
  - *Safety meetings*
  - *Apparatus, equipment, protective clothing specifications*
  - *Fire department safety activities*

In addition to these duties, the fire department health and safety officer, through the fire chief, shall have the authority and responsibility to identify and recommend correction of safety and health hazards. The fire department health and safety officer shall maintain a liaison with staff officers regarding changes in equipment, procedures, and recommended methods to eliminate unsafe practices and reduce existing hazardous conditions.

The term *health and safety officer (HSO)* is used regardless of the rank of the person assigned to the position. A chief officer or other member of the fire department may be assigned to this position. Some departments may have a non-uniformed safety and health professional serve in this capacity. The person assigned must meet the educational and skills requirements of NFPA® 1521, *Standard for Fire Department Safety Officer.* Smaller agencies may use other methods to meet these requirements, such as using the training officer as the HSO with assistance from other staff members. Organizations may also contract private or outside agencies to provide the HSO function. Regardless of the official rank of the person serving as the HSO, the fire chief must delegate authority to fulfill the responsibilities of this position. In addition, the fire chief must determine if this is a full-time or part-time position based on the department's size, level of risk, and past safety related incidents.

16 Firefighter Life Safety Initiatives

In 2004, a Firefighter Life Safety Summit was held to address positive changes to the safety culture of the fire service and improve the safety of firefighters. During the summit, the 16 Firefighter Life Safety Initiatives were created as well as the Everyone Goes Home® program. Because of their relevance and positive effect on firefighter safety, the 16 Firefighter Life Safety Initiatives will be highlighted throughout this manual. The Initiatives are as follows:

1. Define and advocate the need for a cultural change within the fire service relating to safety; incorporating leadership, management, supervision, accountability and personal responsibility.

2. Enhance the personal and organizational accountability for health and safety throughout the fire service.

3. Focus greater attention on the integration of risk management with incident management at all levels, including strategic, tactical, and planning responsibilities.

4. All firefighters must be empowered to stop unsafe practices.

5. Develop and implement national standards for training, qualifications, and certification (including regular recertification) that are equally applicable to all firefighters based on the duties they are expected to perform.

6. Develop and implement national medical and physical fitness standards that are equally applicable to all firefighters, based on the duties they are expected to perform.

7. Create a national research agenda and data collection system that relates to the initiatives.

8. Utilize available technology wherever it can produce higher levels of health and safety.

9. Thoroughly investigate all firefighter fatalities, injuries, and near misses.

10. Grant programs should support the implementation of safe practices and/or mandate safe practices as an eligibility requirement.

11. National standards for emergency response policies and procedures should be developed and championed.

12. National protocols for response to violent incidents should be developed and championed.

13. Firefighters and their families must have access to counseling and psychological support.

14. Public education must receive more resources and be championed as a critical fire and life safety program.

15. Advocacy must be strengthened for the enforcement of codes and the installation of home fire sprinklers.

16. Safety must be a primary consideration in the design of apparatus and equipment.

NOTE: For more information about the 16 Firefighter Life Safety Initiatives, see Understanding and Implementing the 16 Firefighter Life Safety Initiatives published by Fire Protection Publications and the National Fallen Firefighters Foundation (NFFF).

Health and Safety Officer as Safety Advocate

The HSO is the catalyst in a fire department's mission to identify, analyze, and mitigate risk and champion safety. The main responsibility of the HSO is to manage and administer the fire department's occupational safety and health program. The HSO should administer the programs according to the minimum requirements of NFPA® 1500, *Standard on Fire Department Occupational Safety and Health Program*. This standard applies to public, military, private, and industrial fire departments providing emergency services, including:

- Rescue

- Fire suppression

- Emergency medical services (EMS)

- Hazardous materials mitigation

- Special operations

Risk management – outlined in Chapter 5, Organizational Risk Management, and Chapter 6, Operational Risk Management – is a significant portion of the HSO's responsibilities. The HSO must ensure the development of a comprehensive risk management plan to meet the goals of the organization's occupational safety and health policy. Risk identification, developing and revising risk mitigation steps, and assessing the overall compliance with risk reduction goals are critical components of the HSO responsibilities. The HSO should ensure a committee of key stakeholders is assembled to assist with this process. In order for this committee to be successful, members must become committed to its success. To achieve this, there must be a clear delegation of authority from the fire chief, support from management, and involvement at all levels of the organization.

In addition to the HSO, the incident safety officer shares responsibility for firefighter health and safety, but the positions have distinctly different perspectives. The HSO works proactively to mitigate risk throughout the organization, while the ISO works in the operational arena **(Figure 1.1, p. 14)**. The HSO, for example, ensures that an Incident Management System (IMS) is

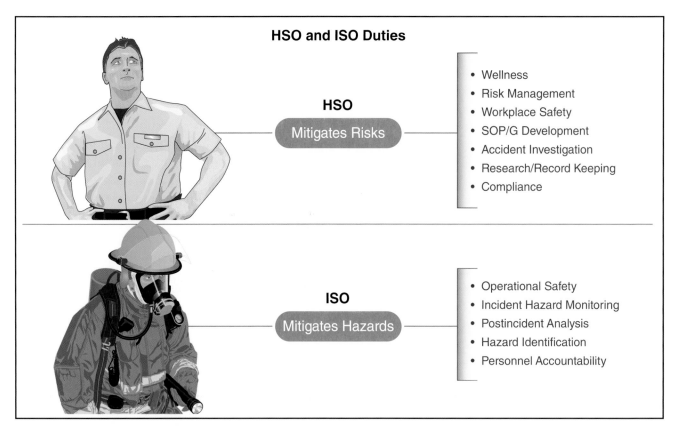

HSO and ISO Duties

HSO

Mitigates Risks

- Wellness
- Risk Management
- Workplace Safety
- SOP/G Development
- Accident Investigation
- Research/Record Keeping
- Compliance

ISO

Mitigates Hazards

- Operational Safety
- Incident Hazard Monitoring
- Postincident Analysis
- Hazard Identification
- Personnel Accountability

Figure 1.1 Both health safety officers (HSO) and incident safety officers (ISO) have safety functions in a fire and emergency services organization. HSOs more frequently deal with risk factors, while ISOs mitigate hazards at emergency scenes.

developed, implemented, and followed. The ISO functions within the IMS at emergency incidents and training evolutions to ensure personnel are following safe operational practices.

The assignment of an HSO may be a staff position in the hierarchical structure. The assignment of an ISO, on the other hand, must meet the needs of the incident and be a flexible component of the ICS. In addition, the position of an ISO can be assigned to a chief officer, a company officer, or another qualified fire department member meeting NFPA® 1521. Having a single staff member fill the ISO role at all or most incidents may not be realistic due to geographic distances or other job responsibilities that delay immediate response. Some fire departments have the same person assigned to HSO and ISO responsibilities. What is important is the assignment of the functions and responsibilities of both the HSO and ISO to address risk and ensure safe operational practices.

Health and Safety Officer Job Functions

The occupational safety and health program defines the scope of the HSO's responsibilities within the fire department. Although the fire chief has the ultimate responsibility for the implementation of an **occupational safety and health program**, the HSO has the assigned task of developing and implementing the program, if such a program is not already in place **(Figure 1.2)**. If one is in place, the HSO manages the program to ensure a safe and healthy work environment.

Occupational Safety and Health Program — Collectively, all departmental programs intended to reduce risks associated with emergency service as an occupation; should have clearly outlined components and identify the roles and responsibilities of the fire department and its members.

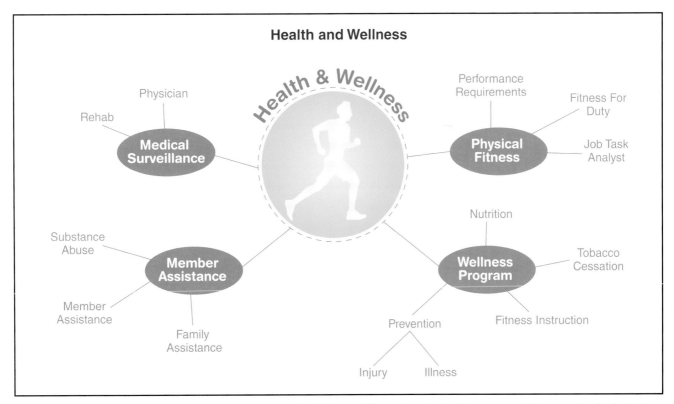

Health and Wellness

Health & Wellness

Physician
Rehab
Medical Surveillance

Performance Requirements
Fitness For Duty
Physical Fitness
Job Task Analyst

Nutrition

Substance Abuse
Member Assistance
Member Assistance
Family Assistance

Wellness Program
Tobacco Cessation
Fitness Instruction

Prevention
Injury   Illness

Figure 1.2 Occupational safety and health programs should be multifaceted and take into account all areas of a firefighter's health and wellness, including physical and psychological fitness for duty.

NFPA® 1521 outlines the job performance requirements for the HSO. According to the standard, the HSO must have the authority, skill, and knowledge to carry out the following:

- Ensure safety training and education
- Manage the accident or loss prevention program
- Investigate accidents or incidents
- Maintain a records management system
- Analyze data
- Develop or revise standard operating procedures/guidelines (SOP/Gs)
- Review equipment specification and assist in acceptance testing
- Ensure program compliance
- Comply with health maintenance requirements
- Serve as internal and external liaison
- Act as infection control officer
- Develop a critical incident stress management plan
- Ensure a procedure to include a safety and health component in the post-incident analyses
- Submit recommendations and reports to the fire chief
- Conduct facility inspections
- Participate in safety committee meetings
- Identify deviations from SOP/Gs

The department's occupational safety and health program consists of several important components, including the following:

- Risk management plan
- Accident, injury, and illness prevention program
- Medical exposure management program
- Member physical fitness and wellness program
- Member assistance program

HSO as a Liaison

The HSO serves as a liaison between the fire chief and the department members. In this role, the HSO advocates for the safety, health and wellness, and risk management of the fire department **(Figure 1.3)**. A critical first step of having an HSO in a fire department is the fire chief delegating authority for the HSO to carry out the responsibilities of the position. A critical second step is assigning a person who brings the skills and knowledge needed, but also with credibility and trust. The HSO must be a person who adheres to the same safety guidelines that he or she sets for others.

Even though the HSO reports to the fire chief, he or she must have good working relationships with all officers and members. The HSO must be able to interact with formal and informal groups within the fire department. These relationships require the HSO to have good communication skills, mutual respect, and compassion. In terms of HSO functions, the following key interactions and communications will occur **(Figure 1.4)**:

- **Communication with fire administration** — the HSO must communicate verbally and in writing to the fire administration staff. This communication will include periodic reporting of safety and health compliance; statistics on injuries, fatalities, and accidents; and recommendations for improvement.

- **Communication with members** — the HSO must effectively communicate with fire department members. The HSO will have frequent interactions with members to ensure compliance with policies; take corrective measures when an imminent threat is witnessed; investigate accidents; and during training sessions. Most of the communication with department members will be in person.

- **Communication with committee members** — the HSO must communicate with the members of the occupational safety and health committee. This communication requires an ability to facilitate meetings and develop a positive team environment.

- **Communication as an external liaison** — the HSO must communicate with agencies and individuals that have direct interaction with the fire department's occupational safety and health program. These parties may include hospital staff, the department physician, risk manager, worker's compensation carrier, or a facility providing medical evaluation testing.

The position is an essential link between management and the firefighter. Ultimately, the HSO works to ensure the safety of all fire department members.

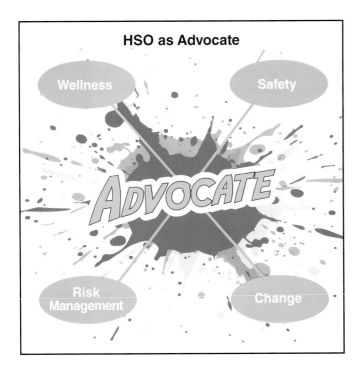

HSO as Advocate

Figure 1.3 One of the HSO's main roles is advocacy for a strong safety culture. This advocacy includes being a change agent when safety, health, and wellness are not a central focus in the organization.

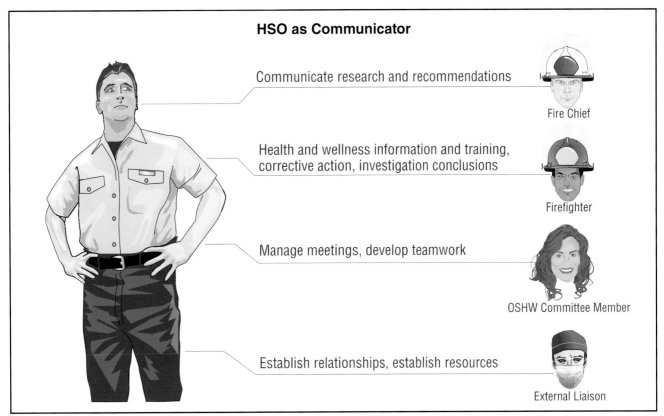

HSO as Communicator

Communicate research and recommendations — Fire Chief

Health and wellness information and training, corrective action, investigation conclusions — Firefighter

Manage meetings, develop teamwork — OSHW Committee Member

Establish relationships, establish resources — External Liaison

Figure 1.4 In order to create a strong safety culture, the HSO must be a good communicator and establish relationships that support a safety emphasis throughout the organization.

Advocate for Cultural Change

Culture is a part of every fire department. It is the method the department adopts in conducting business and how it delivers its services. A fire department's culture is evident by the actions of all members as they carry out their

> **Culture** — The shared assumptions, beliefs, and values of a group or organization.

daily responsibilities. Culture can have a positive and/or negative influence within a fire department. When there is a negative cultural influence, such as with safety, change must occur. **Cultural change** usually takes time. The exception to this is when a significant injury, death, or illness occurs. This wakeup call is unfortunate, but historically common in the fire service. These significant events can drive immediate change. Positive cultural change is seen through the following:

- Improvements in teamwork
- Professional development
- A diverse workforce
- Continued training and education programs
- Initiatives to promote a safe work environment

If the fire and emergency services are to reduce the number of line-of-duty fatalities, injuries, illnesses, and property loss, we must change our culture. The traditional culture that placed an emphasis on heroism at all cost must give way to one that rewards safety. The change must be complete and permanent to ensure that everyone goes home safely and that we do not fall into a cultural drift that takes us back to a time when casualties were an accepted part of our profession **(Figure 1.5)**.

Individual change is not easy. Examples of personal behavioral changes that can take time and resources are firefighters losing weight, making healthy meal choices, or quitting smoking. Cultural change within an organization or profession may be even more difficult because it can mean going against tradition.

In the fire and emergency services, tradition is a powerful, closely-guarded part of the professional image of a firefighter. Firefighters take pride in the fact that they expose themselves to danger in order to protect the citizens of their

Figure 1.5 Firefighters should champion safety as part of their professional identity. Firefighters can only be heroes if they continually keep themselves and their fellow firefighters safe.

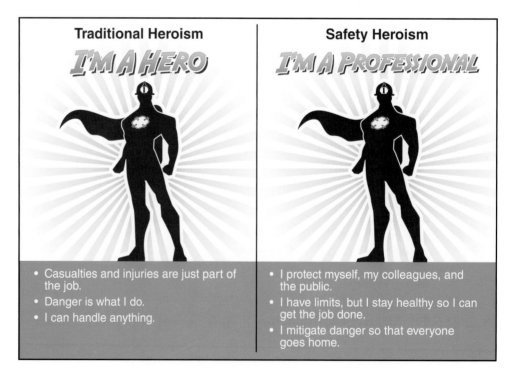

Traditional Heroism

I'M A HERO

- Casualties and injuries are just part of the job.
- Danger is what I do.
- I can handle anything.

Safety Heroism

I'M A PROFESSIONAL

- I protect myself, my colleagues, and the public.
- I have limits, but I stay healthy so I can get the job done.
- I mitigate danger so that everyone goes home.

communities. The citizens also hold firefighters in high regard. These internal and external images can create barriers to the change of firefighter culture.

To create an organizational and professional safety culture, HSOs must take aggressive actions, such as the following to cause the change **(Figure 1.6)**:

- Understanding what current culture is and its foundations
- Recognizing the need for change and the barriers that may inhibit it
- Recognizing the results of the change and knowing the benefits it will bring
- Being aware of the various programs and initiatives that can be used to support the change to a new safety culture

Figure 1.6 Asking questions about an organization's safety culture and seeking out honest answers is a key step in creating change.

Safety Programs and Initiatives

While programs and initiatives supporting health and safety change over time, some initiatives currently available during the completion of this manual include:

- International Safety and Health Week
- IAFC Rules of Engagement for the IC
- International First Responder Seatbelt Pledge
- Crew Resource Management
- Everyone Goes Home®
- 16 Firefighter Life Safety Initiatives

From company-level training to formal department-wide training, safety initiatives should be incorporated into everyday fire department life. As the HSO, it is your responsibility to instill a positive, safety conscious culture in your fire department. Creating this culture may include questioning tradition and not accepting firefighter injuries or fatalities as a part of the job.

Occupational Safety and Health Committee

The purpose of the **occupational safety and health committee** is to conduct research, develop recommendations, study and review safety and health matters, and advise the fire chief on safety matters. Within this scope of responsibility, the committee must analyze data from local, regional, state, and federal databases; and review departmental procedures. The occupational safety and health committee must take a leading role in creating a safety conscious culture. The committee is intended to unify formal and informal networks of individuals and groups toward the common goal of firefighter safety. All committee members must display and share the same message. Safety is everyone's business – the occupational safety and health committee's role is to be advocates for safety and ensure the workplace has the needed preventive measures in place. In addition, the committee should constantly motivate the department to improve its safety culture.

Federal and state OSHA regulations (29 CFR 1960.36-41) set the minimum standard for safety committees. The standards include the frequency of meetings, the committee makeup and size, documenting and posting minutes and agendas, and injury review. Remember, these are minimum standards and each jurisdiction may expand the requirements.

At a minimum, regularly scheduled meetings must be held every six months according to NFPA® 1500. The committee should have the discretion to hold more frequent meetings or special meetings to address issues that arise. Written meeting minutes must be recorded, retained, and made available for all department members. Joint safety and health committees help to improve the communication between management and firefighters and strengthen the commitment to the safety and health program.

Committee Membership

The committee is composed of both administrative staff and operational members, or representatives of member organizations, in addition to the HSO. The total number of members will vary depending on the size and type of organization. Administrative staff should not outnumber operational members. A career organization may use members from each shift, each district/battalion, each division, or other combination depending on the organization's size. Volunteer and combination organizations should recruit a representative cross section of the organization that will provide sufficient diversity of views, opinions, and skills. Additional members may be appointed, including the fire department physician and/or representatives from other nonfire departments within the jurisdiction. Involvement of members at all levels helps reduce an "us-versus-them" perception **(Figure 1.7)**.

A critical element of the committee is to overcome any personal biases, hidden agendas, or inappropriate motivations. The members who agree to serve on this committee must be willing to actively work in the process and look for

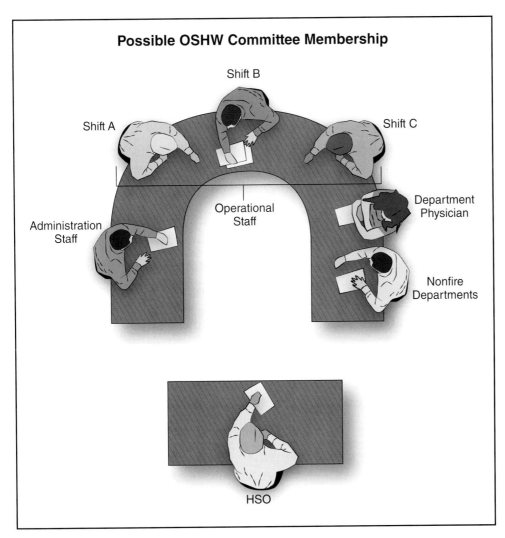

Possible OSHW Committee Membership

Shift B

Shift A

Shift C

Operational
Staff

Department
Physician

Administration
Staff

Nonfire
Departments

HSO

Figure 1.7 In order to include all stakeholders in an organization's safety culture, the occupational safety, health, and wellness committee membership should reflect individuals at all levels of the organization and any partners outside the organization.

solutions. The committee must work to develop a positive working relationship and committee cohesiveness to ensure good productivity.

Role of the HSO

The role of the HSO is to manage the occupational safety and health program committee. Managing the committee requires the ability to work with all members of the committee in an objective manner. Some good traits and abilities of an effective HSO in this capacity include:

- **Management** — the ability to manage time, people, and responsibilities while looking for solutions
- **Leadership** — have a positive influence on the organization to change behaviors through empowerment and inspiration
- **Communication** — the ability to communicate effectively verbally and in writing, listen well, and relay information accurately in the role of liaison
- **Advocacy** — be a safety advocate for all members
- **Credibility** — be a credible individual who consistently exhibits safe conduct
- **Researcher** — be able to conduct research, analyze results, and formulate recommendations

Committee Roles and Responsibilities

The goals of the occupational safety and health committee are to develop and recommend solutions to resolve conflicts. However, one issue that should not be an objective of this committee is disciplinary action. The activities and issues addressed must be within the scope of the committee. As part of their duties, occupational safety and health committee members may be required to perform the following tasks:

- Identify situations that may be a source of danger to members
- Investigate reported violations of the organization's safety policy
- Make recommendations to the fire chief or organization manager on matters reported to the committee and on rules and regulations promoted by outside regulatory agencies that relate to safety issues
- Evaluate safety rules and regulations established by the organization to ensure compliance with state/territorial/provincial mandates
- Review the annual injury and illness report for trends
- Review the safety and health inspection reports to assist in correcting unsafe conditions or practices
- Evaluate the incident investigations conducted since the last meeting to determine if the cause of an unsafe act or unsafe condition was properly identified and corrected
- Evaluate the accident and injury prevention program and make recommendations for improvement where indicated
- Make recommendations to the administration and members for the improvement of members' safety and health
- Recommend, maintain, and monitor safety and health programs and procedures
- Consider forwarded reports from outside agencies addressing safety and health in order to make recommendations to management regarding these issues
- Take and post meeting minutes that include attendance and the topics of discussion at occupational safety and health committee meetings

Conduct Research

The occupational safety and health committee conducts research on topics specific to risk management, safety, accidents, injuries, fatalities, and new technologies and techniques that improve safety. Research validity must be determined before recommending wholesale changes in procedures or implementing new technologies. The committee must weed through the documentation and determine what is credible for consideration. Best practices can provide valuable insight into what is working elsewhere, but it will be up to the committee to find supporting empirical evidence before recommending implementation of a best practice.

Develop Recommendations

The occupational safety and health committee develops recommendations based on research and investigation results, with the intent of improving negative trends. When developing recommendations consider the following:

- **Accidents** — Accidents are unplanned, uncontrolled events resulting from unsafe acts and/or unsafe occupational conditions, which may result in injury, death, or property damage. Determining the root cause of an accident will help prevent recurrence. Read accident reports from investigative agencies to determine if lessons learned can be recommended in your department.

- **Injury, death, and illness reports** — Read reports detailing firefighter injuries, deaths, and illnesses since these significant events provide lessons learned. Evaluate these reports against your department's practices, looking for vulnerabilities.

- **Trends** — Local, regional, state, and national statistics can provide valuable information when developing recommendations. Scan the horizon and look for trends – don't be the trend.

NOTE: Chapter 3, Record Keeping and Data Analysis, includes information on where committee members can conduct research on these topics.

Recommendations for change need to be factually based and presented to the fire chief and/or fire administration chief officers. This report should include the following:

- Behavior or condition that caused an accident (root cause)

- Previously unrecognized hazards

- Apparatus/equipment defects or design flaws

- Additional training needs

- Improvements needed in safety policies and procedures

- Facts that could have a legal impact on an accident case

- Historical trends

Recommendations from the committee are non-disciplinary and not based on the finding of fault or assigning blame. Recommendations are based on how to improve practices, procedures, and technologies that can be implemented to increase the safety of the work environment.

Chapter Summary

The health and safety officer of a fire department is a critical component to ensuring the safety and health of its members. This process starts with the delegation of authority for the HSO and assigning the right person. The ultimate goal of the HSO is developing and/or maintaining a positive occupational safety and health program, including leading a committee of colleagues.

NFPA® 1521 outlines the job functions and requisite knowledge and skills of the HSO. Within this scope, the HSO serves as a liaison between department officers and members, leads the occupational safety and health committee, and administers the comprehensive risk management plan. The HSO also develops recommendations for improvements to work practices, manages the accident prevention program, and conducts investigations for accidents, injuries, illnesses, or deaths. In addition, the HSO is responsible for conducting thorough research and providing a continual assessment of practices, SOP/Gs adequacy and effectiveness, and research of new technologies.

Review Questions

1. How does the health safety officer act as safety advocate for the fire department? (pp. 13-14)

2. What are the job functions of a health safety officer? (pp. 14-20)

3. What are the roles and responsibilities of an occupational safety and health committee? (pp. 22-23)

Safety and Health Laws, Codes, Regulations, and Standards

Chapter Contents

Key Terms

NFPA® Job Performance Requirements

This chapter provides information that addresses the following job performance requirements of NFPA® 1521, *Standard for Fire Department Safety Officer Professional Qualifications (2015).*

4.2.4	4.6.2	4.8.1	4.9.1	4.11.4
4.3.1	4.6.3	4.8.2	4.9.2	4.12.1
4.3.2	4.7.1	4.8.3	4.10.1	4.12.2
4.5.4	4.7.2	4.8.6	4.10.2	

Safety and Health Laws, Codes, Regulations, and Standards

Learning Objectives

After reading this chapter, students will be able to:

1. Define laws, codes, regulations, and standards applicable to the role of the health safety officer. (4.2.4, 4.3.1, 4.3.2, 4.5.4, 4.6.2, 4.6.3, 4.7.1, 4.7.2, 4.8.1, 4.8.2, 4.8.3, 4.8.6, 4.9.1, 4.9.2, 4.10.1, 4.10.2, 4.11.4, 4.12.1, 4.12.2)

2. Recognize federal laws, codes, and regulations to which health safety officers must ensure compliance. (4.3.1, 4.3.2, 4.5.4, 4.6.2, 4.6.3, 4.8.1, 4.8.2, 4.8.6, 4.9.1, 4.9.2, 4.12.1, 4.12.2)

3. Recognize state/provincial and local laws, codes, and regulations to which health safety officers must ensure compliance. (4.3.2, 4.5.4, 4.6.2, 4.8.1, 4.8.2)

4. Identify national standards pertinent to the roles of the health safety officer. (4.2.4, 4.3.1, 4.5.4, 4.6.2, 4.6.3, 4.7.1, 4.7.2, 4.8.3, 4.8.6, 4.9.1, 4.9.2, 4.10.1, 4.10.2, 4.11.4, 4.12.1, 4.12.2)

5. Learning Activity 2-1: Determine compliance with applicable safety and health laws, codes, regulations, and standards. (4.2.4, 4.3.1, 4.3.2, 4.5.4, 4.6.2, 4.6.3, 4.7.1, 4.7.2, 4.8.1, 4.8.2, 4.8.3, 4.8.6, 4.9.1, 4.9.2, 4.10.1, 4.10.2, 4.11.4, 4.12.1, 4.12.2)

Chapter 2
Safety and Health Laws, Codes, Regulations, and Standards

Case History

The Texas Commission on Fire Protection is a state agency charged with regulating certain aspects of the paid fire service in Texas. Local governing bodies are free to staff their fire departments as they see fit, but if they employ paid firefighters, they must meet basic firefighter safety standards. A board comprised of career fire personnel, personnel from other fire protection fields, and members of the public oversees the Commission. The Texas legislature created the Commission in 1969. The Commission's scope was significantly expanded following the deaths of three firefighters in a North Texas church fire in 2001.

The Commission established a number of PPE, SCBA, procedural, and training standards in the interest of, among other things, promoting firefighter safety. Fire departments have to ensure that bunker gear is regularly inspected and maintained and replaced when its service life is over. They must maintain training records, demonstrate the adoption of certain procedures, and report certain types of injuries. Risk-based inspections of local fire departments complement a schedule of biennial inspections in which Commission inspectors examine a department's PPE, SOP/Gs, and records.

The Commission is also tasked by statute with conducting line-of-duty-death investigations for all firefighters in Texas and issuing reports on the same. In 2009, its investigatory scope expanded to include firefighter injuries relating to the failure of protective equipment. In 2013, the Commission regulated 667 entities, which includes fire departments and certain fire marshals' offices and training agencies. Nearly 30,000 firefighters were subject to Commission certification requirements at that time.

The organization's administration should assign its HSO the task of developing and implementing a safety and health program that meets the organization's requirements, demands, needs, and concerns. Developing a safety and health program is made easier if the HSO uses current safety and health laws, codes, regulations, and standards as foundations for program development. Although these safety standards have requirements for employers, the regulations also contain significant requirements for employees. Each employee must comply with the requirements of the occupational safety and health standards. HSOs and their organizations are encouraged to go beyond the minimum requirements of the law.

Occupational safety and health laws are established through either legislative action or through agencies with rule-making authority. The latter procedure is the more common and is more responsive to the need for change. Whether a law comes from a legislative body or an authoritative agency, the law or regulation has the same force and effect. Following laws, codes, regulations, and standards is the best way to manage responders' and responding agencies' legal liability.

This chapter describes some of the prominent laws, codes, regulations, and standards that influence fire department operations. The HSO's responsibility is to stay up-to-date with legal directives from the federal, state/provincial, and local authorities.

16 Firefighter Life Safety Initiatives 5, 11, and 12

The *16 Firefighter Life Safety Initiatives* were discussed in Chapter 1 of this manual. Three of those initiatives are particularly pertinent to the HSO's observation of safety and health laws, codes, regulations, and standards:

5. Develop and implement national standards for training, qualifications, and certification (including regular recertification) that are equally applicable to all firefighters based on the duties they are expected to perform.

11. National standards for emergency response policies and procedures should be developed and championed.

12. National protocols for response to violent incidents should be developed and championed.

Laws, Codes, Regulations, and Standards Defined

The HSO has a responsibility to understand the difference between laws, codes, regulations, and standards and how they influence fire department operations. The HSO must apply any applicable federal, state/provincial, or local law, code, regulation, and/or standard in the following areas of responsibility:

- Developing SOP/Gs
- Developing corrective actions
- Creating a safe work environment
- Investigating accidents
- Reporting accidents and injuries
- Reporting bloodborne pathogens and exposures
- Analyzing an incident
- Recommending safety-related fire apparatus, equipment, and protective clothing and equipment specifications
- Conducting facility inspections
- Developing incident risk management plan
- Distributing safety and health information
- Managing a health maintenance program
- Establishing an occupational safety and health committee

Statutes and Case Law

Statutes, also known as *statutory laws*, pertain to civil and criminal matters. Due to the nature of these laws, they may not take effect for many years. **Case law** is the result of a legal precedent or a judicial decision. These cases serve as rules for the future determinations in similar cases. The impact of these decisions affect emergency responders almost immediately because there is usually no implementation period. Case law, if heard at the federal level, can have nationwide effect **(Figure 2.1)**.

Case law can also set precedent for identifying who the liable party is when an injury or fatality occurs. For example, the Ontario Ministry of Labour found the Village of Point Edward, Ontario partly liable in the training death of a firefighter in 2010. The Ministry fined the town government nearly $94,000. Though the instructor overseeing the training on the day of the fatality was later tried individually, the Ministry set precedent for penalizing a municipality for the actions of its employees, in this case the fire department training instructor.

Some case law decisions can impact emergency responders even though the individual case did not involve emergency response personnel. For example, *Whirlpool Corporation v. Marshall* determined that an employer could not terminate the employment of a worker who refuses to perform an unsafe act

Statute — Federal or state/provincial legislative act that becomes law; prescribes conduct, defines crimes, and promotes public good and welfare. Also known as Statutory Law.

Case Law — Laws based on judicial interpretations and decisions rather than created by legislation.

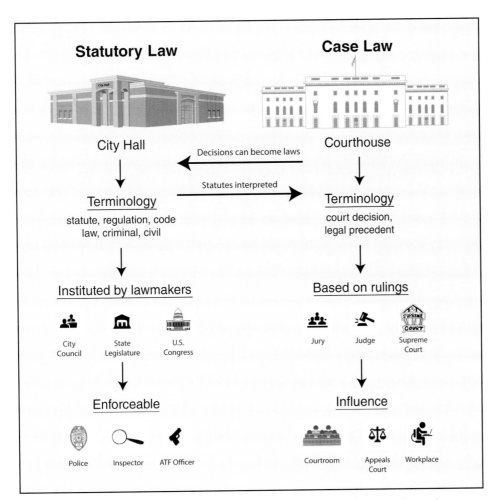

Figure 2.1 HSO's should understand the difference between statutory and case law. They should also be aware of how each affect SOP/Gs and departmental programs.

that he or she considers unacceptably risky. However, case law is always subject to change and can provide precedent to both sides of an issue. The HSO should also be aware of administrative rules and Attorney General opinions that shape the law.

Collective Bargaining

Besides local, state/provincial, and federal safety and health laws, the labor/management agreement between the fire and emergency services organization (or jurisdiction) will also contain safety and health clauses. Collective bargaining, meet and confer, or memorandum of understanding are clauses that may include requirements for protective clothing and equipment, a wellness program, a member assistance program (MAP), or annual medical examinations, and drug testing. The labor/management agreement may directly cite language in a National Fire Protection Association® (NFPA®) standard, essentially adopting that standard for the duration of the agreement. These clauses can influence how the HSO manages some programs.

Code — A collection of rules and regulations that has been enacted by law in a particular jurisdiction. Codes typically address a single subject area; examples include a mechanical, electrical, building, or fire code.

Regulations — Rules or directives of administrative agencies that have authorization to issue and enforce them.

Standard — A set of principles, protocols, or procedures that explain how to do something or provide a set of minimum standards to be followed. Adhering to a standard is not required by law, although standards may be incorporated in codes, which are legally enforceable.

National Fire Protection Association® (NFPA®) — U.S. nonprofit educational and technical association devoted to protecting life and property from fire by developing fire protection standards and educating the public.

Codes, Regulations, and Standards

A **code** is a body of law established either by legislative or administrative agencies with rule-making authority. The code is designed to regulate, within the scope of the code, the topic to which it relates. Fire departments or jurisdictions will adopt codes as the basis for reference in public and life safety compliance. For example, a jurisdiction could adopt NFPA® 101, *Life Safety Code* as its local reference document.

A **regulation** is an authoritative rule dealing with details of procedures or a rule or order having the force of law, issued by an executive authority of government. Regulations usually provide specific application to acts of legislation. The Code of Federal Regulations is an example of federal regulations with consistent applicability across the U.S.

A **standard** is any rule, principle, or measure established by authority. Standards are considered to be criterion documents that are developed to serve as models or examples of desired performance or behaviors and that contain requirements and specifications outlining minimum levels of performance, protection, or construction. Under the Occupational Safety and Health Act of 1970, the term occupational safety and health standard means "a standard which requires conditions, or adoption or use of one or more practices, means, methods, operations, or processes, reasonably necessary or appropriate to provide safe or healthful employment and place of employment." Perhaps the most commonly known standards in the fire service are those developed by the **National Fire Protection Association® (NFPA®)**.

The major difference between a regulation and a standard is that a regulation must have administrative provisions to explain how and when the standards are to be applied. Simply stated, a regulation is a law that may be based on or incorporate a standard. A standard, however, only becomes a law when it is legally adopted by a jurisdiction or included as part of a code. HSOs should seek opportunities to act as stakeholders in the adoption processes in their jurisdictions **(Figure 2.2)**.

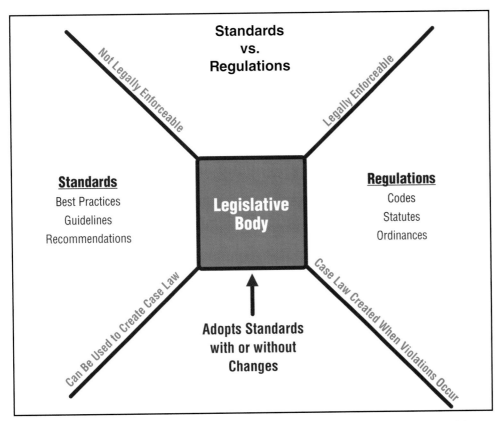

Figure 2.2 Standards must be adopted by a legislative body before they are enforceable as law. HSOs should have a role in the adoption process whenever possible.

A **guide** is an instrument that provides direction or guiding information. Although such guides do not have the force of law, they may be considered as part of what is "reasonable" in a negligence case when determining the standard of care. In addition to using the terms code and standard, NFPA® also uses the term guide. For example, NFPA® 1402 is the *Guide to Building Fire Service Training Centers.*

Guide — Document that provides direction or guiding information; does not have the force of law but may provide the basis for what is reasonable in cases of negligence.

Compliance with Laws, Codes, Regulations, and Standards

Laws, codes, regulations, and standards are in place to protect the work force and the workplace. Unsafe acts and unsafe workplaces put workers and organizations at great risk. Losses can impact the worker or the organization in the following ways:

- Financial loss, fines
- Job security
- Apparatus, personnel, equipment loss
- Loss of reputation, trust, public support

The HSO is responsible for keeping the work force and workplace safe and out of litigation. This task is accomplished with a thorough understanding of the legal system and with a continual assessment of **compliance**. The HSO must evaluate compliance and write corrective action recommendations when deficiencies are found. NFPA® 1500, Annex B, *Monitoring Compliance with a Fire Service Occupational Safety and Health Program* and Annex G, *Sample Facility Inspector Checklists* provide detailed forms for documenting compli-

Compliance — Meeting the minimum standards set forth by applicable codes or regulations.

ance. The IAFC/IAFF Labor-Management Initiative (LMI) is another tool for the HSO. LMI provides training and gives the HSO a broader perspective on the legal constraints that influence program management. **Learning Activity 2-1** combined with the remainder of the information in this chapter will provide more guidance on ensuring compliance.

Federal Laws, Codes, and Regulations

Federal laws, codes, and regulations are typically in place as a minimum requirement and may be supplemented by state/provincial and local level legal directives. For the HSO, the federal level laws, codes, and regulations generally cover worker safety and protection, privacy rules, wages, and accepted best practices that standardize operational policy and procedures. The following federal legal directives are not all encompassing, but summarize some of the critical elements specific to the HSO position.

Health Insurance Portability and Accountability Act (HIPAA) of 1996

HIPAA regulates the sharing of medical records and documents. Patient privacy rights and the protection of personal information have become a bigger concern for individuals over the past decade. Not all emergency medical providers fall under the HIPAA legal mandate. The HSO should visit the HIPAA website and use the flowchart to determine if his or her department is a "covered entity." A covered entity must follow HIPAA. Even if a department is determined to not be a covered entity, following the HIPAA regulation is considered a best practice. The HSO will need to research the HIPAA Act and forward a SOP/G recommendation to the fire chief.

Freedom of Information Act (FOIA)

Enacted in 1966, the **Freedom of Information Act (FOIA)** is specific to federal agencies and does not cover access to state or local governmental records. State-to-state records requests differ, and the HSO must determine legal mandates for releasing records. The federal executive branch has oversight of the FOIA. The Department of Justice's Office of Information and Policy handles compliance oversight. Prior to releasing any fire department record, the HSO must consult with the fire chief and possibly the agency attorney.

Ryan White HIV/AIDS Treatment Extension Act of 2009, Part G – Notification of Possible Exposure to Infectious Diseases

This Act, commonly called the Ryan White Act, provides a means of notification to emergency medical providers in the event of a possible exposure to an infectious disease. It is typically learned through the treatment process in a hospital setting that a patient has an infectious disease. If emergency responders were in contact with a patient (such as those who treated and/or transported the patient) with an infectious disease, then it is permissible to share the pertinent patient history with emergency personnel **(Figure 2.3)**. The HSO should be involved in this notification process and should serve as the liaison between hospital staff and emergency responders. See Chapter 7, Safety and Health Programs for information on the duties of an Infection Control Officer.

Health Insurance Portability and Accountability Act (HIPAA) — Congressional law established to help ensure the portability of insurance coverage as employees move from job to job. In addition to improving efficiency of the health care payment process, it also helps protect a patient's/client's privacy. The law also applies to information pertinent to juvenile firesetting situations.

Freedom of Information Act (FOIA) — Legislation used as a model for many state laws designed to make government information available to the public.

Figure 2.3 Only those individuals who will provide direct care to a patient should receive medical information about that patient.

Occupational Safety and Health (OSH) Act of 1970

The Occupational Safety and Health Act of 1970 (Public Law 91-596) created the **Occupational Safety and Health Administration (OSHA)** and the **National Institute for Occupational Safety and Health (NIOSH)**. This law is commonly referred to as the Williams-Steiger Occupational Safety and Health Act, named after the two legislators who were the primary authors and sponsors. The Act requires standards to be implemented for employers and employees to improve working conditions. The Act includes recommendations for education, training, labor/management cooperation, and state-approved plans.

Occupational Safety and Health Administration (OSHA) — U.S. federal agency that develops and enforces standards and regulations for occupational safety in the workplace.

The federal OSHA is a part of the U.S. Department of Labor, and sets the minimum standards for workplace safety. Application of OSHA regulations vary by state, and HSOs should refer to their state OSHA office for clarification on regulations and enforcement. OSHA has inspection and enforcement rights with private employers and all state-approved plans. OSHA regulations change frequently, so the HSO must stay up-to-date with the effects of any change. Section 18 of the OSH Act of 1970 addresses state-approved plans, covered in a section below. The sections that follow are not all encompassing, but do summarize OSHA CFRs pertinent to health safety officers.

> ⚠️ **CAUTION**
>
> HSOs should refer to their state OSHA office for clarification on regulations and enforcement.

Figure 2.4 Requiring the use of hearing protection in machine shops is one important aspect of a hearing conservation program.

Occupational Noise Protection (29 CFR 1910.95)

This regulation requires a hearing conservation program for workplace noise levels above 85 decibels **(Figure 2.4)**. The HSO is required to perform sound-level tests in all facilities and for all types of apparatus and equipment to determine the level of noise present. Regular monitoring of noise levels is recommended.

Hazardous Waste Operations and Emergency Response (29 CFR 1910.120)

This regulation requires a written safety and health program for members engaging in hazardous waste operations. The HSO will work with other department members to ensure SOP/Gs address hazardous waste operations and response. This process will include an ICS structure, a risk/hazard analysis, member training requirements, personal protective equipment, site control measures, decontamination, and atmospheric monitoring. HSOs must also ensure that any member of their hazardous materials team receives the required medical examination.

Permit-Required Confined Spaces (29 CFR 1910.146)

This regulation covers workplaces that have permit-required confined spaces. In addition to work site employers with confined spaces, emergency responders or rescue teams must comply with this regulation. Rescue and emergency services requirements are addressed in Section K.

Fire Brigades (29 CFR 1910.156)

In addition to fire brigades, this regulation covers industrial fire departments and private or contractual type fire departments **(Figure 2.5)**. This regulation requires employers to provide the necessary training, equipment, and protective clothing to safely carry out their assigned duties.

Protective Equipment (29 CFR 1910, Subpart I)

This regulation covers the protective clothing and equipment necessary for full personal protection. This standard mainly addresses the protection of the head, eyes, face, hands, feet, and respiratory system. The HSO must ensure members are properly trained in the use of protective clothing and equipment and that members are provided the necessary protective clothing and equipment to carry out their duties.

Respiratory Protection (29 CFR 1910.134)

The Respiratory Protection section under Subpart I addresses the training of members, medical evaluation and examination, fit testing, and procedures for operating in an immediately dangerous to life and health (IDLH) atmosphere. The common term associated with IDLH operations is the two-in, two-out rule that requires a rapid intervention crew to be readily deployable. The HSO must be part of the selection team for any protective clothing and equipment, including self-contained breathing apparatus, to ensure that safety requirements are met **(Figure 2.6)**.

Figure 2.5 According to OSHA regulations, employers must provide all necessary training and equipment to fire brigades functioning in industrial environments.

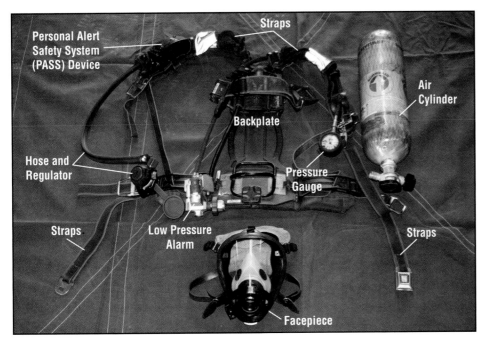

Figure 2.6 The HSO should be involved when selecting replacement or updated SCBA equipment. He or she should also understand the various components that comprise the equipment.

Bloodborne Pathogens (29 CFR 1910.1030)

This regulation covers occupations in which exposure to infectious disease is possible in the workplace. Infectious diseases include, but are not limited to the Human Immunodeficiency Virus (HIV), Hepatitis B Virus (HBV), and Hepatitis C Virus (HCV). Employers are required to have an Exposure Control Plan that addresses all aspects of worker protection. The Needlestick Safety and Prevention Act updated this regulation in 2000 (Public Law 106-430). This amendment specifically addresses definitions and a new safer sharp instrument design. The addition of a sharps injury log is included in this amendment.

Canadian Centre for Occupational Health and Safety Act

This Act established the **Canadian Centre for Occupational Health and Safety (CCOHS)** governed by the Council of the Centre. The Act promotes the safe work environment for all workers in Canada. The Act defines similar research, training and education, and enforcement to the U.S. OSH Act, and similar framework between federal and provincial/territorial regulations as between the federal and state OSHA in the U.S. Canadian federal regulations may be found in the Canada Labour Code.

Public Safety Officer Benefits (PSOB) Act of 1976 and Hometown Heroes Survivors Benefits Act of 2003

The PSOB is a benefit program from the U.S. Department of Justice for those killed or severely injured in the line of duty. The Hometown Heroes Act amended the PSOB to include death benefits for public safety officers who die while on-duty or within 24 hours of an on-duty event that triggers a cardiac or cerebrovascular occurrence. HSOs will most likely serve as the internal and external liaison when there is a **line-of-duty death (LODD)** or injury and must be knowledgeable about the resources available to assist the department, the affected member, and their family. The National Fallen Firefighters Foundation's Local Assistance State Team (LAST) Project is one such resource. This outreach project has local and regional resources to assist a department with a LODD and the filing of death benefit forms. Another valuable resource is the 100 Club, a nonprofit organization that provides financial assistance to public safety officers injured or killed in the line of duty. HSOs should research state, local, or regional resources and have them written into their department's SOP/G. Some of these resources include state firefighter associations, state fire marshal offices, state fire training organizations, and other related organizations.

National Incident Management System (NIMS)

Homeland Security Presidential Directive (HSPD)–5, Management of Domestic Incidents, required the creation of the **National Incident Management System (NIMS)**. The NIMS concept provides a national operational framework for all responders. FEMA states that the "approach to enable government (federal, state, tribal, and local), the private sector, and nongovernmental organizations (NGOs) to work together to prepare for, prevent, respond to, recover from, and mitigate the effects of incidents regardless of the incident's cause, size, location, or complexity." Federal departments and agencies are required to adopt NIMS. State, tribal, and local organizations must adopt and implement NIMS to be eligible for federal preparedness financial assistance.

The **Incident Command Structure (ICS)** is a component of NIMS **(Figure 2.7)**. The ICS provides the modular organizational structure that can expand and contract based on the incident complexity. The HSO is responsible for developing an incident risk management plan that complies with HSPD-5 and incorporates the ICS for all emergency incidents and training evolutions.

National Response Framework (NRF)

Homeland Security Presidential Directive (HSPD)-8, *National Preparedness*, issued in 2003, defines the preparedness of federal agencies and the coordination needed. The original document from this directive was called the *National Response Plan (NRP)*. In 2011, the document was renamed the *National Response Framework (NRF)* and renumbered as Presidential Policy Directive (PPD)-8. It was revised to integrate federal government prevention, preparedness, response, recovery, and mitigation plans into one all-discipline, all-hazard approach to domestic incident management. The NRF and NIMS provide the framework and processes that weave the capabilities and resources of all of the jurisdictions, disciplines, levels of government, and the private sector into a cohesive and coordinated national approach to domestic incident management.

The HSO is responsible for developing an incident risk management plan that complies with PPD-8. Additionally, the HSO must be knowledgeable in all aspects of ICS, including single and multiple agency/jurisdictional incident operations and the Multiagency Coordination Systems (MACS). As the individuals responsible for developing the incident risk management plan, HSOs should utilize the **Federal Emergency Management Agency's (FEMA)** NIMS Training Program manual as a guide to their departments and their own development in NIMS and ICS.

Incident Command Structure (ICS) — Standardized approach to incident management that facilitates interaction between cooperating agencies; adaptable to incidents of any size or type.

National Response Framework (NRF) — Document that provides guidance on how communities, states, the U.S. federal government, and private-sector and nongovernmental partners conduct all-hazards emergency response.

Federal Emergency Management Agency (FEMA) — Agency within the U.S. Department of Homeland Security (DHS) that is responsible for emergency preparedness, mitigation, and response activities for events including natural, technological, and attack-related emergencies.

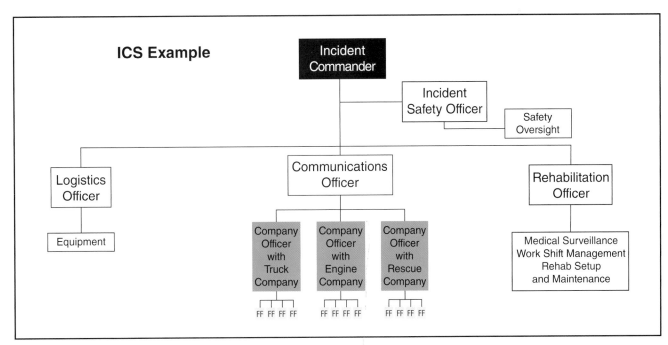

Figure 2.7 The Incident Command Structure (ICS) is designed to be flexible and adaptable to a wide variety of incident sizes and complexities.

State/Provincial and Local Laws, Codes, and Regulations

The safety officer should understand the context of a law before applying it in a jurisdiction. For instance, legal powers in the U.S. and Canada are defined differently. Federal laws, codes, regulations, and standards have overall authority across the country. Federal legal directives apply a consistent authority across the nation and local jurisdictions can have similar directives, but they cannot be less restrictive than federal laws, codes, regulations, and standards.

State/provincial law also has variability with regards to jurisdiction. For example, in Canada, provincial regulations apply to municipal fire departments, but in the U.S. municipal regulations may be different from state law. In addition, federal law may supersede state law or jurisdiction as is the case with airports and military personnel in the United States **(Figure 2.8)**.

State and provincial law can at times have significant impact on fire departments, and historical case law should be examined for precedent setting rulings. The HSO should be familiar with resources that specifically address fire service law. For example, *The Fireman's Rule*, which generally states that firefighters cannot sue land or property owners when injured on the job, is applied differently across the U.S. The HSO should take into consideration pertinent case law as the rulings are based on some of the following legal directives.

A variety of government entities, including municipalities, counties/parishes, special districts, and fire protection districts, create and adopt the local level of legislation. The fire and emergency services organization usually generates fire and emergency services ordinances enacted at this level. For example, NFPA® 1500 *Standard on Fire Department Occupational Safety and Health Program* may be adopted as an ordinance in a jurisdiction. Once the ordinance is adopted, it becomes local law and must be followed.

Figure 2.8 The federal government has a higher legal authority than state or local governments; however, state and municipal governments can create laws that differ from federal laws as long as the state or local laws are stricter than federal law.

Occupational Safety and Health Administration (OSHA) Regulations in the U.S.

The OSH Act of 1970 promotes the adoption of state-approved plans for worker safety and health. State-approved plans can be more stringent, but not less stringent than the federal regulations. States have enforcement rights, will provide consulting services to both public and private employers without penalty or citation, and conduct training and education programs addressing worker safety and health. Not all states have identical legislation, so the HSO should remain current on state specific requirements.

What This Means to You

Fire departments must determine what access rights or limitations exist for detailed annual fit-for-duty and respirator evaluation results. The following OSHA regulations cover some aspects of the access rights:

- 29 CFR 1910.120(f)(7)(ii) for the physician written opinion limitations
- 29 CFR 1910.134(e)(6)(i)(a) for physician written recommendations on a members use of a respirator
- 29 CFR 1910.120(f)(7)(i)(c) for an employer receiving results only when requested by the employee

The CFRs are a guide for the HSO. They are federal regulations and standards across jurisdictions; however, states may apply them or interpret them differently. How they are applied and interpreted at the state level may differ, so researching compliance at the state, provincial, or local level is critical to departmental compliance.

Health and Safety Regulations in Canada

In Canada, the provincial and territorial governments regulate health and safety within their own jurisdictions. Although the Canadian federal government has an **Occupational Health and Safety Agency (OH&S)**, it only regulates the activities of some federal government employees. Other federal employees are regulated by the OH&S regulations of the province/territory in which they are located.

The title of the provincial/territory agency responsible for administration of OH&S regulations varies. Some of the agencies are Worker's Compensation Board (WCB), Workplace Safety and Insurance Board (WSIB), Workplace Safety and Health, among others. The provincial/territory agency may be a government agency, a "crown" corporation (government-regulated but not funded), or a government board.

Just as the titles of agencies vary from province to province, the OH&S regulations also vary. Regulations only apply in the province/territory enacting them and do not have authority in any other province/territory. Some regulations cover fire service specific subjects such as training and certification, respiratory protection, or protective clothing requirements. Other regulations cover general safety issues for all worker portions that apply to firefighters.

Provincial/territorial OH&S regulations typically adopt standards or parts of standards within the regulations. Even though a standard is not formally adopted, such as NFPA® standards, it may be referenced as best practice in a legal proceeding or in government documentation. Once a standard has been adopted as part of a regulation, the standard must be followed. Standards are only enforceable when they are adopted by the appropriate legislative body. The provincial/territorial government retains the responsibility for enforcement, not the standard writing agency.

Occupational Health and Safety Agency (OH&S) — Canadian federal agency that regulates workplace safety for some federal employees; regulation under the OH&S is typically delegated to a provincial agency.

Public Records

States commonly use **public records** or a similar term, instead of FOIA, to refer to any public record available through a request process. Public records requests at the state and local level are not covered under the federal FOIA. All 50 states and the District of Columbia have enacted legislation on open public records **(Figure 2.9)**. HSOs, or any fire department members, should become familiar with their department's responsibility to fulfill an open public record request, and any limitations that may apply within the legislation. For example, HSOs should research through their state law or local legal representative whether quality improvement reviews are discoverable. The HSO should be knowledgeable in state-specific case law that pertains to open public records requests as case law sets precedence for how the law is interpreted. The HSO should also know how HIPAA or personnel records may overrule the Public Records law.

The state/province defines the exact definition and list of records that are available to the public. An example of the definition by one state is as follows:

Public record includes any writing containing information relating to the conduct of government or the performance of any governmental or proprietary function prepared, owned, used, or retained by any state or local agency regardless of physical form or characteristic: All budget and financial records; personal leave, travel and payroll records; records of legislative sessions; reports submitted to the legislature; and any other record designated a public record by any official action by the Senate or the House of Representatives.

Public records include virtually all records of agencies and jurisdictions within the state/province. Those records include documents, maps, photographs, videotapes, handwritten notes, letters, computer data (including e-mails), company issued cell phones, and all other records if they were created or held by a government organization. These records may be subpoenaed in a court case. Records of responses to emergency medical incidents present restricted-access issues because of the requirement for confidentiality established by the Health Insurance Portability and Accountability Act (HIPAA).

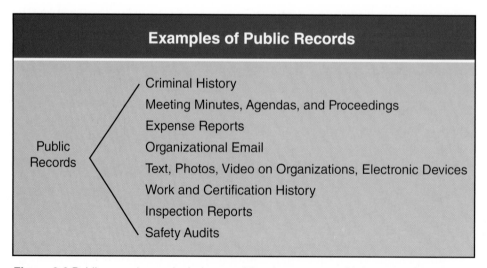

Examples of Public Records

Public Records
- Criminal History
- Meeting Minutes, Agendas, and Proceedings
- Expense Reports
- Organizational Email
- Text, Photos, Video on Organizations, Electronic Devices
- Work and Certification History
- Inspection Reports
- Safety Audits

Figure 2.9 Public records may include any of the documents and information listed here. Local governments or state governments may have other records that are public within their jurisdictions.

Caution

HIPAA prohibits responders from making comments concerning patients to anyone outside the continuity of care.

Record Retention

Public records must be maintained for a specified period. State legislation will define a records retention schedule for the varying document types. The HSO must be knowledgeable in the retention schedule for exposure reports, injuries, illnesses, and medical records related to these incident types. See OSHA 29 CFR 1910.1020(d) "Preservation of records" for specific retention reference. In addition, HSOs should research their state record retention schedules for further document references.

Department of Motor Vehicles

Each state Department of Motor Vehicles (DMV) can have different requirements for driver/operators of emergency vehicles. Commercial Driver's License (CDL) requirements should be understood and may be written into the department's SOP/G. The CDL is issued at the state level and is state-regulated. Regardless of whether a CDL is required, the HSO is responsible for ensuring compliance with state DMV laws. Any deficiency in compliance should be included in the semiannual report to the fire chief with corrective recommendations.

Release of motor vehicle records and/or driver's license information falls under the **Federal Driver's Privacy Protection Act (DPPA)** and may also have state legal implications **(Figure 2.10)**. Access and eligibility criteria for obtaining records must be determined within a given state and written into the department's SOP/Gs. The HSO is responsible for verifying the training and testing of fire department driver/operators, and ensuring proficient knowledge in traffic laws. The HSO may also be responsible for obtaining member driver's license records during an accident investigation. Again, the process for obtaining this record must be written into the department's SOP/G.

The use of seatbelts, or lack thereof, is a significant risk management element the HSO must evaluate. Compliance with seat belt laws is a recurring issue in the fire service. The HSO must work with emergency responders and supervisors to ensure 100% compliance with this life saving device.

Federal Driver's Privacy Protection Act (DPPA) — U.S. Federal law that establishes a limited list of reasons (law enforcement request, insurance underwriting, and others) under which a department of motor vehicles can distribute personal information. State laws based upon the federal statute may vary.

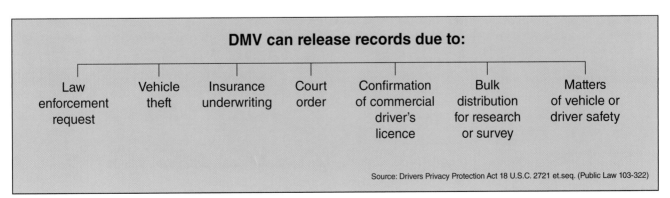

Figure 2.10 In the United States, the Department of Motor Vehicles can only release records under certain, clearly defined situations.

National Standards

National standards in the fire service provide recommended best practices for fire departments. The National Fire Protection Association (NFPA®) is the most influential and renowned authority of standards within the fire service. The NFPA® develops consensus standards that are not considered law unless formally adopted by a jurisdiction. Once formally adopted, the consensus standard becomes a legal mandate. Even if NFPA® standards are not formally adopted, they may be used as a reasonable measure of practice in the event of an investigation. This section contains specific standard information relating to the safety and health of fire service members. It includes information for Canada, from the NFPA®, and national initiatives.

Standards Council of Canada

Standards Council of Canada (SCC) — Federal Crown corporation in Canada that establishes a variety of standards for accepted work practices, technical requirements, and specific terminologies for products, services, and systems. Cooperates with the Canadian Standards Association (CSA) to approve their published standards.

The **Standards Council of Canada (SCC)** is the verification agency for standards writing agencies. This organization is similar to the American National Standards Institute (ANSI) in the United States. ANSI is also a recognized verification agency in Canada. Standards developed by the NFPA® and NIOSH may be adopted in a province/territory because they carry ANSI approval. Standards written by the Canadian Standards Association (CSA) and approved by the SCC may also be adopted or referenced by regulations. Standards may also be listed as reference documents within the OH&S regulations. As a reference document, the cited standard is considered a "recommended practice" that meets the requirements of the OH&S regulation. Fire service personnel in Canada are urged to consult their provincial OH&S agency to determine the appropriate requirements.

NFPA® Standards Relating to Safety and Health

The NFPA® has over 300 consensus standards, with a number of them relating to the safety and health of fire department operations or firefighters. When researching an NFPA® standard, the HSO should consult the *Referenced Publications* or the *Informational References* sections for other reference material that is routinely included. The HSO should research these references, especially if it is the document of origin for a topic. The HSO must also have an understanding of the correlation between the standards and be able to apply the correct code/standard and section. The following is a partial list of NFPA® standards specific to the HSO function.

NFPA® 1250, Recommended Practice in Fire and Emergency Service Organization Risk Management

This document provides a model for developing, implementing, and monitoring a risk management program. This model can be a stand-alone document or a supplement to a jurisdiction's risk management plan. The goal of this recommended practice for risk management is to reduce the risk to members through defined control measures. The HSO will use this standard as a basis for risk management.

NFPA® 1403, Standard on Live Fire Training Evolutions

The HSO is responsible for ensuring the fire department SOP/G addresses having at least one trained safety officer on site at all live fire training evolutions. Large training evolutions may require additional trained safety officers to assist with site safety supervision **(Figure 2.11)**. The HSO is also responsible for ensuring a preburn inspection is conducted with a preburn plan and briefing is completed prior to beginning the evolution. Specific training criteria are covered in Chapter 8, Training Functions.

NFPA® 1451, Standard for a Fire and Emergency Service Vehicle Operations Training Program

NFPA® 1451 provides the minimum requirements for a fire organization's vehicle operations training program. The standard addresses both emergency and nonemergency vehicle operations with the ultimate goal of preventing crashes, injuries, and fatalities related to vehicle operations **(Figure 2.12)**. The

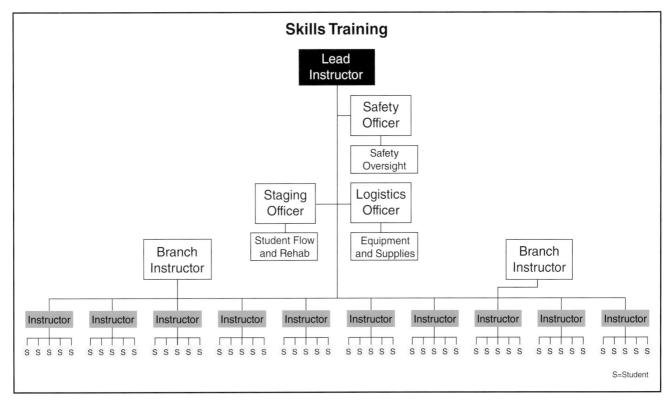

Figure 2.11 Large training evolution should follow both training guidelines, such as assigning one instructor for every five students, and the ICS system for operational, command, and safety functions with instructors functioning as the IC and the ISO.

Figure 2.12 All departments should have a vehicle operations program that complies with appropriate standards and jurisdictional regulations.

current version of the standard also includes new information about safety and training for responses to vehicle incidents. The HSO should use this standard as a guide for creating a vehicle operations program or evaluating an existing program. The standard can also inform SOP/Gs related to response to vehicle incidents and overall apparatus safety.

NFPA® 1500, Standard on Fire Department Occupational Safety and Health Program

This standard is the core document for the fire department's occupational safety and health program that the HSO is responsible for overseeing. Many other NFPA® standards refer to this document. In summary, this standard includes:

- **Chapter 4: Fire department administration** — this chapter includes criteria for developing the risk management plan, roles and responsibilities, the occupational safety and health committee, records and data collection, and an HSO position. The scope of responsibility for the HSO in this section is as manager of the occupational safety and health program.

- **Chapter 5: Training, education, and professional development** — this chapter defines the criteria for reducing firefighter risk through training, education, and professional development. These criteria include qualification of members in their areas of assignment and any additional special skills. The HSO is responsible for ensuring training targets injury and accident prevention activities. The HSO must coordinate with the fire department training division, as roles and responsibilities are closely related.

- **Chapter 6: Fire apparatus, equipment, and drivers/operators** — this chapter defines criteria for improving vehicle operations, marine vessel operation, the maintenance and securing of tools and equipment, and the personnel operating or riding on the apparatus. The HSO will research apparatus design and safety features as it relates to the safety and health of fire department members.

- **Chapter 7: Protective clothing and protective equipment** — this chapter provides extensive reference to full protective clothing and equipment of all types for fire service operations. The HSO will research protective clothing and equipment for functionality, protection, and safety features as it relates to the safety and health of fire department members in the different operational areas **(Figure 2.13)**. In addition, the HSO will reference other NFPA® standards and OSHA CFRs in determining protective clothing and equipment compliance.

- **Chapter 8: Emergency operations** — this chapter defines the criteria for emergency scene operations through the use of the ICS, communications, accountability, risk analysis, scene safety considerations, and rehabilitation of members. The HSO is responsible for ensuring that an operational risk management plan is in place that meets the requirements of this chapter. SOP/G requirements for the operational risk management plan should include:

  — Incident risk management assessment

  — Personnel accountability

  — The use of rapid intervention crews (RIC)

Possible Protective Clothing Needs

Structural Fire Fighting

Bloodborne Pathogens

Station/Work Uniform

Technical Rescue

Swiftwater Rescue

Ice Rescue

Hazardous Materials

Proximity

Figure 2.13 Personal protective clothing and equipment varies depending upon the type of duty being performed. The HSO should ensure that the department has the appropriate variety of equipment based upon the area it serves and its response history. *Ice Photo Courtesy of Iowa Fire Service Training Bureau.*

— Safe scene operations, provisions for rehabilitation

— Radio communication protocols, including use of "clear text" and definitions of "emergency traffic" is clear text.

- **Chapter 9: Facility safety** — this chapter includes criteria for inspecting, maintaining, and repairing fire department facilities to improve the workplace environment. The HSO will be responsible for conducting inspections and safety audits to ensure compliance with legal mandates on workplace safety. The HSO will keep a written record of all inspections and safety audits and any corrective actions taken.

- **Chapter 10: Medical and physical requirements** — this chapter includes the criteria for firefighter fit-for-duty standard, data collection, and wellness. HSOs should consult with legal counsel and their local OSHA office on what kinds of medical information may be obtained by a fire department.

- **Chapter 11: Member assistance and wellness programs** — this chapter addresses the criteria for making member assistance program available to help deal with stress, substance abuse, or other personal issues. In addition, the wellness programs need to provide overall fitness assistance and the elimination of tobacco use among its members **(Figure 2.14)**. The HSO is responsible for ensuring a SOP/G covers these programs.

- **Chapter 12: Critical incident stress program** — this chapter outlines the development of a critical incident stress management program. The HSO will most likely serve as a liaison for this program and develop a SOP/G on its appropriate use in specific situations.

NFPA® 1561, Standard on Emergency Services Incident Management System and Command Safety

This standard provides the framework for utilizing an Incident Management System (IMS). NFPA® uses IMS and ICS interchangeably, and both terms are seen in the NFPA® standards. The HSO is responsible for ensuring the imple-

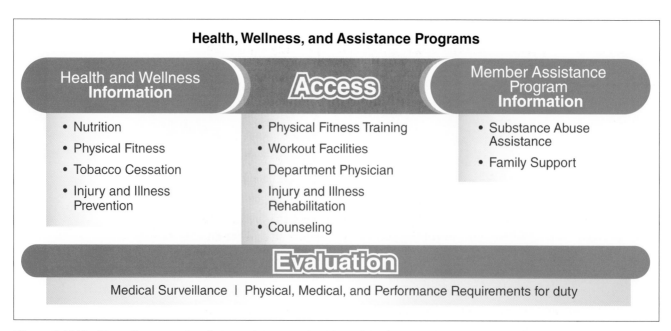

Figure 2.14 Health, wellness, and assistance programs should provide access to everything firefighters need to remain fit-for-duty. The programs should also evaluate firefighters on how well they are maintaining their health and wellness.

mentation of an IMS on all emergency operations and training evolutions. Within this scope, the HSO must ensure personnel are trained to the proper level in which they function in the command structure and ensure that the command structure positions are identified in the SOP/Gs and implemented when needed. The HSO also must ensure SOP/Gs address the accountability of personnel and their rehabilitation prior to returning to any activity.

NFPA® 1581, Standard on Fire Department Infection Control Program

This standard provides criteria for reducing the potential exposure of an infectious disease when members are in the station, on an apparatus, or at an incident scene, or transporting a patient to the hospital. The HSO is responsible for evaluating this standard and OSHA regulations related to infection control and ensuring an Exposure Control Plan is implemented. The HSO must then ensure the department complies with the legal mandates on their written SOP/Gs. Depending on the organizational structure of the fire department, the HSO may also serve as the Infection Control Officer.

NFPA® 1582, Standard on Comprehensive Occupational Medical Program for Fire Departments

This standard provides extensive criteria for the medical evaluation of fire department members. Included in this standard are the essential job tasks for firefighters that a physician should consider when conducting a medical evaluation. Physicians may use the definition of Category A and Category B medical conditions when appropriate. Category A conditions will result in a not-fit-for-duty status. Meanwhile, Category B will result in a fit-for-duty certification if the physician concludes that the condition is not a threat to the firefighter's life when participating in any essential job task. The HSO is responsible for working with the department physician to ensure comprehensive medical evaluations are conducted and comply with this standard.

NFPA® 1583, Standard on Health-Related Fitness Programs for Fire Department Members

This standard provides the criteria for developing a health and fitness program for fire department members. The HSO will work directly with the health and fitness coordinator to ensure data collection on member participation is maintained and that the objectives of the health and fitness program are achieved.

NFPA® 1851, Standard on Selection, Care, and Maintenance of Protective Ensembles for Structural Fire Fighting and Proximity Fire Fighting

The HSO will use this standard to develop or revise SOP/Gs that address the selection, care, and maintenance of protective clothing and equipment. The HSO must have a clear understanding of the tasks to be performed and the environment in which they will be performed. Protective clothing and equipment is the first line of defense in injury prevention and against the elements of the work environment such as heat, cold, fluid contamination, and chemical and toxic materials. The HSO will make recommendations on protective clothing and equipment based on usability of the gear, the level of protection desired, and financial considerations. To extend the life of the protective clothing and

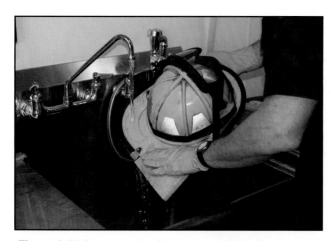

Figure 2.15 A care and maintenance program for personal protective clothing and equipment should be a part of every organization's SOP/Gs.

equipment and to maintain the best possible protection, the HSO must ensure a proper care and maintenance program is made available **(Figure 2.15)**. This task will include provisions for cleaning/servicing of contaminated personal protective clothing and equipment.

NFPA® Standards Relating to Incident Safety or Operations

Both the HSO and ISO must be familiar with the following standards that apply to the operational setting. ISOs need this information to identify hazards, perform safety functions, understand the ICS, or identify situations where additional assistance is needed. HSOs should be familiar with these standards to assist with writing SOP/Gs and operational risk management plans. This is not an all-encompassing list, and safety officers should research other NFPA® standards for applicability.

NFPA® 472, Standard for Competence of Responders to Hazardous Material/Weapons of Mass Destruction Incidents

This standard provides the competence level of responders to hazardous materials (hazmat) and weapons of mass destruction (WMD) incidents. The HSO will use this standard as a reference when developing or revising SOP/Gs that identify components of response, operations, ICS, and certification level of personnel when handling a hazmat or WMD event.

NFPA® 1006, Standard for Technical Rescuer Professional Qualifications

This standard provides the competence level of responders to technical rescue incidents. Technical rescue incidents include but are not limited to:

- High/low angle rescue
- Confined space rescue
- Trench rescue
- Structural collapse
- Vehicle and machinery rescue
- Surface water rescue
- Swiftwater rescue **(Figure 2.16)**

Rescuers can be trained to either Level I (limited techniques) or Level II (advanced techniques). An ISO for a technical rescue incident must be trained to the level of the operation deployed. The term Technical Safety Officer (TSO) is sometimes used to identify an ISO with advanced training.

NFPA® 1026, Standard for Incident Management Personnel Professional Qualifications

The HSO will reference this standard when developing or revising SOP/Gs that identify the components of the ICS. Chapter 5 of this standard is specific to a safety officer functioning at an incident or planned event. Within the ICS, the safety officer is a part of the Command Staff and reports directly to the Incident

Figure 2.16 Swiftwater rescue is a specialized skill that may require the assignment of TSOs as part of departmental SOP/Gs to ensure safety during rescue incidents.

Commander (IC). The primary responsibilities of the ISO are to manage the incident hazards, stop any unsafe act, and report conditions to the IC.

NFPA® 1584, Standard on the Rehabilitation Process for Members During Emergency Operations and Training Exercises

This standard provides the criteria for the rehabilitation process during emergency operations and training exercises. The ISO should ensure a designated area for rehab is established, the provision of hydration, nutrition, and rest is accomplished, and the medical evaluation of members is conducted prior to them returning to activity. The USFA's Emergency Incident Rehabilitation publication is a resource for understanding rehabilitation of members and creating a policy. This document covers heat and cold work environment rehabilitation, as well as after-incident rehabilitation **(Figure 2.17)**.

Figure 2.17 Rehabilitation at both emergency scenes and training evolutions should meet or exceed the requirements of NFPA® 1584.

NFPA® 1710, Standard for the Organization and Deployment of Fire Suppression Operations, Emergency Medical Operations, and Special Operations to the Public by Career Fire Departments

NFPA® 1710 states that "an incident safety officer shall be deployed to all incidents that escalate beyond a full alarm assignment or when firefighters face significant risk." In the ICS, the IC is responsible for all command and general staff functions until they are delegated. Therefore, the IC is the ISO until the incident complexity or span of control require the assignment of an ISO. Larger incidents may require assistant ISOs or technical safety officers (TSOs).

NFPA® 1720, Standard for the Organization and Deployment of Fire Suppression Operations, Emergency Medical Operations and Special Operations to the Public by Volunteer Fire Departments

The ICS is a flexible framework that can expand and contract depending on the incident complexity and size. Regardless of the size or type of fire department, the IC has ultimate decision-making authority in the ICS structure. The IC must maintain both a reasonable span of control over personnel and situational awareness of all aspects of the incident. Failure to do so jeopardizes the safety of those operating on the scene. Having an ISO assigned early in the incident provides the IC with another evaluation of the incident to maintain a positive risk/benefit approach.

NFPA® 1951, Standard on Protective Ensembles for Technical Rescue Incidents

This standard provides the minimum requirements for protective clothing and equipment for personnel operating on technical rescue incidents. The ISO is responsible for ensuring that personnel wear the proper protective clothing and equipment for the situation **(Figure 2.18)**. The ISO has the authority to stop any unsafe act or correct unsafe behavior immediately, including the protective clothing and equipment being worn.

The Fire Service Joint Labor Management Wellness-Fitness Initiative

The initiative began with a collaborative effort between the International Association of Fire Chiefs and the International Association of Fire Fighters. Commonly called the Wellness-Fitness Initiative (WFI), the non-punitive program's goal is to improve the wellness of fire department members. A component of the program is the WFI Health Information Registry (HIR), which is a centralized database collecting specific member information from those in participating fire departments. The goal of the HIR is to produce reliable health and illness data and the result achieved. The HSO can use this initiative when developing SOP/Gs, assisting the department physician or in the occupational safety and health program. See Chapter 7, Safety and Health Programs for detailed information on safety and health programs.

The National Volunteer Fire Council (NVFC) Heart-Healthy Firefighter Program

This program is designed for career and volunteer firefighters, their families, and their fire departments. It promotes nutrition, fitness, lifestyle, and basic cardiac health to improve personal health. The HSO can use this information when developing or revising SOP/Gs and for promoting the health and wellbeing of members.

16 Firefighter Life Safety Initiatives

The National Fallen Firefighters Foundation created the *Everyone Goes Home®* program, which established the *16 Firefighter Life Safety Initiatives* and other training resources promoting a safety culture in the fire service. HSOs can review the information and realistic recommendations of each initiative and compare them to their department's operations and SOP/Gs.

Figure 2.18 The ISO at a scene should be required in SOP/Gs to verify that responders are wearing their protective clothing and equipment properly.

Manual on Uniform Traffic Control Devices (MUTCD)

The *Manual on Uniform Traffic Control Devices (MUTCD)* provides a standardized approach to highway markings and signage, and sets a minimum standard for state and local agencies. The U.S. Department of Transportation, Federal Highway Administration oversees the revisions of the *MUTCD*, which is published under 23 CFR 655, Subpart F. State adoption of the MUTCD was required to be completed by January 2012. The HSO should work as an external liaison with law enforcement agencies to develop a uniform approach to moving traffic around incident scenes. The *MUTCD* provides the

Manual on Uniform Traffic Control Devices (MUTCD) — Nationwide, U.S. standard that road managers use to install and maintain traffic control devices on public streets, highways, bikeways, and private roads that are open to public traffic.

legal foundation for SOP/Gs that coincide with law enforcement practices. HSOs should identify the version of the MUTCD that has been adopted in their state/province.

Chapter Summary

Laws, codes, regulations, and standards continue to play a profound and pivotal role in ensuring firefighter safety. The HSO must determine which federal, state, provincial/territorial, or local legal directives apply within their scope of responsibility. There are many resources available for the HSO to use for ensuring compliance, carrying out their roles and responsibilities, and researching information for data comparison. It is critical for the HSO to be knowledgeable in these laws, codes, regulations, and standards as they evaluate SOP/G compliance, risk management, and occupational safety and health of all fire department members.

Review Questions

1. What are the differences between laws, codes, regulations, and standards? (pp. 30-34)

2. What federal laws, codes, and regulations should the health safety officer follow for compliance? (pp. 34-39)

3. What types of state/provincial and local laws, codes, and regulations should the health safety officer follow for compliance? (pp. 40-43)

4. What national standards are pertinent to the roles of the Health Safety Officer? (pp. 44-54)

Refer to Appendix B: Learning Activity Answers in the back of this manual for suggested responses.

Purpose

Laws, codes, regulations, and standards are created to protect personnel, the workplace environment, and civilians who need assistance. It is the responsibility of the HSO to evaluate compliance with these directives.

Directions

1. Consider the following environments and areas of focus within your department or jurisdiction:

- Protective clothing and equipment use, specifications, and storage

- Apparatus and bays

- Tools and equipment storage

- Air fill station

- Sleeping/housing quarters

- Kitchen/food prep areas

- Training facilities

2. Choose two (2) of these focus areas and brainstorm a list of compliance criteria for inspecting each area. As you work, be sure to research and cite specific laws, codes, regulations, and standards that require compliance.

3. Based on the criteria you identified, create a compliance checklist or inspection form. You may choose whichever style of checklist document works best – yes/no check boxes, numerical rating scales, etc. – but be sure that the checklists meet the specific needs of your department or jurisdiction.

   The checklists should be in your own words, but you can refer to **Figure 2.19, p. 56** as an example. You can also visit the National Institute for Occupational Safety and Health (NIOSH) website and/or U.S. Occupational Safety & Health Administration (OSHA) website for additional checklists related to safety and health topics.

ROUTINE PPE INSPECTION FORM

Name:	Employee #	Unit #	Supervisor Signature:	Date:
Coat Serial #		Trouser Serial #	Turnout Coat/Trouser Manufacturer Date/Age:	

PASS or FAIL P = Pass F = Fail	COAT SHELL	COAT LINER	DRD	TROUSER SHELL	TROUSER LINER	HELMET	HOOD	GLOVES	BOOTS	BRUSH PANT	SCBA MASK
Soiling/Contamination (Fail if present)											
Physical Damage - tears, rips, holes, charring, bubbling, melting, chips, cracks											
Discoloration											
Primary Closure System - Hooks/Snaps											
Secondary Closure System - Velcro Integrity											
Liner Attachment											
Fabric Integrity - shell, liner, moisture barrier, ear covers											
Seam/Stitching Integrity											
Wristlet Integrity - shell or liner, glove											
Hardware Functionality - pockets, accessories, neck protector											
Reflective Trim Functionality / Stitching											
Label Integrity & Legibility											
Elastic - excessive stretching, fatigue											
Suspension System											
Chin Strap/Closure Hardware											
Faceshield/Goggle - function, scratching, discoloration, melting, etc											
Matches - serial number, size											
Exposed steel toe - other boot damage											
Helmet ID System/Name											

EMS Fanny Pack	Eye Glasses	CPR Barrier	Personnel Protection Gown	N95 Mask	Gloves	Sleeves	Anti-Bacterial Cleaner
	☐	☐	☐	☐	☐	☐	☐

Figure 2.19 This form is provided as an example of a possible inspection form.

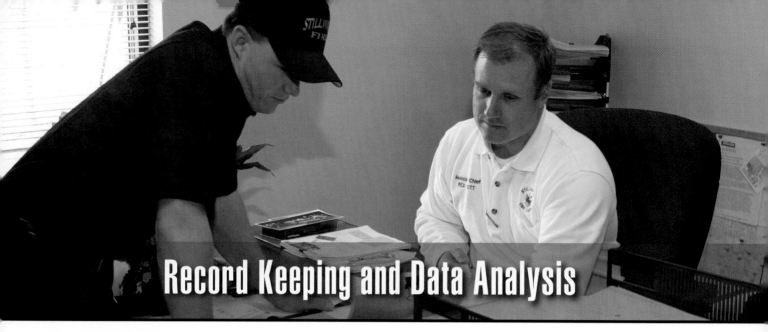

Record Keeping and Data Analysis

Chapter Contents

Key Terms

NFPA® Job Performance Requirements

This chapter provides information that addresses the following job performance requirements of NFPA® 1521, *Standard for Fire Department Safety Officer Professional Qualifications (2015)*.

4.2.1	4.4.3	4.7.1	4.8.2	4.10.1
4.2.2	4.6.1	4.7.2	4.9.1	4.10.2
4.2.3	4.6.2	4.7.3	4.9.2	4.11.3
4.4.2	4.6.4	4.8.1		

Record Keeping and Data Analysis

Learning Objectives

After reading this chapter, students will be able to:

1. Explain ways to manage departmental records. (4.2.3, 4.7.1, 4.7.2, 4.7.3)

2. Determine types of records included in a confidential health database. (4.10.1, 4.10.2)

3. Identify records involving other departments. (4.4.2, 4.7.3)

4. Determine ways to verify departmental inspection and service testing records. (4.7.2)

5. Identify safety and health program components that necessitate documentation. (4.2.1, 4.4.2, 4.4.3, 4.5.1, 4.6.1, 4.6.2, 4.6.4, 4.8.1, 4.8.2, 4.9.1, 4.9.2)

6. Determine methods used for compiling safety and health data. (4.7.1, 4.11.3)

7. Identify skills used for analyzing data. (4.7.1, 4.11.3)

8. Explain ways to perform a cost/benefit analysis. (4.2.1, 4.2.2)

9. Learning Activity 3-1: Create a departmental records and data management system. (4.7.1)

Chapter 3
Record Keeping and Data Analysis

Case History

A Safety Team for a medium-sized fire department met for a regularly scheduled meeting. The lead mechanic for the department's maintenance division was concerned about the number of minor accidents apparatus had been involved in during the last quarter. At the time, no database for motor vehicle accidents existed, so it was difficult to identify common types or numbers of accidents.

The Safety Team developed and implemented an apparatus accident program that collected various types of information related to any type of apparatus damage or any event in which an apparatus was involved in an accident or property damage. The information collected included:

- Diagrams and photos
- Witness and police reports
- Driver training records
- Prior work rest cycles
- Apparatus movement
- Maintenance records
- Road conditions, time of day and weather conditions

Within six months, analysis of the collected data began to yield results. Combined with the fuel and mileage records from the department's Resource Management and Maintenance Division, the Safety Team identified the following:

- The average number of miles that the fleet traveled before it had an accident
- Which battalions were having accidents
- Most accidents happened in close quarters or at low speeds

The Training Division took the information and created a low speed driver training program. The Safety Team issued a report to the department's senior staff that identified which divisions or battalions were having accidents without mentioning names of individuals. The Personnel Division began to keep track of members' driving records to ensure no member had an excessive amount of accidents (more than two in 3 years).

The mileage between accidents improved in the first year from one every 42,000 miles to one every 66,000 miles. Currently, the fleet's accident rate is one every 110,000 miles. Results were due to the increased awareness level and improved training of the drivers and crews. The battalions and divisions also fostered friendly competition among themselves based upon which units had the fewest accidents. In addition, the Personnel Division also identified a member that had a serious, correctable vision problem, and worked with the firefighter to get the problem corrected.

Record keeping and data analysis are two processes that go together and are important functions for all fire departments. Record keeping is the process of documenting, organizing, and storing files of fire department activities and events. There are legal implications, privacy rights, retention schedules, and reporting requirements with strict compliance mandates, all of which apply to record keeping. The HSO must be knowledgeable of the types of records that must be maintained for the safety and health program and the protocol for managing the records. A methodical record-keeping system will be critical to the HSO when meeting the following responsibilities:

- Develop and revise the risk management plan

- Develop safety and health programs to address risks

- Develop, document, and maintain corrective actions

- Produce reports for the fire chief and occupational safety and health committee

- Perform document investigations and inspections

Data analysis is a process that involves collecting, compiling, and assessing the large amounts of information available to the HSO. Knowing what information to look for and where to find it is essential when complying with legal mandates and creating reports for the organization. This chapter outlines the critical elements of record keeping and data analysis as they relate to the HSO and the safety and health program.

16 Firefighter Life Safety Initiatives #7

The importance of data collection is addressed in one of the *16 Firefighter Life Safety Initiatives*:

7. Create a national research agenda and data collection system that relates to the initiatives.

Record Keeping

Record keeping is just one element of the Management Information System (MIS) or Information Technology (IT) system that most organizations depend on today. Information management includes the acquiring, analyzing, organizing, distributing, and storing of data and information that provides managers with timely and useful information. Even with the use of computer systems to store information, some **records** are still maintained as hard copies. These records may include documents from third-party vendors, forms that require signatures, or forms that are completed in the field. Electronic and hard copy documents have identical procedures for access, privacy, and retention. This section will cover the management of records and how it applies to the safety and health program. HSOs will need to become knowledgeable in the methods of their fire department for developing a record-keeping system along with data collection, data analysis, legal requirements, and system maintenance. This section and **Learning Activity 3-1** at the end of the chapter are intended to help HSOs create or revise record management systems in their organizations.

Records — Permanent accounts of past events or of actions taken by an individual, unit, or organization.

Records Management

Good **records management** and data analysis can provide justification for preventive and corrective action. One of the HSO's duties is to collect and analyze this information and recommend corrective action. NFPA® 1521, *Standard for Fire Department Safety Officer* and NFPA® 1500, *Standard on Fire Department Occupational Safety and Health Program* require that departments maintain records on all accidents, occupational deaths, injuries, illnesses, and exposures. In addition, the HSO is responsible for the following tasks:

- Safety and health SOP/Gs
- Maintenance of records pertaining to periodic inspections
- Develop and maintain a wellness program
- Safety testing of department apparatus and equipment
- Verify the inspection and testing of in-service protective clothing and equipment
- Inspection of department facilities
- Accident investigations

When recommended safety corrections are made, the HSO keeps records of those corrections in addition to records of the implementation of safety and health procedures and accident prevention policies. Over time, the HSO will use this information to analyze data from accidents or incidents that result in near-misses, injuries, fatalities, illnesses, or exposures.

The HSO is required to develop a periodic safety and health report that is given to the fire chief and communicated to all personnel according to NFPA® 1521. This report includes information relating to department accidents, near-misses, occupational injuries, illnesses, deaths, and hazardous exposures. The report provides a comparison between the department's records and national fire and industry safety and health data. It also helps to both determine developing trends and understand root causes so that recommendations to mitigate risks can be developed. The goal of this report is to prevent deviations from policies and recurring accidents and incidents.

HSOs should understand that national data may not be current, complete, or dependable. When national data is used, it should clearly state what it represents. Regional variations may not be reflected in the national data collection process.

Records management must comply with NFPA® 1500 and OSHA regulations. Permanent records must be collected in the system for all job-related accidents, injuries, illnesses, exposures to infectious agents, communicable diseases, chemical exposures, and fatalities **(Figure 3.1, p. 64)**.

The federal government requires those states that have adopted OSHA regulations or state-approved plans to collect data on all job-related injuries, illnesses, and fatalities (except for first-aid cases). This requirement is regulated in Title 29 CFR 1904, which provides the record-keeping guidelines. A log and summary of all recordable occupational injuries and illnesses must be kept and provided to the Department of Labor and any employee, former employee, or their authorized representative. Some information will need to

Records Management — Maintenance, review, and security of records including controlling access, ensuring that records are organized, current, and searchable, and that record keeping is compliant with applicable laws, codes, and regulations.

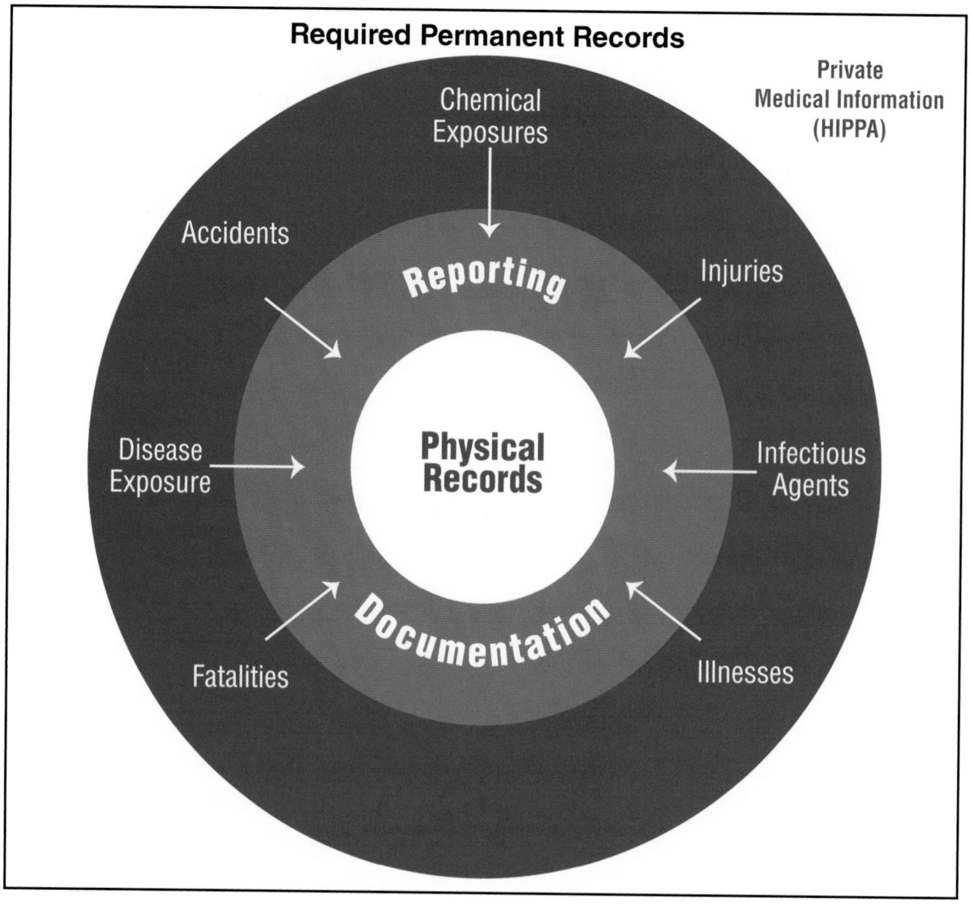

Required Permanent Records

Private Medical Information (HIPPA)

Reporting

Physical Records

Documentation

Chemical Exposures

Accidents

Injuries

Disease Exposure

Infectious Agents

Fatalities

Illnesses

Figure 3.1 Permanent records are defined by NFPA® 1500, OSHA regulations, and the additional needs of the jurisdiction. Medical records are permanent but should have their own, separate storage system.

be redacted from the log based upon who is making the request. OSHA records should be completed using or in keeping with the following Department of Labor/OSHA forms:

- Form 300 *Log of Work-Related Injuries and Illnesses*
- Form 300A *Summary of Work-Related Injuries and Illnesses*
- Form 301 *Injury and Illness Incident Report*

NOTE: Jurisdictions not covered by OSHA or an approved state plan should consult their state/provincial Department of Labor or Workers' Compensation Board.

Chemical Exposure at Fire Incidents

Modern products are more likely to produce chemical hazards, such as the release of cyanide, which must be recognized by fire department members. Research of the health effects of the by-products of fire is on-going. Documenting chemical exposures at fire incidents is becoming more common. The challenge for the HSO is developing a record-keeping process for determining who has been exposed.

Electronic Records

Electronic records are fast becoming the method of choice for developing and maintaining records for many fire departments. Electronic records may be scans of legacy, paper documents or saved digital files. Electronic records may also be part of a searchable database on the organization's server. Some organizations may allow members to document activities in fillable online forms that generate immediate electronic records that need to be maintained and compiled.

Electronic Communication

Electronic communications include email, cell phone calls and texts, all computer-generated forms and documents, and all shared or downloaded photographs and videos (**Figure 3.2**). Regardless of how it is stored, any bit of information is considered legally discoverable. The emergence of social media has created new challenges for all fire officers in monitoring the appropriateness of its use.

Retention Requirements

State/provincial laws and municipal ordinances generally dictate the length of time certain types of records must be retained and how they must be destroyed at the end of that period of time. Additional requirements can be found in the OSHA Code of Federal Regulations Title 29. See **Figure 3.3, p. 66** for more information.

Database — Computer software program that serves as an electronic filing cabinet; used to create forms, record and sort information, develop mailing lists, organize libraries, customize telephone and fax lists, and track presentation and program outcomes.

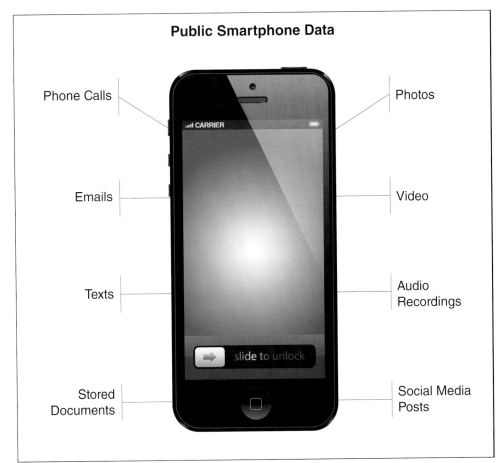

Public Smartphone Data

Phone Calls

Photos

Emails

Video

Texts

Audio Recordings

Stored Documents

Social Media Posts

slide to unlock

CARRIER

Figure 3.2 Any information – regardless of format – stored or transmitted on smartphones that are issued within the organization are considered public record and may be requested under FOIA.

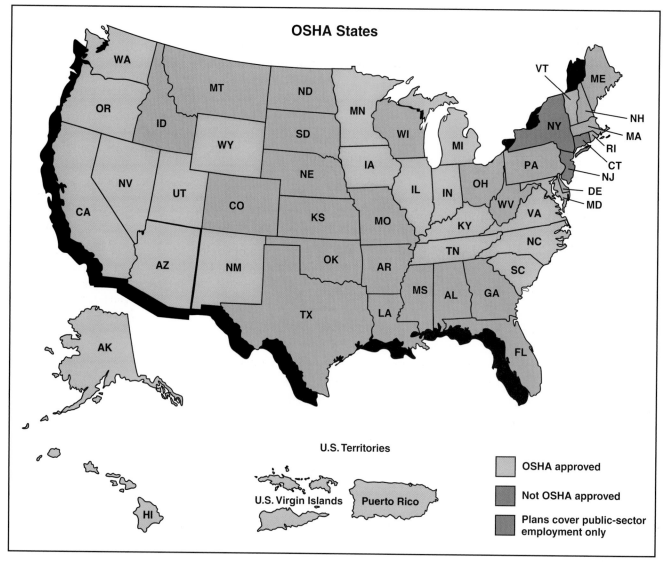

OSHA States

U.S. Territories

U.S. Virgin Islands   Puerto Rico

OSHA approved

Not OSHA approved

Plans cover public-sector employment only

Figure 3.3 In OSHA approved states, Federal Regulations Title 29 provides the requirements for record retention. In nonapproved states, the AHJ sets retention requirements at the state or local level.

Privacy Requirements

Records that must be confidential include personnel files, administrative investigations, individual training records, and medical files. Access to these files must be limited. Training records may also be considered part of an individual's personnel file, a fact that requires an organization to limit access to training records and quality improvement reviews. Even if local laws do not require this practice, organizations should develop and adopt written policies that limit access to personal training records only to those personnel with a legal need to know.

Centralization of Records

All fire department records should be centrally located. Maintaining a centralized record-keeping system promotes a standard filing and retrieval process, an organized search process, and access control. This location may be a computerized storage system that permits access to members of the department via an intranet or internet connection or it may be secured, hard-copy documents.

Even in today's modern fire service, hard-copy documents are still prevalent. Typically, the original hard-copy document will reside in the fire administration office. Secondary copies may be kept in fire stations, maintenance facilities, or with a jurisdictional office. Having a centralized location of records also makes the process of responding to a public record request more efficient.

Record Security

Regardless of the collection system used to store records, all records – even those that are publicly available – should be secured. Public availability of records does not mean that records are open to the public; rather it means that certain records must be provided upon request. Unless requested, records should remain secure. The organization should have a central point of contact, such as a **records management liaison officer (RMLO)**, to process requests for reports and records. Each department in larger organizations may have a point of contact who has the responsibility over the records in that department.

Records' security can be as simple as limiting access to rooms where paper files are stored. More and more, however, records are stored electronically in databases that may be accessed through networked computers throughout the organization or through online portals to users outside the organization. Protection of electronic files should include close collaboration with the organization's information technology staff. Outside users should have to use a password to access files and should be verified as appropriate users before being allowed access. Internal security can be tied to user logins on networked computers with an audit tracking system **(Figure 3.4)**.

Records Management Liaison Officer (RMLO) — Organizational member responsible for processing requests for public records and maintaining the security of departmental or organizational records; serves as the central point of contact between the public and the organization with regards to release of records.

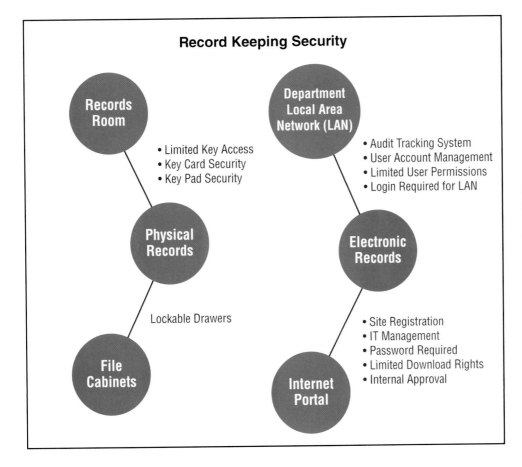

Record Keeping Security

Records Room
- Limited Key Access
- Key Card Security
- Key Pad Security

Physical Records

Lockable Drawers

File Cabinets

Department Local Area Network (LAN)
- Audit Tracking System
- User Account Management
- Limited User Permissions
- Login Required for LAN

Electronic Records

Internet Portal
- Site Registration
- IT Management
- Password Required
- Limited Download Rights
- Internal Approval

Figure 3.4 Records must be kept secure whether the records are part of a network database or paper copies stored in a records room.

Access to Records

In general, fire department records should be open for inspection. Openness includes compliance with open records legal requirements, but also includes allowing fire department personnel access to records. The results of safety audits, inspections, maintenance and service testing of apparatus and equipment, and recommendations of correction must be accessible. The HSO should ensure availability of these records either with a hardcopy or electronic filing system. Specific facility or apparatus reports should be filed in-house in addition to what the HSO maintains. Having readily accessible records and reports improves the risk management program and builds in a system of compliance for all fire department members.

Other personal information that is regulated to ensure privacy include Social Security Numbers and test scores. Many organizations no longer use an employee's Social Security Number for records identification, and some states prohibit its use. The practice of using other identification methods reduces the opportunity for improper use or the potential for identity theft. Laws protect the release of individuals' evaluation/testing scores. In the U.S., the **Family Educational Rights and Privacy Act (FERPA)** prohibits the release of this type of information. Similarly, the Canadian province of Ontario has the Municipal Freedom of Information and Protection of Privacy Act (MFIPPA), which places the responsibility on training officers to know their duties and responsibilities under the applicable legislation within their jurisdictions. Scores and personal data are considered privileged information and are available only to management and a few other designated personnel with authorization and a specific need to know.

While individual personnel records are confidential, other department records are not. Generally, open-meeting laws and open-records acts define the type of records that are available to the public and media. A jurisdiction's open-meeting law will cause the official minutes and any other notes that are made as part of the meeting to be included in the public record (such as the Occupational Safety and Health committee meeting minutes). Care should always be taken in the recording of any information that might potentially become public **(Figure 3.5)**.

Family Educational Rights and Privacy Act (FERPA) — U.S. Legislation that provides that an individual's school records are confidential and that information contained in those records may not be released without the individual's prior written consent.

Figure 3.5 Notes or minutes should be kept of any formal meetings to ensure that the decisions from the meeting are available if requested under open-records laws.

Exemptions to the open-records acts exist in many states, but they are limited and have been interpreted narrowly by the courts. The laws presume that all records are open and place the burden on the jurisdiction to demonstrate that any requested materials are exempt. If a public record contains both exempt and nonexempt material, the exempt portion must be redacted and the remaining nonexempt material disclosed. All fire department officers who are involved with the creation, storage, and distribution of records should be aware of the open-records laws enforced in their jurisdiction. Federal employees must be aware of the application of the Freedom of Information Act (FOIA) on U.S. government agencies. Examples of exemptions are as follows:

- Medical and veterinary records and other materials involving matters of personal privacy

- Records relating to pending investigations

- Records required by the federal government to be kept confidential, such as training, promotional, and educational records

- Trade secrets and certain information of a proprietary nature

- Research data, records, or information that has not been published, patented, or otherwise publicly disseminated

- Confidential evaluations submitted to a public agency in connection with the hiring of a public employee

- Records in which privacy outweighs the public interest

A fire department member may gain access to and request a release of records upon separation of employment. The HSO should ensure a SOP/G addresses the release of records and meets all legal directives.

Confidential Health Database

NFPA® 1500 states that the fire department shall maintain a confidential health record and data base for each member. To protect the member, OSHA has strict requirements regarding the development and maintenance of medical records as contained in Title 29 CFR 1910.1020, *Access to Employee Exposure and Medical Records*. In addition, the HSO should review Title 29 CFR 1910.120, *Hazardous Waste Operations and Emergency Response*, and Title 29 CFR 1910.134, *Respiratory Protection*, for additional limitations on the access to member medical records.

In all cases, confidentiality is a key issue for the proper management of files and databases. The fire department's physician and the employee are the only individuals who have access to an individual's file. Thorough record keeping is also necessary from a legal standpoint because it supports the position of the authority having jurisdiction in cases involving termination, duty status, and denial of employment or membership to candidates. Award of public safety officer benefits may also depend on the availability of the member's records.

Personnel Medical Records

The fire department is required to ensure a medical record is kept by the physician or medical provider. Defining what a medical record is and what is contained in the medical record is crucial for the HSO to ensure compliance with federal, state/provincial, and local regulations. The HSO will serve as a liaison with the physician or medical provider to ensure proper documentation is completed. The fire department's physician only provides the organization with an opinion concerning an individual's ability to perform the required duties and not the detailed description of any malady. Medical records beyond a physician's fit-for-duty opinion shall be kept separate from personnel records.

Physical Fitness for Duty Records

NFPA® 1500 provides detailed guidelines for a department physician or approved medical provider in evaluating fire department member's fitness for duty; and criteria for when a member is not fit for duty. The physical fitness for duty evaluations should be conducted annually, with the written physician opinion maintained in a confidential fire department file. The HSO will serve as a liaison in this process, ensure confidentiality of member information, and ensure compliance with NFPA® 1500 evaluation process.

Exposure Reports

The HSO should ensure a standard form is developed and used for documenting any **exposure**. Any exposure to the following should be reported and documented immediately:

Exposure — Contact with a hazardous material, causing biological damage, typically by swallowing, breathing, or touching (skin or eyes). Exposure may be short-term (acute exposure), of intermediate duration, or long-term (chronic exposure).

- Infectious agents/diseases
- Chemical
- Biological
- Radiological
- Nuclear

A supervisor report may accompany an exposure report, but is not required. Exposure reports should indicate the following:

- Date
- Member name
- Level of exposure
- Any protective clothing and equipment worn when the exposure occurred
- Any signs or symptoms
- Any immediate actions or treatments

If the HSO is serving as the Infection Control Officer, then the HSO will also serve as the liaison and ensure documentation is completed as well as any follow-up information. Retention of an exposure report is typically 30 years past a separation of employment of a fire department member.

State Regulations for Health Records

State/provincial regulations on health records vary. Federal and state OSHA regulations provide the minimum standard. State/provincial regulations will supplement OSHA regulations. HSOs should research their state/provincial laws and regulations to determine compliance.

Release of Health Records

Release of health records is done at the request of the fire department member. An exception to this general rule is during an investigation of an injury, fatality, illness, or exposure while on duty. OSHA 29 CFR 1910.120 and 1910.1020 address the release of medical records. State/provincial regulations may also provide direction on the release of medical records. HIPAA also provides guidance on when releasing medical records is acceptable.

Records Involving Other Departments

In addition to safety and health records, reports, and documentation, the HSO has record keeping responsibilities that will involve other departments within the fire service organization. In some cases, the HSO is providing records that will be maintained in other departments. In other cases, the HSO is verifying that records are being kept in other departments or working with outside entities to maintain records. The sections that follow describe some of these records.

Training Program Records

The HSO is responsible for either providing training on safety and health topics that may include specific classes and seminars or ensuring that such training takes place. Training may also include providing briefings on new SOP/Gs or refresher courses on organizational procedures to new and existing members. All such training should be documented and a record kept of the events. These records are necessary to document both that the HSO is in compliance with training requirements and that fire department members have been trained and informed about safety and health requirements. Records may include attendance lists, dates of classes delivered, and certificates of completion when applicable. These records may be stored with other safety and health records, or they may become part of the training division's records.

Records of Corrective Actions

Corrective actions are recommended to prevent unsafe practices from continuing. They can also decrease the hazards faced, thus improving the workplace environment. The HSO should research injury and accident reports, including near-miss events, to determine any root causes. This research should lead the HSO to develop a list of recommended corrective actions. The HSO will need to monitor corrective actions and determine if they met the goal of eliminating or reducing recurring accidents or incidents.

Records of corrective actions should be maintained after the actions are implemented to provide a history of these actions for the department. The HSO will work with other departments to communicate corrective actions and may assist them with record keeping related to implementing the actions or taking enforcement actions.

Member Assistance Program Records

When a member seeks assistance from the Member Assistance Program, the providing agency retains the detailed records. The only record the fire department receives is an attendance notification. In some organizations, the Human Resources Department receives this attendance record and keeps it confidential.

Corrective Actions — Measures implemented to improve the workplace, reduce hazards, or correct any unsafe acts.

Inspection and Service Testing Records

The HSO is responsible for verifying that inspection and service testing records are kept. The department must maintain inspection and service testing records. All records should follow their local or state retention schedules.

Inspection records include those relating to safety inspections of facilities, apparatus, equipment, and clothing. Service records include those relating to apparatus in-service testing, annual testing of apparatus and equipment, and fit testing of self-contained breathing apparatus (SCBA) masks used by personnel. These records should be maintained in a fashion that promotes easy access for any fire department member or government agency with authorization to request copies, such as OSHA. Having a central computer server that permits access via the Internet is the most practical method because it allows equal access while maintaining document protection from alteration.

Facilities

Any inspection of a fire department facility or fire station must be documented. The HSO is responsible for ensuring a SOP/G addresses the frequency of inspections and the documentation of results. Inspections are crucial to the maintenance of facilities, which mitigates risk in the workplace environment **(Figure 3.6)**. The inspections also ensure compliance with building and fire codes. A sample form for conducting station inspections is found in NFPA® 1500, Annex G, Facility Safety Checklist. Records on each fire department facility should be maintained according to local and state retention schedules.

Apparatus

Chapter 4 of NFPA® 1500 requires that the fire department provide and maintain records relating to the inspection, maintenance, repair, and service of all vehicles used for emergency operations. This requirement can include daily, weekly, monthly, semi-annual, and/or annual apparatus and equipment checks. Justifying apparatus re-

Figure 3.6 Facility inspections should be regularly scheduled, documented, and retained as part of the record-keeping system.

furbishment or replacement is based on accurate and thorough record keeping. The department should have data containing all information collected on each emergency and nonemergency vehicle owned, leased, or assigned to it. Information maintained in the file should include, but is not limited to, the following:

- Safety related issues
- Mechanical repairs and/or recall issues
- Accident involvement
- Reliability
- Original specifications
- Manufacturer's certification for apparatus pumps
- Manufacturer's certification for apparatus ground and aerial ladders
- Acceptance test results
- Annual pump test results
- Annual ground and aerial ladder test results
- Third-party ladder certification generated during the 5-year test
- Vehicle assignment
- Unit inspection records
- Preventive maintenance records
- Major overhauls, refurbishments, or repairs
- Purchase and maintenance costs
- Certification and training of maintenance personnel

Vehicle Standards

The apparatus inspection records for an organization will depend upon which types of apparatus are utilized in that organization. All such records should coincide both with jurisdictional requirements and with one or more of the following NFPA® standards depending on the type of apparatus:

- NFPA® 414, *Standard for Aircraft Rescue and Fire-Fighting Vehicles*
- NFPA® 1901, *Standard for Automotive Fire Apparatus*
- NFPA® 1906, *Standard for Wildland Fire Apparatus*
- NFPA® 1911, *Standard for the Inspection, Maintenance, Testing, and Retirement, of In-Service Automotive Fire Apparatus*
- NFPA® 1912, *Standard for Fire Apparatus Refurbishing*
- NFPA® 1914, *Standard for Testing Fire Department Aerial Devices*
- NFPA® 1915, *Standard for Fire Apparatus Preventative Maintenance Program*
- NFPA® 1917, *Standard for Automotive Ambulances*
- NFPA® 1925, *Standard on Marine Fire-Fighting Vessels*

Equipment

Equipment inspection and service testing includes items attached to apparatus and assigned to qualified personnel. This database includes all documentation on the equipment and the personnel who use it. Because this data may be compiled by a variety of personnel inside and outside the department, the HSO is the logical person to ensure that the necessary information is gathered and maintained in the appropriate file.

Equipment, such as SCBA, has special record-keeping requirements that include both medical and equipment service testing components. The following information on SCBA and facepieces must be maintained **(Figure 3.7)**:

- Personnel files, medical
  - Facepiece fit testing documentation
  - Annual medical exam regarding pulmonary tests (physician written opinion only)
  - Exposure reports
  - Injury reports that involve respiratory injuries
- Personnel files, general
  - Fit testing, pass or fail
  - Documentation and required SCBA training
- SCBA and other respiratory equipment data
  - Design and selection criteria
  - Annual testing and inspection documentation
  - Maintenance records on individual units
  - Air-quality reports
  - Regulator flow testing
- Monthly inspection of hydrostatic test dates on cylinders

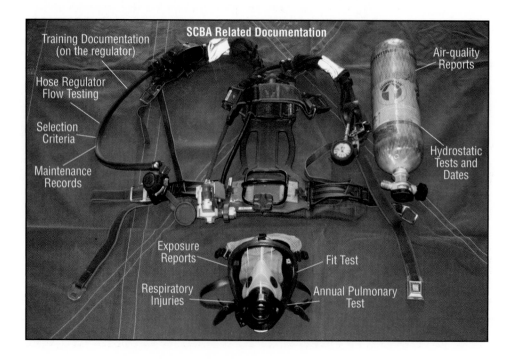

Figure 3.7 SCBAs have special record-keeping requirements including medical and equipment service testing components.

Protective Clothing

Records must be kept on all protective clothing and equipment. The records serve many purposes, including inventory control, budget justification, and liability mitigation. Records may be divided into purchasing, inspection, maintenance, and disposal records. These records may be linked to a common identification number, or bar code, for each individual item of protective clothing and equipment.

Modern records keeping systems permit various types of files to be cross-referenced so that all information can be easily accessed. In some cases, the information is located in remote sites that may even be under the control of a different division or department within the jurisdiction.

The jurisdiction's purchasing department usually maintains purchasing information, although the fire and emergency services department may also retain it. The information ensures that products have been received and that they meet the correct specifications. In addition, the information provides a background for future purchases. Purchasing information includes the following **(Figure 3.8)**:

- Product specifications
- Purchase order
- Purchase contract
- Warranty
- Shipping/delivery papers
- Manufacturer/vendor information

Protective Clothing Purchasing Information

Manufacturer/Vendor Information

Product Specifications

Warranty

Purchase Contract

Purchase Order

Shipping/Delivery Papers

Figure 3.8 Purchasing information for protective clothing should be kept in the record-keeping system for reference when making future purchases.

Local jurisdictions usually establish periodic inspection requirements for protective clothing and equipment. Some of these requirements are based on legal mandates, such as the inspection cycle for SCBA. Inspection information provides a basis for other types of records, including the need for maintenance and disposal, to track inventory, and to determine liability in the event of a protective clothing and equipment-related accident. Inspection information usually includes the following **(Figure 3.9)**:

- Inventory tracking number
- Inspector's name
- Item assigned to (person or location)
- Condition
- Age
- Repairs needed
- Remove from service reason

Maintenance records include information about cleaning, preventive maintenance, and corrective maintenance. Cleaning records should be maintained on protective clothing, ropes, and facepieces. Preventive maintenance should include scheduled repairs, such as periodic battery or parts replacements, calibrations, and any manufacturer's recommended repairs. Corrective maintenance is the result of an inspection or of any reported equipment failure or damage. The protective clothing and equipment is removed from service, and either a permanent or a temporary replacement is issued. Maintenance records generally include the following:

- Inventory tracking number
- Name of person requesting maintenance

Figure 3.9 Protective clothing inspection information should be documented and retained to identify clothing that needs replacement or repair.

Protective Clothing Inspection Information

Item assigned to (person or location)

Inspector's name

Inventory tracking number

Condition

Age

Repairs needed

Remove from service reason

- Name of person performing maintenance
- Type of maintenance
- Reason for maintenance
- Parts used
- Labor (in hours/minutes)
- Cost of parts
- Cost of labor
- Recommendation to dispose of item

All state/provincial and local governments have laws concerning the disposal of property. When protective clothing and equipment reaches its normal end of service life (ESL) or repairs cannot be justified, the item must be disposed of according to those laws. Generally, there are only two ways to dispose of protective clothing and equipment: surplus sale or destruction.

Disposal records include the inventory tracking number, reason for disposal, and final means and date of disposal. If the final disposal is the result of damage or loss that can be reimbursed, then additional information may be included to indicate how and when the item was replaced. Equipment may be disposed of for a number of reasons, including the following **(Figure 3.10)**:

- Age
- Lack of repair parts
- Equipment out of compliance
- Damage and degradation
- Equipment is faulty from the manufacturer
- Equipment has similar faults to previously identified faulty equipment

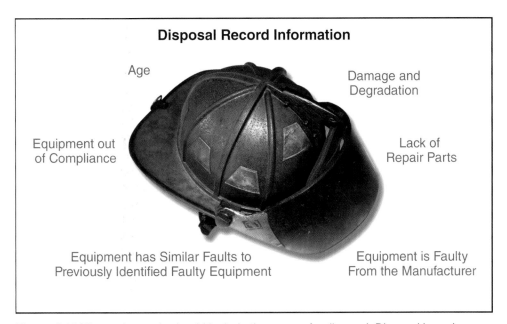

Disposal Record Information

Age

Damage and Degradation

Equipment out of Compliance

Lack of Repair Parts

Equipment has Similar Faults to Previously Identified Faulty Equipment

Equipment is Faulty From the Manufacturer

Figure 3.10 Disposal records should include the reason for disposal. Disposal based upon age is recommended in NFPA® standards or the AHJ's policies.

Code Violations

Any code violations discovered during inspections should be documented and then added to the record-keeping system. These records create a history of violations that can help identify units that are routinely not following organizational equipment policies or local building codes. The violation history can also show improvements over time or identify procedures in need of revision.

Documentation for the Safety and Health Program

Documents are written for specific purposes: to educate, persuade, inform, or enlighten. The ability to write effectively helps to ensure that the intended purpose is attained. Documentation in the safety and health program will be produced from investigations, inspections, accidents, incidents, specifications, and training. Documentation will range from simple checksheets to formal reports.

A fire department has an obligation to its membership, the jurisdiction, the governing body, and the community to document and report on its operations. This obligation includes the safety and health program. The following sections explain documentation specific to the HSO.

Accident, Injury, or Occurrence Investigation Documentation and Reports

The HSO is responsible for investigating incidents that result or could result in hazardous conditions, injuries, illnesses, exposures, and fatalities involving fire department members. Investigations must be documented, so that information from the investigation can be analyzed to determine the root cause of the accident.

Members should follow established SOP/Gs for reporting accidents and injuries using a standard reporting procedure. Documentation may be completed electronically or by hard copy. The HSO will need to develop an acceptable template for completing reports that meet the needs of the department and meet the legal requirements **(Figure 3.11)**. Reports on accidents, incidents, events, and activities should be completed in narrative form. These reports require sections that include descriptions, recommendations, contributing information, findings, and outcomes.

Once an accident has been reported, it must be investigated. Beginning with the report of the incident, the HSO will assist with the gathering of information pertinent to the investigation. In addition to written reports, investigations may include photographs or video footage of the accident or incident. During the investigation phase of the incident, the HSO collects information from many sources, such as the following:

- Dispatch records
- Interviews with participants **(Figure 3.12, p. 81)**
- Emergency incident reports
- Incident action plan
- Incident safety plan
- Police reports

- Photographs and videotapes of the scene or incident
- Site diagrams
- Physical property involved in the incident
- Chain of custody documentation
- Laboratory analysis of evidence relating to the incident
- Testimony from experts
- Incident safety officer report

Figure 3.11 Having templates for various reports, such as this accident reporting form, are important for standardizing reporting procedures. *Courtesy of City of Pitt Meadows Fire Rescue.*

PITT MEADOWS FIRE & RESCUE SERVICE INCIDENT ACCIDENT/INCIDENT/NEAR MISS INVESTIGATION REPORT

EMPLOYER NAME **PITT MEADOWS FIRE RESCUE SERVICE**	Firefighters Attending Investigation #
	Firefighters Absent #

ADDRESS WHERE INCIDENT OCCURRED:

INCIDENT OCCURRED:

PLACE	DATE YY/MM/DD	TIME	
			☐ AM ☐ PM

INJURED PERSON(S) or NON-INJURY ☐

LAST NAME	FIRST NAME	JOB TITLE
1) 2)		

NATURE OF INJURY

1) 2)		

EQUIPMENT FAILURE/DAMAGED

YES/NO DESCRIBE:

MEMBERS INVOLVED AND/OR WITNESSES

NAME	RANK	ADDRESS IF NOT FD MEMBER	TELEPHONE
1)			
2)			
3)			
4)			

ACCIDENT/INCIDENT DESCRIPTION

Briefly describe what happened, including the sequence of events preceding the incident

CONTRIBUTING FACTORS AND CAUSES

List of any unsafe conditions, acts, procedures or factors that in any manner contributed to the incident

RECOMMENDATIONS

Identify any corrective actions that have been taken and any recommended actions to prevent similar incidents

RECOMMENDED CORRECTIVE ACTION	ACTION BY WHOM	ACTION BY DATE
1)		
2)		
3)		
4)		
5)		
6)		

JOSH INVESTIGATION COMMITTEE

NAME	SIGNATURE	TYPE OF REPRESENTATIVE			DATE
		☐ EMPLOYER	☐ WORKER	☐ OTHER	
		☐ EMPLOYER	☐ WORKER	☐ OTHER	
		☐ EMPLOYER	☐ WORKER	☐ OTHER	
		☐ EMPLOYER	☐ WORKER	☐ OTHER	
		☐ EMPLOYER	☐ WORKER	☐ OTHER	

Figure 3.11 Continued

This information provides the HSO with a fairly accurate description of the incident. A written report is then compiled on the incident relating to health and safety issues. This report is the basis for the postincident analysis and any corrective actions that the department needs to take. The finalized report may include diagrams as an explanatory tool for understanding an accident or incident. Computer software programs are available to make this process easier.

Figure 3.12 When reviewing accident and incident reports, the HSO may hold follow-up interviews with firefighters.

Establishing Checks for Completion

Before submitting a report or document, the report writer should thoroughly review the information included. Corrections and changes should be made at this time to ensure the most accurate report possible.

When reports are submitted, a review process should be included. This review process should start at the supervisory level above the report writer and continue through the chain of command. Each supervisor within the report's chain of responsibility should review it for accuracy and completeness.

Addendums

Once documents are completed and submitted, revisions to the original document should not be done. If a revision needs to be made, the report writer should submit an addendum. It may be tempting and easy to alter a word processor-produced document; however, once submitted, the original document should not be altered. Computer-generated documents have a date and time stamp of the last correction. Having conflicting information could be detrimental in a legal action.

Supervisors should never make changes or alter a report written by another department member. Supplemental reports or addendums are the appropriate means to address items or include additional comments.

Hand-written reports may have spelling errors. The report writer can easily correct these spelling errors by placing a single line through the word and initialing the error. The correct word is then written. Scratching out a word or using multiple lines should never be done **(Figure 3.13)**.

Reports on Department Functions

While the HSO focuses a lot of attention on reports of injuries or fatalities, instances where there was the potential for an injury or accident but none occurred are of equal importance. Reporting and keeping records of these occurrences is a proactive way for the HSO to make recommendations for change before a firefighter has been injured or killed rather than learning lessons after the fact. The sections that follow describe some department functions that may not have resulted in accidents, but are nevertheless vital information for an HSO.

Figure 3.13 Hand-written reports should be edited before being submitted as permanent records. The editing marks should be clear and offer a recommended correction.

Vehicle Incident Reports

Vehicle incidents can range from a traffic accident involving fire department vehicles, apparatus and apparatus equipment failures, to property damage as a result of improper backing **(Figure 3.14, p. 84)**. Any of these occurrences may result in a firefighter injury or fatality. Accidents are generally investigated even in the absence of injury. Apparatus failures need to be reported so that the HSO can account for aging equipment when assessing equipment specifications.

Near-Miss Reports

A **near-miss** is defined as an occurrence that had a high likelihood to cause an injury or fatality, but the injury or fatality was avoided. Near-miss documentation and reporting is valuable because near-misses often identify behavior that firefighters may think is safe but still needs correction. A near-miss may also indicate unsafe habits or actions that firefighters have been engaging in for a long time without incident, even though the practices are against procedure. Near-misses may also indicate incidents that are likely to occur in the future that the HSO can address before they result in an injury or fatality.

Near-Miss — occurrence that had a high likelihood to cause an injury or fatality, but the injury or fatality was avoided.

Equipment Malfunction or Failure Reports

Similar to apparatus malfunctions, equipment malfunctions or failures indicate occurrences that could have caused an injury or fatality. If these occurrences are not reported and documented, then no proactive measures can be taken to ensure that the faulty equipment does not harm a firefighter in the future. HSOs rely upon this information when making recommendations about the purchase or repair of equipment.

Training Documentation

The HSO is responsible for ensuring procedures are in place for conducting and documenting live fire training evolutions. Documentation of all fire department training should follow NFPA® 1401, *Recommended Practice for Fire Service Training Reports and Records*. The training report will document the who, what, where, when, why, and how of the evolution. The training evolution procedures should follow NFPA® 1403, *Standard on Live Fire Training Evolutions*. The HSO will participate in a post-training critique and must be able to document the need for any changes based on safety considerations.

Using acquired or fixed facility structures for live fire training evolutions can present unique challenges for each type. NFPA® 1403 provides guidance on the use of acquired structures and fixed facilities for live fire training. The HSO will need to ensure permits are obtained and preburn inspection documentation is complete **(Figure 3.15, p. 86)**. This requirement will depend on local and state regulations.

The HSO is also responsible for reviewing postincident reports from training exercises to ensure that training meets the same compliance standards as emergency response. Firefighters respond according to how they have trained. While the training environment should be safer than an actual incident, the higher level of safety should not be an indication that SOP/Gs are optional or do not apply.

PLEASE FAX ACCIDENT REPORT TO IRMA WITHIN 5 DAYS 630-932-9680
IRMA NON-WORKERS COMPENSATION ACCIDENT REPORT FORM

Please complete the sections of the report that are applicable. Please print in ink. The individual having responsibility for reporting the accident should complete the report **by the close of the work shift**. The claimant should not complete this form.

The supervisor/department head of the employee who filled out the form should complete section IX. The report shall then be forwarded to your claims coordinator **by the end of the work shift or within 24 hours**. This completed form shall then be forwarded to IRMA the **same day** the claims coordinator receives it.

I. MEMBER INFORMATION

NAME OF IRMA MEMBER (MUNICIPALITY)	CONTACT PERSON NAME AND PHONE NUMBER - -	DEPARTMENT

DATE OF LOSS / /	TIME OF LOSS A.M. P.M.	ESTIMATE OR LOSS DAMAGE $	WAS EMPLOYEE INJURED YES ☐ NO ☐

LOCATION OF LOSS	EMPLOYEE NAME	EMPLOYEE STATUS ☐ FULL ☐ PART ☐ SEASONAL ☐ OTHER

POLICE OR FIRE DEPT. REPORT #	STREET/SIDEWALK CONDITIONS: ☐ DRY ☐ OTHER ☐ WET ☐ SNOW/ICE	WEATHER CONDITONS: ☐ CLEAR/CLOUDY ☐ RAIN ☐ SNOW ☐ OTHER

II. MEMBER PROPERTY DAMAGE

ITEMS DAMAGED:	AGE OF ITEM (S) DAMAGED	VIN NUMBER:	
MAKE OF OUR VEHICLE/MOBILE EQUIPMENT:	YEAR:	MODEL:	LICENSE NUMBER (S)

III. MEMBER DESCRIPTION OF ACCIDENT

DOES MEMBER ANTICIPATE FURTHER ACTION FROM CLAIMANT? ☐ YES ☐ NO   PLEASE EXPLAIN:

IV. TYPE OF ACCIDENT (Please check which applies)

SLIPS, TRIPS, FALLS ☐   PROPERTY ☐   POLICE PROFESSIONAL LIABILITY ☐

AUTOMOBILE LIABILITY ☐   EMPLOYMENT LIABILITY ☐   OTHER/PLEASE EXPLAIN ☐

V. CLAIMANT ACCIDENT / INJURY INFORMATION

NAME:		SEX:	AGE/D.O.B. / /
BUSINESS PHONE: - -	HOME PHONE: - -	ADDRESS:	
NATURE OF INJURY/PART OF BODY: ☐ FATALITY		WHAT WAS INJURED PERSON DOING?	
WHERE TAKEN? (Name of hospital/clinic, address, phone number)			

VI. CLAIMANT AUTOMOBILE INFORMATION

OWNER OF OTHER VEHICLE	AGE	ADDRESS	CITY	STATE	ZIP	PHONE - -
DRIVER, IF OTHER THAN OWNER	AGE	ADDRESS	CITY	STATE	ZIP	PHONE - -

MAKE OF VEH	YEAR	MODEL	LICENSE NO.	VIN NO.	AREA OF DAMAGE	ESTIMATE OF DAMAGE $

IS VEHICLE INSURED? ☐ YES ☐ NO	COMPANY/AGENCY NAME, POLICY NO. & PHONE NO.	WHERE VEHICLE CAN BE SEEN

Figure 3.14 Vehicle incident reports may be completed in forms similar to those used for non-vehicular accidents. One form may cover all types, but in either case the reports should be completed for every incident. *Courtesy of the International Risk Management Agency.*

VII. CLAIMANT NON-AUTO PROPERTY DAMAGE (i.e. fence, building, etc.)						
OWNER OF PROPERTY	ADDRESS	CITY	STATE	ZIP	PHONE - -	
DESCRIBE DAMAGED PROPERTY:		LOCATION OF PROPERTY:				
IS PROPERTY INSURED? ☐ YES ☐ NO	COMPANY/AGENCY NAME, POLICY NO. & PHONE NO.					

VIII. WITNESS INFORMATION					
NAME:	AGE/D.O.B.: / /	ADDRESS:	BUS PHONE - -	HOME PHONE - -	
NAME:	AGE/D.O.B.: / /	ADDRESS:	BUS PHONE - -	HOME PHONE - -	

IX. ADDITIONAL COMMENTS

Unsafe conditions (Describe any unsafe conditions or defects contributing to the accident):

Unsafe acts (Describe any unsafe acts or procedures contributing to the accident):

What precautions should have been taken to avoid accident (if any?):

Remedy (As a supervisor, what action have you taken or do you propose taking to help prevent a similar accident?)

Was the member aware of any problems or conditions to the property prior to this accident: ☐ Yes ☐ No

If so, how, when and where was it made known?

Comments:

SUPERVISOR/DEPT. MANAGER: DATE:

CLAIMS COORDINATOR: DATE:

PLEASE FAX ACCIDENT REPORT TO IRMA WITHIN 5 WORKING DAYS.
PLEASE SEND ANY SUPPORTING MATERIAL, SUCH AS AVAILABLE REPORTS, NEWSPAPER ACCOUNTS,
PICTURES, REPAIR ESTIMATES AND/OR BILLS,
POLICE REPORTS / AMBULANCE REPORTS / AS SOON AS POSSIBLE.
NOTE: IF MEMBER PROPERTY IS DAMAGED BY A CLAIMANT VEHICLE, PLEASE FILE A STATE OF ILLINOIS ACCIDENT
FORM WITH THE SECRETARY OF STATE.

Page 2 of 2

Figure 3.14 Continued.

Figure 3.15 Preburn inspections should be conducted before all live-fire evolutions and should become part of the permanent records of the training event.

Documentation of Corrective Actions

Corrective actions are implemented to improve the workplace, reduce hazards, or correct any unsafe acts. Determining the root cause of an incident and preventing future adverse effects is the goal of implementing corrective actions. A thorough inspection and maintenance program and a review of accident/incident reports will allow the HSO to detect most deficiencies in the workplace. Some deficiencies will be found during the course of the normal work routine, in the training environment, or during incident response activities. The HSO is responsible for continually monitoring the workplace for corrective action needs. Corrective actions must be documented and disseminated to the workforce if they are to be effective. Reevaluation is needed to ensure improvement is made.

Technology Specifications

The HSO plays an integral part of the design and review of new specifications for fire apparatus, equipment, and protective clothing. Technological advances drive changes in design, function, and safety. These changes are reflected in the revision of regulations and standards. The HSO needs to become knowledgeable of the revision cycles of regulations and standards of apparatus, equipment, and protective clothing and how they can influence the process of purchasing. Consideration of the most up-to-date regulations and standards affects not only new purchases, but the refurbishment of used apparatus, equipment, and protective clothing.

Facilities Inspection Documentation

Facility inspections are conducted on a regular basis. The station crew will perform some inspections, while other inspections will involve fire administration staff, jurisdictional risk management personnel, building safety personnel, and/or third-party vendors. Regardless of the formality of the inspection, all inspections must be documented and maintained in a file. The fire department should establish standard forms for the routine inspections **(Figure 3.16, p. 88)**. These reports may be spreadsheets or checksheets that easily record pertinent items. There should be room on the form to record notes of deficiencies or ongoing issues. The HSO is responsible for ensuring the inspections meet the objectives of the safety and health program as well as the risk management plan. Further information on facility inspections and addressing code violations is covered in Chapter 10, Facilities Inspection.

Infection Control Documentation

To meet the record-keeping requirements of Title 29 CFR 1910.1030, the fire department must maintain complete records of both the exposures to members and member training. The exposure report forms, completed at the time of the exposure, must contain the following:

- Name and Social Security Number of the individual
- Copy of the individual's hepatitis B vaccination status
- Copy of the results of all examinations, medical testing, and follow-up procedures
- Copy of the fire department physician's written opinion
- Description of the employee's duties at the time of the incident
- Documentation of the circumstances of the exposure
- Results of the source individual's blood testing
- All medical records relevant to the treatment of the employee

These records must be retained for thirty years from the employee's date of termination. They must remain confidential and may only be released with the permission of the employee.

Training records for exposure awareness, which are retained for three years from the time of training, shall include the following:

- Dates of training sessions
- Summary of the training given
- Names and qualifications of the training personnel involved
- Names and job titles of all those attending training sessions

Personnel Interaction, Interviews, and Surveys

In carrying out the responsibilities of the safety and health program, the HSO must interact with personnel, conduct interviews, and gather information on surveys. These functions will help the HSO understand any issues that are impacting members, or where improvements can be made. These are simple tools for the HSO to incorporate in the safety and health program. More importantly, it gets people talking about safety.

Accident Prevention Information

The HSO will submit recommendations on the Accident Prevention Program to the fire chief. Information on accident prevention can be obtained through interactions with personnel in their environment. The HSO must remain alert

MONTHLY SAFETY INSPECTION CHECKLIST
FIRE DEPARTMENT FACILITIES

Location:_____   Date:_____

Inspected By:_____   SAT: Satisfactory

Reviewed By:_____   NA: Needs Attention

SAFE WORK PRACTICES	SAT	NA	COMMENTS (Location, Nature of Problem, etc.)
1. Employees observe no smoking policy.			
2. Employees observe general safety rules.			
3. Unattended files and/or desk drawers closed.			
4. Hose Tower Winch inspected and in good working order.			
5. Equipment used properly.			
6. Employees keep work area (floors, furniture, storage) clean & neat.			
7. Protective equipment available and in good condition, (eye and hearing protection, face shields).			
8. No obstructions or tripping hazards.			

HOUSEKEEPING	SAT	NA	COMMENTS
1. Floors & aisles uncluttered.			
2. Sufficient number of trash cans convenient & in good condition.			
3. No overflow in garbage cans.			
4. Floors, aisles, stairways in good repair.			
5. Liquid spills, melted snow, etc. cleaned properly.			
6. Stair railings secure.			
7. Office furniture in good condition.			
8. Proper storage of cleaning supplies.			

FIRE CONTROL	SAT	NA	COMMENTS
1. Fire doors closed/free of obstructions.			
2. Exits clearly marked.			
3. Fire instructions posted.			
4. Periodic fire drills conducted.			
5. Fire extinguishers marked for type of use, and inspected monthly. Tested annually.			

Figure 3.16 Using a standard inspection form for daily, weekly, and monthly facility inspections helps to ensure that nothing is overlooked. *Courtesy of the Wilmette Fire Department*

		SAT	NA	COMMENTS
6.	Furnace and water heater clear of any stored materials.			
7.	Flammable liquid and pressure cylinders stored properly.			

	ELECTRICAL	SAT	NA	COMMENTS
1.	Permanent wiring boxes, switches, outlets & lights secured.			
2.	Breakers & fuse boxes properly maintained and closed.			
3.	No overloading of outlets.			
4.	Wires and plugs securely connected.			
5.	Lighting adequate to perform work.			
6.	Combustibles a min. of 3' clearance.			

	HEALTH & SANITATION	SAT	NA	COMMENTS
1.	Eating facilities clean.			
2.	Bathrooms clean and properly maintained.			
3.	First aid supplies readily available and adequately maintained.			
4.	Eyewash station(s) functioning properly.			
5.	AED's inspected per checklist			

	BULLETIN BOARD & RECORDS	SAT	NA	COMMENTS
1.	OSHA & IDOL labor posters present.			
2.	OSHA records current; OSHA-200 and 300.			
3.	Safety Committee minutes posted.			

ADMINISTRATIVE INSPECTION SECTION

	FLEET SAFETY MANAGEMENT	SAT	NA	COMMENTS
1.	Annual review of driver's record by management.			
2.	Written policies and safety rules governing use of all vehicles are detailed and distributed to all drivers annually.			
3.	Vehicle accident reporting procedures are communicated to all drivers and reporting supervisors annually.			

	EMERGENCY PLANS	SAT	NA	COMMENTS
1.	Emergency evacuation plan posted.			
2.	Floor plan posted			

Figure 3.16 Continued.

to the current work environment and the potential for improving that environment. The HSO can also conduct specific interviews with personnel, especially if a concern, suggestion, or recommendation has been raised.

Finally, surveys can be a valuable tool in gathering information from the membership. Surveys can be conducted anonymously or with names attached. Anonymous surveys present an opportunity for personnel to voice opinions not usually shared. This method also provides personnel with the opportunity to voice their complaints anonymously. Those who do include their names on surveys can be contacted again to clarify information and gain a greater perspective. The HSO will need to weigh both the pros and cons of surveys and choose the best option for the department.

Training Information

Training can be mandated by regulation or department policy, or can be the result of an accident, an incident, an unsafe act, or the needs of the membership. The last of these should be an important consideration in any training program. The best way to obtain the needs of the membership is by asking. The HSO can work with the training division staff to elicit information through interaction, interviews, and/or surveys. All methods can have a positive outcome in the development of training. The HSO should focus on the safety and health aspect and ensure discussions and considerations of safety are included **(Figure 3.17)**.

Figure 3.17 Providing physical fitness information to firefighters can be as informal as posting weight training information in common spaces and discussing the information with firefighters.

Recommendations for the Health and Wellness Programs

Annually, more fire department members die of cardiac-related events than any other cause. This topic is a sensitive issue in some jurisdictions for fear that the health and wellness program is punitive. If a health and wellness program is to be successful, it must have the full support of all fire department members. Allowing personnel to speak openly, in private interviews, or via a survey is a step in the right direction. Recommendations for the health and wellness program must include membership input. Before submitting recommendations, the HSO should discuss the following with fire department members and staff:

- Annual fit-for-duty evaluations
- Physical fitness assessments
- Physical fitness training (on-duty/off-duty) **(Figure 3.18)**
- Nutritional advice
- Physical ability testing
- Process for managing those unfit for duty

The overall health and wellness of fire department members is the goal of this program. Making recommendations will involve a process of discussions and information gathering. The HSO will need to collaborate with labor and management in the development of recommendations.

Interactions with Personnel and Other Departments

Risk management and the safety and health program touch all fire departments. To gain an understanding of the factors that impact safety in their department, HSOs need to talk to personnel. Emergency responders and field supervisors are valuable sources of information. They can inform the HSO of new hazards or where SOP/G improvements are needed.

Figure 3.18 As part of physical fitness training, the HSO may take the time to discuss the exercises with firefighters to ensure they are doing them properly.

The HSO should also connect with other fire departments locally or out of the jurisdiction. Reaching out through networks or just contacting other departments can provide the HSO with advice, recommendations, or answers to issues. Making safety and health recommendations should not be done in isolation. Recommendations should be developed from a foundation of broad knowledge gained from many sources.

Collecting and Compiling Data

Developing effective safety, health and wellness, and risk management programs depends on accurate and current information. Information is based on data that must be gathered from a variety of sources. Gathering the data requires time and effort. Once gathered, the data must be categorized by type and then evaluated to determine what information it provides. **Data mining**, or *knowledge discovery*, is the process of collecting data and analyzing it for meaning. Advances in computer science have led to data mining software that assist in this analysis process. Fire departments across the country input data daily. The **National Fire Incident Reporting System (NFIRS)**, located at the National Fire Academy in Emmitsburg, Maryland, is a widely recognized and utilized data collection point for the fire service. Data mining provides a newer research methodology in the form of statistical analysis as the fire service improves its data reporting capability.

To be effective at researching a topic, you must know what to look for, where to look for it, and how to determine the validity of the data that is collected. The topic helps determine the data to be collected. For example, if the topic involves developing a safety program, the data collected would include the following:

- Local accident, injury, and line-of-duty death reports
- Similar reports for other fire departments in the region or of similar size
- National statistics on firefighter injuries and line-of-duty deaths (LODDs)
- Statistics on similar injuries and deaths in other high-risk occupations based on similarity of activity
- Insurance industry statistics
- Fire and emergency responder pension program statistics
- Worker's compensation data
- Data compiled by governmental agencies

Sometimes, it is just as difficult to determine what to exclude as it is to decide what to include within the search parameters. If the focus of this project were injuries and fatalities, as in this example, then data on illnesses would not be needed.

The first step of the process is to write down the topic that is to be researched. List all possible topics that are similar to the main topic. Next, list the various types of data that may support the topic, such as internal reports, regional or national reports, legislation, product reviews, and cost estimates. Then list the possible sources for each information type. Your department should identify other fire departments in which a comparison may be helpful. In this context, look for other departments of similar size and organizational structure that serves similar demographics. This type of comparison may be more useful than a national statistic. Index cards can be used to record this information

Data Mining — the process of collecting, searching, and analyzing a large amount of data in a database or other record system in order to identify patterns or relationships within the data. *Also Known As* Knowledge Discovery.

National Fire Incident Reporting System (NFIRS) — National fire incident data collection system managed by the United States Fire Administration. Local fire departments forward incident data to a state coordinator. The coordinator collects statewide fire incident data and reports information to the USFA.

and the sources. The information can also be placed in a computer database for easy retrieval and sorting. The information types may include the following (**Figure 3.19**):

- **Expert opinions** — Statements by credible experts in a particular field or someone who has analyzed or experienced a similar situation. Personal knowledge is an acceptable starting point when looking for this type of information; that is, what you or the person doing the research knows about the subject.

- **Trends** — Patterns that can be traced over time and used to forecast the future. Trends may be developed from raw data, such as incident scene strains/sprains over time.

- **Models** — Frameworks composed of accepted practices that an organization can adapt to its own needs such as a model fitness program.

- **Similar situations** — Information from interviews with other people on how they handled particular situations. Sources for this type of research include industry journals, newspaper articles, or simply networking with peers through professional organizations.

- **Quantitative data** — Raw numbers such as lost-time injury leave or cost of overtime.

- **Examples** — Representative images of situations, processes, items, or anything else that a researcher can use to illustrate concepts. Good examples can create a benchmark; that is, something that is considered an informal standard or a goal that an organization attempts to attain. From using benchmarks, an organization can determine how well it has done in reaching or surpassing the standard.

- **Analyses** — Third-party testing laboratories, universities, and other organizations that continually evaluate equipment, procedures, and trends and produce written analytical reports of the behavior of those items. The resulting reports can provide researchers with objective reviews without having to perform the testing.

- **Demographics** — Collected information on the population in a specific area or of a specific group, such as the members of the fire and emergency services organization. This type of information is probably the easiest to obtain because it is readily available.

- **Recommended/suggested practices** — Suggestions for how to do something; usually based on trial-and-error experiences of other people or scientific research. The Hazen-Williams Water Flow Tests are examples of this type of information because they provide a basis for determining nozzle pressures on hoselines.

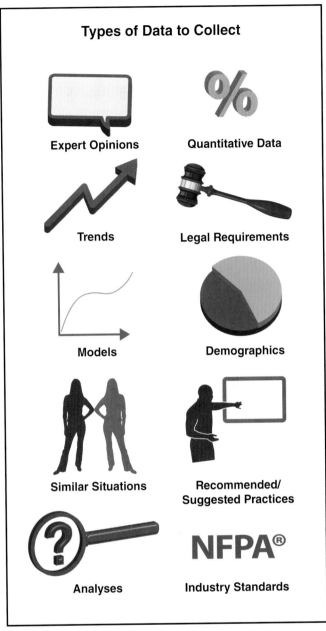

Types of Data to Collect

Expert Opinions

Quantitative Data

Trends

Legal Requirements

Models

Demographics

Similar Situations

Recommended/ Suggested Practices

Analyses

NFPA®

Industry Standards

Figure 3.19 Data that informs decision-making in the organization can come from a wide variety of sources.

- **Industry standards** — Generally accepted methods for accomplishing some task or function (similar to recommended practices). For example, the NFPA® provides industry standards for fire and life safety. Other types of standards are developed by engineering and scientific testing organizations such as the American Society of Mechanical Engineers (ASME) or American National Standards Institute (ANSI).

- **Legal requirements** — Laws, codes, ordinances, and decrees that are legally binding requirements created at most levels of government to ensure the safety and welfare of a society. In the U.S., the *Code of Federal Regulations (CFR)* applies to many areas of the fire and emergency services, while the Americans with Disabilities Act (ADA) affects the design of facilities to ensure access for people with physical impairments.

With the knowledge of what to look for, the next step is to start locating the sources of the information. However, you should be prepared to seek assistance from a professional research firm if necessary. The savings in time, effort, and frustration can easily offset the cost of hiring a research organization that specializes in the particular field of research. Resources used in data analysis are discussed below.

Creating Record Categories

Records management and data analysis require organization. By developing a categorization of information, the HSO will be able to retrieve data easily, gather only the data that is needed, and use the data for analysis.

Organization can be achieved by creating record categories. Categories may be required by local, state/provincial, or federal legal directive. There may also be a local or organizational preference in types of record categories established. The HSO will ensure the creation of categories related to the safety and health program. These categories include but are not limited to the following **(Figure 3.20)**:

- **Injuries** — describe the injuries incurred including their frequency and severity. Include the activity engaged in when injured, the type of injury, and the body part injured.

- **Fatalities** — describe any fatalities with the activity engaged in at the time of death.

- **Illnesses** — describe any illnesses that are attributed to workplace activity. Include the type of illness.

- **Exposures** — describe any exposures that are attributed to workplace activity. This will include exposure to infectious diseases and hazardous materials.

- **Accidents** — describe any accidents involving personnel and/or apparatus. This will include traffic collisions, striking a pedestrian/cyclist, striking a stationary object, or single-vehicle accidents.

- **Incidents and Near-Misses** — describe any incidents involving personnel, apparatus, and/or equipment. Include the location of the incident and any deviation from the SOP/Gs.

- **Financial** — describe the financial loss the fire department incurred; for example, the cost of medical treatment, worker compensation, apparatus or equipment repair/replacement, and/or reparation to outside parties.

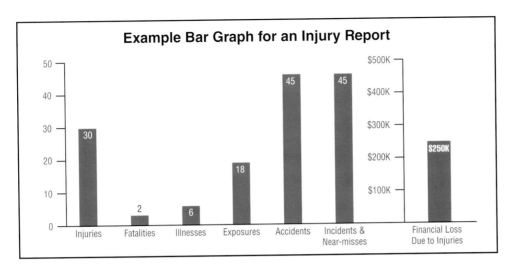

Example Bar Graph for an Injury Report

Figure 3.20 Graphs are a useful tool for showing injury, illness, and fatality data quickly and effectively.

Summarizing Fire Department Experience

The HSO will summarize the fire department experience as it relates to the safety and health program in a document using the categories outlined above. The summary should be limited to the HSO's fire department. It is a way to document the historical experience of a fire department as a reference. Having this information will prove useful when conducting a data comparison from a historical perspective, from a trend analysis perspective or when assessing corrective actions and control measures. Remember, this is a summary of the historical experience of a fire department and not a detailed investigative report.

Resources for Safety and Health Data Comparison

Safety and health data comparison can be accomplished from a myriad of resources. HSOs must become familiar with the different reports and data analysis tools that are available to them. As the department's safety and health advocate, the HSO must analyze data and incorporate important key points in the training and education of members, SOP/G compliance, and the semi-annual report on accident mitigation.

Conducting research to find comparative data depends upon the topic being researched and the scope of the comparison (such as national vs. local). Regardless of the scope, the quality of research is based upon the credibility of the sources; the more credible the source, the more trusted the conclusions of the research **(Figure 3.21, p. 96)**. A high level of credibility is generally associated with the following sources:

- Government agencies
- Libraries
- Educational institutions
- Testing and standards organizations

Canadian and U.S. government agencies at all levels are the best sources of data on fire and emergency services topics. Laws, ordinances, and statutes that affect the fire service and emergency services exist at national, state/provincial, and local levels. Agencies responsible for transportation, manufacturing, and natural resources maintain information on incidents that occur on highways, airways, railroads, and ship channels and in factories, national forests, and grasslands.

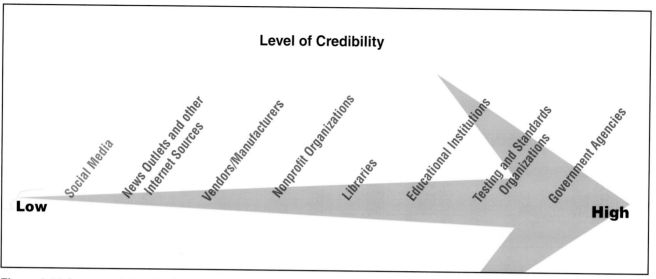

Level of Credibility

Social Media

News Outlets and other Internet Sources

Vendors/Manufacturers

Nonprofit Organizations

Libraries

Educational Institutions

Testing and Standards Organizations

Government Agencies

Low

High

Figure 3.21 Sources of data that have a higher level of credibility add to the credibility of reports generated from the data.

Nonprofit organizations and vendors or manufacturers are also credible sources of some types of information. These organizations may have agendas that influence the information that they provide, such as social causes or profit margins, so safety officers are advised to weigh the information that they receive from these sources carefully before including the information in research.

Most of these agencies and organizations provide the majority of their research information online. Any online information from a credible source carries the same value in research as print information from the same source. Just as in the print media world, information on the Internet may not be credible or may appear credible but require more scrutiny. Information obtained through social media sites, for example, should be traced back to its original online or print source to verify its credibility before being included in data comparison research **(Figure 3.22)**. The following organizations and agencies provide credible information that can be used for data comparison.

Department of Labor (DOL) and OSHA Investigations

The DOL has several divisions with investigation and enforcement authority that may affect fire department personnel. Data comparison information from the DOL or any of its divisions can provide the HSO with rulings and claims statistics. For instance, the Fatality and Catastrophe Investigation Summaries and fact sheets provide information on investigations or rulings. The U.S. and state DOLs can provide data on worker's compensation claims. This data can provide a view of the length of rehabilitation time required for injuries, the cost, and the types of injuries that are more prevalent.

National Institute for Occupational Safety and Health (NIOSH)

NIOSH investigates and publishes reports on firefighter LODDs as well as alerts on a variety of topics important to firefighter safety. The HSO will analyze NIOSH reports for incident information and research the lessons learned or recommendations. This information is valuable when assessing the adequacy and effectiveness of SOP/Gs, when making the semiannual report on accident mitigation, and when making recommendations from the accident prevention program.

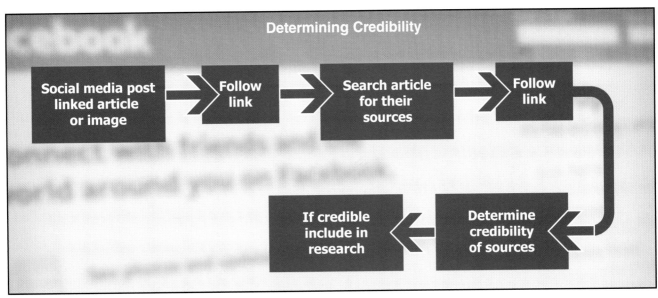

Figure 3.22 Judging the credibility of a piece of information means tracking the information to its source and determining the credibility of the source material.

NIOSH is a part of the Centers for Disease Control and Prevention (CDC) in the Department of Health and Human Services. NIOSH conducts research on work-related injuries and illnesses, and publishes investigative reports that include recommendations to improve the workplace environment – such as the firefighter fatality investigation and prevention program. Through the NIOSH website, resources and publications are available that are specific to the fire service. HSOs can use NIOSH reports in their data collection process. These reports provide valuable information on incidents and lessons learned that may be included in the semiannual reports for SOP/G compliance, and the mitigation of occupational accidents.

NIOSH's **Health Hazard Evaluation (HHE)** program is another resource. Any private sector, federal, state, or local workplace (management or labor representative) or employee can request an HHE (see OSHA 42 CFR 85). Employee requests/complaints can be confidential. This evaluation will assess the workplace for hazardous materials exposures or dangerous conditions and report findings to the organization. The HSO will most likely serve as the liaison between the investigators and fire department management. Any findings of correction needed in a workplace will be the responsibility of the HSO as a part of the occupational safety and health program.

United States Fire Administration (USFA)

The **U.S. Fire Administration (USFA)** provides a wide range of reporting tools and resources for the HSO to use when researching injuries and fatalities developing recommendations. The HSO should become familiar with the USFA Publications Center for online, printed, and digital publications.

The **National Fire Data Center** is a division in the USFA that manages the National Fire Incident Reporting System (NFIRS). NFIRS is a central fire service data collection and reporting system. NFPA® 901, *Standard Classification for Incident Reporting and Fire Protection Data*, is the foundation for the NFIRS incident entry. This system standardizes the data collected

Health Hazard Evaluation Program (HHE) — Program funded through the National Institute for Occupational Safety and Health (NIOSH) intended to learn whether workers are exposed to hazardous materials or harmful conditions in their workplace. Any private sector, federal, state, or local workplace (management or labor representative) or employee can request an HHE.

U.S. Fire Administration (USFA) — U.S. agency whose aim is to reduce the nation's fire deaths. Promotes better fire prevention and control, supports existing programs of research, training, and education, and encourages new programs sponsored by state and local governments. Administers an extensive fire data and analysis program and co-administers a program concerned with firefighter health and safety. USFA is a division of the Federal Emergency Management Agency (FEMA), which itself is a division of the Department of Homeland Security (DHS).

from any participating fire department. With this standard data entry tool, NFIRS can produce detailed reports on fire service incidents, casualties, and fire loss.

The USFA's *Fire Data Analysis Handbook* is another useful tool for the HSO, or any fire officer. This 71-page book is available on the USFA website or in print edition and provides methods for conducting statistical data analysis. The HSO will be responsible for generating charts and other documents that describe specific data elements.

The **National Fire Academy (NFA)** and the **Emergency Management Institute (EMI)** are other divisions in the USFA. The HSO can attend courses at the NFA or EMI specific to safety and health topics.

National Fire Protection Association® (NFPA®)

In addition to the consensus codes and standards, the NFPA® also provides valuable information for the HSO. The four areas the HSO should become familiar with are:

- **Fire analysis and research** – this division of NFPA® provides thirteen statistical reporting tools for the HSO.

- **Fire investigations** – this division of NFPA® provides reporting of fire behavior characteristics and injury and fatality losses.

- **Fire protection research foundation** – is an independent nonprofit that supports the NFPA® mission.

- **Charles S. Morgan library** – maintains the archives for all NFPA® publications.

National Institute of Standards and Technology (NIST)

The **National Institute of Standards and Technology (NIST)** provides research resources from experiments and other testing processes. The HSO should consult the NIST website for specific topics and the results of experiments and testing conducted. For example, The Report on Residential Fireground Field Experiments is a well-known NIST report published in 2010. The HSO should review NIST reports for specific information relating to the occupational safety and health of fire department members.

Underwriters' Laboratories (UL)

Third-party testing and certification organizations provide statistics on the quality of equipment and products and the ability of that equipment or product to perform a specific task. Most fire and emergency services personnel are familiar with the testing that is performed by **Underwriters' Laboratories Inc.**, Underwriters' Laboratories of Canada, Factory Mutual, and other similar organizations. Test results, specifications, and performance criteria are available from these organizations and may assist in writing specifications or in establishing testing criteria for internal equipment evaluations.

American National Standards Institute (ANSI)

The **American National Standards Institute (ANSI)** provides assistance to organizations, such as NFPA®, for their standards development process. In addition, ANSI provides accreditation to agency generating standards and to product certification agencies. The HSO should be familiar with the standards that impact protective clothing and equipment, apparatus, and/or equipment specification design and purchase.

Canadian Standards Association

In Canada, the **Canadian Standards Association (CSA)** improves worker safety through the development of standards. The CSA scope extends beyond the workplace safety environment to include several other programs such as product and industrial safety certification labeling and hazardous materials site certification.

ASTM International

ASTM International, formerly American Society for Testing and Materials (ASTM), is a nonprofit organization that assists in the development of standards for materials, products, systems, and services. Some of the main topics of ASTM standards for the HSO are industrial hygiene and safety; search and rescue operations; firefighter equipment, apparatus, and protective clothing; and emergency medical services.

Center for Public Safety Excellence (CPSE)

The **Center for Public Safety Excellence (CPSE)** is a nonprofit organization that promotes quality fire service improvements through its programs. The Commission for Fire Accreditation International (CFAI) and the Commission for Professional Credentialing (CPC) are programs within CPSE. CPSE and CFAI also serve as a network of fire service professionals who can reach out when needed. Data comparisons between fire departments can include criteria of being Accredited or non-Accredited, and serving similar geographic and demographic characteristics. The HSO can use this network when developing SOP/Gs and revising the risk management plan or the occupational safety and health program.

Other Fire and EMS Professional Organizations

Fire and emergency services professional organizations are also sources for safety-related data, information, and model programs. Among these organizations that can benefit HSOs in carrying out their roles and responsibilities are:

- American Society of Safety Engineers (ASSE)
- Canadian Association of Fire Chiefs (CAFC)
- Canadian Society of Safety Engineers (CSSE)
- Canadian Volunteer Fire Services Association (CVFSA)
- Centers for Disease Control and Prevention (CDC)
- Congressional Fire Services Institute (CFSI)
- Fire Department Safety Officers Association (FDSOA)
- International Association of Fire Chiefs (IAFC)

Underwriters' Laboratories, Inc. (UL) — Independent fire research and testing laboratory that certifies equipment and materials, which can be approved only for the specific use for which it is tested.

American National Standards Institute (ANSI) — Voluntary standards-setting organization that examines and certifies existing standards and creates new standards.

Canadian Standards Association (CSA) — Develops worker safety standards, safety certification labeling, and other related services for Canada.

ASTM International — Voluntary standards-setting organization that sets guidelines on characteristics and performance of materials, products, systems and services; for example, the quality of concrete or the flammability of interior finishes.

Center for Public Safety Excellence (CPSE) — Nonprofit organization that promotes quality improvement of fire and emergency services organizations.

Other Fire and EMS Professional Organizations (cont.)

- International Association of Fire Fighters (IAFF)
- International Association of Women in Fire & Emergency Services (iWomen)
- International Fire Service Training Association (IFSTA)
- International Society of Fire Service Instructors (ISFSI)
- National Fire Fighter Near-Miss Reporting System
- National Registry of Emergency Medical Technicians (NREMT)
- National Volunteer Fire Council (NVFC)
- State/provincial training organizations
- State department of health services
- Volunteer Fire Insurance Service (VFIS)
- World Health Organization (WHO)

State/provincial level organizations associated with these groups may also be able to assist in the gathering of data. Membership may be required to take advantage of the services offered by these organizations.

Colleges and Universities

Colleges and universities can provide certified individuals who can serve as the health and fitness coordinator for the department. These individuals will have the background, experience, education, and training needed to serve in this capacity. In addition, the HSO should work to develop professional relationships with educators to be able to request assistance when researching topics, conducting experiments, or finalizing a statistical analysis. Some colleges and universities have elaborate training facilities for fire, technical rescue, hazmat, marine vessel, aircraft firefighting, and flammable/combustible liquid incidents. Other colleges and universities that do not have fire service programs have classrooms, chemistry laboratories, and demonstration facilities that may be used for presentations. Many institutions have interactive video facilities that can be used to access regional or national training seminars over the Internet.

Some colleges and universities are research institutions and promote advancing medical procedures through experimental programs. These programs can be partnerships between fire service or emergency medical service agencies and the research institution. The HSO may serve as a liaison and assist with developing a program. Even if training sessions are not conducted at college campuses, the college might accredit courses taught off campus, which is a great benefit to students and the credibility of the course being taught.

The library is a valuable resource in any college or university **(Figure 3.23)**. When researching a topic or needing an interlibrary loan of a reference, library staff have the expertise to assist with your project. HSOs should develop a working relationship with library staff of their local educational institution as a resource in meeting their data collection, research, and report writing responsibilities.

Figure 3.23 University libraries are excellent sources for data. Many university libraries may be able to provide departments with Internet access to their materials.

The Learning Resource Center (LRC), located at the NFA, is another valuable library resource. The LRC has the largest collection of fire and emergency service related books, articles, videos, and publications in the U.S.

Data Analysis

Analyzing data is often the topic of advanced research and evaluation methods. Certain basics can help make sense of reams of data. First, always start with the evaluation goal or the reason for the evaluation. This goal helps organize the data and focus the analysis. For example, if the goal is to improve an organization/program by identifying its strengths and weaknesses, then organize the data into organization/program strengths, weaknesses, and suggestions for improvements. If the desired result is to understand how a program works, organize data in chronological order based on how customers go through the program. If an outcome-based evaluation is used, categorize data according to the measurements or indicators for each outcome.

Comparing Data

Interpreting the results of an analysis involves placing the information into perspective. Perspective can be achieved in the following ways:

- Comparing results to the desired results or common standards for the fire and emergency services **(Figure 3.24, p. 102)**.

- Comparing results to the original organizational/program goals.

- Comparing results to indications of accomplished outcomes or descriptions of the organization/program's experiences, strengths, and weaknesses.

- Considering any recommendations submitted by customers to help improve the organization/program.

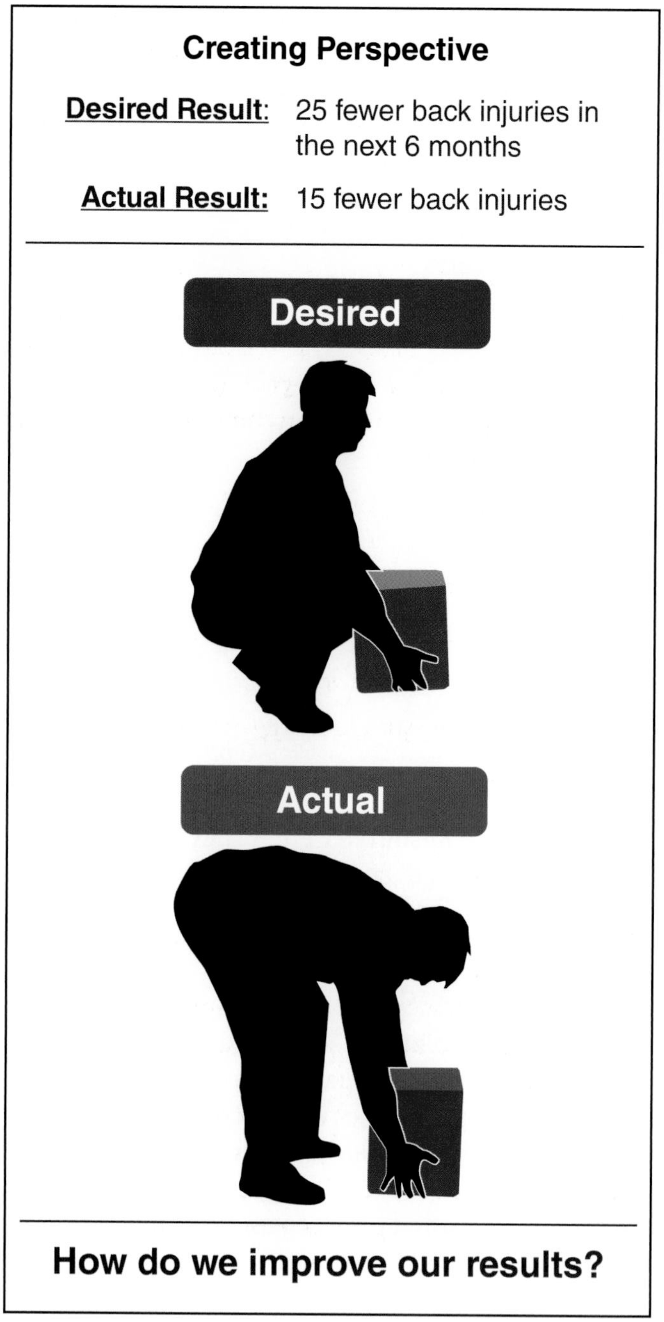

Creating Perspective

Desired Result: 25 fewer back injuries in the next 6 months

Actual Result: 15 fewer back injuries

Desired

Actual

How do we improve our results?

Figure 3.24
Comparing the desired result to the actual result of a program creates perspective on the success of the program and may indicate needed revisions.

Record conclusions from data analysis and make recommendations in a report document for the organization's chief or the authority having jurisdiction. All conclusions or recommendations must be justified based on the analysis of the information gathered.

Comparing To National Trends

The HSO can compare local incidents or accidents and the related injuries, deaths, illnesses, or exposures to national data and determine if a trend exists. A national trend can provide a broad picture of an issue in the fire service. For example, the national trend of firefighter injuries and deaths due to not wearing a seat belt can be compared to local information. Using a national trend can help prevent a similar event from occurring locally. It can also help show where a fire department is above, average, or below a national trend.

Although most departments are too small to rely on their own database for a statistically valid trend, national averages and trends are available from the NFPA® and the National Fire Academy. National data is not always complete or accurate due to collection inconsistencies, and a time lag of one to two years is required to collect, analyze, and publish it.

Comparing To Other Jurisdictions

Research can begin by surveying fire and emergency services organizations in other jurisdictions. Depending on the topic, a survey may include organizations that serve similar demographics, geographic areas, hazards, or accreditation status. Any comparison should include information on the other jurisdictions and why they are included. Common safety and health comparisons include but are not limited to:

- Injuries, fatalities, illnesses, and exposures – rates, frequency, severity, costs/loss
- Specifications for and purchasing of equipment and apparatus
- Specifications for and purchasing of protective clothing and equipment
- Facility design and features
- Communication system design and features
- Manufacturer support
- Control measures

Comparing To Other Occupations and Industries

Comparing the fire service to other occupations and industries may provide clues as to what is working and what is not. The U.S. Department of Labor publishes statistics on job-related injuries, fatalities, illnesses, and exposures. These statistics could provide general data analysis comparisons. For example, comparing the fire service to other hazardous occupations may show if worker injuries are increasing or decreasing. Further analysis could show why a certain occupation or industry has experienced a change in its injury rate. Other occupations and industries may also provide comparative data on equipment, protective clothing and equipment, apparatus, workplace safety programs, or new technologies.

Basic Statistical Analysis

Data collected may be quantitative or qualitative. *Quantitative* data includes numerical ratings, rankings, or simple *yes* or *no* answers. *Qualitative* information involves the answers that are received in interviews, focus groups, or written commentaries on the quality of the service, organization, or program **(Figure 3.25, p. 104)**.

Quantitative

Although **quantitative analysis** is not simple, a basic approach can be used. Using the measures of central tendency (mean, median, and mode) provides differing views of data. The mean is the average of a set of data and is one of the most commonly used measures. The median is the center of a set of data or numbers, while the mode is the data, or numbers, occurring most often in a data set.

Quantitative Analysis — Means of assessment that uses numbers and statistical data to compare different materials and methods, is likely to be more sophisticated than qualitative methods, and involves formal testing; intended to discover quantifiable data.

Quantitative Data	Qualitative Data
Overview: • Deals with numbers • Data can be measured • The what, when, where information • Numerical Ratings/Rankings • Facts • Objective Quantitative ⟶ Quantity	**Overview:** • Deals with descriptions • Data can be observed but not always measured • Why it occured • How it occured • May be subjective • May include opinion • May be quantified when analyzing results Qualitative ⟶ Quality

Figure 3.25 Quantitative and qualitative data are both useful when completing statistical analysis, but each provides a different emphasis.

Mean — Statistical term that refers to the "average" of a set of numerical values scores; calculated by adding all of the set of values and dividing by the total number of values.

Median — Statistical term that refers to the numerical value in a set of values that represents the middle value, or midpoint of the values when they are arranged or ranked in size (order) from high to low.

Mode — Statistical term that refers to the numerical value that appears most frequently in a set of values.

Qualitative Analysis — Examination of nonmeasurable data such as firefighters' opinions about or reactions to a certain program.

Before beginning any analysis, make draft copies of all the surveys or questionnaires that were collected. Maintain the originals in the archives and use the copies for analysis. For ratings and rankings, compute a **mean** for each question. The **median** can measure or assess interval time stamps on all incidents, because they are minimally skewed by outlier data. The **mode** indicates the result that appeared most frequently and can further help to identify outliers. The mode also gives a numerical value to the most common occurrences in the data **(Figure 3.26)**.

More advanced statistical analyses include the measure of dispersion (range, variance, and standard deviation) of a data set. Further statistical analysis requires applying the correct analysis tool. The HSO should refer to FEMA's *Fire Data Analysis Handbook* or a statistics course for further information.

Qualitative

The first step of the **qualitative analysis** is the same as the quantitative analysis — create draft copies and store the originals. Next, read all the data. Highlight or note various types of information that can help in subsequent steps. Now, organize and label, called coding, the comments according to similar categories, such as the following:

• Concerns

• Suggestions

• Strengths

• Weaknesses

• Similar experiences

• Program inputs

• Recommendations

• Outputs

• Outcome indicators

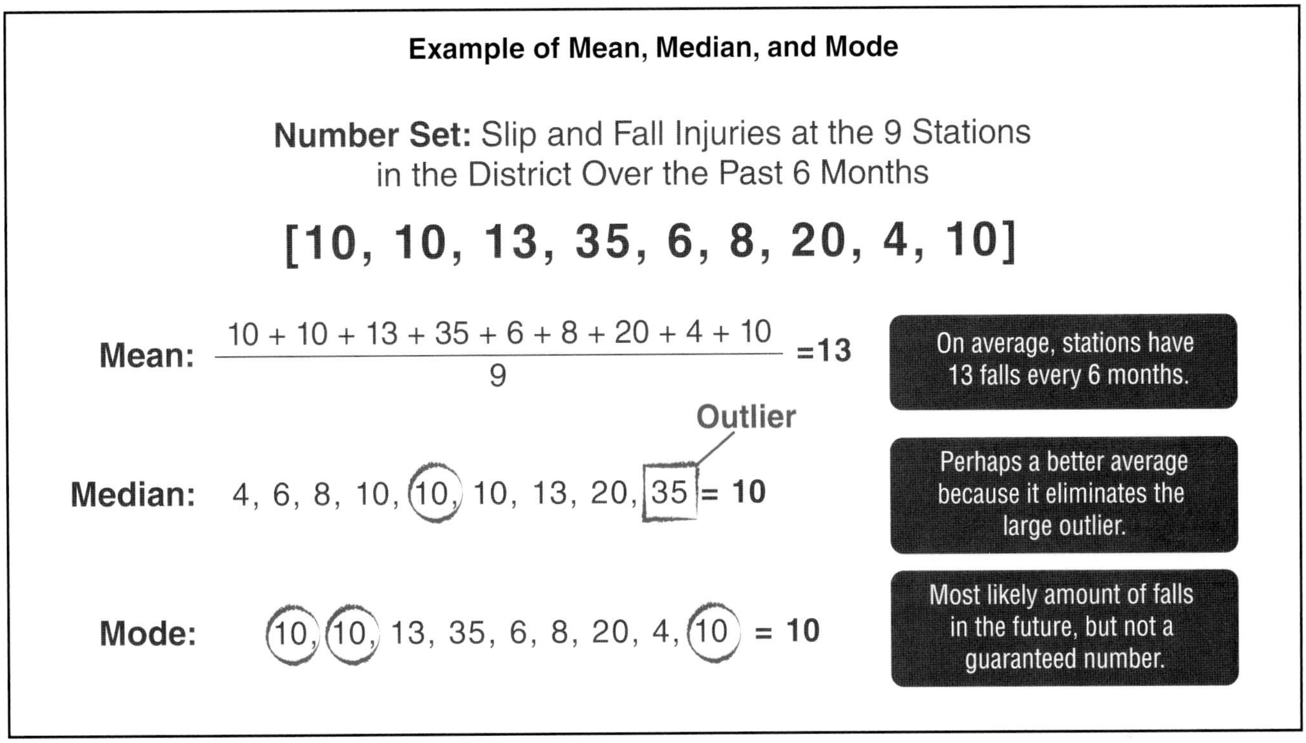

Example of Mean, Median, and Mode

Number Set: Slip and Fall Injuries at the 9 Stations
in the District Over the Past 6 Months

[10, 10, 13, 35, 6, 8, 20, 4, 10]

Mean: $\dfrac{10 + 10 + 13 + 35 + 6 + 8 + 20 + 4 + 10}{9} = 13$

> On average, stations have 13 falls every 6 months.

Outlier

Median: 4, 6, 8, 10, (10), 10, 13, 20, |35| = 10

> Perhaps a better average because it eliminates the large outlier.

Mode: (10), (10), 13, 35, 6, 8, 20, 4, (10) = 10

> Most likely amount of falls in the future, but not a guaranteed number.

Figure 3.26 The mean, median, and mode are three ways to analyze a set of numbers. Which one is used depends upon what information is needed.

Identify patterns, associations, or causal relationships in the themes. For example, do all the customers who used the program have similar concerns? Do most customers live in the same geographic area? What is the average educational background of the respondents? What types of services did each of the customers use? Retain the original data and analysis as part of the organizational evaluation for future reference.

The HSO can utilize various computer software tools to develop data analysis reports. Data collection results can be organized in spreadsheets and/or pivot tables and graphs. These tools provide basic and advanced formulas that can be inserted for automatic tabulation of data arranged in columns and/or rows. In addition, software programs are available specifically for quantitative and qualitative data analysis. For example, qualitative researchers utilize one or more computer-assisted analysis of qualitative data software (CAQDAS). These programs help the researcher organize, group, code, and retrieve data more readily.

Data Analysis Methodology

The method used to analyze data depends upon the question being asked. For example, the question *Are we likely to have more incidents in the next five years than in the previous five years?* may simply require collecting the total amount of incidents over the past five years and determining whether the number is trending up, down, or remaining the same. However, answering the question *Are we likely to have more back injuries in the next five years than in the previous five years?* will require identifying a certain type of injury among all other injuries and then assessing the trend. Further questions might arise such as

What can be done about the high numbers of back injuries in our organization? The sections that follow describe methodologies for data analysis that the HSO can use to find answers to similar questions.

Top-Down Approach

A top-down approach begins with the biggest category possible and then subdivides the sampling into categories to identify topics of interest. For an HSO, a top-down approach usually begins with the number of fatalities, injuries, accidents, and exposures in the organization over a period of time (1 year, 6 months). Once the number is known, the HSO uses records and documentation to identify what types of injuries are occurring and creates subcategories based upon individual records. The subcategories may vary depending upon the organization and the types of response over the specified time period **(Figure 3.27)**.

Subcategories should be as detailed as possible. For example, illness is a broad category that includes many possible subcategories. Information about heart health-related illnesses is more useful information than illnesses in general. The same applies to injuries. Subcategories that are unique to a particular occurrence should still be included in the analysis, but may be seen as outliers in the data. Generally, the subcategory process is meant to identify those topic areas that represent a larger portion of the broader topic.

A top-down approach benefits from creating percentages based upon the numbers of incidents per category. It is easier and more understandable to report that 40 percent of all injuries in the organization were related to vehicle accidents than to give the particular number. Percentages also allow for easier and more accurate comparisons with external data.

What This Means to You

You are the HSO at a large metropolitan department. Over the last 6 months, you have had 50 accidents, injuries, illnesses, exposures, or fatalities reported. In your top-down analysis, you discover the following:

- Fatalities — 0 (0 percent)
- Illnesses — 4 (8 percent)
- Exposures — 6 (12 percent)
- Injuries — 30 (60 percent)
- Accidents — 10 (20 percent)

You look further into the high percentage of injuries and discover that most of them happened in nonemergency settings as follows:

- Lower back strains — 10 (33 percent)
- Sprained ankles/twisted knees — 10 (33 percent)
- Bruises and contusions — 5 (17 percent)
- Burns — 3 (10 percent)
- Head trauma — 2 (7 percent)

Now that you have the data showing a high rate of back and leg injuries on the job in your organization, you can look into why the injuries occurred in such high numbers. You can also investigate what remedies may be available to reduce these injuries in the future.

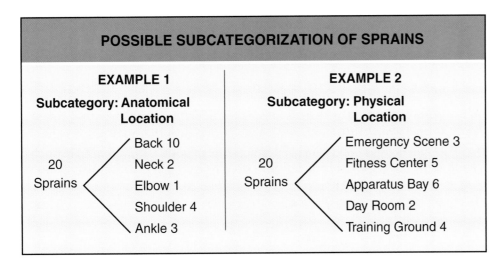

POSSIBLE SUBCATEGORIZATION OF SPRAINS

EXAMPLE 1

Subcategory: Anatomical Location

20 Sprains
- Back 10
- Neck 2
- Elbow 1
- Shoulder 4
- Ankle 3

EXAMPLE 2

Subcategory: Physical Location

20 Sprains
- Emergency Scene 3
- Fitness Center 5
- Apparatus Bay 6
- Day Room 2
- Training Ground 4

Figure 3.27 Creating subcategories in data analysis depends upon what outcomes are being analyzed, for example, what body part did firefighters injure vs. where were firefighters when they were injured.

Topic-Based Approach

A topic-based approach involves identifying a topic for study and analyzing all of the data associated with that topic. While a top-down approach provides raw, numerical data, a topic-based approach seeks to answer why and how a particular category or topic is worthy of study. Topic-based approaches also help to identify solutions that can improve trends in the future **(Figure 3.28)**.

For example, if there have been numerous vehicle incidents regarding backing of apparatus over a certain time, a topic-based approach would look at these incidents and categorize the cause of each. Identifying the causes should show trends, such as the absence of backing assistance from firefighters or failure to adequately block traffic in front of a station. With this information, the HSO can identify whether new procedures for apparatus backing are needed. The

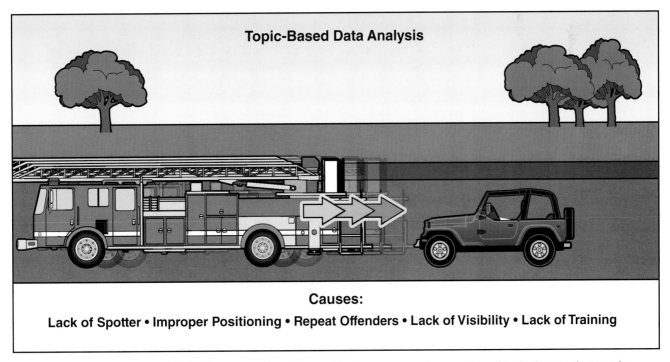

Topic-Based Data Analysis

Causes:

Lack of Spotter • Improper Positioning • Repeat Offenders • Lack of Visibility • Lack of Training

Figure 3.28 A topic-based analysis of apparatus backing accidents may generate a number of topical areas that require further study.

HSO may also identify certain individuals who continually appear on the reports and have not been following established backing procedures. Analyzing data from a topic-based approach such as this one is often the beginning of a root cause determination.

Finally, a topic-based approach can include comparison data on the same topic from surrounding jurisdictions or national data. To continue the previous example, data from the neighboring jurisdiction over the same period of time may show no incidents of property damage due to improper backing. HSOs can include this data in their findings and then investigate how the neighboring jurisdiction has prevented backing incidents.

Cost/Benefit Analysis

Cost/benefit analysis is based on the relationship between the effort (cost) and the result (benefit). To be effective, the benefit must match or exceed the cost to justify the program, process, or purchase. Public officials sometimes refer to this benefit as *return on investment*. It can be applied to the purchase of a new piece of equipment; staffing; facility construction, design, or location; and many other situations.

Cost/Benefit Analysis — Examination of the proposed expense of an effort and deciding if the overall benefit is worth the investment of money and/or time.

What This Means to You

Your department plans to replace ten sets of protective clothing and equipment in the next fiscal year. While your current protective clothing and equipment has performed according to specifications, there is a new type of material available that has been shown in recent studies to provide better protection. Replacement of your current protective clothing and equipment using the same material you have now will cost $2,000 a set. Protective clothing and equipment made of the newer material will cost $3,000 a set. Moving to the newer material will cost the department an additional $10,000 per year ($1,000 per set).

While the less expensive material you are using has protected most firefighters, research suggests that the newer material sheds heat better when used within the manufacturer's heat tolerance levels. Manufacturer tests indicate that the newer material will reduce burn incidence and severity by 25 percent and 50 percent respectively.

The human resources department has provided you with information on the direct cost of treating the burns over the past year and the associated salary costs paid to firefighters who were not on duty due to burn injuries. You study the data for the reported burns to determine if spending an additional $10,000 would decrease the amount spent on burn care and recovery in your department. If so, then the *benefit* to making the change would outweigh the *cost* of current practice. If not, then there may be other reasons to make the change, such as new equipment specifications and standards that require the new material even at a higher cost. If the cost does not outweigh the benefit, then the department may have to look for other resolutions to the increase in burn incidents, such as improved training or new procedures.

When conducting a cost/benefit analysis, several factors should be considered. Asking the following questions will help the HSO chart important considerations:

- **What is the cost of implementing the control measure?** — This includes estimated costs associated with new purchases, upgrading or refurbishing apparatus/equipment, and training.

- **What is the benefit of implementing a control measure?** — This can be a qualitative and/or quantitative data analysis. A qualitative analysis will include the benefit to the working environment and perceived safety improvements. It can also be related with a quantitative estimation in the reduction of costs associated with future injuries, maintenance and repair costs, apparatus/equipment downtime, and liability. This estimate will be based on historical data leading up to the analysis.

- **Historically, what is the cost associated with not implementing a control measure?** — This includes known costs associated with injuries, lost work time, maintenance and repair costs, apparatus/equipment downtime, and legal liability potential.

- **What is the benefit of not implementing a control measure?** — This is a complex question to ask. The HSO should step back and assess the potential benefit of not implementing a control measure. This may be associated with delaying the implementation because new technology is imminent, the cost of implementation is too high and an alternate, more affordable control measure is considered, and another control measure may address the same issue. HSOs must keep the safety and health of all fire department members in the forefront of this analysis, but they should not focus too narrowly on an issue. Consider alternatives and look for the right benefit for your department.

The answers to these questions will lead to a comparison of data about the pros and cons in the cost/benefit decision-making process. Cost benefit analysis is a process, and reevaluation is needed to determine if the decision to implement or not implement led to a positive or negative outcome. Improvements can be made in the process, and the HSO should document each analysis in a manner that sets the stage for the future analyses and decisions. Additional considerations that the HSO will need to include when presenting a cost/benefit analysis are the time commitment for implementation, a revision cycle or life cycle of a control measure, and who is responsible for implementation and monitoring of a control measure. The HSO will perform cost/benefit analysis in the following areas of responsibility:

- Risk management plan
- Incident risk management plan
- Apparatus and equipment specification design
- Corrective action recommendations
- Control measures
- Safety, health, wellness, and fitness programs

Chapter Summary

Developing an organized record-keeping system is a critical function of the HSO and is viewed as an essential function to the operation of a modern fire and emergency services organization. This system includes the management of records, access and privacy rights, legal mandates on record retention, and documentation of inspections and maintenance. Keeping up with technology requires constant monitoring. Developing specifications requires knowledge of the latest technology, but also the regulations and standards that govern the design of apparatus, equipment, and protective clothing. Reducing the liability of the organization is one fundamental consideration in the record-keeping system.

Collecting, compiling, and analyzing data accompany the management of records. The HSO and department personnel must be able to readily access records to recommend improvements in the risk management plan and the safety and health program. Recommendations and reports will include data comparisons and trends that come from collecting, compiling, and analyzing data from a myriad of sources.

Review Questions

1. What methods can the health safety officer use to manage departmental records? (pp. 63-67)

2. What types of records are included in a confidential health database? (pp. 69-71)

3. How does the health safety officer interact with other departments to maintain records? (p. 71)

4. How can the health safety officer verify departmental inspection and service testing records? (pp. 72-78)

5. What safety and health program components necessitate documentation by the health safety officer? (pp. 78-92)

6. How can the health safety officer compile safety and health data on behalf of the fire department? (pp. 92-101)

7. What types of skills are used for analyzing fire department data? (pp. 101-108)

8. How is a cost/benefit analysis performed? (pp. 108-109)

3-1
Create a departmental records and data management system.

LEARNING ACTIVITIES

Refer to Appendix B: Learning Activity Answers in the back of this manual for suggested responses.

Purpose

The HSO is responsible for the collection and retention of large amounts of departmental data – from safety and health program information to inspection records and accident investigation data. Because of the sheer volume of this information, a well-organized retrieval system is one of the most crucial components of good records management.

Directions

Consider the following departmental areas and programs that require records collection and management:

- Safety and Health SOP/Gs
- Inspection and Service Testing
- Corrective Actions
- Accident, Injury, Occurrence Investigations
- Personnel Interactions, Interviews, Surveys

- Wellness Program
- Technology Specifications
- Training Program
- Member Assistance Program
- Infection Control Documentation

1. Identify any other areas within your own department or jurisdiction that would necessitate documentation and storage of records. If more can be identified, add them to the list above.

2. Design a *computer file folder structure* that would make the records for this information easily manageable and retrievable. You can describe the records system with text or visuals – whichever is easiest for you.

    NOTE: Use the following questions to help you determine the proper electronic file folder structure for your records:

- What is the quickest, easiest way that I can sort or categorize these files? By date? Department? Program? Personnel?

- What subcategories should I create?

- How do I file the information so that the records can be accessed, destroyed, or archived quickly and efficiently?

Standard Operating Procedures

Chapter Contents

Key Terms

NFPA® Job Performance Requirements

This chapter provides information that addresses the following job performance requirements of NFPA® 1521, *Standard for Fire Department Safety Officer Professional Qualifications (2015)*.

4.2.5   4.9.1

4.3.1   4.10.1

4.4.3   4.10.2

4.6.2

Standard Operating Procedures

Learning Objectives

After reading this chapter, students will be able to:

1. Describe the process for establishing standard operating procedures or guidelines related to an occupational health and safety program. (4.3.1)

2. Identify live-fire training exercise requirements that must be included in safety procedures. (4.4.3)

3. Identify key areas that must be addressed when developing medical emergency procedures. (4.2.5)

4. Describe components in standard operating procedures or guidelines related to accident and injury reporting and investigations. (4.6.2)

5. Explain requirements for developing health and safety facility inspection standard operating procedures or guidelines. (4.9.1)

6. Identify methods for incorporating infection control procedures into a fire department health maintenance program. (4.10.1, 4.10.2)

7. Learning Activity 4-1: Create a standard operating procedure or guideline based on departmental documents or materials. (4.3.1)

Chapter 4
Standard Operating Procedures

Photo Courtesy of the United States Air Force.

Case History

In 2010, a nationally recognized educational institution experienced an explosion in a fire sciences laboratory that resulted in laboratory damages and injuries to a student. The postincident investigation revealed that there were systematic deficiencies within the institution. Of particular interest was the lack of a policy and procedures manual in the laboratory.

After the investigation was complete, the program administrators implemented a number of postincident controls to address the deficiencies. Program administrators surveyed fire instructors and students who used the lab about current safety procedures at the facilities. The administrators catalogued the various equipment used in the lab and incorporated manufacturer's recommendations into the new SOP/Gs and noted how the equipment was currently being used. They also compared current practices against OSHA regulations to identify where SOP/Gs needed to be legally compliant. They created a procedures manual, and A Safety Awareness and Education Program was implemented to provide a "Safety Protocols and Procedures" course every six months. A Safety Compliance Assurance Program was also created, which included policies for monitoring SOP/Gs and human behavior in the labs over time.

The majority of fire and emergency services organizations have written organizational policies and procedures. Depending on the AHJ's adopted definition, the document(s) may be called a standard operating procedures (SOPs), standard operating guidelines (SOGs), or policy and procedures manual (PPM). Each fire department will need to determine the name of its manual.

One method of compiling a departmental manual is to divide it into administrative *policies* and operational *procedures*. The administrative documents contain the mission statement, responsibilities, and authority of the organization and each of its branches and functional positions. The *policies* may include everything from sick leave to the organization's smoking policy. Operational *procedures* describe the specific processes of how members function as a part of the fire department. The processes exist in, but are not limited to, training manuals, operational manuals, and maintenance manuals. The individual policies and procedures within a manual will vary depending on the fire department's local operational environment. All policy and procedure documents and manuals have some basic similarities, including providing the expected performance of its members. For the purposes of this manual, the abbreviation SOP/G is used to refer to the policy and procedure manual.

The HSO will serve on a team of fire department members for the development, evaluation, and revision of SOP/Gs. The HSO's responsibility is to ensure that the SOP/Gs address the safety and health elements of the workforce and workplace. The HSO's role is to ensure policies and procedures are in place, that an evaluation process is established, and that a process for addressing safety and health issues is established. The following list explains HSO responsibilities that relate to SOP/Gs:

- Ensuring the development of a policy for risk management
- Identifying policy and procedure deficiencies and making recommendations to the appropriate organizational authority
- Training personnel on safety procedures
- Evaluating personnel training procedures
- Developing corrective actions
- Ensuring training evolution procedures are established
- Ensuring preburn inspection procedures are established for all live-fire training evolutions
- Ensuring procedures for safety investigations
- Ensuring procedures are established for treating and transporting injured or ill members
- Ensuring procedures are established for incident rehabilitation of members
- Ensuring a procedure to include a safety and health component in the postincident analysis

16 Firefighter Life Safety Initiatives 1, 2, 3, and 9

The *16 Firefighter Life Safety Initiatives* were discussed in Chapter 1, Health Safety Officer Responsibilities. Four of those initiatives are particularly pertinent to the HSO's responsibilities related to SOP/Gs:

1. Define and advocate the need for a cultural change within the fire service relating to safety; incorporating leadership, management, supervision, accountability and personal responsibility.

2. Enhance the personal and organizational accountability for health and safety throughout the fire service.

3. Focus greater attention on the integration of risk management with incident management at all levels, including strategic, tactical, and planning responsibilities.

9. Thoroughly investigate all firefighter fatalities, injuries, and near misses.

Occupational Safety and Health Program Procedures

Written policies and procedures are essential for the effective and efficient operation of any fire and emergency services organization. Procedures identify benchmarks for behavior and performance that remain static in a dynamic workplace or response environment. The procedures place into writing the organization's expectations based on the organizational model and the strategic and operational plans. Procedures may need to be created for the following reasons:

- A safety issue is identified that requires new procedures.
- Changes have occurred in industry standards, accepted best practices, or laws, codes, and regulations.
- A safe work behavior is identified that the organization wants to formalize through the procedure development process, such as wearing seatbelts on apparatus at all times.

The general steps for determining the need for a new policy or procedure are summarized below:

- **Identify the problem or requirement for a policy or procedure** — determine whether a policy or procedure is necessary to address the problem. Some problems may be best addressed on an individual basis and do not require a formal policy.
- **Collect data to evaluate the need** — use data that may be quantitative or qualitative and may come from personnel interviews, product literature, or activity reports. Data collection may also involve determining best practices, industry standards, and regulations.
- **Select the evaluation model** — use one of the evaluation models: goals-based, process-based, or outcome-based. See Chapter 5, Organizational Risk Management, for detailed information.
- **Establish a timetable for making the needs evaluation** — consider the length of time required to evaluate the problem, which depends on the complexity of the problem and the amount of information that must be evaluated **(Figure 4.1)**.
- **Conduct the evaluation** — follow the recommended steps for the model that is most appropriate for the problem.

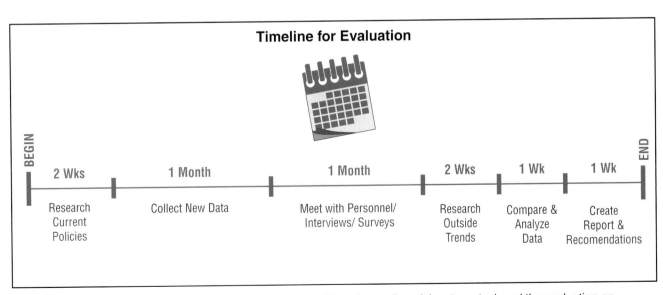

Figure 4.1 Program evaluations need an established time table to keep all participants on task and the evaluation on schedule.

- **Select the best response to the need** — determine the best policy or procedure to solve the problem. Remember that this selection may include no policy or procedure at all.

- **Select alternative responses** — select a second best choice if a contingency is indicated. External influences may make it necessary to select a policy or procedure other than the first choice. Personnel safety should be the priority in selecting alternatives.

- **Establish a revision process or schedule** — create a revision process as part of the policy or procedure. This process may be general for all policies and procedures or may be one that is specific to the policy that has been selected.

- **Recommend the policy or procedure that best meets the need** — the HSO will make recommendations on policy and procedure approval based on the operational need.

- **Consider the need for legal adoption of policy and procedure** — consider that because policies and procedures may have the effect of law, the jurisdiction may need to formally adopt them. Formal approval requires that the policy or procedure be supported by documentation.

NOTE: FEMA's *Developing Effective Standard Operating Procedures for Fire and EMS Departments* is a resource that can assist the HSO with developing SOP/Gs as a part of the fire department team.

Effectiveness Assessment and Criteria

Stating that your fire department has a SOP/G manual may be easy. However, it is more difficult to answer how effective the documents within that manual are on a daily basis. The SOP/G manual is a collection of documents that must address the administrative and operational needs of the department. The individual documents in the manual must be reviewed regularly for appropriateness and effectiveness. Each fire department needs to determine the frequency schedule of the SOP/G manual review. In addition to scheduled reviews, unscheduled reviews will occur when specific SOP/Gs are identified in a postincident analysis or as a part of an investigation **(Figure 4.2)**. An SOP/G review should include those operations that were successful as well as those that were unsuccessful. The SOP/Gs should be assessed within the scope of the incident in which they apply. This assessment may include everyday fire department operations in addition to emergency or nonemergency incidents and training evolutions.

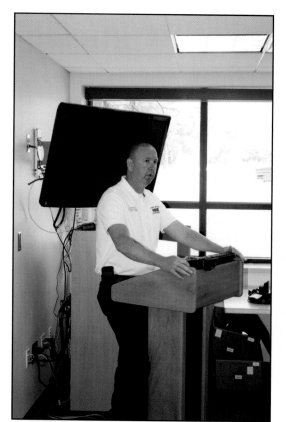

Figure 4.2 As part of postincident analysis briefings, the chief may discuss concerns about current SOP/Gs based upon the outcome of the incident and the incident investigation.

CAUTION
When SOP/Gs change too frequently, they lose their effectiveness. Change SOP/Gs only as necessary or during scheduled review.

Each incident or training exercise is unique in some way. SOP/Gs must provide the guidance necessary to address the all-hazards, multi-discipline nature of the modern fire service, but with enough flexibility to be useful in a myriad of situations. When determining the criteria for assessing the effectiveness of SOP/Gs, the HSO should concentrate on the safety and health aspects. The criteria may be answered by asking the following questions:

- Did the incident or exercise come to a successful conclusion? Why or why not?
- Did the SOP/Gs provide enough guidance for a coordinated team effort?
- Were the typical SOP/Gs applicable and relevant to current practices?
- Did the SOP/Gs provide enough flexibility for crews to adapt to the situation?
- Did any injuries, fatalities, illnesses, or exposures occur?
- Did the incident risk analysis lead to a positive incident strategy and subsequent tactics?
- Did a deviation of SOP/Gs occur? Was the deviation appropriate or inappropriate?
- Did any SOP/Gs or actions of responders violate any laws, codes, regulations, or standards?

When answering these questions, the HSO should remember that the goal is to improve the performance of responders while ensuring that their improved safety and health are considered part of the goal. These questions will guide the process of determining if the department's SOP/Gs are adequate and effective. The HSO should ensure the effective management of the policy and procedure review process.

Fire Department Operations

Fire department operational SOP/Gs should be standardized to provide consistent expectations of performance during incidents. The SOP/Gs should not be so detailed as to limit the ability of members to carry out their tasks. However, they should provide direction or guidance as to what to accomplish. When assessing the effectiveness of SOP/Gs for fire department operations, the review team (including the HSO) should evaluate the overall performance during an operation in relation to the guidance of the SOP/G. The team should determine if the SOP/G is effective and provided the needed guidance for the responders to bring the incident to a successful conclusion. The HSO's role on the team is to assess the SOP/G and the incident to determine if the safety and health aspects were addressed. The HSO will play a more significant role if any injury, fatality, illness, or exposure occurred during an operation. The HSO should also determine any **mutual aid** or **automatic aid** operational differences that may affect responder safety and health.

Training Practices

When evaluating training practices, the HSO serves mainly in the proactive phase prior to training being conducted. The HSO ensures procedures are in place, so training evolutions can provide and replicate the realistic response environment in a safe and prudent manner. This replication is beneficial in assessing training practices and allows for testing the adequacy and effec-

Mutual Aid — Reciprocal assistance from one fire and emergency services agency to another during an emergency, based upon a prearranged agreement; generally made upon the request of the receiving agency.

Automatic Aid — Written agreement between two or more agencies to automatically dispatch predetermined resources to any fire or other emergency reported in the geographic area covered by the agreement. These areas are generally located near jurisdictional boundaries or in jurisdictional "islands."

tiveness of SOP/Gs in a controlled environment. The HSO will also assist in evaluating SOP/Gs after training evolutions are conducted. This process can be viewed as a cyclical sequence of reviews. The same scrutiny can be used to assess the training environment.

Safety Subjects to Include

The HSO's role is specific to the safety and health concerns of fire department members. In this role, the HSO will focus on topics that improve safety in the workplace. The HSO should consider the following list of safety subjects when assessing the effectiveness of SOP/Gs as they relate to the safety and health of members in all fire department operations **(Figure 4.3)**:

- Emergency vehicle operations
- Use of the Incident Command System and accountability of all members
- Use of incident safety officers and technical safety officers
- An Incident Action Plan that includes a risk analysis of the incident
- Recurring or frequent injuries based on organizational records, such as sprains and strains
- Include the importance of member physical fitness
- Training, inspection, and use of proper protective clothing and equipment
- Use of rapid intervention crews (RICs)
- Use of backup teams
- Rehabilitation of members
- Compliance with safety and health laws, codes, regulations, and standards
- Training on newly implemented practices and any new apparatus or equipment that will be put into service

Compliance with Laws, Codes, Regulations, and Standards

As stated in Chapter 2, Safety and Health Laws, Codes, Regulations, and Standards, litigation is a legitimate consideration in the development and revision of SOP/Gs. SOP/Gs place operational practices on paper, so all members have the same expectations. The HSO will serve on a team or committee of fire department members that addresses compliance with SOP/Gs. The HSO's role is to ensure the department's SOP/Gs are in compliance with the following safety and health requirements **(Figure 4.4, p. 122)**:

- State, provincial, and/or federal regulations, including but not limited to OSHA regulations
- State, provincial, and/or local traffic and vehicle operation laws
- Apparatus, equipment, and protective clothing specifications standards
- FOIA or state/local open records laws and retention schedules
- HIPAA regulations
- NFPA® consensus standards, codes, and guides
- NIMS and ICS compliance
- Environmental protection regulations that may influence SOP/G development/revision

Safety Subjects for SOP/Gs

Emergency vehicle operations

An Incident Action Plan that includes a risk analysis of the incident

Training on newly implemented practices and any new apparatus or equipment that will be put into service

Include the importance of member physical fitness

Recurring or frequent injuries based on organizational records, such as sprains and strains

Use of rapid intervention crews

Training, inspection, and use of proper protective clothing and equipment

Compliance with safety and health laws, codes, regulations, and standards

Use of backup teams

Use of the Incident Command System and accountability of all members

Rehabilitation of members

Use of incident safety officers and technical safety officers

Figure 4.3 SOP/Gs should comprehensively cover safety subjects that are relevant to the department or organization and comply with all appropriate codes and regulations in the jurisdiction. *Rehabilitation photo courtesy of Ron Jeffers.*

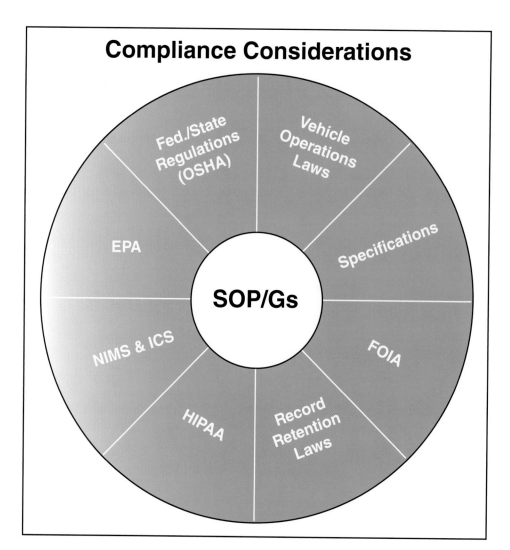

Figure 4.4 A wide variety of laws and regulations affect the writing of SOP/Gs. All of these plus additional local and state/provincial regulations should be reflected in completed SOP/Gs where applicable.

SOP/G Creation

During an assessment of current departmental SOP/Gs, the HSO should have identified any new SOP/Gs that need to be created to better ensure firefighter safety and health. The need for new procedures may also result from other research such as new equipment specifications or new research regarding nutritional health. The HSO should use a standard format that matches the format used for other SOP/Gs in the AHJ's procedures manual. He or she should also consider transcribing material from other sources that inform the creation of the procedure into the SOP/G. See **Learning Activity 4-1** for an exercise designed to provide practice at creating SOP/Gs based upon an identified need.

SOP/G Format and Template

Generally, the procedures manual contains a statement of purpose, a statement of scope, a contents page, the procedures or policies organized according to specific topic or function, and appendices that contain copies of forms that are referred to in the body of the text. Structurally, each page contains basic information at the top that assists the reader in navigating the document. This basic information includes the following **(Figure 4.5)**:

- **Subject** — what the policy/procedure is about.
- **Procedure number** — assigned to the specific procedure for tracking purposes.

Booneville Fire and Rescue
SOP/G - Cover Sheet

Dates: _06-10-2014_

Subject: _Decontamination at structure fires._

Procedure Number: _5.12_

Supersedes: _5.11_

Approvals: _Chief Harrison_   **Signature:** _Bill Harrison_

Distribution: _All company officers and command staff._

Applicability: _Applies to all structure fires regardless of the structural contents or the absence of hazardous materials._

Pages: _5_

Revisions: ☐ Original _____ ☑ Revised _05-08-2014_

Forms Used: _None_

Figure 4.5 SOP/Gs generally begin with a cover sheet indicating some basic information about the rest of the procedure or guideline.

- **Dates** — original date of implementation plus any revision dates.

- **Supersedes** — procedure number that is replaced by the current page.

- **Approvals** — initials of the authority approving the policy/procedure.

- **Distribution** — list of persons or groups to whom the policy/procedure is issued.

- **Applicability** — persons or groups to whom the policy/procedure applies.

- **Pages** — number indicating the position within the document.

- **Revision** — indicates whether the current SOP/G is an original or a revised document and any applicable numbering system.

- **Forms used** — indicates the appropriate form used to fulfill the policy/procedure.

Because the policy and procedures manual must be revised periodically, the number and location of each copy must be available to the administration. Archived copies should be retained for future reference. The HSO should follow all AHJ procedures for including new and revised procedures to the current and archived policies and procedures manual.

New SOP/Gs may be distributed in a variety of ways to the organizational membership, including paper documents or email distribution lists. Using a networked server system to upload SOP/Gs, to a central database ensures that all members can access the most current revision at any time and be alerted to updates. HSOs should use the method approved in their jurisdiction. The HSO's responsibilities may include training the membership on new or revised health and safety procedures; however, this responsibility may be delegated to the training division.

Material Added from Other Sources

SOP/Gs are written from a broad spectrum of information from other sources. When using the following sources as information in SOP/Gs, ensure that the source for the information is properly cited or acknowledged:

- **Laws, codes, regulations, or standards** — as stated, compliance with legal mandates is required in many areas of the fire service. The HSO must ensure all applicable safety and health legal mandates are incorporated into the department's SOP/Gs.

- **Other jurisdictions' SOP/Gs** — this will be necessary when writing procedures for mutual aid/automatic aid assignments and multijurisdictional events. This can include cooperating with or giving assistance/receiving assistance from other fire agencies, law enforcement agencies, emergency medical service transportation agencies, special operations teams, and incident management teams.

- **Reports from research and investigative agencies** — fire science research can provide valuable technical information that can be reviewed for adaptability into SOP/Gs. Investigative reports should be reviewed for lessons learned and recommendations.

- **Manufacturer recommendations** — manufacturers of apparatus, equipment, and protective clothing and equipment can provide specific maintenance, inspection, testing, or care requirements and recommendations. These requirements or recommendations may meet or exceed NFPA® standards.

- **Federal, state, and local emergency management plans** — the FEMA *National Response Framework (NRF)* outlines the responsibilities at the different governing levels. In the event of a disaster, the local jurisdiction is the focal point of responsibility for the response and recovery effort. Requesting assistance or resources from outside the jurisdiction requires specific steps to be followed. SOP/Gs need to break down the comprehensive plan into operational practice for responders to employ.

- **Postincident analyses** — a postincident analysis should define which SOP/Gs were utilized on an incident or event. Reviewing actual incidents or events can provide valuable insight into what is working, what needs to be changed, or what is missing.

- **Manuals** — the fire service has numerous sources of information manuals, operation manuals, and education/training manuals. Some useful resources for the HSO in researching rehabilitation of responders are: FEMA *Emergency Incident Rehabilitation* and the National Fire Service Incident Management System Consortium Model Procedures Committee *Model Procedures Guide for Structural Firefighting*.

SOP/G Revision

An effectiveness assessment may also indicate existing SOP/Gs that require revision. Revising SOP/Gs should be done only when there is a need. The HSO should learn to recognize when there are deviations from existing, well-written procedures and when the procedures themselves are poorly-written, no longer current, or no longer effective. For newly created and revised SOP/Gs, the HSO should monitor the implementation of the new procedures and verify that they are being followed as intended.

Verification of Procedures

SOP/Gs are written to provide guidance and expectations for job performance. SOP/Gs are living documents that are written, followed, reviewed, and updated or removed. This cyclical pattern includes verification that SOP/Gs are used appropriately. The HSO will verify SOP/G use during the postincident analysis process. In addition, verification of SOP/G use will occur during any accident/incident investigation involving an injury, fatality, illness, or exposure. The HSO will also determine if any deviation in SOP/G occurred. If any deviation occurred, the HSO will document the facts and outcome of the incident. The HSO should not police the operational setting. Instead, the HSO can rely on company and chief officers supervising fire department operations within the fire department's chain of command structure. This process places the enforcement of policy within the command structure at a supervisory level, and maintains the **unity of command** concept.

Unity of Command — Organizational principle in which workers report to only one supervisor in order to eliminate conflicting orders.

SOP/G Revision Process

A process for revising policies and procedures should be established to ensure that they are flexible enough to adapt to changing operational and organizational requirements. The revision process is included in the policy or procedures manual and is based on answers to the following questions:

- When does the policy or procedure need to be revised? Is there a specific timetable?

- What conditions or circumstances would cause the policy or procedure to need revision?

- How should the policy or procedure be revised: completely, partially, or not at all?

The answers to some of these questions will be up to the AHJ to determine. Indications that a policy or procedure needs to be revised may include the following **(Figure 4.6)**:

- Increase in policy infractions.

- Injuries or property loss due to a failure of the procedure.

- Change in the resources used to accomplish the task.

- Change in the problem that the policy or procedure was intended to solve.

The policies and procedures of the organization must be continually monitored for effectiveness. Policies and procedures are most effective if they are dynamic documents that are subject to constant scrutiny, review, and revision. When it becomes apparent that a policy or procedure must be revised, replaced, reviewed, or abandoned, the actual process steps are generally the same as those used earlier for the creation of the new policy or procedure.

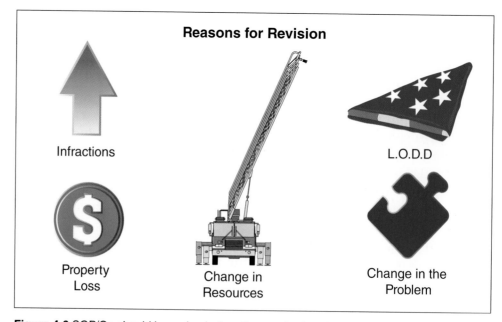

Figure 4.6 SOP/Gs should be revised when the need arises but not so frequently that they lose their meaning.

Live-Fire Training Procedures

All live-fire training procedures must follow applicable laws, codes, regulations, and standards. Live-fire training evolutions must be treated like real world incidents. The common saying of "Train like you fight" puts this into context. In order to conduct live-fire training evolutions, the HSO is responsible for ensuring SOP/Gs are in place and address the safety and health of all members participating. Live-fire training procedures must cover all types of live-fire exercises that the department conducts **(Figure 4.7)**. Firefighter injuries and fatalities during live-fire training in fixed facility and acquired structures, as reported by NIOSH, should be reviewed for lessons learned and recommendations. These reports provide valuable information that the HSO should review and determine if a revision to SOP/Gs is needed.

Figure 4.7 Live-fire training procedures should be in keeping with NFPA® standards and cover the entire scope of training that the organization conducts.

The HSO will work with the Training Division in this process to ensure full compliance with legal mandates. NFPA® 1403, *Standard on Live Fire Training Evolutions,* is the guiding document for conducting live-fire training; however, state/provincial and local regulations, such as acquiring burn permits, will also influence the organization's SOP/Gs.

NIOSH Fire Fighter Fatality Reports between 2000 – 2013[1]

- F2000-27 Fatality at acquired structure live-fire training exercise.
- F2001-38 Fatality and injury at acquired structure live-fire training exercise.
- F2002-34 Fatalities at acquired structure live-fire training exercise.
- F2003-28 Fatality and injury in a simulated marine vessel live-fire training exercise.
- F2003-41 Injuries in a mobile flashover training simulator.
- F2005-31 Fatality after a live-fire training exercise at a training academy.
- F2007-09 Fatality at an acquired structure live-fire training exercise.

Requirements for Live-Fire Training

All live-fire training evolutions share some common safety and health requirements. The HSO's main responsibility is to ensure procedures are in place that address the safety and health concerns for members during all live-fire training evolutions. The HSO should consider the inherent dangers of the following topics in live-fire training SOP/Gs:

- Class A, B, C, D, and K fires **(Table 4.1)**
- Interior versus exterior setting requirements
- Fuel loading and location of fire
- Weather
- Safety officer(s) present **(Figure 4.8, p. 130)**
- Safety officer training that includes specific knowledge of the type of fire
- Rapid Intervention Crews (RICs)
- Rehabilitation and emergency medical procedures
- Preburn inspection procedure
- No live victims at any time **(Figure 4.9, p. 130)**
- Reassessment of the structure/facility after each live-fire evolution

In addition, procedures should address the following requirements of live-fire training:

- Protective clothing and equipment inspections
- Water supply needs
- Emergency plans
- Communications plans
- Resource allocation considerations

Requirements Unique to Fixed Facilities

Fixed facilities for live-fire training have specific requirements in NFPA® 1403. While fixed facilities can provide a more controlled environment, age and technological features of the facility will vary. The HSO is responsible for ensuring that procedures are in place for the inspection of the facility. This review includes a preburn inspection, an annual structural inspection, and a 5-year structural inspection performed by a licensed engineer. These inspections must include an evaluation that all openings and safety devices are operational and functioning as designed. In addition, destructive or non-destructive testing may need to be performed if structural damage is found. The AHJ or building owner shall evaluate the structural integrity annually, per NFPA® 1403. NFPA® 1403 further states that this inspection shall include core sampling of the concrete to determine if delamination has occurred.

Requirements Unique to Acquired Structures

Using acquired structures in live-fire training can be dangerous. Acquired structures are typically in severe disrepair and ready for demolition. Live-fire training exercises in acquired structures are never completely controlled. For example, there are no control switches for turning off the fuel source or automatically opening ventilation holes.

Table 4.1
Classifications of Fire

Class Name	Letter Symbol	Image Symbol	Description
Class A or Ordinary Combustibles	A — Ordinary Combustibles		Includes fuels such as wood, paper, plastic, rubber, and cloth.
Class B or Flammable and Combustible Liquids and Gases	B — Flammable Liquids		Includes all hydrocarbon and alcohol-based liquids and gases that will support combustion.
Class C or Electrical	C — Electrical Equipment		This includes all fires involving energized electrical equipment.
Class D or Combustible Metals	D — Combustible Metals		Examples of combustible metals are: magnesium, potassium, titanium, and zirconium.
Class K or Kitchen	K — Cooking Oils		Includes unsaturated cooking oils in well-insulated cooking appliances located in commercial kitchens.

Reproduced with permission from Wayne State University, Detroit, MI.

The HSO is responsible for ensuring the following specific acquired structure considerations are addressed in a SOP/G prior to any live-fire training **(Figure 4.10, p. 131)**:

- Permits and permission documents are obtained
- Site evaluation to ensure hazards are removed prior to live-fire training (such as asbestos, vegetation, debris, household items, storage, containers)
- Neighboring properties are not endangered
- Ingress and egress routes are unobstructed
- Inspection of the structural integrity, wall/floor openings, stairwells, etc.
- Inspection of the structure for any persons or animals present
- Securing of utilities

Figure 4.8 SOP/Gs should require a safety officer to be present to document and evaluate any live-fire training evolution.

Figure 4.9 Although there is no set standard or regulation preventing the use of live victims in training evolutions, U.S. case law has set precedent that manikins should be used at all times to prevent unnecessary injury to individuals acting as victims during training. If an injury to a live victim were to occur, the training organization could be held legally liable for those injuries.

Figure 4.10 SOP/Gs for using acquired structures for live-fire training should include a comprehensive inspection list for the structure that complies with NFPA® 1403.

Preburn Inspections of Acquired Structures

Preburn inspections must be completed on acquired structures prior to live-fire training. Acquired structures present some unique challenges that must be addressed to ensure the safety and health of all members participating in the training exercise. The HSO is responsible for ensuring procedures are established for acquired structures to comply with NFPA® 1403. An SOP/G must be written requiring that all of the following actions are taken before training in an acquired structure:

- Ensure the structural integrity of the building.
- Remove hazardous materials from the structure.
- Repair structural members that may create a hazard.
- Repair stair treads, risers, and railings.
- Secure holes in floors.
- Secure loose floorboards.
- Secure or patch walls and ceilings.
- Secure or remove loose bricks in masonry walls or chimneys.
- Provide adequate roof level ventilation.
- Shut off utilities.
- Remove trash and debris that may cause a hazard.
- Remove low-density combustible fiberboard wall coverings.
- Remove vermin and insects from the structure and surrounding area.
- Provide exposure protection for adjacent structures.

- Remove vegetation from the area of the burn building.
- Provide sufficient egress routes.
- Develop a predetermined evacuation plan.
- Ensure that all participants understand the incident management system to be used.

The use of the acquired structure for live-fire training should not take place if firefighter safety and health procedures have not or cannot be completed. If any of the above listed actions cannot be completed, then the structure cannot safely be used for a live-fire evolution. Acquired structures that cannot be made to meet the requirements of live-fire training may be useful for other types of training such as ladder raises, forcible entry, or simulated ventilation.

Medical Emergency Procedures

All emergency service organizations should have SOP/Gs addressing accidents or incidents where a member is injured or becomes ill. NFPA® 1584, *Standard on the Rehabilitation Process for Members During Emergency Operations and Training Exercises*, is the guiding document for rehabilitation considerations for members on emergency incidents and training exercises. When faced with taking care of our own, having established SOP/Gs provides a guideline for decision-making in determining the best course of action. Having these guidelines in place before an injury or illness can ease some of the stress in making the right decisions.

Development of an SOP/G on medical emergency procedures should address the following key areas **(Figure 4.11)**:

- Recognizing the signs and symptoms of injuries and illnesses
- Providing rehabilitation at emergency scenes and training evolutions
- Evaluating the seriousness of the injury/illness
- Treating the injured/ill member or members
- Notifying the immediate supervisor of the injured/ill member or members
- Obtaining the right medical transportation resource for the member or members
- Having the member or members transported to the appropriate medical facility, if necessary

To help organize the information in a standard format, the HSO can use ICS Form 206, *Medical Plan*, from the Incident Management System (IMS). This form can be distributed and kept on all apparatus for ease of reference, especially command vehicles.

In addition to the above guideline steps, the immediate supervisor or commanding officer will have additional responsibilities that may include:

- Notifying the fire chief through the chain of command
- Notifying other fire department members (this may be limited to life-threatening injuries/illnesses)
- Notifying the family (when the injured/ill member or members are unable to do so)

- Ensuring the proper paperwork is completed and forwarded through the chain of command
- Having Critical Incident Stress Management (CISM) services available for those requesting assistance

Vital Sign Measurements

Medical surveillance is important to ensure firefighter health during a response and should be a part of the rehabilitation function at an incident. Each fire and emergency services organization should determine vital sign values to be measured during rehabilitation. Research opinion on the vital sign levels that are acceptable as part of medical surveillance vary among authoritative sources. When developing SOP/Gs for rehabilitation, the HSO can use any of the following sources to guide what are the acceptable vital signs for a firefighter being checked as part of the rehabilitation:

- NFPA® 1584, *Standard on the Rehabilitation Process for Members During Emergency Operations and Training Exercises*
- FEMA FA-314 *Emergency Incident Rehabilitation*
- NFSIMS, *Model Procedures Guide for Structural Firefighting*

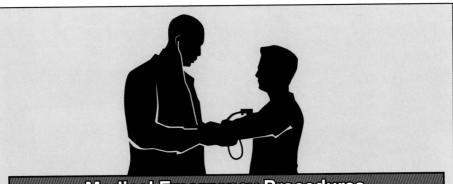

Medical Emergency Procedures

1. Recognizing the signs and symptoms of injuries and illnesses

2. Providing rehabilitation at emergency scenes and training evolutions

3. Evaluating the seriousness of the injury/illness

4. Treating the injured/ill member(s)

5. Notifying the immediate supervisor of the injured/ill member(s)

6. Obtaining the right medical transportation resource for the member(s)

7. Having the member(s) transported to the appropriate medical facility, if necessary

Figure 4.11 Medical emergency procedures should include these key areas as well as any jurisdictional requirements.

Procedures should outline *who* is responsible for *what* in order to prevent duplicate or missed responsibilities **(Figure 4.12)**. The procedures should be general enough so those individuals filling a position understand their responsibilities. As with other SOP/Gs, the HSO must follow up during accident investigations and postincident analysis to ensure that the medical emergency procedures are being followed.

Identification of Appropriate Medical Facilities

Identification of appropriate medical facilities will depend on the severity and type of the injury/illness, the geographical location of the person and the facility, and the mode of transportation to be used. In small communities, there may be only one choice in selecting the initial medical facility. In large

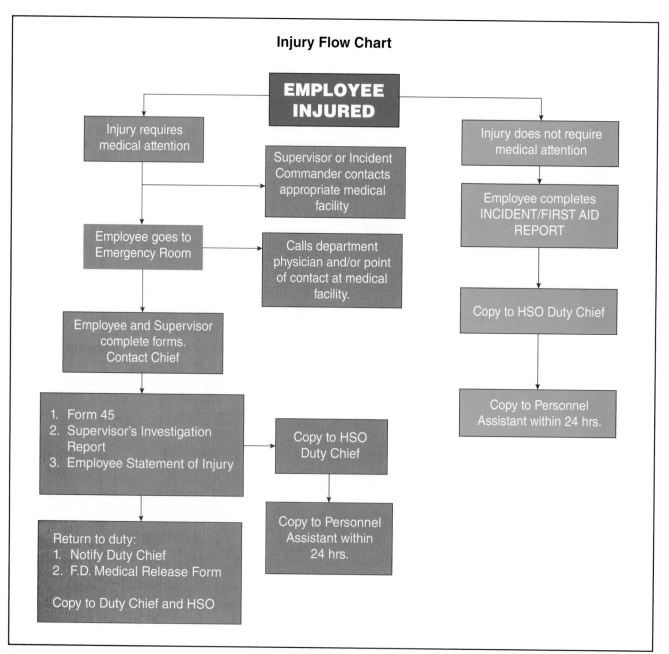

Figure 4.12 This example of an injury flow chart shows which person (who) has which responsibility (what) at what point in the process (when). *Courtesy of Village of Wilmette Fire Department with modifications.*

metropolitan areas, there may be numerous choices for medical facilities. Using the ICS Form 206 as a supplement to the SOP/G, the HSO will help identify the most appropriate medical facility in the decision-making process. Typically, local medical procedures that EMS personnel use to determine the appropriate medical facilities for community residents will be the same procedures used for fire department members. Appropriate medical facilities specific to life-threatening situations include, but are not limited to:

- Burn centers
- Trauma centers (Level I-IV)
- Neurologic specialty centers
- Cerebrovascular specialty centers
- Cardiovascular specialty centers
- Hyperbaric oxygen therapy centers

Some medical facilities will provide more than one specialized service. Local protocol will guide the decision in finding the closest and most appropriate facility.

Treatment and Transport Procedures

Treatment and transport procedures provide a guideline for decision-making processes. These two elements are often talked about together, but are distinctly different steps in the process of caring for an injured or ill member. Some departments may address treatment and transport in separate SOP/Gs, while other departments may address them in a single SOP/G. The membership should be knowledgeable about the procedure regardless of how it is written.

Treatment

Treatment will depend on the type and severity of the injury/illness and the available level of medical care on the scene. Minor injuries or illnesses may be treated on site or at the fire station. NFPA® 1403 states at a minimum **basic life support (BLS)** care shall be provided at live-fire training exercises.

The SOP/G should provide guidance on the decision-making process and give options for caregivers to choose from. These decisions will depend on jurisdictional resources and capabilities. For example, some jurisdictions use a tiered emergency medical services system, while others may have an all-paramedic level service. Some of the options include:

- **Basic life support (BLS)** — this may be appropriate for minor or non-life-threatening injuries or illnesses. BLS care refers to basic emergency medical technician (EMT) level care **(Figure 4.13, p. 136)**.

- **Advanced life support (ALS)** — this may be appropriate for non-life-threatening or life-threatening injuries or illnesses. ALS care refers to intermediate emergency medical technician level care, and may also include cardiac monitoring capabilities.

If ALS or Advanced Cardiac Life Support (ACLS) care is needed and is not on site, the SOP/G must outline how assistance will be obtained. Emergency medical systems vary across the country, and the process for requesting ALS support should not be taken for granted.

Basic Life Support (BLS) — Emergency medical treatment administered without the use of adjunctive equipment; includes maintenance of airway, breathing, and circulation, as well as basic bandaging and splinting.

Advanced Life Support (ALS) — Advanced medical skills performed by trained medical personnel, such as the administration of medications, or airway management procedures to save a patient's life.

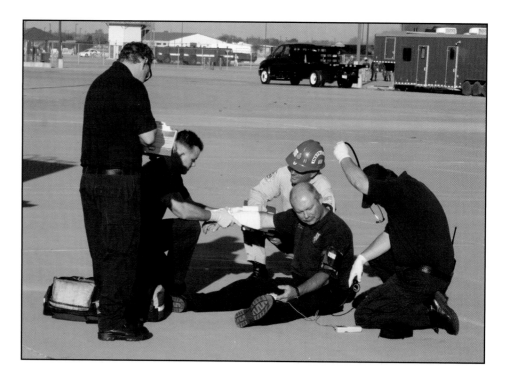

Figure 4.13 Basic life support (BLS) may have to be provided at a scene to firefighters or victims. SOP/Gs should reflect the proper procedures for providing this care.

Transport

Transportation of an injured or ill fire department member will again depend on the severity and type of injury, the distance to an appropriate medical facility, and the level of care needed. In a minor injury/illness situation, a member may be driven in a fire department vehicle to an urgent care or other non-hospital type facility. If a member is to be transported directly to a hospital, then transportation should be by one of the following transport options:

- **Ground basic life support ambulance** — may be appropriate for minor and non-life-threatening injuries or illnesses.

- **Ground advanced life support ambulance** — may be appropriate for life-threatening injuries or illnesses. It may also be appropriate when a basic life support ambulance is not available or not used in a jurisdiction.

- **Air medical transport** — may be appropriate for life-threatening injuries or illnesses for which advanced life support care is required and the transport time to the medical facility is a critical factor.

The SOP/G should provide enough guidance to be flexible to the situation and promote good decision-making options. In addition, local EMS protocol should be followed in regards to the treatment and transport of any injured or ill member.

> ## WARNING!
> Ill or injured responders should never be allowed to transport themselves to a medical facility for treatment, regardless of the apparent severity of their condition.

Accident and Injury Reporting Procedures

The HSO will investigate incidents that result in hazardous conditions, injuries, illnesses, exposures, and fatalities involving organization members. Property damage and near-miss occurrences shall be investigated with the goal of preventing future events. Included with this are incidents involving apparatus, vehicles, facilities, and equipment owned and operated by the organization. Review the procedures in use at the time of the incident and develop corrective procedures as necessary. Some aspects of investigation SOP/Gs are as follows:

- **Immediate responsibility** — Ensure that transportation and medical treatment are provided for any injured personnel. Develop and implement procedures that ensure this care is provided at the most appropriate health-care facility (may include establishing appropriate contracts with health-care facilities and private ambulance services not provided by the jurisdiction).

- **Agency cooperation** — Work closely with law enforcement agencies to ensure complete and accurate reporting in the event of litigation or liability. Include this information as part of the postincident analysis.

- **Deviations or drift from policy** — Evaluate any deviation or drift in policy.

- **Incident review** — Include recommendations to the organization's chief/manager or AHJ for corrective action to prevent future injuries, fatalities, or property-loss incidents.

- **Investigating and reporting** — Develop and review procedures periodically; ensure compliance with federal, state/territorial/provincial, and local requirements.

Reporting Procedures

The HSO should ensure SOP/Gs address the reporting requirements for all fire department members. A main purpose of this documentation for the HSO is to record the incident for analysis and look for trends, control measures, or corrective actions that may prevent a recurrence. In addition, worker's compensation claims and disability claims require thorough documentation. To help the HSO research trends, the organization should have a searchable database management system for storing and analyzing organizational records.

Typically, the reporting process will involve affected members notifying their immediate supervisor, or instructor if in a class or training, of the situation **(Figure 4.14)**. The immediate supervisor then makes the appropriate notifications, which follow the organization's chain of command. In addition to the internal notification process, an SOP/G must address the reporting to the local law enforcement agency responsible for conducting accident investigations. Some fire departments require a police accident report on all accidents or incidents involving apparatus regardless of severity.

Figure 4.14 Reports of all injuries, even minor ones like this student's nose bleed, need to be reported on the proper forms and investigated later.

Federal and state OSHA regulations require reporting of certain injuries, fatalities, illnesses, or exposure events that occurs with a fire department member. OSHA 29 CFR 1904 requires reporting of any of the following occurrences:

- Death
- Days away from work
- Restricted work or transfer to another job
- Medical treatment beyond **first aid**
- Loss of consciousness
- A significant injury or illness diagnosed by a physician or other licensed health care professional

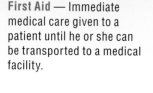

First Aid — Immediate medical care given to a patient until he or she can be transported to a medical facility.

OSHA Definition of First Aid[2]

According to OSHA 29 CFR 1904.7, *first aid* means:

- Using a non-prescription medication at non-prescription strength
- Administering tetanus immunizations
- Cleaning, flushing or soaking wounds on the surface of the skin
- Using wound coverings, such as bandages, Band-Aids™, and gauze pads
- Using hot or cold therapy
- Using any non-rigid means of support, such as elastic bandages, wraps, non-rigid back belts
- Using temporary immobilization devices while transporting an accident victim
- Drilling of a fingernail or toenail to relieve pressure
- Using eye patches
- Removing foreign bodies from the eye, using only irrigation or a cotton swab
- Using finger guards
- Using massages
- Drinking fluids for relief of heat stress

NOTE: These are the federal OSHA regulations; some states follow the federal regulations while others have state regulations based upon OSHA.

An SOP/G should provide a flowchart of decision points and notifications with accidents and injuries. This standardized process will ensure an important element is not missed. HSOs should be versed in their local jurisdictional requirements, as OSHA requirements are the minimum standard.

Investigation Procedures

The HSO should develop or ensure SOP/Gs address the steps in the investigation process. The SOP/G should address the individual responsibilities in the investigation, the documentation process of the investigation, and the final written report. The policy should define accidents and establish both the authority for investigating each type of accident and a procedure for accident investigation. The HSO and the safety and health committee will have the ultimate authority for accident analysis. Initial accident investigation responsibilities will be dependent on the AHJ and outlined in the SOP/G manual.

When an accident occurs, an investigation is conducted to determine the root cause or the most basic reason for the accident and its source or origin. Accident investigations should be objective, impartial, and directed toward fact-finding, not fault-finding. Investigations should never be intended as punishment for those involved. Investigations should result in recommendations for SOP/G review and/or revision and how to prevent future accidents, injuries, and losses. Several reasons to investigate workplace accidents are to identify and document the following conditions:

- Root cause of an accident
- Previously unrecognized hazards
- Apparatus/equipment obsolescence, defects, or design flaws
- Additional training needs
- Improvements needed in safety policies and procedures
- Facts that could have a legal impact on an accident case
- Prevent future accidents from occurring
- Historical trends

When a workplace accident investigation is conducted, all participants and witnesses should be interviewed and all relevant factors documented. Some further information on conducting investigations can be found in Chapter 9, Accident Investigations.

NOTE: Accident investigations are not limited to accidents according to NFPA® 1500, *Standard on Fire Department Occupational Safety and Health Program.* Job-related injuries and illnesses, fatalities, and exposures to infectious diseases and hazardous materials or atmospheres are also investigated.

Facility Inspection Procedures

Inspection procedures will vary depending on the type of fire department facility being inspected. The HSO is responsible for ensuring procedures are in place for fire department facility inspections and that they comply with any applicable law, code, regulation, or standard. This process will include the frequency schedule and the assignment of responsibility for the inspection. Some inspection requirements may vary among states/provinces, so the HSO should be knowledgeable of local mandates. The HSO will also need to ensure inspections are documented and filed in a centrally accessible location. Fire department facilities with unique inspection criteria include:

- **Fire administration, office buildings, and classrooms** — building safety and fire codes. The fire prevention staff typically inspects these buildings on an annual basis.

- **Fire stations** — building safety and fire codes, NFPA® standards, and OSHA regulations. Fire station personnel may inspect fire stations every month **(Figure 4.15)**. Annual fire station inspections may involve a consortium of persons representing the fire prevention bureau, risk management division, health department, contractor, and/or OSHA. The HSO should coordinate this inspection and ensure documentation is completed.

- **Fleet maintenance facilities** — building safety and fire codes, EPA and OSHA regulations. The fleet staff may inspect fleet maintenance facilities every month. Annual inspections of fleet maintenance facilities may involve a consortium of persons representing the fire prevention bureau, risk management division, EPA, and/or OSHA.

- **Training facilities** — building safety codes, structural engineer inspection, EPA regulations, and NFPA® standards. Training facility inspections have several timelines. First, prior to any live-fire evolution a preburn inspection must be conducted. Second, an annual inspection should be performed to assess the overall structural integrity, operational doors and windows, and functioning safety control devices. Third, a licensed engineer must perform a 5-year inspection to assess the overall structural integrity.

    NOTE: Facility personnel should inspect all apparatus, equipment, and protective clothing at training facilities on a regular basis. This documentation should be available for review during facilities inspection.

- **Storage facilities** — building safety and fire codes. The fire prevention staff typically inspects these buildings on an annual basis.

Figure 4.15 A schedule (daily, weekly, monthly, annually) and corresponding inspection checklists should be included in SOP/Gs for the regular inspection of all fire department facilities.

A SOP/G should address special inspections. These inspections will occur after a significant natural event, such as an earthquake, severe weather, or other destructive force; but also occur at the request of the risk manager or OSHA inspector.

Infection Control Procedures

The fire department is responsible for ensuring an **infection control officer** is appointed. This person may be the HSO. In some departments, the infection control officer may be assigned to the EMS Division or another organizational department, such as Human Resources. If the positions are assigned separately, the HSO and the infection control officer will work closely to ensure compliance with all applicable legal mandates. The HSO is responsible for assessing the infection control program and ensuring SOP/Gs are in place to protect the workforce. The HSO must be knowledgeable of and ensure SOP/Gs include requirements in and comply with the following:

- NFPA® 1500, *Standard on Fire Department Occupational Safety and Health Program*
- NFPA® 1581, *Standard on Fire Department Infection Control Program*
- NFPA® 1582, *Standard on Comprehensive Occupational Medical Program for Fire Departments*
- 29 CFR 1910.132 *Personal Protective Equipment*
- 29 CFR 1910.134 *Respiratory Protection*
- 29 CFR 1910.1020 *Access to Employee Exposure and Medical Records*
- 29 CFR 1910.1030 *Bloodborne Pathogens*
- Ryan White HIV/AIDS Treatment Extension Act of 2009, Part G – Notification of Possible Exposure to Infectious Diseases

An **infectious agent** exposure can occur in a fire department facility, on a fire department apparatus, at an emergency or nonemergency event, or while cleaning or disinfecting apparatus and/or equipment. Infectious diseases are not detectable by the senses – they are invisible. What must be recognized is the potential of exposure and proper steps for protection and preventing transmission of the disease. The HSO is responsible for ensuring SOP/Gs are established and provide guidance on preventing infectious disease exposure and transmission. The following list provides some highlighted topics from NFPA® 1581:

- **Training and education** — the infection control program must include annual training and education as required by law.
- **Fire department facilities** — fire department facilities must be cleaned and disinfected. This cleaning includes offices, kitchens, common areas, sleeping quarters, bathrooms, and apparatus bays.
- **Fire department apparatus, equipment, and clothing** — apparatus and equipment must be cleaned and disinfected and protective clothing and equipment must be laundered, disinfected, or properly discarded. Contaminated protective clothing and equipment should not be permitted to be taken home **(Figure 4.16, p. 142)**. All protective clothing and equipment must be kept on the apparatus or designated storage room. Protective cloth-

Infection Control Officer — Designated individual from the fire or EMS division whose responsibilities include managing the infection control program and investigating exposures to infectious agents.

Infectious Agent — Biological agent that causes disease or illness to its host.

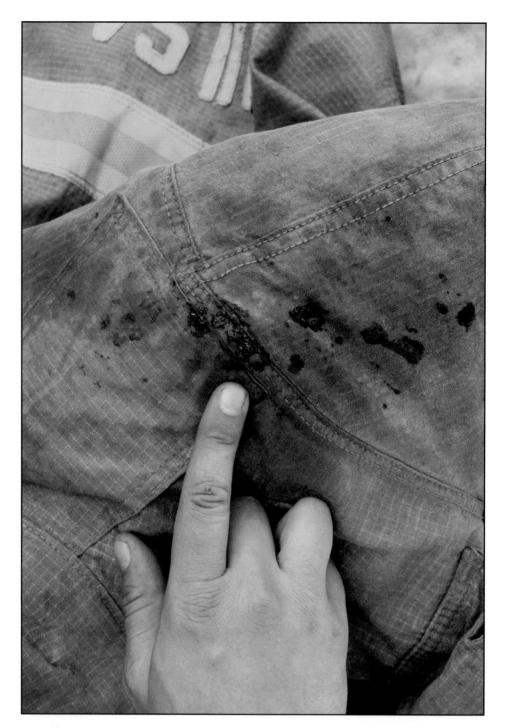

Figure 4.16 SOP/Gs should state that contaminated equipment should not be taken home. The equipment should be cleaned at the station or by an authorized third party.

Titers — Measurement of a concentration of a substance in a solution; in the case of immunizations, a measurement of the concentration of certain antibodies in the blood stream to determine the need for new inoculations against diseases such as hepatitis or tetanus.

ing and equipment should never be worn inside the living quarters, day rooms, offices, or as everyday station work attire. Prior to conducting fire station tours or on-site safety talks, all protective clothing and equipment on display or worn must be clean.

- **Immunizations and infectious disease screenings** — procedures must address the process for members to receive immunizations and infectious disease screening, including post-immunization **titers**.

- **Biohazard disposal and identification** — this includes the placement of warning labels on containers and the proper disposal of contaminated items.

SOP/Gs must address the before, during, and after phases of a potential exposure. By ensuring all three phases are addressed in SOP/Gs, exposure and disease transmission can be minimized. First, the before or prevention phase procedures should include the awareness of the potential for exposure, the allocation of protective clothing and equipment, vaccinations and immunizations, and training. Second, during any potential situation where an infectious agent exposure exists, members must have the knowledge to recognize the potential, the protective clothing and equipment to protect themselves, and the training to properly deal with the situation. Third, the after or post-exposure phase will include documentation of the exposure, any needed follow-up evaluations and procedures, counseling, and required notifications.

Chapter Summary

SOP/Gs are in place to provide guidance on expected performance in all aspects of fire department operations. Fire department members must know what is expected of them and SOP/Gs provide the guiding principles of action. SOP/Gs should be viewed as policies and procedures. Policies help guide proper member conduct while procedures guide members' operational performance in a standardized manner. The goals of SOP/Gs are to improve safety in the working environment and prevent firefighter injuries and fatalities while reducing the potential legal liability.

Review Questions

1. What process should the health safety officer follow when establishing occupational safety and health program standard operating procedures or guidelines? (pp. 116-126)

2. What requirements must be included in safety procedures for live-fire training evolutions? (pp. 128-131)

3. What key areas should the health safety officer address when developing medical emergency procedures? (pp. 132-136)

4. What components make up the standard operating procedures or guidelines related to accident and injury reporting and investigations? (pp. 137-139)

5. What requirements must the health safety officer follow when developing standard operating procedures or guidelines for facility inspections? (pp. 139-141)

6. How can the health safety officer incorporate infection control procedures into the fire department's health maintenance program? (pp. 141-143)

Chapter 4 End Notes

1. National Institute of Occupational Safety and Health (NIOSH)

2. OSHA 29 CFR 1904 *Recording and Reporting Occupational Injuries and Illnesses*

LEARNING ACTIVITIES

4-1

Create a standard operating procedure or guideline based on departmental documents or materials.

Refer to Appendix B: Learning Activity Answers in the back of this manual for suggested responses.

Purpose

One of the most important duties of the HSO is to work with fire department personnel in developing, evaluating, and revising standard operating procedures or guidelines (SOP/Gs). In this capacity, the HSO will often need to investigate problems or issues within the jurisdiction, accumulate the appropriate amount of data, and ensure that policies and procedures are in place and that they address workplace and workforce safety and health elements.

Directions

For this activity, you will practice creating SOP/Gs based on various departmental documents or materials. The documents are presented in various formats (memo, e-mail, letter, etc.) and communicate real-world problems within a jurisdiction — specifically, problems related to the five major topics discussed in Chapter 4:

- Live-Fire Training Procedures
- Medical Emergency Procedures
- Accident and Injury Reporting Procedures
- Facility Inspection Procedures
- Infection Control Procedures

1. Choose one of the documents provided in the Student Worksheet.

2. Analyze the problem or situation presented by your chosen document.

   NOTE: As you work, you should ask certain questions while performing your analysis and investigation. Those questions include (but may not be limited to):

   - What exactly is the problem?
   - What further data may be needed to evaluate the situation?
   - What should be the timetable for making the needs evaluation?
   - What is the best response to the need (the best policy or procedure to solve the problem)?
   - What are any alternative responses that the situation may offer?

3. Brainstorm a list of criteria that would need to be included in a departmental standard operating procedure or guideline (SOP/G).

4. Transcribe your material(s) into the blank SOP/G form provided in the Student Worksheet. The draft SOP/G should accomplish the following:

   - Seek to address all the requirements integral to your chosen document
   - Include references to and support from any laws, codes, regulations, and standards
   - Concentrate on the safety and health aspects of the situation

5. Repeat the process with the additional documents, if necessary.

   NOTE: More information on SOP/G development — including templates and examples — can be found at FEMA's website.

4-1
Create a standard operating procedure or guideline based on departmental documents or materials. (cont.)

Refer to Appendix B: Learning Activity Answers in the back of this manual for suggested responses.

Student Worksheet

Document 1 – Live-Fire Training Procedures

To: HSO Jones

CC: Fire Chief Evans

From: Assistant Chief Burke

Date: 2/17/2014

Re: Live-Fire Training Procedures

As you know, our fire department has recently experienced an increase in college-style apartment home fires. These apartments typically have 2-4 separate sleeping/bathing rooms, with shared kitchen, dining, and living spaces. These buildings in the jurisdiction are usually 3-5 stories high, with multiple units on each level.

Fire department personnel are struggling with the facility layout, accessing the appropriate apartment home, proper ventilation procedures, etc. As the newly assigned HSO, it will be your responsibility to ensure that departmental procedures are established to address this concern. The first step will be to ensure that we have the proper training evolution procedures in place to handle these types of operations. Fire Chief Evans and I have spoken extensively about this need and feel it is something that should be put into action as soon as possible. We will, of course, help provide whatever tools or resources you need as you begin this process.

Please see me if you have any questions.

LEARNING ACTIVITIES

4-1

Create a standard operating procedure or guideline based on departmental documents or materials. (cont.)

Refer to Appendix B: Learning Activity Answers in the back of this manual for suggested responses.

Document 2 – Medical Emergency Procedures

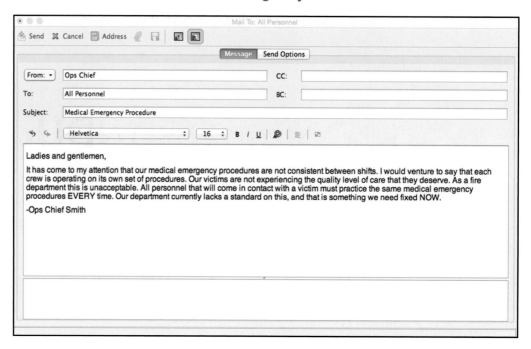

Mail To: All Personnel

Send Cancel Address

Message Send Options

From: Ops Chief

To: All Personnel

Subject: Medical Emergency Procedure

CC:

BC:

Helvetica 16 **B** *I* U

Ladies and gentlemen,

It has come to my attention that our medical emergency procedures are not consistent between shifts. I would venture to say that each crew is operating on its own set of procedures. Our victims are not experiencing the quality level of care that they deserve. As a fire department this is unacceptable. All personnel that will come in contact with a victim must practice the same medical emergency procedures EVERY time. Our department currently lacks a standard on this, and that is something we need fixed NOW.

-Ops Chief Smith

4-1
Create a standard operating procedure or guideline based on departmental documents or materials. (cont.)

LEARNING ACTIVITIES

Refer to Appendix B: Learning Activity Answers in the back of this manual for suggested responses.

Document 3 – Accident and Injury Reporting Procedures

MEMORANDUM
Anytown Fire Department

To: HSO Jones

From: Fire Chief Evans

CC: Assistant Chief Burke

Date: 5/29/2014

Re: Accident and Injury Reporting

In the last month, our fire department has lost one firefighter to a rock-climbing injury, two firefighters to snowboarding injuries, and three firefighters to home-related strains and sprains. Losing six firefighters is significantly impacting the department's operational readiness capabilities. Due to the increase in off-duty related injuries, there is a need for procedures on accident and injury reporting of off-duty mishaps.

LEARNING ACTIVITIES

4-1

Create a standard operating procedure or guideline based on departmental documents or materials. (cont.)

Refer to Appendix B: Learning Activity Answers in the back of this manual for suggested responses.

Document 4 – Facility Inspection Procedures

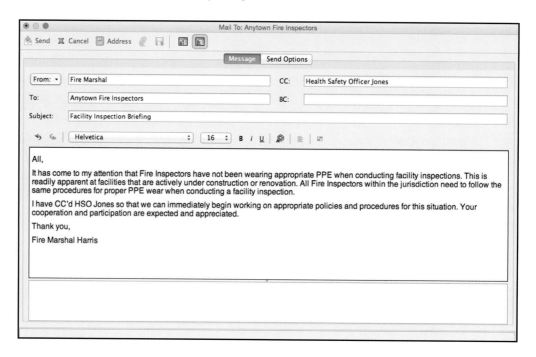

4-1
Create a standard operating procedure or guideline based on departmental documents or materials. (cont.)

Refer to Appendix B: Learning Activity Answers in the back of this manual for suggested responses.

Group 5 – Infection Control Procedures

May 29, 2014

ER Director Abrams
1234 Hospital Drive
Anytown, My State, 55555

Fire Chief Evans
Anytown Fire Department
4321 Fire Department St.
Anytown, My State, 55555

Dear Fire Chief Evans:

I have noticed over the past two weeks that members of the Anytown Fire Department are not practicing infection control procedures when caring for patients. Just yesterday, a patient suffering from a severe laceration was transferred via the fire department. The paramedics providing care were both covered in the patient's blood, and neither took the steps necessary to protect themselves. This is a serious problem.

With the increase in bloodborne pathogens, it is more important than ever to practice infection control. I am deeply concerned that fire department personnel are not taking this issue seriously. Without a change in operational procedures, the Anytown Fire Department will no longer be part of the solution, they will soon be part of the problem.

Sincerely,

Larry Abrams

ER Director Abrams

Create a standard operating procedure or guideline based on departmental documents or materials. (cont.)

4-1

Refer to Appendix B: Learning Activity Answers in the back of this manual for suggested responses.

Sample SOP/G Form

FIRE DEPT.	**Anytown Fire Department** **Standard Operating Procedure/Guideline** **Procedure/Guideline #** **Date:** **Revision Date:**	P. # of # Revision ☐ New ☐

SUBJECT:

I.   PURPOSE:

II.   SCOPE/APPLICABILITY:

III.   POLICY:

IV.   PROCEDURE:

V.   RESPONSIBILITIES:

VI.   SUPERSEDES:

VII.   DISTRIBUTION:

APPROVALS:

4-1
Create a standard operating procedure or guideline based on departmental documents or materials. (cont.)

Refer to Appendix B: Learning Activity Answers in the back of this manual for suggested responses.

	Anytown Fire Department	P. # of #
	Standard Operating Procedure/Guideline	

Procedure/Guideline #
Date:
Revision Date: Revision ☐ New ☐

DETAILED POLICY/PROCEDURE:

_____
_____
_____
_____
_____
_____
_____
_____
_____
_____
_____
_____
_____
_____
_____
_____
_____
_____
_____
_____
_____
_____
_____
_____
_____

Organizational Risk Management

Chapter Contents

Key Terms

NFPA® Job Performance Requirements

This chapter provides information that addresses the following job performance requirements of NFPA® 1521, *Standard for Fire Department Safety Officer Professional Qualifications (2015)*.

4.2.1	4.5.1
4.2.2	4.8.1
4.2.3	4.8.2

Organizational Risk Management

Learning Objectives

After reading this chapter, students will be able to:

1. Determine the process for developing an organizational risk management plan. (4.2.1, 4.5.1)

2. Identify risks associated with emergency operations. (4.2.1, 4.8.1, 4.8.2)

3. Determine risks associated with nonemergency operations. (4.2.1, 4.8.1, 4.8.2)

4. Describe ways to evaluate risks identified in a risk management plan. (4.2.3)

5. Identify ways to establish priorities for action. (4.2.1, 4.2.3)

6. Explain techniques for controlling risks. (4.2.1, 4.2.3)

7. Identify ways to implement an organizational risk management plan. (4.2.1, 4.2.2, 4.2.3)

8. Identify methods for monitoring the effectiveness of a risk management plan. (4.2.1, 4.2.2)

9. Learning Activity 5-1: Identify risks inherent in a motor vehicle collision (emergency). (4.2.1, 4.8.1, 4.8.2)

10. Learning Activity 5-2: Identify risks inherent in a live-fire training evolution (nonemergency). (4.2.1, 4.8.1, 4.8.2)

Chapter 5
Organizational Risk Management

Case History

Different fire departments use different and creative means to address the challenge of risk management. The following leading fire departments are excellent examples of using creative solutions to meet and exceed the risk management requirements described in this chapter.

Kootenai County, Idaho

Kootenai County Fire and Rescue approaches risk management with a forward focus on identifying future challenges. At regular meetings, key stakeholders in the department meet and review each department's functions. This process is augmented with a strategic plan. Long-term key goals have been identified, mid-range objectives listed, and short-term action items clearly developed. This process has helped to galvanize all ranks with a safety-first attitude. As a result of this review process, Kootenai County Fire and Rescue has an excellent safety record that validates its highly successful risk management approach.

Clackamas County, Oregon

Clackamas Fire District #1's Organizational Risk Management program identified sprains and strains as the major contributor to injuries to its firefighters. Some of these injuries caused long leaves of absence and in some cases were career-ending. To address this issue, Clackamas Fire District #1 developed a position for a fitness coordinator. This employee's responsibility is to assist each firefighter in a personal fitness program. The program includes fitness and nutritional training. Each employee has access to the fitness coordinator to regularly monitor his or hers progress. The results have been overwhelming. Being fit helps the firefighters enjoy a better quality of life, and the department is experiencing fewer sprains and strains. Having a fitness coordinator who is a department employee has been a win-win for both the firefighters and the department in Clackamas.

Tualatin, Oregon

Tualatin Valley Fire and Rescue recognized health and wellness as a significant organizational risk many years ago. In the 1990s, TVF&R hired a full-time nurse who specializes in the needs of the fire department. The position has remained as a staff position ever since to provide industry leading health and wellness support to its staff. The duties include full annual physicals, exposure assistance, inoculations, health wellness coaching, and most recently interfacing with workers' compensation claims adjusters. Modern medicine has proven many types of injuries have a better recovery time when quick quality care is made available to the patient. Tualatin Valley Fire and Rescues staff nurse shepherds injuries through the workers' compensation system quickly and efficiently to provide firefighters with the best possible outcome. This process has resulted in healthier firefighter recoveries and cut the costs of lengthy disabling injuries.

Case History

Kitsap County, Washington

Kitsap Risk Management Group has an intergovernmental agreement between South Kitsap Fire and Rescue, Central Kitsap Fire and Rescue, Poulsbo Fire and Rescue, and Bainbridge Fire and Rescue. Over a decade ago, these fire departments were suffering from frequent severe losses. At the time, their combined loss ratio (the ratio of claims cost to insurance premiums paid) exceeded 200%. The departments jointly focused on organizational risk management throughout their service areas. Within 24 months, the combined loss ratio was reduced to under 15% and has been maintained at that level ever since. The groups have participation from each department's management staff and elected officials. The group meets bimonthly for 2 to 3 hours. The agenda includes a claims review, training update, national trends, regional trends, safety alerts, and other risk management issues. This robust regional approach promotes the sharing of data among the departments without removing each department's autonomy. Each department maintains separate safety committees that review the department's injuries, near-misses, and property losses. The departments strive to identify areas where written policy and practice in the field are misaligned. This approach to cultural drift has successfully identified risk that could have gone unnoticed until an injury occurred.

NOTE: These departments are leaders in the fire service when it comes to risk management and have agreed to be named explicitly in this publication. In addition, the risk management plans in these departments exceed NFPA® and OSHA requirements.

Regardless of the size of the community or service area, every fire and emergency services organization should develop, implement, and use a risk management plan to guide its operations. The risk management plan is not a stagnant document that is developed, described in a printed document, and placed on a shelf. Essentially, a risk management plan serves as documentation that risks have been identified and evaluated, and that a reasonable control plan has been implemented and followed. An effective risk management plan has a positive effect on firefighter safety and the department.

The department chief is responsible for the development of a risk management plan. The chief may have the option of delegating the responsibility to the organization's HSO. Regardless of who is responsible for the plan, all organizational members must be familiar with the plan. Personnel who are assigned the responsibility for the risk management plan must be capable of performing multiple skills, such as training, investigating, evaluating, analyzing, implementing, and communicating. Each of these skills can be applied to the tasks required of the HSO. In each task, however, the HSO is the risk manager, applying the elements of risk management to each of the various tasks.

The overall risk management plan should have three distinct sections **(Figure 5.1)**. The first section is community risk assessment. While this section is not a direct function of the HSO, the information from this process will provide the HSO with known risks in the community that responders may be exposed to. The second section is the organizational risk management plan. This section evaluates risks and hazards that can affect the organization and provides control measures to reduce the frequency, severity, and probability

Risk Management Settings

Planning	Organizational	Operational
District Surveys	Shift Work	NIMS - ICS
Preincident Planning	Health and Wellness	Incident and Safety Officer
Site Safety Plans	Task Analysis	Personnel Accountability
	Inspections	Executing Plans and Procedures
	Safety Audits	

Legal Compliance

Figure 5.1 Risk management should be a consideration in planning, day-to-day organization activity, and emergency operations. All risk management policies should comply with applicable laws, codes, and standards.

of a negative event from occurring. The third section is the operational risk management plan. This plan will be discussed in Chapter 6, Operational Risk Management, and will focus on the risks and hazards associated with response to incidents and incident management control measures. All three sections of the risk management plan provide the fire and emergency services organization with a foundation to address the inherent regulatory and legal risks that can harm the organization and its members.

An understanding of the concepts of risk management and system safety is essential to all fire officers and the personnel who fill the position of HSO. These concepts are the basis for the majority of the roles and responsibilities for those officers who plan, develop, and manage the safety and health program.

16 Firefighter Life Safety Initiatives 1, 3, and 16

The *16 Firefighter Life Safety Initiatives* were discussed in Chapter 1, Health Safety Officer Responsibilities. Initiatives 1, 3, and 16 are specifically pertinent to the HSO's responsibilities related to organizational risk management.

1. Define and advocate the need for a cultural change within the fire service relating to safety; incorporating leadership, management, supervision, accountability and personal responsibility.

3. Focus greater attention on the integration of risk management with incident management at all levels, including strategic, tactical, and planning responsibilities.

16. Safety must be a primary consideration in the design of apparatus and equipment.

Organizational Risk Management Plan Components and Development

In Chapter 4 of NFPA® 1500, *Standard on Fire Department Occupational Safety and Health Program,* the requirements of the **risk management plan** are simply stated: "The fire department shall adopt an official written risk management

Risk Management Plan — Written plan that identifies and analyzes the exposure to hazards, selects appropriate risk management techniques to handle exposures, implements those techniques, and monitors the results.

Organizational Risk Management Plan — Portion of the overall risk management plan that focuses on safe work practices outside of the operational environment.

plan that covers administration, facilities, training, vehicle operations, protective clothing and equipment, operations at emergency incidents, operations at nonemergency incidents, and other related activities." The **organizational risk management plan** requires a systematic approach.

Hazard or Risk

In everyday conversation, the terms hazard and risk are often used interchangeably; however, they describe two different things. The term hazard usually refers to an unsafe act or condition that is the source of a risk. A risk, on the other hand, is the potential of loss, injury, or suffering harm from a hazard. Risk can also be thought of as the potential for failure or loss. In other words, risk is the exposure to a hazard. A hazard is a condition, substance, or device that can directly cause an injury, fatality, or property loss **(Figure 5.2)**.

These terms can be used when discussing safety and health issues of the members of the fire and emergency services organization. The hazards are those that the individual must face while performing the duties of firefighter or emergency responder. Those hazards include those found at the emergency scene and that exist in the organization's facilities, apparatus, and nonemergency operations.

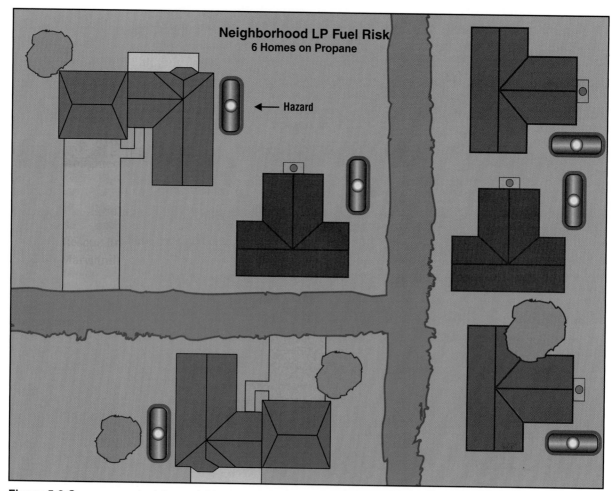

Figure 5.2 One propane tank in a neighborhood presents an individual hazard. A neighborhood where all the homes have propane tanks represents a risk that needs to be managed.

Components

The five distinct components of the organizational risk management plan are (**Figure 5.3, p. 160**):

- **Risk identification** — risks are identified in the community and within the organizational and the operational settings at emergency and nonemergency incidents.

- **Risk evaluation** — risks are evaluated on their probability and potential for negative consequences, including the anticipated severity and frequency of occurrence.

- **Establishment of priorities for action** — a ranking of the identified risks will be based on the degree of severity and frequency.

- **Risk control techniques** — control measures will be identified for each significant risk.

- **Risk management monitoring** — monitoring of the risk control measures will be an ongoing process. Recommendations for plan revision will be based on the monitoring process.

These components provide the elements of a cyclical risk management process. While this is a primary responsibility of the HSO, all members of the fire and emergency services organization have a responsibility and vested interest in ensuring the plan is utilized to its fullest potential.

Development Strategies

An organizational risk management plan should be written specifically for each fire and emergency services organization because unique differences exist in organizational structures, community characteristics, and services provided. Development of an organizational risk management plan is a dynamic process that includes all organizational members. Considerations or strategies for developing an organizational risk management plan include, but are not limited to:

- **Correlating the plan to the organization's mission** — the mission of the organization and the associated risks should be identified and directly connected to the risk management plan.

- **Reviewing reports** — NFPA® 1500 states that the development of the organizational risk management plan shall identify and categorize risks from injury reports, vehicle incident reports, near-miss or equipment malfunction or failure reports, and any other reports important to the organization.

- **Identifying, implementing, and monitoring control measures** — control measures must be identified, implemented, and monitored throughout the risk management process.

- **Cooperating with other agencies** — many fire and emergency service organizations have mutual aid and/or automatic aid agreements. Departments should have immediate access to maps, preincident plans, or other documentation on target hazards in jurisdictions where a request for assistance is likely.

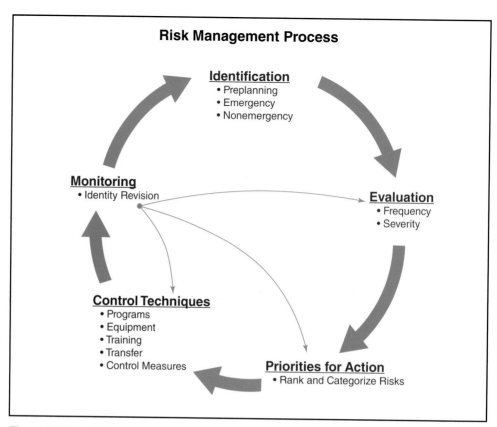

Risk Management Process

Identification
- Preplanning
- Emergency
- Nonemergency

Monitoring
- Identity Revision

Evaluation
- Frequency
- Severity

Control Techniques
- Programs
- Equipment
- Training
- Transfer
- Control Measures

Priorities for Action
- Rank and Categorize Risks

Figure 5.3 The risk management process has five distinct components and is cyclical. Monitoring identifies when the process needs to start again based upon incoming data.

- **Being proactive** — risk management is a continual process. Being proactive in the risk management process puts the organizational members in a position of having the knowledge and skill to effectively handle risks. The risk management plan also allows the organization to proactively handle the mitigation of incidents efficiently when they occur.

- **Involving organizational membership** — the risk management process requires the involvement of all members, including sworn and non-sworn members in all divisions and within each specialty **(Figure 5.4)**. A robust plan will have widespread member involvement.

- **Using additional resources** — the risk management process should involve using resources to help understand the risk management process, identify and assess risk, identify control techniques, determine national and local trends, and review investigative reports.

The HSO should seek out literature and resources when developing or revising the risk management plan. Some useful literature and resources include:

- NFPA® 1250, *Recommended Practice for Fire Service Risk Management*
- NFPA® 1500, *Standard on Fire Department Occupational Safety and Health Program*
- NFPA® 1561, *Standard on Emergency Services Incident Management System and Command Safety*
- FEMA: *Risk Management Practices in the Fire Service*
- FEMA: *Fire and Emergency Medical Services Ergonomics*

Figure 5.4 Getting the input from personnel with different expertise and perspectives is important to managing risks at incident scenes and in the organization as a whole.

- NFFF: *Fire Service Vulnerability Assessment Project*
- NFFF: *Everyone Goes Home®* and *16 Life Safety Initiatives*
- USFA: Firefighter Statistics and Reports
- NIOSH: Fire Fighter Fatality Investigation and Prevention Program
- NIOSH: Research Programs: Program Portfolio
- NFA: numerous courses on risk management
- U.S. Department of Defense: System Safety Program
- CPSE/CFAI *Standards of Cover*

Risk Identification

To identify the risks, the HSO compiles a list of all emergency and nonemergency operations and duties in which the organization participates. Ideally, the HSO should take into consideration the worst possible conditions or potential events, including major disasters and multiple events **(Figure 5.5)**. There are many sources to assist with this identification process.

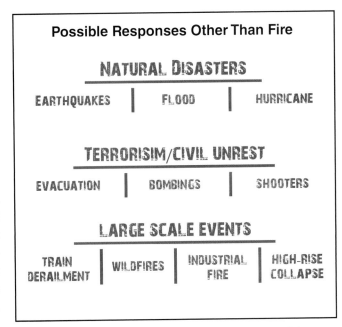

Possible Responses Other Than Fire

NATURAL DISASTERS

| EARTHQUAKES | FLOOD | HURRICANE |

TERRORISIM/CIVIL UNREST

| EVACUATION | BOMBINGS | SHOOTERS |

LARGE SCALE EVENTS

| TRAIN DERAILMENT | WILDFIRES | INDUSTRIAL FIRE | HIGH-RISE COLLAPSE |

Figure 5.5 In an all-hazards response environment, risks other than fire need to be considered as part of the risk management plan.

The first (and possibly the most effective) is the department's loss prevention data, which consists of annual fire-loss reports categorized according to occupancy type, loss value, frequency, and other criteria. Although most departments are too small to rely on their own database for a statistically valid trend, national averages and trends are available from NFPA® and the National Fire Academy (NFA). National data is not always complete or accurate due to collection inconsistencies, regionally or department-wide, and a time lag of 1 to 2 years that is required to collect, analyze, and publish the data.

The HSO should seek input and ideas from the following:

- Department personnel
- Trade journals
- Workers' compensation insurer
- NFPA® annual injury report
- State Fire Marshal
- Professional associations
- Other service providers, such as law enforcement to identify the potential risks

When using information provided by other fire departments or organizations, the HSO should consider local circumstances that might present a different set of emergency and nonemergency operations and duties. Other risk identification sources include risk management plans developed by local industry and hazardous substance sites, vulnerability analyses, and the U.S. Environmental Protection Agency (EPA) plans, among others.

Emergency Risks

Emergency risks are those associated with first responders getting to an incident, stabilizing the situation, and returning to service. The operational setting may require some forethought before responders are placed in hazardous conditions. The assessment of emergency risks is an ongoing process that requires open communication between the line personnel (responders) and the staff officers (chief officers, HSO). The HSO must thoroughly understand the risks associated with response, clothing and equipment, operational setting, and with expanded services.

Response

Motor vehicle collisions rank highly on the list of causes of firefighter injuries and fatalities. In addition, the backing or moving of apparatus has been known to cause injuries and fatalities. The HSO should evaluate the risks associated with all vehicle operations and all apparatus types. Consideration should be given to:

- Policy and procedures, especially seat belt use
- Crew supervision
- Driver/operator training
- The use of spotters **(Figure 5.6)**

- Geographical layout of the jurisdiction
- Preemptive signaling device options
- Weather
- Speed zones
- Road hazards
- Other drivers and distracted drivers

Figure 5.6 The use of spotters whenever an apparatus is backing should be a part of all risk management plans. *Courtesy of Ron Jeffers.*

Improper Backing Can Be Fatal

Proper backing procedures are often overlooked, especially at chaotic scenes. Apparatus can be deadly at even slow speeds. Never assume that because a job task is routine that safety measures can be ignored in favor of speed.

There are many examples of injuries and fatalities associated with backing procedures. For example, in May, 2013, a firefighter in Phoenix, AZ was crushed between two apparatus when a driver/operator was backing one of the apparatus without using a spotter. This scenario may be all too familiar to firefighters in other departments as well. Regardless of the experience of the driver/operator, the use of spotters and extra personnel to provide situational awareness during backing procedures should never be considered optional.

Figure 5.7 Seat belt use saves lives and prevents injury. The HSO should insist that risk management SOP/Gs include the use of seatbelts at all times. *Courtesy of Ted Boothroyd.*

Member behavior and attitude toward safety can play a key role in the success of the risk management plan. For example, the use of seat belts has been shown to have mixed compliance. Annually, the USFA reports firefighters lose their lives as a result of not wearing their seat belt. The HSO should advocate for 100 percent compliance with seat belt use and make recommendations to the fire chief as needed in the occupational accidents report **(Figure 5.7)**. One valuable resource for the HSO is the NFFF's program, *Everyone Goes Home®*, which promotes the use of seat belts. HSOs can raise awareness, develop training using this program as a resource, and promote the International First Responder Seat Belt Pledge in their departments. In addition, member behavior and attitude toward safety should be examined.

Firefighter Fatalities and Injuries During Response[1]

According to NFPA® research, 12,350 collisions involving fire department emergency vehicles occurred in 2013, resulting in 730 injuries. In addition, there were 850 collisions involving firefighters' personal vehicles, resulting in 185 injuries. Injuries from collisions are only part of the 4,015 injuries classified as Responding to or Returning from an Incident occurred. These injuries from collisions and other acts during response accounted for 6 percent of all firefighter injuries in 2013.

In addition to the injuries, there were 16 deaths associated with response in 2013. Ten of these fatalities were attributed to vehicle crashes, while the other six were firefighters being struck by vehicles. The reported reasons for their deaths are as follows:

- Lack of seat belt use (four firefighters were not wearing seat belts, three of whom were ejected from their vehicles)
- Excessive speed
- Driver inattention or inexperience
- Poor weather conditions
- Failure to maintain control of a vehicle
- Reckless driving or ignoring traffic laws to reach a scene
- Drunk driving
- Struck by vehicle

Deaths during response accounted for 18 percent of all fatalities during 2013. The eight deaths directly related to collisions accounted for 10 percent of all fatalities and just over 60 percent of all response-related fatalities.

Protective Clothing and Equipment: Proper Use, Selection, and Limitations

Use of protective clothing and equipment should not result in any injuries or fatalities when the proper protective clothing and equipment is used to mitigate its intended hazard. Injuries and fatalities may result when protective clothing and equipment is not used appropriately. Selecting the correct type and level of protection is critical **(Figure 5.8)**.

At the same time, protective clothing and equipment can cause firefighters to place too much confidence in it and expose themselves to dangers that the garment was not designed to withstand. For instance, structural fire fighting clothing and equipment can provide so much thermal protection that the wearer may not notice rapid temperature changes inside a structure that typically precede a flashover. This lack of awareness exposes the wearer to flashover conditions that the clothing cannot withstand.

The organization should identify the proper clothing and equipment for the operational setting and provide it prior to any operational assignment of personnel. Not providing the correct type of PPE or continuing to use out of date, contaminated, or damaged PPE can contribute to firefighter injuries or fatalities. The organization should also provide training and education on the proper use and limitations of protective clothing and equipment. Emergency service administrators continually evaluate the clothing and equipment provided to ensure that it is adequate to the challenges for the hazardous conditions and situations that responders will face.

To address these concerns, the HSO should ensure the following are explained in the SOP/Gs:

- Selection of appropriate PPE for the response environment
- Inspection, care, and regular cleaning of PPE
- Years of service for each type of PPE
- Discarding, donating, or destroying of PPE

Emergency Operational Risks

Emergency operational risks should be identified and evaluated with appropriate control measures instituted in the organization. This review will include that a job task analysis be performed to assess the associated risks in the operational setting. Established SOP/Gs should address how the organization will provide for the safe working environment of its members. These

Matching Protection and Hazard

Figure 5.8 Risk management plans should outline the selection of the correct personal protective clothing and equipment for each likely response in the jurisdiction.

SOP/Gs will address areas such as apparatus, equipment, personnel, facilities, PPE, and training. Basically, the SOP/G will encompass all the programs in a fire and emergency services organization that provide some element of safety and health in the risk management plan. It will focus on the proactive, behind-the-scenes work that allows responders to carry out their operational responsibilities.

Risks Associated with Expanded Services

The fire service has been called upon to increase the types of services that it provides. Improvements in technology have helped address some of the new requirements as well as increase the effectiveness and efficiency of the services. It is no longer possible to isolate risk management to fire suppression activities or emergency medical service response. The modern fire and emergency services organization responders receive requests for assistance in an all-hazard and threat operational environment, and are finding themselves in a multidisciplined service delivery. Fire and emergency services organizations are expected to have personnel knowledgeable in responding to and handling terrorism events, weapons of mass destruction, pandemic outbreaks, and technical rescue in addition to fire incidents. The HSO must think beyond the everyday service delivery requests and consider the potential risks associated with the all-hazards response environment.

An **all-hazard concept** provides a coordinated approach to a wide variety of potential incidents **(Figure 5.9)**. All responders use a similar, coordinated approach with a common set of authorities, protections, and resources. As a result, when emergency responders plan and train for a particular emergency, they have a higher state of readiness to handle a variety of incident types. The all-hazard concept is used to categorize and prioritize types of hazards, the potential exposure they pose, and therefore the risk level they generate.

Nonemergency Risks

The USFA reports that the nonemergency causes of firefighter fatalities almost equal those from emergency situations. The annual USFA firefighter fatality reports categorized nonemergency duties as those associated with administration, training, other functions, and postincident illness or injury. The HSO must consider risks that have the potential to inflict harm in administration, facilities, training, and vehicle inspection and maintenance.

Administrative Activity Risks

Because the office is a nonemergency work environment, safety is often overlooked. Injuries associated with this environment should be considered for their monetary costs and lost work time. Employees acting or behaving unsafely are the cause of many office injuries, especially tripping or falling injuries. The HSO should ensure that consideration is given to the type and quality of office furniture purchased. Office environments should meet the requirements of the following:

- OSHA/EPA compliance
- Ergonomic needs of members **(Figure 5.10, p. 168)**
- Membership assistance program
- **Hazard Communication Program** and **Employee Right-to-Know**

All-Hazard Concept — Coordinated approach to a wide variety of incidents; all responders use a similar, coordinated approach with a common set of authorities, protections, and resources.

Hazard Communication Program — OSHA mandated safety program stating that an employer must clearly communicate any hazardous materials on-site using the appropriate hazardous communication signage, placards, labels, and internally generated documents.

Employee Right-to-Know — Section of OSHA and other workers' rights laws that states that employees have a right to information about hazards that exist in their workplace; these rights extend to chemical hazards, changes to worker rights, exposure data for the facility, illness and injury reports associated with the facility, and the employee's medical records.

Vehicle Accident

  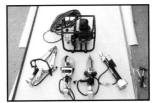 

Fire Fighting

Technical Rescue

Haz Mat

 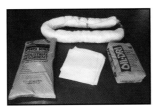  

Figure 5.9 In order for firefighters to function in an all-hazards environment, they need the correct equipment to respond to a variety of incidents. *First column of Photos Courtesy of Mike A. Wieder, Chris Mickal, Ron Jeffers, and the United States Fire Administration respectively.*

Facilities Risks

The HSO is part of the administrative team that is responsible for the creation and maintenance of a safe working environment for department personnel whether they are at an incident or in quarters. When dealing with safety issues in and around fire department facilities, the HSO must ensure that the physical structure provides a safe environment. Safe environments are accomplished through the design and construction of new facilities that meet all applicable codes and standards and through the inspection and renovation of older existing structures. The HSO must also educate the department members in the safe use of their facilities, including proper cleaning, storage, and maintenance techniques **(Figure 5.11, p. 168)**. Because the fire department enforces safety-related fire codes within the community through building inspection and fire prevention inspection programs, all fire department facilities must meet or exceed those same requirements.

Ergonomic Needs of Members

Backbrace: Repeated Lifting

No High Shelves

Dollys for Moving Things

Proper Workstations for Offices

Work Table Height

Figure 5.10 Office environments, such as those for administrative staff and storage areas, should meet ergonomic needs.

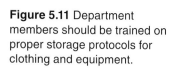

Figure 5.11 Department members should be trained on proper storage protocols for clothing and equipment.

Firefighters are sometimes asked to engage in high-risk activities while at fire department facilities, such as making repairs to the facility. These activities should not be considered part of the firefighter's normal job function, but should be accounted for as part of the potential risks at facilities. If firefighters engage in construction projects at facilities or have additional maintenance duties, such as painting the exterior of the station's second story, the risk management plan should include safe practices for performing these activities in addition to normal firefighter duties.

In addition to the safety requirements found in NFPA® 1500 and 1521, NFPA® 1581, *Standard on Fire Department Infection Control Program*, mandates safety and health-related policy, protocol, and design criteria for fire department facilities. Included in this standard are the requirements for an infection control officer, a written risk management plan for infection control, and training and education of all personnel in infection control. The infection control officer may be the HSO or another officer who is delegated the responsibility for infection control. The written risk management plan includes identification, evaluation, control, and monitoring of risks associated with infection exposure in the following areas:

- While in fire department facilities
- On and around fire department apparatus
- While cleaning or disinfecting personal protective equipment, station wear uniforms, or emergency medical equipment
- Any other situations that might lead to exposure or contamination from infectious materials

The HSO deals with identifying the risks associated with the health hazards and physical hazards at facilities. Both types of hazards can be addressed through changes in structural design and through the education of personnel. Health hazard concerns include (but are not limited to):

- Contaminated clothing and equipment
- Indoor air pollution
- Apparatus emissions
- Water quality
- Proper personal hygiene
- Infection exposure
  Physical hazards include:
- Slipping, tripping, or falling
- Physical fitness equipment
- Injuries from basic housekeeping duties
- Poor internal and external lighting of facilities (illumination)
- Noise pollution
- Electrical hazards
- Specific areas of hazard (shop areas, apparatus maintenance shops, apparatus bays, offices, and fitness areas) **(Figure 5.12, p. 170)**
- Hazardous building materials (asbestos)

Shop Areas

Cuts, Bruises, Abrasions

Apparatus Maintenance Shop

Cuts, Bruises, Abrasions, Slips & Falls, Strains & Sprains

Apparatus Bay

Slips & Falls, Strains & Sprains Impact

Offices

Tripping Hazards, Ergonomic Injuries

Fitness

Strains & Sprains Cardiac Stress

Figure 5.12 Certain types of injuries may occur more frequently in specific areas of a facility.

As stated, building design, training, and administrative policy can mitigate these potential hazards. By far, the best option is to eliminate the potential hazard during the design phase and thereby remove the need for an administrative policy.

Training Risks

Over the past ten years, the USFA statistics show that training accounts for approximately eight to twelve firefighter fatalities each year, indicating the risk identification in training needs improvement. The training environment must be realistic and safe. The HSO should work with the training division and the occupational safety and health committee in this process. Many of the same considerations given for emergency scene operations will directly translate to the training environment. NFPA® 1403, *Standard on Live Fire Training Evolutions,* provides detailed considerations that should be assessed in all live-fire training in fixed facilities and acquired structures.

Training Injury and Fatality Statistics[1,2]

According to the NFPA®, 7,770 training-related injuries occurred in the United States in 2013, accounting for just under 12 percent of all fire service injuries. Most of the training injuries were strains, sprains, muscular pain (60 percent) or wounds, cuts, or bruises (19 percent). The percentages for these injuries occurring during training are higher than the percentages for these injuries occurring during emergency operations.

Seven training-related fatalities occurred in 2013, accounting for 7 percent of the fatalities for the year. Of the seven fatalities, five were sudden cardiac deaths, one of which occurred during a department training exercise at a training facility. Sudden cardiac deaths have received more attention as a hazard at incident scenes, but HSOs should recognize that these deaths can occur during training as well. Fitness for duty should not just apply to emergency response but also the ability to train safely and effectively.

NFPA® 1521 defines the role of the HSO in three areas of training and education **(Figure 5.13)**. First, the HSO is responsible for ensuring that all members receive training in safety procedures related to all departmental operations and tasks. This responsibility may include locating training materials, scheduling and conducting safety training classes, and documenting class attendance. Second, the HSO is responsible for developing the safety procedures within the department's SOP/Gs for all live-fire training exercises. These procedures must be documented and comply with the requirements of NFPA® 1403. The HSO should work with the training division to develop these procedures and to monitor their use and effectiveness. Third, the HSO is responsible for developing safety information for distribution to the members, including providing access to health care professionals.

Figure 5.13 HSOs have specific training responsibilities within an organization.

These responsibilities do not mean that the HSO must personally participate in all training operations or teach all safety-related classes. Through delegation of authority to training officers, topic development by the health and safety committee, and "train-the-trainer" programs, the HSO can create a systematic approach to training and education.

The HSO must also consider the impact of the environment on the personnel involved in the training. The argument is often made that firefighters must be prepared to engage in emergency operations in all types of weather. This may be true; however, training in harsh weather must not endanger the firefighters' health and safety. The HSO advises the training division when it is believed the weather conditions would have an unsafe effect on training. High winds, lightning, sleet, heavy fog, or icy roads are obvious conditions that would warrant the canceling of training operations. Conditions that would make it difficult to drive to the training site should also be considered. These considerations include days when the weather conditions could cause an increase in ozone emissions that would damage the environment. The HSO also considers factors such as the wind chill index and the heat stress index. The HSO should also teach members of the training division to be aware of environmental hazards and make decisions that are in the best interest of training safety.

Vehicle Inspection and Maintenance Risks

Fire department maintenance can be performed either in a work area within the fire station or in a dedicated maintenance facility. Uniformed personnel or nonuniformed personnel may be responsible for maintenance work. Nonuniformed personnel are usually only responsible for equipment or apparatus maintenance. (see NFPA® 1071, *Standard for Emergency Vehicle Technician Professional Qualifications*).

To ensure a safe working environment in the maintenance areas, the HSO needs to develop policies that include requirements for personal protection, including the wearing of eye and face protection, hearing protection, and respiratory protection **(Figure 5.14, p. 172)**. These policies may also indicate training requirements and documentation of training in the use of these types of protection. For instance, the policy may require posting signs stating that eye, hearing, or respiratory protection is required while operating a certain tool or performing a certain task. Eye and face protection may consist of chemical goggles, safety glasses, faceshields **(Figure 5.15, p. 172)**, or equipment-mounted shields. Additionally, emergency eyewash sinks and showers should be provided in the work area in the event of an eye injury or exposure to caustic liquids.

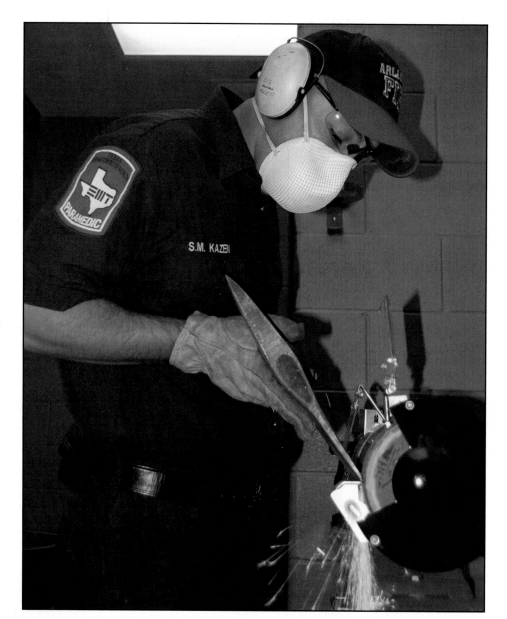

Figure 5.14 Safety procedures should outline what protective clothing and equipment needs to be worn in different areas of the facility.

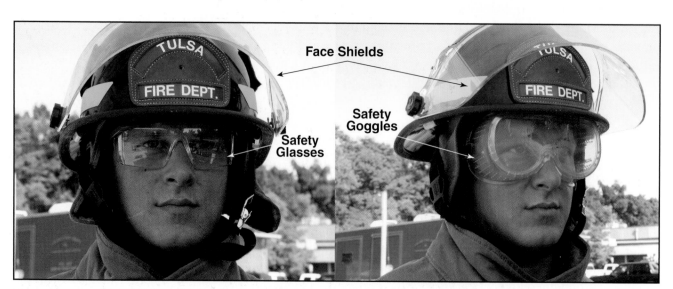

Figure 5.15 Eye protection varies but is an integral part of protective equipment that should not be overlooked.

Risk Evaluation

Once the HSO identifies risks, they can be evaluated from a frequency, severity, and/or probability standpoint. Evaluating risks will involve determining the frequency of exposure along with the potential negative outcomes. The data for this evaluation will lead to a determination of significance that will be the foundation for establishing priorities for action.

Generally, high-frequency incidents with high severity must have the highest priority in the risk analysis, while low-frequency incidents with low severity receive the lowest priority. The method for calculating the risk will vary from one department to another. The evaluation should include those risks associated with the department's operations, risk situations, and prior losses. **Learning Activities 5-1** and **5-2** provide practice scenarios for identifying and evaluating risks.

According to NFPA® 1561, the fire and emergency services organization should consider the following risk assessment factors **(Figure 5.16)**:

- Territory and jurisdiction served
- Entity or segment of the public served
- Plans, policies, services, and operations
- Premises, apparatus, and equipment
- Personnel
- Compliance with applicable laws, codes, standards, and recommended practices

Skills Proficiency Evaluation

Members who lack skills proficiency are at risk of becoming injured when performing functions for which they have not trained. The risk management program should identify those skills that require periodic assessment. Once

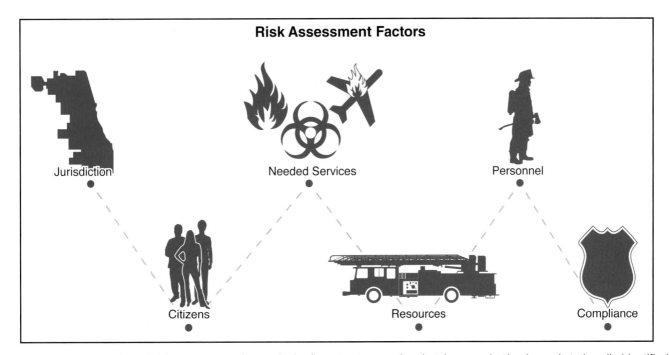

Figure 5.16 Analyzing all risk assessment factors is the first step to ensuring that the organization is ready to handle identified risks in the jurisdiction.

an assessment has been completed, members who lack proficiency should be identified and trained before being allowed to conduct those operations again. The HSO may also consider implementing or advocating for a skills retraining program, even though such programs are not always required. The HSO will work with other divisions and personnel to ensure skill assessments are completed in accordance with SOP/Gs and documented in the training record **(Figure 5.17)**. Skills assessments should also comply with any applicable state and national standards. Some common examples of skills proficiency testing include, but are not limited, to the following:

Figure 5.17 HSOs should coordinate with the training division to make sure that all skills training follows established safety procedures.

- **Fire company proficiency skills** — may include basic fire fighting skills, such as raising ladders, donning SCBA, and wearing turnout gear. This test may also include single and multicompany drills and exercises.

- **Emergency medical proficiency skills** — may include skill assessment for all certification levels, such as airway control, cardiac arrest situations, and proper equipment operation **(Figure 5.18)**. EMS proficiency skill assessments may also be based on state and national standards.

- **Hazardous material proficiency skills** — annual training to the member's skill level (awareness, operations, or technician) in accordance with OSHA 29 *CFR* 1910.120.

- **Technical rescue proficiency skills** — annual drill or exercise that is required for continued certification, such as for confined space entry (see OSHA 29 *CFR* 1910.146).

- **Driver/Operator proficiency skills** — any driver evaluations and those required by the state Department of Motor Vehicles.

- **Incident Commander evaluation** — advancements in technology include command labs where personnel can refresh and sharpen their IC skills.

Frequency and Severity of the Risk

Frequency, referred to as *incidence rate* by the U.S. Occupational Safety and Health Administration (OSHA), addresses the likelihood of occurrence. Frequency is generally defined as either high or low. Each fire and emergency services organization will need to determine the frequency of each risk based upon past injury occurrences and likelihood of exposures within the jurisdiction. Typically, if a particular type of incident such as injuries related to lifting has occurred repeatedly, it will continue to occur until a job hazard or task analysis has been performed to identify the root causes and effective control measures **(Figure 5.19)**.

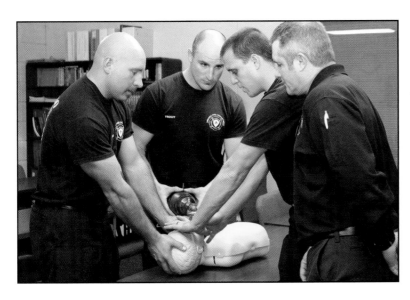

Figure 5.18 Emergency medical skills proficiency training is often part of the training program.

Figure 5.19 Injuries can occur in any part of station facility. In each case a job hazard or task analysis should be performed to identify the root cause.

High occurrence of trips and falls.
- Wet floor sign not set up

Low incidence of injury.

High instance of sprains and strains.
- Firefighters working out alone too frequently

Sometimes there is an overemphasis on either exotic or common risks that fire and emergency service organizations may encounter **(Figure 5.20 a and b)**. On the other hand, the everyday risk may produce repetitive negative consequences. The HSO should be alert for both high and low frequency events and ensure realistic control measures are implemented. Complacency is an additional consideration for the HSO. Complacency can creep into an organization when repetitive skills or incidents occur. Complacency can be identified through the postincident analysis or an investigation process.

The **severity** of a risk is the potential degree for which negative outcome could result. In other words, severity refers to an incident's degree of seriousness. Severity can be measured in a variety of ways:

- Lost time away from work
- Cost of damage
- Cost of and time for equipment repair or replacement
- Service disruption
- Insurance costs
- Legal costs

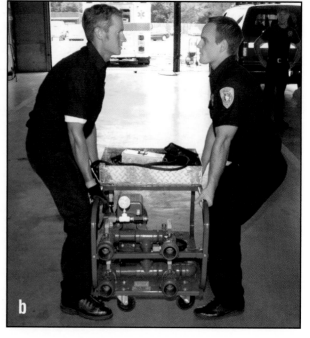

Figure 5.20 a and b
Both uncommon (a) and common (b) risks should be assessed as part of the risk management plan.

Risk Management Formulas[3]

The following formulas may be used to calculate the frequency or incident rate and the severity of incidents. The Occupational Safety and Health Administration (OSHA) calculated the frequency (incident rate) as follows:

$N / EH \times 200,000 = IR$

Where:

N = number of injuries and /or illnesses

EH = total hours worked by all employees during the calendar year

200,000 = base for 100 full-time equivalent (FTE) employees (provides standardization between agencies and companies)

IR = incident rate

OSHA calculates the severity as follows:

$LWD / EH \times 200,000 = S$

Where:

LWD = loss work days

EH = total hours worked by all employees during the calendar year

200,000 = base for 100 full-time equivalent (FTE) employees

S = severity rate

Another method is to assign values to the frequency and severity in the following formula:

$R = S \times IR$

Where:

R = risk

S = severity

IR = incident rate

Assessment of Incident Rate

7. Frequent — Occurs weekly.

6. Very likely — Occurs once every few months.

5. Likely — Occurs about one a year.

4. Occasional — Occurs annually in the United States.

3. Rare — Occurs every 10 to 30 years.

2. Exceptional — Occurs every 10 to 30 years in the United States.

1. Unlikely — May occur once in 10,000 years within the global fire service.

Assessment of Severity

8. Extreme — Multiple deaths or widespread destruction may result from hazard.

7. Very High — Potential death or injury or severe financial loss may result.

6. High — Permanent disabling injury may result.

5. Serious — Loss time injury greater than 28 days or considerable financial loss.

4. Moderate — Loss time injury of 4 to 28 days or moderate financial loss.

3. Minor — Loss time injury up to 3 days.

2. Slight — Minor injury resulting in no loss of time or slight financial loss.

1. Minimal — No loss of time injury or financial loss to organization.

NOTE: The information expressed here is from OSHA and may not directly correspond with NFIRS and USFA data collection criteria.

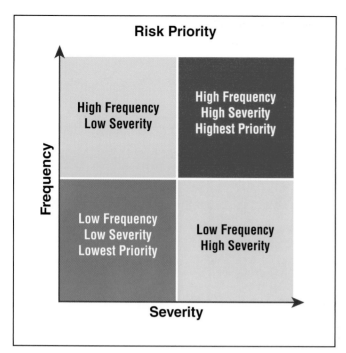

Risk Priority

Frequency

High Frequency
Low Severity

High Frequency
High Severity
Highest Priority

Low Frequency
Low Severity
Lowest Priority

Low Frequency
High Severity

Severity

Figure 5.21 Risks should be prioritized based upon frequency and severity. Severe risks that occur frequently should have the highest priority.

Establishment of Priorities for Action

Taken in combination, the results of the frequency and severity assessments help to establish priorities for determining action. Any risk that has both a high probability of occurrence and serious consequences is considered a high-priority item that deserves immediate action. Nonserious incidents with a low likelihood of occurrence are lower priorities and can be placed near the bottom of the action-required list **(Figure 5.21)**.

Setting Priorities

Establishing priorities for action will involve assessing the risk severity and frequency. There is no single priority list for fire and emergency services organizations to follow. An organization will list the high severity of risk potential at the top of its priority list and low severity risks at the bottom. Setting the priorities will require an in-depth look at the community risks, such as:

- Chemical plants
- Industrial process plants
- Transportation (road, rail, air, water)
- Environmental
- Target hazards
- Geographical hazards

The organization should be assessed for risk potential in the following areas:

- Administration
- Facilities
- Training
- Vehicle operations
- Protective clothing and equipment
- Emergency scene operations
- Nonemergency scene operations
- Other activities

Incorporating the concept of the hierarchy of controls, described later in this chapter, will assist the organization with setting priorities. This process will not only place the high-frequency/high-risk incidents at the top of the priority list, but it will also integrate the best control solution possible.

Identifying Ways to Minimize Risks

Mitigation is a proactive way of reducing the probability, severity, and frequency of risk. Minimizing risk should be a dynamic, multifaceted process. While eliminating risk *entirely* in the fire and emergency services organization is

Mitigation — In terms of risk management, refers, generally, to the reduction of the probability, frequency, and severity of risk.

impossible, mitigating the risks involved is possible and includes implementing control measures to provide the safest possible working environment.

The following list provides some common areas where risk mitigations should be considered:

- Building construction standards
- Fire and life safety code adoption and enforcement
- Apparatus, equipment, and clothing specification and purchasing
- Training and education of members on safety and health topics (including SOP/Gs)
- NIMS/ICS adoption for all incidents, drills, and exercises
- Health and safety program implementation that includes annual physical/medical evaluation, physical fitness training and nutrition guidance, and rehabilitation
- Evaluating and revising current policies in a timely manner
- Comparing national statistics and trends in the fire and emergency services industry and other related occupations to your local organization

Setting Goals and Objectives

Setting goals and objectives are just one part of an overall planning process. Any planning process will define the organization's mission. Each specific program implemented by an organization must be designed so that the organization accomplishes its mission.

Setting goals gives the risk management planning process a target to aim for. Goals must be attainable, desirable, and quantifiable; they must also fit the organization's mission statement as well as any legal mandates. Establishing objectives creates a series of steps that are necessary to reach a goal. Objectives must also be attainable within the limits of the resources available.

The HSO must include goals and objectives to address the everyday operations and the complex operations of the organization. Effective goals and objectives will put the organization in a position to effectively manage the risks that have been identified, evaluated, and prioritized.

Risk Control Techniques

Once risks are prioritized, it is time to apply risk control techniques. Once control measures have been implemented, they need to be evaluated to measure their effectiveness. The sections that follow describe several approaches for controlling risks.

Risk Avoidance

Risk avoidance is the best risk control choice. Simply put, avoid the activity that creates the risk **(Figure 5.22, p. 180)**. This approach frequently is impractical in a fire and emergency services organization. For example, lifting a stretcher presents a serious back injury risk, but personnel cannot avoid this risk and still provide effective service. Training in the use of safe-lifting techniques and/or safer equipment would be solutions that are more acceptable. An example of risk avoidance as a viable option might include a policy

Risk Avoidance — Method of controlling a risk in which an identified risk is completely removed as a possible hazard; often impractical in the fire and emergency services.

Figure 5.22 Exterior fire attack is sometimes an example of risk avoidance; if it is unnecessary to enter the structure, then doing so would be an unacceptable risk. *Courtesy of Bob Esposito.*

prohibiting smoking by departmental/organizational candidates when they are hired, thereby reducing the potential for lung cancer and other smoking-related illnesses among members.

Risk Transfer

Risk Transfer — Method of controlling risk in which the individual who should assume the risk instead transfers or shares the risk with others.

Risk transfer can be accomplished in one of two primary ways: physically transferring the risk to someone else or through the purchase of insurance. Risk transfer may be difficult, if not impossible, for a fire or emergency medical services (EMS) organization. For example, when jurisdictions hire private contractors to clean up and dispose of hazardous materials, risk is transferred from the jurisdiction's haz mat team to the private contractor. The contractor assumes the liability for the risk associated with the cleanup and disposal.

As a risk transfer option, the purchase of insurance should not be seen as a substitute for safe practices. The purchase of insurance only transfers financial risk and does nothing to affect the likelihood of occurrence. Buying fire insurance for the station, while highly recommended to protect the assets of the department, does nothing to prevent the station from burning. Insurance is no substitute for effective control measures, such as installing an automatic sprinkler system.

Risk Control Measures

Control Measures — Specific actions taken to reduce risks through a reduction in either the frequency or severity of the risk.

Effective **control measures** (risk reduction) are the most common method used for risk management. While control measures will not eliminate the risk, they can reduce the likelihood of occurrence or mitigate the severity. Effective control measures include safety, health, and wellness programs; ongoing training and education programs; and well-defined standard operating procedures or guidelines (SOP/Gs). Typical control measures instituted to control incident scene injuries include the use of accountability systems, use of full protective clothing, mandatory respiratory protection plans, training and education sessions, and health and wellness SOP/Gs **(Figure 5.23)**.

For example, the risks associated with backing apparatus into station bays can often be mitigated with driver/operator training or painted guidelines on the apparatus bay floors **(Figure 5.24)**. A policy that requires a second person to guide the backing operation from the rear of the vehicle is also effective. A more expensive solution would be the replacement of older single-door stations with new drive-through stations.

Control Measures

Nonemergency

Safety Programs

Wellness Programs

Health Programs

Emergency

Personnel Accountability

Protective Clothing

Respiratory Protection

Rapid Intervention Crews

Training

Figure 5.23 Control measures should be identified and used for both emergency and nonemergency operations. Training programs should emphasize these same control measures.

Figure 5.24 Parking lines painted on apparatus bay floors are one example of control measures in place to mitigate the risks of backing apparatus into bays.

Hierarchy of Controls

The **hierarchy of controls** is a risk management concept that provides a common framework and approach to worker safety **(Figure 5.25)**. NIOSH and OSHA describe the hierarchy of controls in terms of five control solutions that eliminate or reduce a specific identified hazard in the workplace. This concept promotes the best hazard control solution when setting priorities for emergency and nonemergency operations. The goal is to eliminate or reduce a hazard without creating any unintended consequences or additional hazard(s).

According to NIOSH and OSHA, the five control solutions are:

- **Elimination** — this step targets the hazard at the source and eliminates it. This is the most preferable control solution.

- **Substitution** — this step targets substituting one process for another to improve worker safety with a lesser severity hazard. It may include substituting a lesser severity hazard for one that is a higher hazard.

- **Engineering Controls** — engineering controls will either eliminate an exposure to a hazard or place a separation from the hazard. This may also include the reduction of the hazard level if it cannot be completely eliminated. This step involves workplace changes in response to an identified hazard. For more information on engineering controls, see Chapter 7, Safety and Health Programs.

- **Administrative Controls** — administrative controls require worker and/or organizational action and may include developing or revising work practices (usually rules, policies, procedures, training, staffing, and rest breaks).

- **Protective Clothing and Equipment** — Protective clothing and equipment is considered the least preferable control solution and used as a last resort.

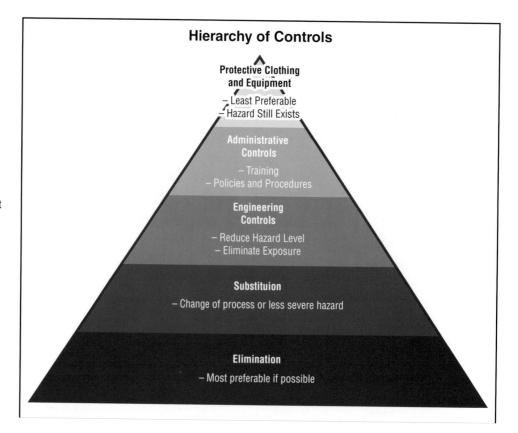

Figure 5.25 The hierarchy of controls lists risk management strategies from most effective to least effective.

The hazard still exists, and the protective clothing and equipment provides protection within its limitations. Protective clothing and equipment is used when other control measures are not effective in removing all of the risk or as an added layer of protection if other control measures fail.

Risk Management Plan Implementation

Implementation of the risk management plan requires communication, training, and application. The plan, produced in written form as part of the organization's SOP/Gs, is distributed to the membership. The distribution includes the public acknowledgement by the administration and the jurisdiction leadership of the plan's importance.

The application of the plan takes place daily as officers and members follow the prescribed policies and procedures. The risk control techniques must become second nature to all personnel. Whether these techniques involve applying proper lifting techniques when picking up heavy objects or putting on respiratory protection when entering a contaminated atmosphere, they must be performed naturally without questions.

Creating an Action Plan for Risk Management

With the risk management goals and objectives set, it is time to develop an action plan. An action plan assigns responsibility for specific objectives, gives time frames for completion, and tracks progress. Chart models can be used to incorporate concepts from operational/administrative plans. The HSO may select from three generally accepted models for plan development that visually display the progression of a program. Risk management is an ongoing, cyclical process, and the use of these charts should not signify an end point but a point along a continuum. The sections that follow described some commonly used methods to monitor an implementation project.

Program Evaluation and Review Technique (PERT)

PERT is a project management system for determining in advance the amount of time required to complete a project. Each step in the process is assigned a likely estimate for the time to completion. The PERT chart **(Figure 5.26, p. 184)** has four elements, as follows:

- Charts plot the project, evaluate the success of each step, depict the individual tasks, depict the time required for each task, and show the interrelationship or dependency of the various steps with each other.

- Chart lines form a network that connects the steps or tasks. The chart is complete when all the tasks are connected to the final or completion point.

- Tasks included are the steps for documentation writing, documentation editing, project report writing and editing, and report reproduction.

- Each tasks is usually time-consuming, thus the time for each is considered when determining the total time for completion.

Critical Path Method (CPM)

CPM identifies the critical paths of dependent tasks that together take the longest time to complete **(Figure 5.27, p. 184)**. The critical path from beginning to completion is indicated. Although rare, a CPM chart can define multiple,

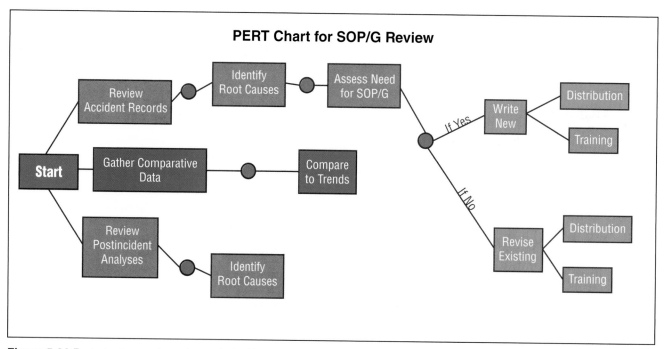

Figure 5.26 Pert charts may be color-coded with each color representing the time needed to complete that step of a project.

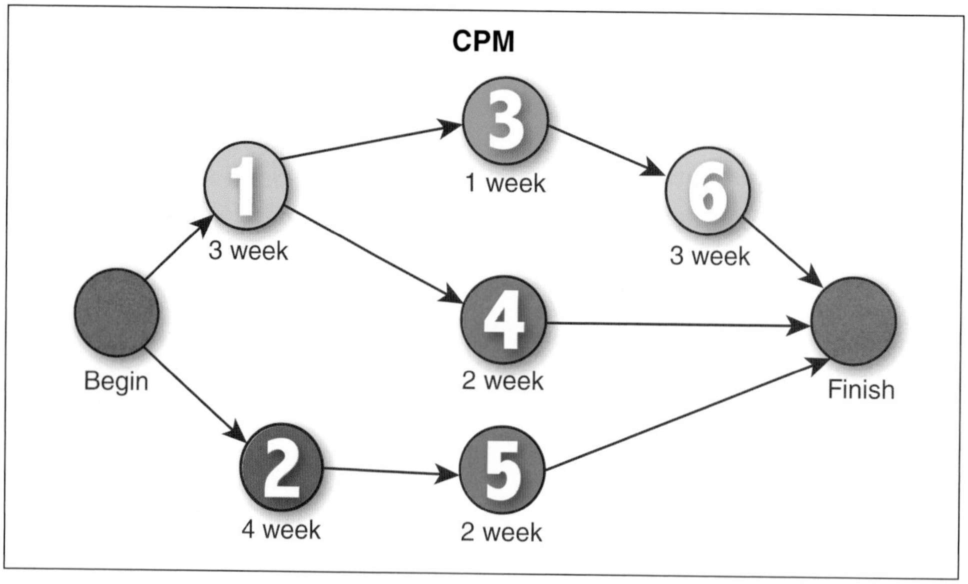

Figure 5.27 Critical path management charts are useful for managing multiple teams on a project, all trying to reach the same goal at the same time.

equally critical paths. Those tasks that fall on the critical path are noted in some way so that they can be given special attention, such as drawing critical-path tasks on the chart with a double line instead of a single line. CPM charts are similar to PERT charts and are sometimes known as PERT/CPM.

Gantt Charts

A Gantt Chart is a matrix that lists on the vertical axis all the tasks to be performed (**Figure 5.28**). Each row contains a single task identification that usually consists of a number and name. The horizontal axis is headed by columns indicating estimated task duration, resources, and name of the person assigned to the task, followed by one column for each period in the project's

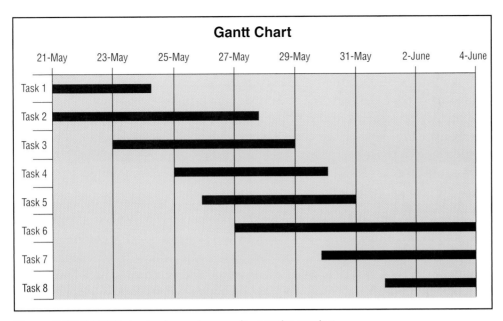

Figure 5.28 GANTT charts show where various tasks overlap.

duration. Tasks that are dependent on other tasks can be linked to indicate when they can be done. Each period may be expressed in hours, days, weeks, months, and other time units.

Communicating the Plan to the Organization

Once the risk management plan is developed, or revised in any manner, it must be communicated to the organization's membership. This communication must include a statement of administration support. This support is essential to membership acceptance and helps to ensure a positive response from not only the members but also the public and stakeholders.

Communication of the plan or its revision can be in the form of a printed copy of the plan and/or computer access to the plan. Either communication method is acceptable as long as the available plan is the most current. If the plan is stored on the organization's computer system, the document must be in a view-only format so no changes can be made. Regardless of how the plan is distributed, the HSO should ensure that training is provided to members on any changes that are being implemented. Risk management plan responsibilities should be communicated and assigned in order to track the plan to completion.

Training must be organization-wide and begins in the entry-level training for new employees. Training sessions for changes in the plan as well as refresher training sessions are provided periodically to current members of the organization. The effectiveness of the program depends on proper training.

Developing Safety and Health Programs

The HSO is usually assigned the task of developing and implementing a safety and health program that meets the requirements, demands, needs, and concerns of the organization. Developing a safety and health program is made easier if the HSO uses current safety and health laws, codes, and standards as foundations for program development. Although these safety standards have requirements for employers, the regulations also contain significant requirements for employees. Each employee must comply with the requirements of the occupational safety and health standards.

One of the HSO's principal tasks is to manage the organization's safety and health program. The HSO is the catalyst who initiates proven safety programs that reduce injuries and fatalities within a fire and emergency medical organization. Supervisors and members have a responsibility to support and abide by these programs in the interests of improving safety in the work environment. Essential to the program's success is documented and public support from the top level of management.

The safety and health program should include the following components:

- **Accident, injury, and illness prevention program** — this component will include hazards/corrective measures identification with specific focus on departmental physical injuries/illnesses and program-related facilities, occupational illness, motor vehicle-related accidents, hearing loss, respiratory injury or illness, and hazardous materials exposure.

- **Medical exposure management program** — this component will include infection control and hazardous materials exposure control.

- **Employee physical fitness and wellness program** — this component will include physical fitness considerations (task analysis, exercise plans, and equipment), and wellness considerations (nutrition, back care, heart and lung diseases, stress recognition and control, critical incident stress management, and member assistance programs).

The HSO may administer the appropriate sections of the local jurisdiction's safety and health plan as it applies to the organization's membership. This plan may include sections on workers' compensation, workplace violence, smoking, and drug and alcohol abuse. If the local jurisdiction does not have a policy, then these issues need to be included in the comprehensive safety and health program.

The development, implementation, and operation of an occupational safety and health committee is one of the instrumental and valuable components of a safety and health program. As described in Chapter 1, Health Safety Officer Responsibilities, the organization's HSO is the chair of this committee and facilitates its work. This individual is the ultimate manager of the safety and health program and reports to the organization's chief/manager. The roles and responsibilities of this position are also discussed in this section.

Implementing Safety and Health Programs

Implementation of safety and health programs will follow the general procedures mentioned above for the risk management plan. The HSO will need to ensure training and education is provided to members that are included in a specific program. For example, smoking cessation and tobacco use may target all staff and line personnel, while medical exposure consideration will target only responders. The HSO will need to work with the fire department physician, peer-fitness trainers, and any external agency providing services to members of the department to ensure implementation of safety and health programs has the needed resources to be effective.

Risk Management Monitoring

The plan's effectiveness becomes evident through monitoring. Monitoring entails keeping a constant evaluation process in progress. Formal, scheduled evaluations of the plan should also be in place, so that risk management is dynamic and continuous. Any problems that occur in the process have to be revised or modified.

As part of risk management monitoring, the HSO should help to establish a culture in which any firefighter who sees an unsafe practice is empowered to intervene and immediately correct the unsafe practice. All organizational members have an obligation to ensure their safety.

Enforcement of the risk management plan belongs within the organization's chain of command. However, when a deviation from the policy is recognized, it is best handled at the lowest supervisory level. Gaining compliance with risk management policy or components is more effective in this setting. Continued deviation or major infractions may ultimately be handled with a progressive disciplinary process. The HSO does not serve in the disciplinary process of the general organization membership. However, the HSO provides recommendations in the semiannual report when common themes or trends develop that deviate from SOP/Gs.

Process and Outcome Evaluations

Programs must be evaluated periodically to determine effectiveness. An effective program will be assessed to determine if it is meeting its intended goals and reaching its planned outcomes. Three generally accepted types of evaluations used for programs are as follows (**Figure 5.29, p. 188**):

- **Goals-based evaluations** — determine how well a program is meeting the original goals or objectives that were established for it.

- **Process-based evaluations** — determine how a program actually works and highlight its strengths and weaknesses; particularly useful for long-standing programs or if a program is determined to be inefficient and complaints are being generated about it.

- **Outcomes-based evaluations** — identify the benefits to the community or consumer of the service. The term *outcome* refers to the actual benefits enjoyed by the community, such as reduced fire loss or improved quality of life. The primary source of data used by the fire service is NFIRS. NFIRS can provide information for data comparisons.

These evaluations may be formative or summative. A **formative evaluation** is one where the intent is to improve a program, isolate any evident weaknesses, or understand the program's strengths and build on them. A **summative evaluation** is one where the intent is to assess the achievements or outcome of the program. In addition, the method may be either quantitative or qualitative, depending on the data available. In any case, the evaluation results need to be made public to the people who are affected by the program. Any changes need to be implemented as soon as possible.

Evaluate Safety and Health Programs

Evaluation of the safety and health program by the chief or HSO compares the desired results with the actual results of the plan. In the evaluation, any variance between policy and practice should be identified. This review will help

Goals-Based Evaluation — Summative assessment of whether or not a given program has met its intended goals.

Process-Based Evaluation — Formative assessment of how well a program functions after it has been implemented and is currently in progress; measures strengths, weaknesses, and efficiency.

Outcomes-Based Evaluation — Summative assessment of what community or consumer benefit was gained or enhanced as a result of a particular program.

Formative Evaluation — Evaluation of a new or revised program in order to form opinions about its effects and effectiveness as it is in the process of being developed and tested (piloted). Its purpose is to gather information to help improve the program while in progress.

Summative Evaluation — Evaluation of a program after all of its various components have been implemented and established; the evaluation is intended to measure achievement of intended goals and the effect of the program on the public (outcomes).

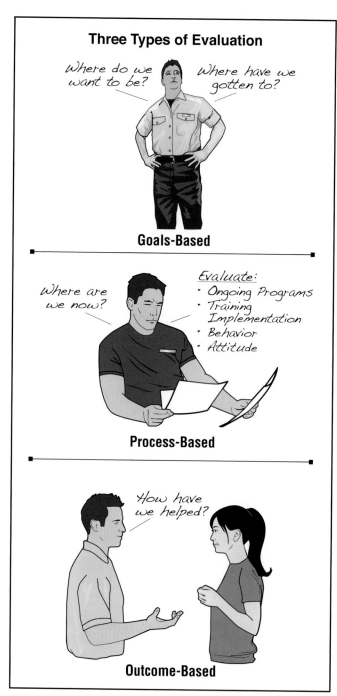

Figure 5.29 Program evaluations often fall into three categories, each of which are intended to show different aspects of the program's success.

identify recommendations for improving a policy, a practice, or both. Data for making the comparisons include injury and fatality reports, amount of participation in safety training, fitness testing results, pre-employment physical fitness reports, and alterations that have been made to address preplan risks. The sources for the data include the target risks or hazards, policies and procedures intended to eliminate the risks, emergency incident reports, daily attendance reports, medical leave requests, training records, and physical fitness reports.

The results of the comparisons, which include either an increase, decrease, or no change in the risks, determine the effectiveness of the risk management plan. If there is a decrease in the risk, indicated by a reduction in medical leave taken or lost-time injuries, then the plan may be considered effective. If, however, the evaluation indicates that there is no change or an increase in the number of injuries, then the implemented risk control techniques must be reviewed and alternate solutions applied.

It will also be important to determine if the cost/benefit is appropriate; is the cost of the risk control techniques less than the cost of the results of the risk? For example, if the cost of altering apparatus storage compartments is greater than the cost of lost-time injuries due to back strains resulting from removing equipment from the compartments, then it may not be worth the control cost.

Evaluate the Effectiveness of the Plan

Evaluating the effectiveness of the safety and health plan requires the collection of data. Participation statistics can be difficult to assess, especially in non-mandatory programs. If the plan is mandatory, then the collection of participation data is permitted and can be used as a monitoring tool. However, the program must be flexible enough so that nonparticipation for legitimate reasons is not punished. Rather, alternative programs should be available to the membership. If the program is effective, then job-related injuries and occupational illnesses should decrease over time.

Reasons to Revise a Risk Management Plan

Fire officers and the HSO should be aware of the reasons why revisions may be necessary, and be able to recognize these reasons when they appear in the plan evaluation. Some reasons may include the following:

- Increase in injuries, fatalities, or loss due to the target risks

- Increase in medical leave requests

- Increase in risk-related costs
- No apparent change in the risk results
- Ineffective cost/benefit
- Changes in the target risks
- Ineffective training

Plan Modification and Revision

Revision procedures are included in the risk management plan when it is developed. The revision process involves following the same steps that the initial risk management plan followed, although it only focuses on those risks that require revision and not the entire plan. The HSO should evaluate the previous year of occurrences within the department for areas where risk control measures were not sufficient. Plan modification should address areas of deficiency and not the actions or lack of action of an individual or crew.

This plan must be reviewed and revised periodically, as defined by the authority having jurisdiction. A good guideline is to conduct a review and revision on an annual basis with an external audit performed every three years. Responsibility for the review and revision may be assigned to the HSO, the occupational safety and health committee, or the fire chief. The plan may be a part of the overall community/jurisdiction plan and may be the responsibility of that organization's risk manager, such as the community health and safety manager or loss control manager.

Chapter Summary

Risk management is a process that involves many parts. Risk management is separated into sections that are the community, the organization, and the operational setting. The organizational risk management section must include an ongoing process for improving the workplace environment. This process includes risk identification, risk evaluation, the setting of action priorities, risk control techniques, and risk monitoring in the emergency and non emergency settings. Through this process, SOP/Gs will be able to specifically address the risks and hazards identified with the associated control measures to enhance member safety. For the risk management plan to be successful, involvement from all members is essential.

Review Questions

1. What process should the health safety officer follow when developing an organizational risk management plan? (pp. 157-161)

2. What risks are commonly associated with emergency operations? (pp. 162-166)

3. How can nonemergency operations pose risks to the fire department? (pp. 166-172)

4. How can the health safety officer evaluate risks identified in a risk management plan? (pp. 173-177)

5. What methods can the health safety officer follow to establish priorities for action? (pp. 178-179)

6. What techniques can the health safety officer use to control risks to the fire department? (pp. 179-183)

7. What steps should the health safety officer take to implement an organizational risk management plan? (pp. 183-186)

8. How can risk management plan components be monitored for their effectiveness? (pp. 187-189)

Chapter 5 End Notes

1. Fahy, Rita F.; LeBlanc, Paul R.; and Molis, Joseph L. "Firefighter Fatalities in the United States – 2013," June, 2014: NFPA®

2. Karter, Michael J. Jr.; and Molis, Joseph L. "U.S. Firefighter Injuries – 2013," November, 2014: NFPA®

3. OSHA Incident Rate Worksheet and *OSHA Technical Manual (OTM)*

Refer to Appendix B: Learning Activity Answers in the back of this manual for suggested responses.

Purpose

Identification of risks is an important function for a health safety officer. For this activity, practice identifying and evaluating hazards and risks in an emergency situation, in this case, a motor vehicle collision.

Directions

1. Read the description of the motor vehicle collision below.

2. Identify and list all hazards and their accompanying risks. See **Table 5.1** in the Learning Activities Answer Key at the back of the manual for a suggested method of listing your answers.

   NOTE: Make sure you understand the difference between a hazard and a risk. Review p. 158 if necessary.

3. Evaluate the identified risks on their probability and potential for negative consequences, including the anticipated severity and incident rate. Use the scales "Assessment of Incident Rate" to estimate IR, and "Assessment of Severity" to estimate S (p. 177).

4. Rank the identified risks based on the formula R = S x IR (p. 177) in order to establish a priority list of risks.

   NOTE: One risk has been identified in **Table 5.1** in the Learning Activities Answer Key.

Scenario

Members of the St. Florian Fire Department are called to a motor vehicle incident on a busy two-way city street. This street is infamous for frequent motor vehicle collisions. Over the past five years, this street has averaged about one collision per month. According to dispatch, a pickup truck has rear-ended a 4-door compact car. Upon arrival at the scene, firefighters observe that the front engine of the pickup truck is dented, and there is smoke emerging from the engine. The pickup truck is seen to have five or six 50 lb (23 kg) bags of fertilizer in the bed. The rear half of the compact car is crumpled, and both rear doors have been deformed in the impact. Both drivers have safely exited their vehicles; however, there is a 2-year-old child in a child seat in the passenger side back seat of the compact car. Due to the deformed back doors, neither back door can be opened. The child is crying loudly, and the driver is frantically trying to pull the child out of the car seat through the passenger front seat. It is a cold day, about 30° F (-1° C), lightly snowing, and the sun is setting.

Purpose

This activity centers on identifying hazards and risks in a nonemergency situation, in this case, a live-fire training evolution.

Identify risks inherent in a live-fire training evolution (nonemergency).

5-2

Refer to Appendix B: Learning Activity Answers in the back of this manual for suggested responses.

Directions

1. Read the scenario below.

2. Identify and list all hazards and their accompanying risks. See **Table 5.2** in the Learning Activities Answer Key at the back of the manual for a suggested method of listing your answers.

   NOTE: Make sure you understand the difference between a hazard and a risk. Review p. 158 if necessary.

3. Evaluate the identified risks on their probability and potential for negative consequences, including the anticipated severity and incident rate. Use the scales "Assessment of Incident Rate" to estimate IR, and "Assessment of Severity" to estimate S (p. 177).

4. Rank the identified risks based on the formula R = S x IR (p. 177) in order to establish a priority list of risks.

   NOTE: One risk has been identified in **Table 5.2** in the Learning Activities Answer Key.

Scenario

Members of the St. Florian Fire Department are planning a live-fire training evolution inside an acquired apartment building. The structure consists of three above-ground stories plus a basement. Although operations will be conducted on all floors, only one fire is planned to be ignited at any given time.

The training is scheduled for a day in August. The average high temperature for the month is 94° F (34° C), with winds up to 20 knots (23 mph or 37 kph). One instructor has been assigned for three rotating teams of seven trainees, with two safety officers overseeing all operations, for a total of three instructors.

Activities planned include:

- A fire on the top (third) floor to be accessed via exterior ladder placement

- A fire on the second floor to be accessed via the front door and stairs

- A fire on the first floor to be accessed via the front door

- A fire in the basement to be accessed via the front door and wooden basement stairs

Operational Risk Management

Chapter Contents

Photo courtesy of Bob Esposito.

Key Terms

NFPA® Job Performance Requirements

This chapter provides information that addresses the following job performance requirements of NFPA® 1521, *Standard for Fire Department Safety Officer Professional Qualifications (2015).*

4.2.4

4.11.2

4.11.5

Operational Risk Management

Learning Objectives

After reading this chapter, students will be able to:

1. Explain the health safety officer's role in the preincident planning process. (4.11.2)

2. Identify risk-based information and assistance that should be provided to members of a jurisdiction. (4.11.5)

3. Describe the components of an operational risk management plan. (4.2.4)

4. Learning Activity 6-1: Gather information for a preincident plan for a public building. (4.11.2, 4.11.5)

Chapter 6
Operational Risk Management

Case History

An Incident Commander reported to a large fire at an auto body shop. The shop was close to the station, so both the IC and the necessary resources to fight the fire arrived quickly. The IC had all of the resources he needed and had them positioned ideally. Rapid Intervention Crews were stationed at appropriate positions to monitor the safety of two crews inside the building. Two Incident Safety Officers had been assigned with these crews to monitor activities on either side of the large structure. Aerial apparatus were positioned perfectly to provide support streams and exposure protection to nearby buildings.

The IC was very confident about the progress at the incident. His interior crews appeared safe and were fighting the fire effectively. The IC said later that his situational awareness began to become secondary to his feeling of confidence about the incident. He started checking in with his safety officers less frequently. Fortunately, they were continuing to maintain situational awareness.

One of the ISOs communicated a retreat from the structure. This communication came as a surprise to the IC, who asked for clarification. The ISO stated that he had observed twisted, weakened steel trusses above one of the crews leading the direct attack in the interior of the structure. All the firefighters retreated, and the incident concluded with exterior attacks only.

It was discovered later that the trusses could have failed at almost any time that the interior crews were fighting the fire. Because the IC followed his procedures and assigned competent Incident Safety Officers at the scene, he had extra personal dedicated to helping him with his situational awareness. When the IC lost focus, the personnel were in place to stop operations that could have resulted in the loss of firefighters.

Operational risk management applies both to training evolutions and emergency incidents. Emergency incidents should be evaluated based upon the facts about the incident, whether the incident was a common type of response or a more infrequent type of incident.

The preincident or pre-emergency planning process provides the opportunity to identify hazards, distractions, and risks that are typical or predictable in the normal daily operational setting. Each type of emergency incident will create potential risks for responders; therefore, learning the normal daily operations of a location will provide valuable knowledge to responders about the potential hazards and risks present. Multiple risks could exist at any incident, or risks could arise at incidents where they are not expected.

Responders must be prepared for the unexpected. They must also use proper personal protective clothing and equipment, adhere to the department's standard operating procedures or guidelines (SOP/G), and follow the orders that are given through the chain of command.

Operational risk management includes a plan for managing incidents in a coordinated manner. Use the Incident Management System (IMS) framework starting when the first arriving unit begins the process of safely and efficiently handling a situation. The IMS provides a consistent management framework that includes a hierarchy of structure, safety of personnel, accountability, and communication. The HSO is responsible for ensuring the development of an operational risk management plan within the department's SOP/G manual. The plan and SOP/Gs must address the preincident or pre-emergency planning process and the emergency incident management strategy.

Organizational vs. Operational Risk Management

Chapter 5, Organizational Risk Management, illustrates risk management strategies for the organization outside of the emergency response environment. HSOs should realize that all risk management, regardless of environment, contributes to the global risk management of the organization. Operational, work place safety, and training safety should all be considered a part of the organization's overall safety culture. For the purposes of this manual and NFPA® 1521, *Standard for Fire Department Safety Officer,* the different aspects of risk management are discussed separately to avoid confusion.

16 Firefighter Life Safety Initiatives 3, 4, 11, and 12

The 16 Firefighter Life Safety Initiatives were discussed in Chapter 1, Health Safety Officer Responsibilities. Initiatives 3, 4, 11, and 12 are pertinent to the HSO's responsibilities related to operational risk management:

3. Focus greater attention on the integration of risk management with incident management at all levels, including strategic, tactical, and planning responsibilities.

4. All firefighters must be empowered to stop unsafe practices.

11. National standards for emergency response policies and procedures should be developed and championed.

12. National protocols for response to violent incidents should be developed and championed.

Preincident Planning —
Act of preparing to manage an incident at a particular location or a particular type of incident before an incident occurs.

Preincident Plan —
Document, developed during preincident planning that contains the operational plan or set procedures for the safe and efficient handling of emergency situations at a given location, such as a specific building or occupancy.

Preincident and Pre-Emergency Planning

Operational risk management should begin with the preincident or pre-emergency phase. **Preincident planning** is an important aspect to the effective and efficient response of the fire and emergency service organization. The goal of the **preincident plan** is to provide responders with location information (such as the layout of the location, potential risks and hazards, site and building features, access and egress points, water supply, and fire suppression features) so strategic and tactical decisions can be made more intelligently **(Figure 6.1)**. Knowing the location details promotes a safer, more efficient operation for responders.

NOTE: Preincident planning has many referenced names in the fire service, including Prefire Inspection, Prefire Planning, Preincident Inspection, Preincident Survey, or Preplanning. Be aware that your jurisdiction may use slightly different terminology to describe this process.

The process for creating a risk management plan for the organization described in Chapter 5, Organizational Risk Management can also be used to assess the hazards at a location during the preincident planning process. If hazards are identified during the preincident planning process, details should be included about the hazard along with strategic and tactical options for responders to consider. For example, a potential collapse zone area could be

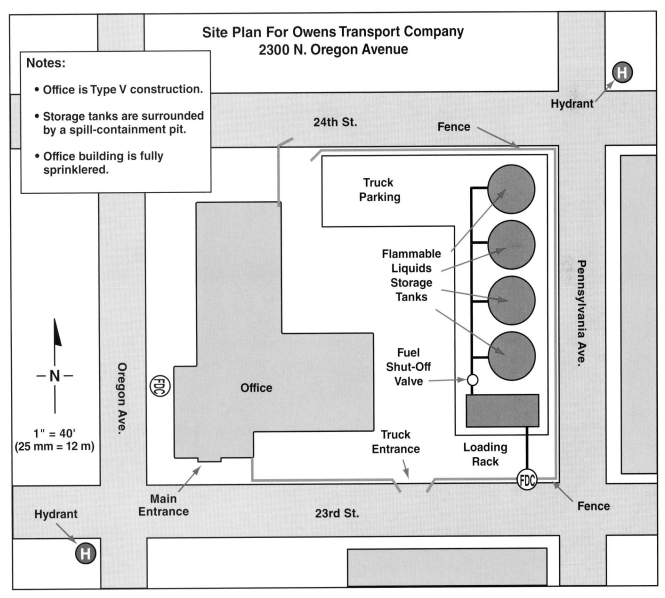

Figure 6.1 Preincident plans should include site maps that provide details about the site that may be important to firefighters or other responders.

identified along with alternate apparatus placement options **(Figure 6.2)**. The HSO should work with the fire prevention staff to advocate for safety related building standards to improve the operational environment. The HSO can act as the facilitator between fire prevention and emergency response to ensure that the two meet the needs of each.

Because of the variety of risks and hazards in any community, all fire departments should conduct assessments of their communities in order to identify these risks and hazards. Knowing what hazards exist helps the department design an all-hazards response plan that meets the community's needs.

A preincident survey is a familiarization tour of a site or structure performed periodically depending on local requirements **(Figure 6.3)**. The survey provides basic information that can be used to develop a preincident plan. **Learning Activity 6-1** provides practice at gathering information for preincident surveys.

The **preincident survey** provides information about:

Preincident Survey — Assessment of a facility or location made before an emergency occurs, in order to prepare for an appropriate emergency response.

- Site access
- Structure
  - Construction type
  - Occupancy type

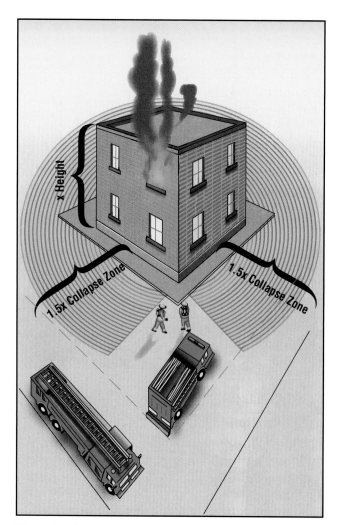

Figure 6.2 Apparatus should be positioned outside of collapse zones to protect them in case of a structural collapse.

Figure 6.3 Firefighters should conduct preincident surveys during the construction process whenever possible.

- Change in occupancy through remodeling
  — Fire protection system(s)
  — Content fuel load
  — Unique characteristics or hazards
  — Access
- Available water supply
- Utilities and supplemental sources of power and water
- Resource needs
- Neighboring risk within a specified geographical area of a known target hazard

Generally, fire departments conduct and update surveys annually or biannually, when there has been a change of occupancy type, and whenever renovations or alterations have been made to the structure. The HSO again should facilitate communication between the fire prevention staff and operational personnel with any updated information learned during inspections. Surveys should also be made at construction sites as a means of learning about how the building is being built. Remember that construction sites are vulnerable to fires and your survey is a way of preparing for that possibility.

NFPA® 1620, *Standard for Pre-Incident Planning*, provides details on the information and considerations to be integrated into the preincident plan. Your department may already have a survey checklist of information needed to gather. During the survey, the HSO should assist personnel in understanding the safety and health considerations at a location and how these could impact operations. The following list provides features that are usually included in preincident surveys:

- Life safety concerns for firefighters and occupants
- Building construction type and material to determine resistance to fire spread
- Building services, including utility shut-offs, high-voltage equipment, generators, elevators, and HVAC
- Building access and egress, including lock box location
- Building age
- Building area and height
- Contents, to estimate fire load
- Building use, to determine life safety and fire load
- Exposures
- Collapse zone
- Location and capacity of available water supply
- Location of fire control and protection system control valves and connections
- Hazardous materials or processes, including flammable/combustible liquids and gases
- Location of Safety Data Sheets (SDS) as revised in the Globally Harmonized System (GHS) of Classification and Labeling of Chemicals

- Occupancy load at all hours
- Names and telephone numbers of contact or responsible persons for owner/occupant
- Estimated quantity of water required to extinguish a fire in the structure or a portion of it (fire flow)
- Emergency evacuation plan

    NOTE: Some locations may have unique features not included in this list.

    Once this information is gathered, a preincident plan can be developed. The preincident plan should be completed on a standard department form. Some departments have computer software programs that can incorporate architectural drawings of the site and floor plans in addition to the information from the survey. Once digitized, preincident plans can be made available on the organization's computer system, on apparatus mobile data terminals, and on the computer aided dispatch system.

    Computer software can also integrate **geographic information system (GIS)** data with the preincident plan **(Figure 6.4)**. For example, road closures, hazard control zones, and hydrant availability can be updated in real time for responders and dispatchers to see on their screens. This information can

Geographic Information Systems (GIS) — Computer software application that relates physical features on the earth to a database to be used for mapping and analysis. The system captures, stores, analyzes, manages, and presents data that refers to or is linked to a location.

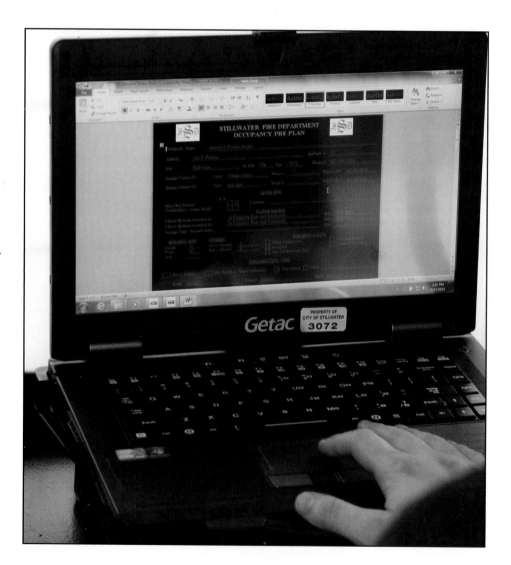

Figure 6.4 A variety of computer software packages can provide and record GIS data when conducting preincident surveys.

improve both the responders' decision-making and operational efficiency and effectiveness. Some jurisdictions also make the preincident plans available to neighboring departments when mutual and automatic aid assignments are common.

Assisting with District Surveys

The **district survey** is a dynamic evaluation conducted as frequently as needed of a geographically assigned area to identify potential hazards, especially those safety and health aspects that can affect response. The HSO must ensure personnel are informed of what to look for and how to report potential hazards. Depending on the size and structure of the fire and emergency service organization, responsibility for the district survey will vary. Some organizations place this responsibility with the fire prevention bureau, while others place the responsibility at the Company level. Regardless of where the responsibility lies within the organization, district surveys are a vital tool to a successful risk management plan.

The HSO is responsible for assisting field personnel in the development of possible control measures for handling various types of incidents involving target hazards. The HSO should provide the forecasting of potential hazards and risks, as they relate to the safety and health of responders at a location, and options for mitigating them. A site visit is one of the best ways to forecast hazards and risks. The site visit provides personnel with the opportunity to see first-hand the details of a location and interact with site personnel.

District Survey — Evaluation of an entire response district to identify hazards on a broader scale than preincident planning; may also involve identifying standards of coverage needs for the district or jurisdiction.

Standards of Cover

Standards of Cover (SOC), also referred to as Standards of Coverage or Deployment Analysis, is one system for determining if a department is properly deployed and staffed to meet all of the risks and possible response needs of a community. An SOC is generally a document that includes everything from the number of fire stations needed in a district to the apparatus, personnel, and equipment they are likely to need. The SOC also includes anticipated strategy and tactics where applicable as well as studies of the coverage population and concentration. Guidelines for completing an SOC vary; resources include:

- OSHA
- Insurance Services Office (ISO)
- NFPA®
- Commission on Fire Accreditation International (CFAI)

The effect that an incident may have on the environment is another consideration that must be addressed. Foam, contaminated water, or hazardous materials have to be contained and removed from the site. Preincident planning in coordination with the facility's response plan can help to reduce the potential damage to the surrounding area. Conveying environmental concerns to site personnel shows professionalism and a genuine concern for business recovery. Once these preincident plans are created, they must be reviewed and revised periodically to adjust for changes at the site or within the department. Revisions can be based on subsequent inspections or on a postincident analysis report.

Providing Information to Personnel

The HSO has the responsibility of communicating safety and health risk information that has the potential of affecting and/or posing a risk to operations. Therefore, as personnel prepare for a district survey or site visit at a target hazard, the HSO should be consulted for historical information about a location. The HSO can research occurrences at a specified location for previous responses and any associated accidents, injuries, fatalities, illnesses, or exposures. These occurrences can be found by researching postincident analyses and incident-related reports. In addition, the HSO should seek out historical knowledge from within the department's membership. Personnel can provide information otherwise lost by time or that which predates computer information storage. By providing any previous department experience at a location, personnel can gain a perspective of the potential risks and hazards in order to effectively manage operations. The sections that follow describe health and safety information collected during preincident and district surveys that should be provided to or readily available to firefighters.

Hazards that Could Affect Operations

A hazard usually refers to a condition, substance, activity, or device that can directly cause an injury, fatality, or property loss. When surveying a district or creating a preincident plan, the HSO should assist responders with identifying conditions, substances, or devices that can affect operations. The preincident plan should identify these hazards along with appropriate control measures to address the hazard. Hazards that can affect operations include but are not limited to the following:

- **During the response** — traffic hazards are a significant concern for the safety and health of responders. The HSO should assist in identifying traffic hazards that are common and unique to each district **(Figure 6.5)**. Incident operations can be affected if responding resources are involved in an accident or otherwise delayed during a response.

    — Roads: road hazards include narrow lanes, sharp turns, blind intersections, medians, one-way roads, speed humps, and poorly maintained road surfaces. Additional considerations should include flooding, landslides, or other conditions that may block a chosen response route.

    — Bridges: bridges may have height and weight restrictions, single-lane alternating traffic patterns, narrow lanes, and reduced visibility when entering or exiting.

    — Construction zones: road construction projects create ever-changing conditions that may catch responders unaware. People and machinery may block traffic, lanes may be reduced in width with roadway markers, and traffic congestion can delay a response.

    — Traffic: traffic congestion, distracted drivers, bicyclists and pedestrians, and vehicles stopping without pulling to the right may create hazardous driving conditions.

Figure 6.5 Common traffic hazards and construction notes on maps provide useful information to responding units.

- **Violence** — firefighters may need to rely on law enforcement to secure the area before operations begin. In addition, some jurisdictions are developing response policies to hostile situations that may include SWAT medic programs. The risk/benefit analysis conducted by the IC in violent situations is critical to the strategy employed. Communication with law enforcement is essential to coordinating activities.

  — Civil disorder: history has shown that responders may be targeted during civil disorders.

  — Weapons: knives, firearms, bats, rocks or other improvised objects are a significant hazard to responders. Clearing a scene of weapons by law enforcement should be a priority prior to responders entering a scene.

  — Explosives: the use of explosives not only produces the initial event but additional devices may intentionally target responders or Good Samaritans.

  — CBRN event: the use of chemical, biological, radiological, and/or nuclear substances can produce a significant hazard to victims and responders.

- **Weather** — weather would most likely be addressed in an SOP/G and not the individual preincident plans. It is noted here as a hazard that can affect the operations and place personnel at risk. Consideration should be given to apparatus, in addition to personnel, when factoring in weather conditions. Weather events that can impact operations include:

  — Thunderstorms: lightning, heavy rain, wind, and flash floods.

  — Winter: snow, blizzards, icy conditions, extreme cold temperatures, fog, wind, and impassable roads.

  — Summer: extreme heat and/or humid conditions.

  — Significant natural events: tornadoes, hurricanes, flooding, tsunamis, earthquakes, and volcanoes.

Locations that Present Safety and Health Risks

Local SOP/Gs should include a process to determine the factors that indicate which occupancies to survey and how often. The potential fire and life safety hazards at a site along with local SOP/Gs determine which occupancies to survey and how frequently. Referred to as *target hazards*, these sites contain life safety concerns for firefighters as well as occupants, hazardous processes or storage that may have a high frequency or severity of fires, government buildings, prominent structures, and/or high content or structure value (**Figure 6.6**). A few examples are:

- Life safety concerns:
    - Schools, colleges, universities
    - Auditoriums, theaters, restaurants
    - Places of worship
    - Hospitals, nursing homes, daycare centers
    - Multifamily dwellings, hotels, motels, dormitories
    - Institutions, jails, prisons

Figure 6.6 Certain occupancies represent a greater life safety concern than others.

Life Safety Concerns Associated with Certain Occupancies

- Nonambulatory Occupants
- Hazardous Materials
- Bloodborne Pathogens
- Biohazardous Waste

- Hazardous Materials
- Flammable Liquids & Gases
- Large Interior Spaces
- Multiple Exposures

- High Fuel Load
- Variety of Fuels
- Large Interior Spaces
- Stacked Fuels

- Hazardous processes or storage:
  - Spray paint operations
  - Metal plating
  - Chemical plants
  - Automobile fueling stations
  - Compressed gas storage
  - Paint storage warehouses
- High contents/structure value:
  - Mercantile occupancies
  - High-rise structures
  - Office buildings
  - Warehouses

Site Safety Plans

Businesses create **site safety plans** to identify their potential hazards and risks to employees and the public, and to identify the control measures implemented to mitigate them **(Figure 6.7, p. 208)**. Not all business and industry locations require site safety plans, but OSHA 29 CFR 1910.120 and 29 CFR 1926.65 *Hazardous Waste Operations and Emergency Response* (HAZWOPER), requires plans for certain hazardous waste sites. In addition, Tier II reporting under the Emergency Planning and Community Right-to-Know Act (EPCRA) and 40 CFR 370 has implications for local, tribal, state/provincial, and federal governments as well as industry. Fire and emergency service organizations should be aware of any location that has an OSHA-required site safety plan.

Site safety plans should illustrate any site features that might be a hindrance to emergency responses at the site including:

- **Access and egress points** — access and egress restrictions may delay operations. Units and personnel must be able to access a location and gain entry into all portions of a structure(s) in a reasonable time. Any restricted point should be identified with options for gaining access and/or egress **(Figure 6.8, p. 208)**.

- **Building construction and characteristics** — This information is critical to the safe deployment of resources during interior operations. Both positive and negative structural aspects should be identified, such as areas protected by a fire suppression system, fire walls and draft stops, possible ventilation points, breaches in walls and floors, and known structural weaknesses.

- **Limited or no water supply** — having a steady, reliable water supply can be a critical element during a fire fighting operation. Alternative sources of water, including the nearest reliable water source, should be identified in the preincident plan.

- **Fuel type and load** — the fuel type and load are significant considerations for a preincident plan. For example, a warehouse that stores fertilizers, pesticides, and other agricultural chemicals can have different fire suppression recommendations. Some of these chemicals react with water and may be stored in an isolated room. Having this information readily available

Site Safety Plan — Facility plan that identifies potential hazards and risks to employees and the public at businesses that meet certain hazardous criteria such as hazardous waste storage facilities.

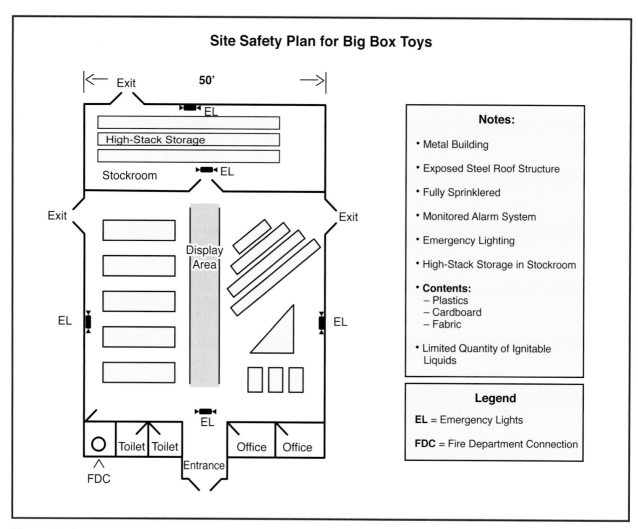

Figure 6.7 Site safety plans identify safety hazards and potential safety hazards at a location.

Figure 6.8 Access and egress to sites under construction may require forcing through fencing around the scene. Unfinished structural components make identifying egress paths even more important.

The content within Figure 6.7 includes:

Site Safety Plan for Big Box Toys

Exit — 50' —

EL

High-Stack Storage

Stockroom

EL

Exit

Display Area

Exit

EL

EL

EL

Toilet | Toilet

Office | Office

FDC

Entrance

Notes:

• Metal Building

• Exposed Steel Roof Structure

• Fully Sprinklered

• Monitored Alarm System

• Emergency Lighting

• High-Stack Storage in Stockroom

• **Contents:**
  – Plastics
  – Cardboard
  – Fabric

• Limited Quantity of Ignitable Liquids

Legend

EL = Emergency Lights

FDC = Fire Department Connection

Figure 6.9 Razor wire atop security fencing presents an access challenge for responders and should be marked in preincident surveys.

for responders can be critical for the appropriate strategy to be employed for incident stabilization. Locations with flammable and/or combustible materials, such as liquefied petroleum gas facilities or crude oil refineries, can produce significant fire and/or explosive hazards.

- **Security features** — certain security features can pose a hazard to responders and should be identified in the preincident plan **(Figure 6.9)**. Some buildings require electronic key card access in multiple areas. This type of lock can limit the access and escape of responders. Loud alarms can impair the hearing of responders both inside and outside the structure, and critical communications can be lost. Security dogs are another hazard that must be identified.

As part of the risk management plan, fire and emergency service organizations should build cooperative relationships with local businesses and industries. The fire chief, fire marshal, or a designated official, such as the HSO, should serve as the point of contact for working with local businesses and industries. Through a collaborative effort with facility personnel, preincident survey and preincident plans can lay the foundation for improved safety and coordination efforts when an emergency occurs.

ICS Form 208 provides a standard way to document a site safety and health plan. This form is compliant with 29 CFR 1910.120 and is mainly used for oil and chemical spills.

Recommending Control Measures

The adoption of effective control measures (risk reduction) is the most common method used for risk management. While control measures will not eliminate the risk, they can reduce the likelihood of occurrence or lessen the severity. Some control measures are already engineered into buildings, such as deluge sprinkler systems or smoke control devices **(Figure 6.10, p. 210)**. Control measures should be coordinated with the fire marshal's office and/or other code setting and enforcement organizations in the community.

The use of preincident plans and district surveys is one way to determine control measures. These plans and surveys are designed to identify specific hazards or risks at a location or in a general geographical area. Fire personnel

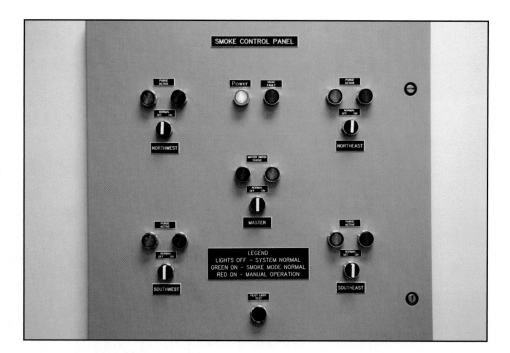

Figure 6.10 The location and use of building systems, such as smoke control panels, should be include, in preincident surveys.

can then customize control measures to the specific hazard or risk through the use of hierarchy of controls, which could reduce the time to control the situation, improve responders' safety, and reduce the financial loss to the business. Defining control measures should be a holistic approach that includes prioritizing safety measures based on information gathered during district surveys and preincident planning.

The district survey and/or preincident plan will identify needed control measures based on the hierarchy of controls concept that may include **(Figure 6.11)**:

- Eliminating hazards at the source (such as having utilities secured)

- Reducing or substituting processes to mitigate the hazard (such as fire suppression techniques based on location of fuels)

- Creating a separation with engineering controls between the responder and the hazard (such as new apparatus designs with enclosed cabs and hearing protection)

- Implementing management or administrative controls that ensure resource needs are identified and addressed in SOP/Gs for specific target hazards (such as apparatus, equipment, and/or personnel)

- Identifying PPE needs based on known location hazards (such as hazardous material specific PPE)

Operational Risk Management Plan

According to NFPA® 1521, the HSO is responsible for developing an operational risk management plan that addresses the risks and hazards that responders potentially face in the operational setting. Fire and emergency services organizations respond to a wide range of emergency situations and incidents. Each incident and training exercise presents its own hazards, placing responders' health and safety at risk. The leading causes of fatalities that occur before,

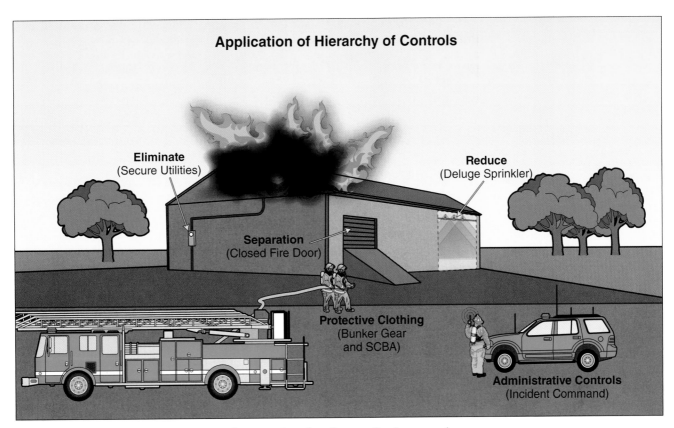

Application of Hierarchy of Controls

Eliminate
(Secure Utilities)

Reduce
(Deluge Sprinkler)

Separation
(Closed Fire Door)

Protective Clothing
(Bunker Gear
and SCBA)

Administrative Controls
(Incident Command)

Figure 6.11 The hierarchy of controls applies to various functions on the fire ground.

during, and shortly after emergency operations involve trauma, sudden cardiac arrest, and vehicle accidents. Many of the accidents occur in firefighters' civilian vehicles.

To effectively handle the variety of emergency incidents, the fire and emergency service organization must have an incident management framework, which is applied to all incident types. NFPA® 1500, *Standard on Fire Department Occupational Safety and Health Program*, Chapter 8, Emergency Operations, details the requirements of emergency scene operations and states the ICS shall also be applied to training exercises and other hazardous situations that are similar to an actual emergency. The HSO should refer to NFPA® 1500, Chapter 8, when developing the operational risk management plan to ensure it addresses the following components:

- Incident Management System
- Communications
- Risk Management During Emergency Operations
- Personnel Accountability During Emergency Operations
- Members Operating at Emergency Incidents
- Established Hazard Control Zones
- Traffic Incident Procedures
- Rapid Intervention Crews (RIC)
- Rehabilitation During Emergency Operations
- Violent Scenes, Civil Unrest, and Terrorism
- Postincident Analysis

NFPA® 1521 emphasizes the establishment of clear incident management, command structure, and safety considerations. The sections that follow describe those topics.

NOTE: The incident safety officer section of this manual (beginning with Chapter 13) describes other subject areas from NFPA® 1500, Chapter 8. Some topics are beyond the scope of this manual and should be researched in their corresponding NFPA® standards or other source documentation.

Incident Management System

Every fire and emergency service organization must implement a locally adopted incident command system (ICS) based on the National Incident Management System NIMS-ICS. The ICS should be used, in varying forms, on all incidents. The ICS model adopted by many jurisdictions in North America is based on NFPA® 1561, *Standard on Emergency Services Incident Management System*. The ICS provides guidance and direction for the management and control of all types of emergency incidents, ranging from single company responses to multiple agency and jurisdiction incidents.

The HSO must ensure the incident management system complies with the following:

- NFPA® 1500, *Standard of Fire Department Occupational Safety and Health Program*
- NFPA® 1521, *Standard for Fire Department Safety Officer*
- NFPA® 1561, *Standard on Emergency Services Incident Management Systemand Command Safety*
- HSPD-5 *Management of Domestic Incidents*
- HSPD-8 *National Response Framework* (NRF)
- Federal, state/provincial, and local laws, codes, regulations, and standards

ICS is the basic operating system for all incidents within a jurisdiction. By design, the ICS can grow from a small-scale incident to a large-scale and/or multiagency operation depending on the needs of the incident. The HSO must be knowledgeable about the ICS and ensure the following components are included in an SOP/G to provide the basis for clear communication and effective operations:

- Common terminology
- Modular organization
- Integrated communications
- Unified command structure
- Consolidated action plans
- Manageable span of control
- Predesignated incident facilities
- Comprehensive resource management

Establishment of an Incident Safety Officer (ISO)

The HSO should ensure that organizational SOP/Gs address the establishment, duties, and authority of the ISO. Fire and emergency service organizations may differ on how the ISO is assigned. During an incident, the Incident Commander (IC) should assign this function to an individual designated as the ISO **(Figure 6.12)**. This function may require the assignment of assistants. In smaller departments, ICs may find that they have to perform this function along with other duties. Regardless of the type of incident, the role of the ISO must be defined in the fire and emergency service department's SOP/Gs, which can vary across departments. NFPA® 1521, outlines the role of the ISO and is a good starting point for developing the SOP/G.

Figure 6.12 The assigned ISO and the IC work together to monitor safety at emergency incidents.

Division — NIMS-ICS organizational level having responsibility for operations within a defined geographic area. It is composed of a number of individual units that are assigned to operate within a defined geographical area.

Group — NIMS-ICS organizational subunit responsible for a number of individual units that are assigned to perform a particular specified function (such as ventilation, salvage, water supply, extrication, transportation, or EMS) at an incident.

Span of Control — Maximum number of subordinates that one individual can effectively supervise; ranges from three to seven individuals or functions, with five generally established as optimum.

According to NFPA® 1561, the types of situations that may need a specific SOP/G for a safety officer include:

- Commercial and residential fires
- Multiple-alarm fires
- Firefighter injury or firefighter transported for treatment
- Hazardous materials incident
- Technical rescue incident
- Incident command request

Today's modern fire and emergency service organization responds to emergency and nonemergency incidents categorized in an all-hazards environment. Fire personnel should incorporate an incident's size and complexity in their considerations for establishing an ISO. They should also include the IC's ability to effectively assess all safety considerations and maintain an appropriate span of control at the incident. The SOP/Gs should also detail the assignment of assistant incident safety officers and their responsibilities at the incident.

Tactical-Level Management

Complex emergency situations often exceed the capability of one officer to effectively manage the entire operation. **Divisions** or **Groups** can be established to direct operations in specific geographic areas or to manage incident-related functions. Establishing these tactical groups should reduce **span of control**. Generally, the best span of control consists of three to seven subordinates, with five being the preferred number **(Figure 6.13)**.

Tactical-level supervisors direct operational activities toward specific objectives. Tactical-level supervisors oversee grouped resources and are responsible for functions or specific geographic areas. A tactical-level assignment comes with the authority to make decisions and assignments within the boundaries of the overall plan and safety conditions. The accomplished goals of each tactical group should contribute to executing the strategy outlined in the incident action plan.

Tactical Components

The NIMS-ICS assigns Divisions and Groups as tactical-level management components that assemble units and/or resources for a common purpose. *Divisions* are the organizational level that have responsibility for operations within a defined geographic area. The Division level is organized into Single Resources, Task Forces, Strike Teams, or Branches. For situations where the incident has an odd geographical layout (no obvious North, South, East, or West), the front of the building is designated *Division A*, and the remaining sides are given a designation of B, C, or D in a clockwise manner. For clarity of purpose during radio communications, the phonetic designations of *Alpha*, *Bravo*, *Charlie*, and *Delta* are suggested **(Figure 6.14)**. In multi-story occupancies, Divisions will usually be indicated by floor number or basement level.

Groups are an organizational level responsible for the specific functional assignment. The Group level is also organizationally between Single Resources, Task Forces, or Strike Teams and the Branch. Examples are Salvage Group, Search Group, Rescue Group, Haz-Mat Group, and Medical Group.

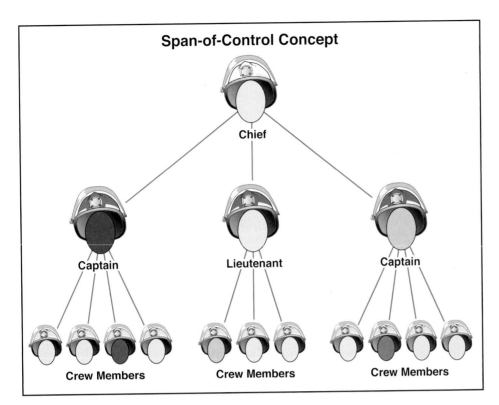

Figure 6.13 Manageable span of control is an important control measure for emergency scene management.

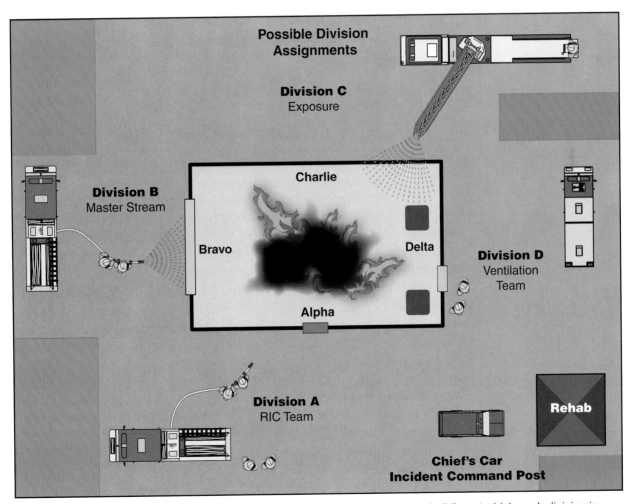

Figure 6.14 Division assignments can be organized according to the side of the building at which each division is located: A, B, C, D; or Alpha, Bravo, Charlie, Delta.

Scalability for Size and Complexity

According to NFPA® 1561, fire personnel should assess incidents for their cause, needs, size, and complexity when establishing the incident command structure. A major incident will initially have more tasks that need to be completed than the available resources can accomplish. There is a tendency to start performing these tasks immediately upon arrival, thereby postponing the establishment of ICS. *Doing so is a major error.* The lack of direction will result in confusion and lack of coordination. This action increases the risks to emergency personnel and decreases the likelihood of a successful operation. The HSO is responsible for ensuring the SOP/Gs address the establishment of an ICS from the first arriving unit. The SOP/Gs must also detail the flexibility to expand the ICS and the transfer of command.

CAUTION
Do not postpone the establishment of ICS or take action before needed resources are available.

FEMA Categories of Complexity[1]

According to FEMA, incidents are categorized based on the following levels of complexity:

- **Type I** — the most complex type of incident that requires national resources and a written IAP. The command structure will have all command and general staff positions filled along with the use of Branches. Operational periods will typically have 500 personnel or more assigned.

- **Type II** — the second-most complex type of incident that requires resources from outside the local jurisdiction and has multiple operational periods. Most or all of the general and command staff positions are filled and a written IAP is required. Operational periods will typically have less than 200 personnel assigned.

- **Type III** — this type of incident will exceed the capabilities of the jurisdiction and may have multiple operational periods. A written IAP may be required. The expansion of the ICS should match the complexity of the incident.

- **Type IV** — this type of incident may have several resources, including a task force or strike team. The expansion of the ICS should match the complexity of the incident. Typically, a written IAP is not required and the incident does not extend past one operational period.

- **Type V** — this type of incident is usually managed with one or two single resources. The ICS does not require the assignment of general or command staff positions other than the incident commander. No written IAP is required and the incident is contained in less than one operational period.

Staff Organization

To understand the application of ICS, the HSO should know the major operational position descriptions within the ICS structure. These descriptions include Command, Command Staff, and the General Staff positions. Personnel may be assigned to any of these positions based on their ICS training level, knowledge, skills, and abilities. The IC holds the responsibility of all ICS structure positions until those duties are delegated and formally assigned **(Figure 6.15 a and b)**.

Command

The **Incident Commander (IC)** is the fire officer in overall command. The IC is ultimately responsible for all incident activities, including the development and implementation of an incident action plan. This process may include making a number of critical decisions and being responsible for the results of

Incident Commander (IC) — Person in charge of the incident command system and responsible for the management of all incident operations during an emergency.

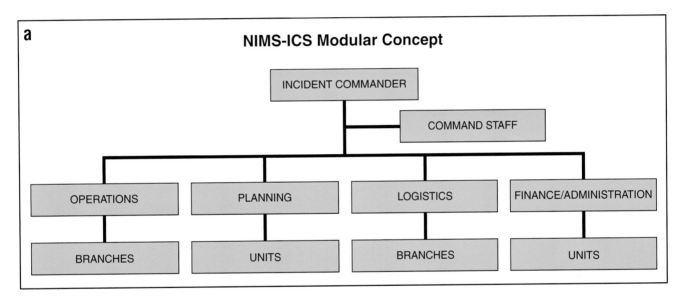

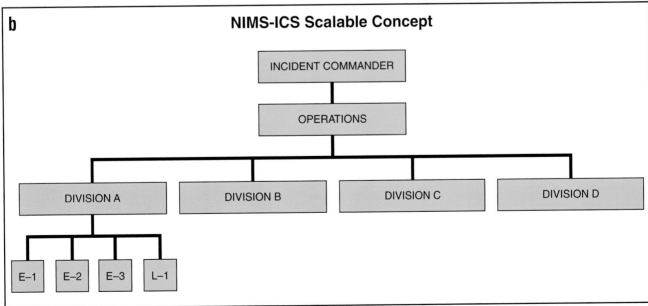

Figures 6.15 a and b The ICS model is designed to scale or change depending upon the complexity, size, and need of the incident. Organization may be according to division or to assignment.

Command Staff — In a fully developed fireground organization, the Public Information Officer (PIO), Safety Officer, and Liaison Officer, who report directly to the IC.

Safety Officer — Member of the IMS command staff responsible to the incident commander for monitoring and assessing hazardous and unsafe conditions and developing measures for assessing personnel safety on an incident.

Liaison Officer — Point of contact for assisting or coordinating agencies; member of the command staff.

Public Information Officer (PIO) — Member of the command staff responsible for interfacing with the media, public, or other agencies requiring information direct from the incident scene.

General Staff — Group of incident management personnel: operations section chief, planning section chief, logistics section chief, and finance/administrative section chief.

those decisions. The IC has the authority to request and release resources to and from the incident. If the size and complexity of the incident requires it, the IC may delegate authority to other firefighters, who form the Command and General Staffs along with the IC. At single-unit incidents, the IC will perform the functions normally assigned to the Command Staff.

Command Staff

The **Command Staff** reports directly to the IC by providing management support in functions that are not directly involved with the operational tasks. Command staff positions include the following assignments:

- **Safety Officer** — assesses hazardous conditions and unsafe situations and develops an incident safety plan that ensures the safety of personnel at the incident. The Incident Safety Officer (ISO) has the authority to alter, suspend, or terminate activities that are imminently dangerous to the life of an occupant or responder.

- **Liaison Officer** — acts as a point of contact for other agencies and jurisdictions and coordinates the activities with them.

- **Public Information Officer (PIO)** — provides accurate and complete information on the incident to the media. During a larger incident, the public information officer provides information to other governmental agencies that need information concerning the incident **(Figure 6.16)**.

General Staff

As an incident becomes larger and more complex, additional tasks must be performed which requires the addition of more personnel. These personnel comprise the **General Staff**. The General Staff represents the major functional sections, including Planning, Operations, Logistics, and Finance/Administration.

Figure 6.16 Public information officers are assigned at large events to act as a liaison with the media. *Courtesy of Steve Baker*

- **Planning** — the Planning Section Chief is responsible for the collection, evaluation, dissemination, and use of information concerning the development of the incident. Planning is also responsible for tracking the status of all resources assigned to the incident as well as the situation status. Command uses the information compiled by Planning to develop strategic goals and contingency plans.

- **Operations** — Staff assigned specific functions at a scene such as fireground support or rapid intervention crew (RIC). Operations may be divided into Divisions or Groups with a recommended five members per group. If an Operations Chief has more Divisions/Groups than what is considered reasonable, Branches may be organized with Divisions/Groups assigned to them.

- **Logistics** — Logistics is responsible for providing the facilities, services, and materials necessary to support the incident. There are two Branches within Logistics – Support and Service.

- **Finance/Administration** — Finance/Administration has the responsibility for tracking and documenting all costs and financial aspects of the incident. Generally, Finance/Administration will be activated only on large-scale, long-term incidents. Day-to-day mutual aid and automatic aid responses are usually considered to be reciprocal and do not require interagency reimbursement. Administration is also responsible for the legal aspects of the incident, such as monitoring contracts with vendors, agreements with other agencies, and compliance with state/provincial, and national laws.

Safety Enforcement

The IC has responsibility for the safety and health of all members operating at an emergency incident. At small incidents, the IC may be effective at enforcing safety-related issues; as the incident grows in size and/or complexity, the IC's situational awareness with respect to safety may diminish. The IC will need to expand the command structure in order to maintain optimal situational awareness. Overall, the ICS system has the potential for multiple layers of safety enforcement. Safety awareness and compliance should begin at the personal level with each member following safety SOP/Gs and accepted best practices. Members should look out for each other and speak up if they recognize an unsafe act or unsafe condition. Company officers provide the next level of safety enforcement and can provide the directive for corrective action to be taken. Division and Group Supervisors provide safety enforcement in the geographic and function areas. These supervisors must look at the overall scene and ensure personnel are not freelancing or otherwise operating in an unsafe manner or location. The ISO is the scene safety enforcement supervisor who has the authority to immediately stop actions. The ISO will report any immediate corrective action stoppage to the IC for contingency plan considerations.

Chapter Summary

The operational risk management plan, which is managed by the HSO, will mitigate or eliminate hazards identified during the preincident planning process. The HSO will assist responders with identifying the many hazards that are common or unique in a given area or at a location. Control measures can then be recommended based on the district survey or preincident plan information. Use of the ICS is an essential component of the operational risk management plan. It also provides a framework for ensuring a coordinated response is established and communicated, appropriate incident strategy and tactical decisions are made, personnel are accounted for, and the overall safety of personnel is addressed.

Review Questions

1. What is the health safety officer's role in the preincident planning process? (pp. 198-204)

2. What risk-based information and assistance should the health safety officer provide to members of a jurisdiction? (pp. 204-210)

3. What are the components of an operational risk management plan? (pp. 210-219)

Chapter 6 End Notes

1. ICS Resource Center at FEMA's website.

6-1
Gather information for a preincident plan for a public building.

Refer to Appendix B: Learning Activity Answers in the back of this manual for suggested responses.

Purpose

Preincident or pre-emergency plans are a vital part of operational risk management. For this activity, practice gathering the types of information required to develop a preincident plan for a potential emergency situation.

Directions

1. Choose a local public building in your community, such as a library, school, or gymnasium. You will want to choose a building that does not require permission to enter, and one which you will be able to easily observe without appearing odd or out of place.

2. Make a list of the information needed for a preincident plan. See pp. 198-210 for ideas or consult your agency's preincident plan forms.

   NOTE: You will want to consider the building's layout, exposures, potential risks and hazards, site and building features, access and egress points, water supply, and fire suppression features at minimum.

3. Take some time to visit the public building. Gather as much information from your list as you are able to as an observer.

   NOTE: Although it is not necessary to interview or speak with anyone for this assignment, you may wish to inform the building manager (or other responsible party) about your visit and purpose.

4. Compare the information you have gathered to any information on file at your department. Note what information you were unable to obtain and why. Also note any discrepancies in your information and the information on file with the department. If you see any areas where the department's information is outdated or in error, bring it to the attention of your department's health safety officer.

   NOTE: You may also take the opportunity to examine other preincident or pre-emergency plans on file.

Safety and Health Programs

Chapter Contents

Key Terms

NFPA® Job Performance Requirements

This chapter provides information that addresses the following job performance requirements of NFPA® 1521, *Standard for Fire Department Safety Officer Professional Qualifications (2015)*.

4.5.1	4.10.2
4.5.3	4.11.4
4.5.4	4.12.1
4.10.1	4.12.2

Safety and Health Programs

Learning Objectives

After reading this chapter, students will be able to:

1. Describe guidelines for coordinating fire department safety and health programs. (4.10.1, 4.10.2, 4.11.4)

2. Explain the components of a fire department's health maintenance program. (4.10.1, 4.10.2)

3. Recognize the components of a fire department accident prevention program. (4.5.1)

4. Describe processes used when conducting a safety audit for compliance with federal, state/provincial and local laws. (4.5.4)

5. Describe all aspects of a jurisdictional infection control program. (4.12.1, 4.12.2)

6. Identify all aspects of an emergency vehicle safety program. (4.5.3)

7. Learning Activity 7-1: Identify safety and health programs based on departmental needs. (4.5.1, 4.5.3, 4.5.4, 4.10.1, 4.12.1)

Chapter 7
Safety and Health Programs

Case History

The safety committee in a combination fire district (paid and paid-on-call firefighters) noticed a trend in national research that back injuries were on the rise on EMS-related calls. Because the average age of the firefighters in the district was only 28 years old, no one had yet considered the potential for back injuries until the trends were discovered. Upon reviewing local incident and injury reports, the committee discovered many practices that could have caused back injuries within the district.

The health safety officer began expanded research to assist the committee in creating a new safety plan. The HSO provided the committee with workers' compensation information, possible pension issues in the future, and other related costs that could increase if the number of back injuries also increased. This data was added to the committee discussions, and a proactive risk management approach that appeared to offer the best possible outcomes was agreed upon.

The first priority was to reevaluate the safety training within the district. Both the training division and the insurance loss control team were included in the evaluation. Once current training practices had been identified, additional support materials were selected to fill gaps in the program regarding lifting techniques and back injury prevention. After the training division and district had approved the new materials, they were added to the proposal as part of the back safety program.

Second, the safety committee reviewed the individual firefighter fitness program. They ensured that the fitness program included emphasis on exercise that would help prevent back injuries. They also improved their efforts to promote the fitness plan among the membership and included this in their proposed plan.

Third, the committee identified new technology and equipment that could control or eliminate the need for heavy or difficult lifting on the job. They reviewed mechanical cots, cot lifts, and ergonomic equipment designs; and selected new equipment to recommend to the administration as part of their proposed plan.

Lastly, the committee and HSO worked with the EMS division to write and revise lifting policies and procedures. These were also added to the proposal for the administration.

All of the components – research, training adjustments, fitness program changes, new equipment recommendations, and new policies and procedures – were presented to the district administration. After the administration's approval, the back safety program was implemented. Training began, and the HSO and safety committee reviewed accident and injury reports closely for the next two quarters to track the effectiveness of the training. They also implemented a schedule for evaluating the program at least annually to monitor and adjust the program.

The organization's administration should assign its HSO the task of developing and implementing a safety and health program that meets the organization's requirements, demands, needs, and concerns. The foundation of the safety and health program should include current safety and health laws, codes, and standards. Although these safety standards have requirements for employers, the regulations also contain significant requirements for members. Each member must comply with the requirements of the occupational safety and health standards.

The HSO is the catalyst that initiates proven safety programs that reduce injuries and fatalities within a fire and emergency services organization. Supervisors have a responsibility to take a leadership role, and all members should be required to actively participate in these programs in the interests of improving safety in the work environment. The program's success depends upon management's documented establishment of safety as the organization's core cultural value.

The following are important reasons for implementing an occupational safety and health program:

- Fulfills an ethical obligation to prevent injuries, illnesses, and fatalities while supporting organizational members and their families during times of loss

- Reduces property losses and minimizes the financial impact on organizations and membership due to injuries, illnesses, and fatalities

- Reduces the frequency and severity of injuries and fatalities

- Reduces the organizations' workers' compensation and liability insurance costs and expenditures

- Protects the department from citations, fines, and other financial penalties

- Ensures compliance with applicable national, state/provincial, and local laws, codes, and standards

16 Firefighter Life Safety Initiatives 2, 5, 6, and 13

The *16 Firefighter Life Safety Initiatives* were discussed in Chapter 1, Health Safety Officer Responsibilities. Initiatives 2, 5, 6, and 13 are pertinent to the HSO's responsibilities related to managing and implementing the safety health programs:

2. Enhance the personal and organizational accountability for health and safety throughout the fire service.

5. Develop and implement national standards for training, qualifications, and certification (including regular recertification) that are equally applicable to all firefighters based on the duties they are expected to perform.

6. Develop and implement national medical and physical fitness standards that are equally applicable to all firefighters, based on the duties they are expected to perform.

13. Firefighters and their families must have access to counseling and psychological support.

The safety and health of department/organization members is a paramount issue for the successful operation of an organization. A comprehensive approach will help ensure a successful process that includes an across-the-board team effort, management support, and member participation. This chapter outlines the various programs that should be implemented and managed to meet NFPA® standards for safety and health programs. The HSO's responsibility is to implement, manage, evaluate, and revise these programs in order to provide a safety conscious culture and healthy firefighters for the organization.

General Guidelines for Program Coordination

Programs in the fire service are ongoing, have no defined duration, and are established to meet mission and strategic planning goals. Programs are generally centered on services provided, public outreach, and personnel management. Program coordination requires continuous administrative oversight. For the HSO, this responsibility focuses on analyzing and coordinating the safety and health programs with the crucial purpose of eliminating or significantly decreasing the severity, frequency, and probability of injuries, fatalities, illnesses, and exposures. The programs in this chapter focus on positively influencing personnel in meeting this goal. **Learning Activity 7-1** offers practice at identifying needed programs and planning for their implementation.

Projects are under the umbrella of programs. Projects concentrate on specific objectives in meeting a greater goal. In addition, projects have a defined beginning and ending point and are technical in nature. For example, the process of designing, budgeting, and constructing an exercise facility is a project that would help the organization meet its goals for its health and fitness program.

Administrative oversight of a program and/or project is based on the organizational structure of the department. Some departments may delegate this responsibility to chief officers, while other departments may delegate responsibility at any level in the organization. For the safety and health programs, the administrative responsibility is with the HSO.

For safety and health programs to be effective, there must be SOP/Gs addressing the following:

- Statements of purpose
- Strategies for accomplishing the purpose
- Expected performance of members
- Administrative oversight responsibilities
- Methods of measuring the program
- Processes to recommend and implement improvements

Establishing a department safety and health committee is one effective method of accomplishing these program goals. In a collaborative manner, committee members should address all aspects of fire department safety and health, including member individual responsibilities, management accountability, and the overall safety culture of the organization.

Comprehensive management of a wellness program is dependent on the willing participation of members. Participation is essential for the program to be successful. All members must willingly take responsibility for their own health in order for the program to be successful.

A comprehensive program should be derived from the following:

- A well communicated definition of safety and health that guides the program
- Clarification of the program mission, vision, and values
- Clearly defined goals, objectives, and action items that members can follow to remain participatory in the program and take personal responsibility for their involvement
- Input and validation from members at all organizational levels, including the Occupational Safety and Health Committee, labor representatives (if any), and management

A safety and health program model can only be selected and implemented to create cultural change after the organization has recognized the need to change its safety culture. Members must have developed an awareness of a problem before they will be willing to change their behavior. Ongoing open communications, discussion of problem issues, and agreement on a course of action contribute to policy, procedure, equipment, and apparatus changes.

Health Program Analysis

NFPA® 1521, *Standard for Fire Department Safety Officer* states that the HSO is responsible for analyzing and coordinating the components of the health program. The core components of the program include requirements for:

- Medical evaluations **(Figure 7.1)**
- Physical performance
- Physical fitness
- Health and wellness
- Health database
- Infection control procedures
- Fire department physician
- Fitness-for-duty evaluations
- Recommendations to correct program deficiencies

Essential to proceeding with final development of a department health program is a careful review by the safety and health committee of data relative to health and fitness in general. Such research should be completed with recommendations and included in a regularly scheduled report to the fire chief and the department.

Researching historical data on departmental injuries, illnesses, and medical issues, as well as job-related fatalities can indicate problem areas. Members' privacy should be protected during this research.

Departmental research should be expanded, particularly in small or newer agencies as those agencies may not have sufficient experience to be meaningful. The USFA and NFPA® create annual reports and multi-year summaries of firefighter injury and fatality data and analysis, which should prove useful

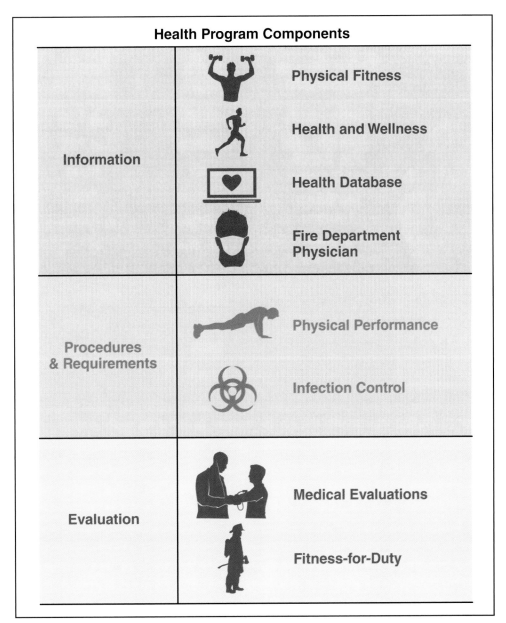

Health Program Components

Information	Physical Fitness
	Health and Wellness
	Health Database
	Fire Department Physician
Procedures & Requirements	Physical Performance
	Infection Control
Evaluation	Medical Evaluations
	Fitness-for-Duty

Figure 7.1 It is the HSO's responsibility to establish and/or coordinate the core components of the organization's health program.

to any agency initiating a safety and health program. A health program must include measures to screen personnel for existing health problems during the pre-employment process and throughout an individual's career, improve members' nutrition, and establish a fitness program that supports overall wellness.

Committee review should also include a best practices review and recommendations regarding medical requirements for a firefighter. NFPA® 1582, *Comprehensive Medical Program for Fire Departments*, provides a basis against which the department's current practice can be compared. Any changes and recommendations for improvement should be carefully documented and reported to the fire chief.

Any review of physical or medical requirements related to firefighter duties should also be well researched and reported to the fire chief. It is not acceptable to assume that modern fire departments can require specific physical

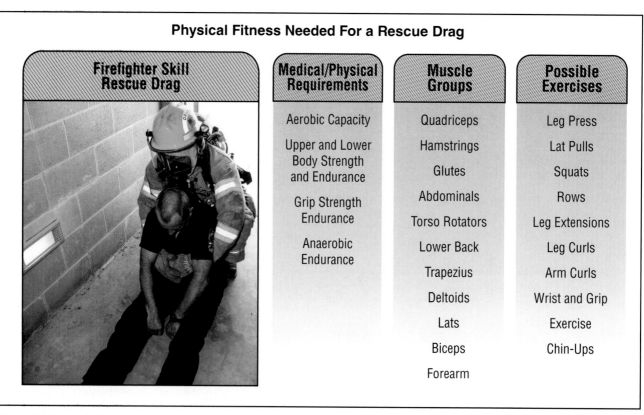

Physical Fitness Needed For a Rescue Drag

Firefighter Skill Rescue Drag	Medical/Physical Requirements	Muscle Groups	Possible Exercises
	Aerobic Capacity	Quadriceps	Leg Press
	Upper and Lower Body Strength and Endurance	Hamstrings	Lat Pulls
		Glutes	Squats
	Grip Strength Endurance	Abdominals	Rows
		Torso Rotators	Leg Extensions
	Anaerobic Endurance	Lower Back	Leg Curls
		Trapezius	Arm Curls
		Deltoids	Wrist and Grip
		Lats	Exercise
		Biceps	Chin-Ups
		Forearm	

Figure 7.2 Every firefighter skill has certain physical requirements that can be improved as part of the health program.

or medical requirements without demonstrating the relationship of those requirements to the essential firefighter duties **(Figure 7.2)**. Those requirements, if not proven to be job-related, can – and likely will – be challenged in court.

Properly executed, a health program will allow employees to openly discuss with a physician their health and develop a treatment or wellness program to improve their physical fitness for the job. Benefits should be seen in improvements in employee longevity and operational effectiveness as well as reductions of health care costs, turnover, and absenteeism.

Equipment and Resources

The facilities and equipment for a physical fitness plan vary depending on the finances available to the organization **(Figure 7.3)**. The HSO and safety and health committee provide the administration with a list of recommended equipment necessary to implement the plan. The organization must determine what equipment will be provided and how to fund the plan. The organization might find it more economical to enter initially into a contract with a local health-care facility or gymnasium for the use of its weights and machines. The investment in achieving member well-being is a justified cost that will likely reduce the cost of lost-time injuries.

Additionally, resources must be available to the health and fitness coordinator and peer fitness trainers to properly conduct fitness assessments. NFPA® 1582, Annex C, *Protocols for Evaluation of Fitness of Members*, provides an explanation of the assessment elements along with the needed equipment and resources. The role of health and fitness trainers and coordinators will be explained in more detail later in this chapter.

Not all fire and emergency service organizations will be able to have in-house exercise rooms, equipment, and/or peer fitness trainers. The following may be options for departments that may not have on-site facilities:

- Establish agreements with local businesses that can provide these services
- Use apparatus bays or other areas at the station for exercise sessions
- Use facilities at local schools or public recreational centers
- Collaborate with colleges and universities in the area that have physical fitness training programs **(Figure 7.4)**

Figure 7.3 Some departments will have their own fitness facilities in their fire stations. Others may contract with local gyms to provide discounted rates or free memberships for fire service personnel.

Figure 7.4 Colleges and universities often have trainers and training facilities that fire service organizations can use for physical fitness programs.

Safety Precautions

The HSO and health and fitness coordinator should evaluate the organization's ability to safely administer the components of the safety and health program. This task includes an evaluation of department facilities or other facilities that members may use for health and wellness. Before the department establishes a physical fitness program, a physician familiar with the demands of fire fighting should evaluate all members. In addition, prior to program implementation, members must be provided training and education that includes but is not limited to:

- Proper physical fitness exercises (these can and should be tailored to the individual)
- Proper stretching exercises
- Proper weight lifting techniques
- Proper use of fitness equipment **(Figure 7.5)**
- Recognition of injury, illness, or overexertion **(Figure 7.6, p. 234)**
- Proper nutrition and fluid replenishment before, during, and after exercise

Department members should recognize that some injury-prone activities should not be permitted on-duty. The SOP/Gs should list acceptable and not acceptable activities with considerations toward acceptable risk of injury based on the activity.

Fire Department Physician

In order to develop and implement an effective health and fitness program, the department should efficiently manage and direct the implementation. The selection and appointment of a **fire department physician** is a crucial element. The requirements for the fire department physician are found in OSHA 1910.134, as well as NFPA® 1500, *Standard on Fire Department Occupational Safety and Health Program*, and NFPA® 1582.

In order to provide an NFPA®-compliant medical certification program, the fire department physician must have a clear understanding of the services the department provides. It may be necessary to provide training for the fire department physician in the tasks, operating procedures, and evolutions inherent in fire fighting. Smaller departments could join together to hire a physician to provide services for all of them as a cost-saving approach. The HSO should refer to NFPA® 1582, Section 4.2, for a list of fire department physician responsibilities.

When the department has an assigned physician who conducts all medical evaluations, that physician should be familiar with NFPA® 1582 and NFPA® 1583, *Standard on Health-Related Fitness Programs for Fire Department Members*. The physician should also be aware of the demands of the essential tasks assigned to a firefighter **(Table 7.1, p. 235)**. If the department does not have the resources to have an assigned physician, the physician who is selected to conduct the medical evaluations should receive more than just a briefing on the essential tasks. The physician should be provided an opportunity to observe and perhaps even participate in many of the tasks associated with the work that firefighters perform. The briefing should include but not be limited to documentation regarding the essential job and tasks, as well as

Fire Department Physician — Physician designated by a fire department to treat members of the department.

Proper Use of Exercise Equipment

Pull-ups

Dumbbell Flys

Seated Medicine Ball Twists

Barbell Squats

Dumbbell Squats

Figure 7.5 Physical fitness equipment is only effective if used properly and with good form. Improper use can lead to injury rather than improved fitness.

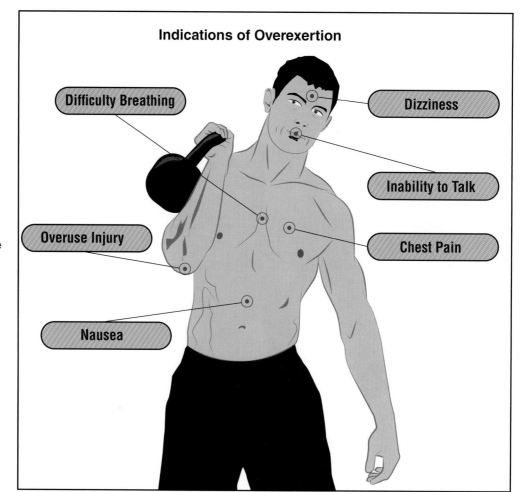

Indications of Overexertion

Difficulty Breathing

Dizziness

Inability to Talk

Overuse Injury

Chest Pain

Nausea

Figure 7.6 Recognizing the signs of overexertion is important for safe physical fitness training. Appearance of these indicators during training is a warning to stop and rest to avoid injury.

the psychological and physiological demands of the work. Participation on the safety and health committee also helps the physician assimilate into the fire service.

Fitness-for-Duty Evaluations

NFPA® 1582 provides specific details of medical evaluations that should be performed in examining the health and fitness of firefighter candidates and incumbents. **The fitness-for-duty evaluation** is intended to determine health and fitness as they relate to the demands of the work of a firefighter. The recommended medical evaluations consist of a comprehensive examination of a number of functions and systems, including:

- Head and neck
- Eyes and vision
- Ears and hearing
- Dental
- Nose, oropharynx, trachea, esophagus, and larynx
- Lungs and chest wall
- Aerobic capacity
- Heart and vascular system

Fitness-for-duty Evaluation — Health evaluation administered by a fire department physician to determine an individual's ability to perform fire service tasks; evaluations may be physiological or psychological in nature depending on need.

Table 7.1
Energy Expenditures During Common Sports and Fire Fighting Activities

Common Sports Activities	Average Expenditure (in METs)
Basketball	8.3
Cycling (10 mph [16 kph])	7.0
Football (touch)	8.0
Racquetball	9.0
Weight (circuit) Training	9.1

Common Fire Fighting Activities	Average Expenditure (in METs)
Climbing an Aerial Ladder	9.3
Chopping at Medium Speed	11.0
Dragging a Supply Hoseline	10.2
Raising a Ladder 40 - 50 feet (12 – 15 m)	9.2
Climbing Stairs in PPE/SCBA/Hotel Pack	11.0
Carrying Victim Down a Ladder	10.1

NOTE: One MET is defined as the energy expenditure for sitting quietly, which, for the average adult, approximates 3.5 ml of oxygen uptake per kilogram of body weight per minute (1.2 kcal/min for a 70-kg individual). For example, a 2-MET activity requires two times the metabolic energy expenditure of sitting quietly.

- Abdominal organs and gastrointestinal system
- Metabolic syndrome
- Reproductive system
- Urinary system
- Spine and axial skeleton
- Extremities
- Neurological disorders
- Skin
- Blood and blood-forming organs
- Endocrine and metabolic disorders
- Systemic diseases and miscellaneous conditions
- Tumors and malignant diseases
- Psychiatric conditions
- Chemicals, drugs, and medications

The examining physician should also understand the environmental conditions to which firefighters will be exposed. Firefighters have a number of protective clothing and equipment requirements that must be considered in the medical evaluation. The full ensemble of boots, pants, coat, hood, and helmet, as well as the requirement for self-contained breathing apparatus (SCBA) in addition to tools carried and work performed, place specific demands on the firefighter. Those firefighters assigned to enter and perform work in hazardous atmospheres may require full Level A suit protection, and the demands, especially from heat in those suits, must be considered in performing the medical evaluation. Finally, firefighters who will perform wildland fire suppression will face longer durations of physical stress. Physicians may not be fully aware the extraordinary demands that layers of protective clothing and safety devices place on the body. The examining physician may not be that familiar with the amount of heat buildup and should be thoroughly briefed prior to performing any medical examinations **(Figure 7.7)**.

A return-to-duty policy could also incorporate some form of a *restricted* or *limited (light)* duty assignment that will return the firefighter to some capacity of work while continuing to rehabilitate from an injury or illness **(Figure 7.8)**. That policy must be well defined, coordinated and equitably applied with relevant sick leave, injury leave, and family leave policies. Work assignments need to be carefully evaluated and compared to the restrictions established by the fire department physician to ensure that the activities will not aggravate existing injuries or illnesses or contribute to new injuries or illnesses. Fire departments have a substantial investment in the training and experience of firefighters; developing a **light duty policy** allows for the transition of valuable employees back into the work force while the organization benefits from the work that they can complete.

Light Duty Policy — Department policy that indicates certain assignments that may be given to firefighters who are recovering from injuries; the assignments should be evaluated to ensure that they will not interfere with injury rehabilitation.

Figure 7.7 Firefighter personal protective clothing is designed to capture heat and prevent its convection to the skin. Fire department physicians need to be informed about the rate of heat build-up and the additional physical stress that heat causes to a firefighter's body.

If firefighters are unable to perform the essential duties of their position due to a line-of-duty injury or illness, the department should have a well-defined policy to manage workers' compensation issues. In these cases, the medical treatment and rehabilitation may be the same; however, the department is obligated to support the treatment and rehabilitation of that firefighter. Return-to-duty and light duty may be treated in much the same manner for either on- or off-duty illness or injury; however, the use of sick/injury leave may not be required of the employee for on-duty illness or injury. State laws differ regarding workers' compensation issues. The organization must seek consultation from an experienced risk manager, workers compensation carrier, or legal advisor to coordinate the agency's policy with relevant state law.

Medical Requirements

Policies must be in place that not only define the medical criteria for being hired but also for continued employment and separation of employment. These policies may be associated with the labor/management agreement, protect the employee, and establish the rights of management. Medical requirements must follow all applicable OSHA regulations, NFPA® standards, and industry best practices. The medical requirements should include:

- Annual medical evaluations **(Figure 7.9)**
- Return-to-duty criteria
- Medical leave criteria
- Disability separation or termination criteria
- Limited duty guidelines

Levels of Fitness

As part of assessing fitness-for-duty, departments may want to define what duties may be assigned to personnel with various levels of fitness. Including these designations in the program may help ensure that firefighters or support personnel are not performing actions at scenes that could be detrimental to their health.

Based on NFPA® 1582, any candidate who is determined to have any Category A preexisting conditions shall not be certified for employment. Category A conditions may present a significant risk to the individual or other personnel. Category B medical conditions must not prevent the candidate from fulfilling the duties of a firefighter. Applicants with Category B medical conditions that, based on the severity or degree of

Figure 7.8 Firefighters who have received minor injuries that prevent them from responding to emergencies may still be able to perform light-duty work around stations or other facilities.

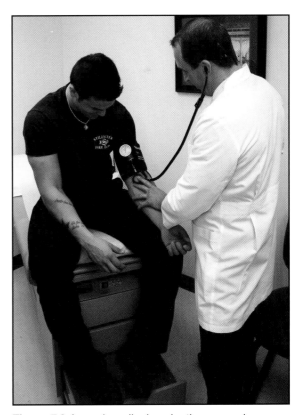

Figure 7.9 Annual medical evaluations are a key component of any fitness-for-duty evaluation program.

the condition, would prevent them from performing the duties of a firefighter in training or at an emergency incident shall not be certified as fit for duty. However, the AHJ can make reasonable accommodations to allow such an individual to perform other assigned functions.

Categories A and B

NFPA® 1582 has two classifications for medical conditions: Category A and Category B. The categories define two levels of severity for an injury or medical condition. Chapter 6 of the standard provides details for a variety of injuries described in terms of these categories. In general, a Category A medical condition indicates that an individual cannot meet the medical requirements of NFPA® 1582 and is therefore not recommended as fit-for-duty. Category B conditions are allowed, assuming that the candidates with the medical condition can still perform job functions without posing a safety and health risk to themselves or others.

In the standard, for example, an individual with vertigo due to inner ear injuries or conditions would be considered Category A and would not be fit-for-duty. An individual who has unequal hearing in both ears would be considered Category B and would be fit-for-duty, assuming that there is no indication that the hearing loss will endanger the firefighter or other firefighters.

Job Task Analysis — Process of evaluating firefighter job tasks and determining the best medical, physical fitness, safety, and health requirements and programs to help ensure that firefighters can perform those tasks safely and without injury.

Job Performance Requirement (JPR) — Statement that describes a specific job task, lists the items necessary to complete the task, and defines measurable or observable outcomes and evaluation areas for the specific task.

Candidate Physical Ability Test (CPAT) — Optional, nationally recognized physical fitness examination for firefighter candidates which is oriented toward firefighter job tasks with established benchmarks.

Incumbent Physical Ability Test (IPAT) — Physical fitness test developed within an individual jurisdiction to assess fitness-for-duty of firefighter candidates.

Performance Requirements

NFPA® 1500 states that a fire and emergency services organization must develop physical performance standards for all personnel who engage in emergency operations. Job performance requirements for fire department members must be based on the job description for the duties performed. The job description is based on a detailed **job task analysis** that will provide the fire and emergency services organization with the verified essential job tasks for each position within the organization. The essential job tasks and associated job description must include only those verified through a validation process and be specific to the services provided by a fire and emergency services organization. NFPA® 1582 Chapters 5 and 9 also include a list of 13 Essential Job Tasks and Descriptions that can be used to compare the services provided by a specific fire department. This comparison of the NFPA® standard to local circumstances allows departments to tailor performance requirements.

Job performance requirements (JPRs) that correlate to the accepted essential job tasks can be applied to initial and annual ability testing. Each fire and emergency services organization must determine performance and ability testing criteria. Potential firefighter candidates are often given the **Candidate Physical Ability Test (CPAT)** **(Figure 7.10)**. This test has standardized the entrance fitness test through a rigorous validation process. Under the CPAT process, incumbent firefighters are not required to take or pass this test. While some incumbent firefighters take this test, it is on a voluntary basis. Some departments have approved an **Incumbent Physical Ability Test (IPAT)** or *Work Performance Evaluation (WPE)*, but as of the publishing date of this manual, no national standard has been approved.

Fitness Requirements

The general approach to physical fitness in the fire service continues to improve. Empirical research of firefighter health data continues to show that cardiac-related deaths are the number one cause of firefighter deaths in the United States. Physical fitness programs are highly recommended as one of many preventative measures to reduce risk factors that have been shown as contributing to sudden cardiac death.

There are several firefighter fitness programs intended to help reduce sudden cardiac death events including:

- The International Association of Fire Fighters (IAFF) and the International Association of Fire Chiefs (IAFC), *The Fire Service Joint Labor Management Wellness-Fitness Initiative*, support this standard in which the manual establishes a best practice for firefighter health and wellness.

- The National Fallen Fire Fighters *Everyone Goes Home®* program and Life Safety Initiative 6 *Medical and Physical Fitness* provide recommendations and support for improving firefighter health and fitness.

- The National Volunteer Fire Council's *Heart Health Firefighter Program* also provides valuable resources for improving firefighter health and fitness.

As a part of the fitness requirements, fire and emergency services organizations should have a health and fitness coordinator to administer annual assessments. The health and fitness coordinator may be the HSO or may perform these specific functions under the supervision of the HSO. The annual assessments are outlined in NFPA® 1583 and are based on the following five fitness categories (**Figure 7.11, p. 240**):

- Body composition
- Muscular strength
- Muscular endurance
- Aerobic capacity
- Flexibility

Specific measurement criteria are outlined in NFPA® 1582 Annex C. The initial and annual fitness assessments of candidates and incumbent members of the organization must be preceded by a medical clearance from a physician who is informed of the essential job tasks and job description of the person being examined.

Figure 7.10 Many jurisdictions use the standardized CPAT test to evaluate potential recruit firefighters. The test simulates a number of firefighter skills and assesses the recruit's ability to perform them.

Annual Assessments Categories

Muscular Strength

Aerobic Capacity

Flexibility

Body Composition

Muscular Endurance

Figure 7.11 NFPA® 1583 requires certain fitness categories be part of annual physical fitness assessments for firefighters.

Monitoring Changes in Personnel Performance

Confidential personnel performance is typically monitored with the comprehensive medical and fitness evaluations and an annual physical ability test. A baseline evaluation should be obtained at the time of hire. During a career, three important levels of assessment can catch a decline in performance before it becomes an issue **(Figure 7.12)**:

- **Level I: Organizational/Annual assessments** — the HSO, the health and fitness coordinator, and the fire department physician must work together in monitoring personnel performance and the overall health of members.

- **Level II: Individual/self-care** — individuals play a significant part in their own health and wellness condition. The goal is for fire and emergency services members to effectively perform their jobs, but also to retire healthy after a full career.

- **Level III: Supervisory** — a firefighter's performance should be constantly under review by immediate and secondary supervisory officers with the expectation that the performance will meet or exceed standards. Any observed failure to perform can then be evaluated to determine the cause for failure to perform.

Should any level of assessment reveal that there is a possible physical, emotional, or psychological problem relative to performance, a mandatory fitness-for-duty evaluation can be requested in addition to annual evaluations. The procedures for requiring a fitness-for-duty evaluation must clearly indicate that the decision is based on observed and documented observation of the firefighter's inability to perform the assigned duties. Drug and alcohol screenings also fit into the category of fitness for duty. Member assistance programs can provide assistance in getting members back to a fit-for-duty status.

What This Means to You

Requesting a mandatory fit-for-duty evaluation for a fellow firefighter can be a difficult decision, especially when the decision calls into question a psychological problem. Imagine that you are the HSO of a small, full-time department. During a committee meeting, a firefighter who you know well suggested that he had had recent thoughts of suicide. Many other firefighters at the meeting became uncomfortable enough to report to you about the individual who was struggling with these thoughts. The question for you as the HSO is what to do.

This situation occurred just as described in a real department. The HSO in the real-world case made the difficult decision to notify the department's human resources director and the department chief. The HSO interviewed the firefighters who had been at the committee meeting. He kept all of these notifications and interviews confidential. There was no clear indication from the interviews that the firefighter was in danger of suicide, but the HSO also knew this firefighter personally and knew through private conversations that the concerns were likely true.

The decision was made to remove this firefighter from duty for a psychological fitness-for-duty evaluation. The firefighter attended mandated professional counseling for a few weeks and then returned to work authorized as fit-for-duty by his counselor. A few months later, the firefighter left the fire service after 10 years on the job.

Other members of the department felt that the HSO had forced the troubled firefighter to leave the profession, but the HSO knew differently. The firefighter who had been struggling with suicidal thoughts confided in the HSO after leaving the profession. He thanked his friend and senior officer for what he had done, saying, "Had you not intervened, I certainly would have gone through with it." Sometimes the hard decisions are the right ones, and though others may not understand them, they can have a profound impact on the lives of firefighters.

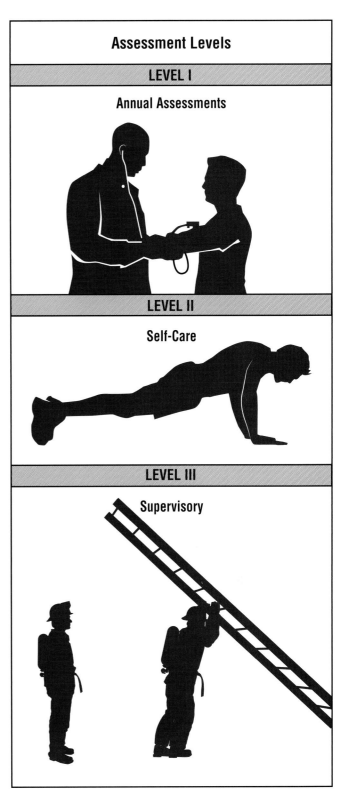

Figure 7.12 Three entities or individuals are responsible for assessing a firefighter's physical fitness: the organization, the firefighter's immediate supervisor, and the firefighter him or herself.

Health Maintenance Programs

The employee health program is intended to improve the health of the individual firefighter or emergency responder. Individual health improvement is accomplished through wellness education, medical surveillance, physical fitness training, member assistance, and professional counselling when appropriate. A holistic approach is proactive, attempting to address potentially injurious situations before they occur.

The overall health of fire and emergency services members is critical to the mission they serve. Ill or injured members cannot function in their assigned role. Members may be at significant additional risk if the illness or injury occurs during an emergency scene operation. This situation potentially places the members' coworkers at risk as they care for and/or rescue a downed crewmember. Preventing illnesses, injuries, fatalities, and exposures is the goal of the health maintenance program.

The HSO needs to consider the physical and psychological health, wellness, and fitness levels of fire and emergency service members through an integration of programs and resources. The key responsibilities for the HSO in the overall health maintenance program is to analyze the data, coordinate the logistics, and serve as a liaison in the management of the program.

Medical Surveillance Program — Series of medical evaluations based upon medical fitness-for-duty requirements for firefighters which begin when the firefighter is hired and continue on a regular basis throughout the firefighter's career.

Medical Surveillance Program

The **medical surveillance program** is the first component of the health maintenance program. The medical surveillance program begins with an initial medical evaluation during the hiring process and continues throughout a member's career. In addition, a long-term medical surveillance program provides the resources and detailed personal medical information to combat possible cardiac events. The HSO should consult with the department physician in determining specific medical evaluation tests based on the age, gender, and job task analysis of the member(s).

When developing and implementing a medical surveillance program, the fire and emergency services organization should follow the legal mandates and standard guidelines outlined in the following:

- OSHA 29 CFR 1910.120, *Hazardous Waste Operations and Emergency Response*
- OSHA 29 CFR 1910.134, *Respiratory Protection*
- NFPA® 1500, *Standard on Fire Department Occupational Safety and Health Program*
- NFPA® 1582, *Standard on Comprehensive Occupational Medical Program for Fire Departments*
- NFPA® 1583, *Standard on Health-Related Fitness Programs for Fire Fighters*

Medical surveillance can also include rehabilitation at emergency incidents and training exercises in accordance with NFPA® 1584, *Standard on the Rehabilitation Process for Members During Emergency Operations and Training Exercises*. All members functioning on these events should be evaluated per local SOP/Gs prior to being released back to duty **(Figure 7.13)**. The HSO should work with the department physician in determining vital sign criteria, length

Figure 7.13 Firefighters should receive medical evaluations during rehab before being allowed to return to duty at an emergency scene.

of rest periods, and thermal regulation measures. Having the fire department physician directly or indirectly involved in incident rehabilitation promotes a more complete medical evaluation process and can be the key to preventing premature cardiac death of members.

Physical Fitness Program

The physical fitness program is designed to help members maintain a qualified status. **Physical performance requirements** of a fitness program are based on accepted industry best practices. According to NFPA® 1500, personnel who engage in emergency operations must be annually qualified with a physical performance assessment that is approved by the department. *The Fire Service Joint Labor Management Wellness-Fitness Initiative*, from the IAFF and IAFC, states that an exercise program is individualized to the member and considers the current fitness level, job duties, and self-improvement goals (**Figure 7.14, p. 245**).

Each fire and emergency services organization must determine the physical performance requirements of its members. The HSO should work closely with the fire department physician and the health and fitness coordinator in the development and implementation of these requirements.

Job Task Analysis for Physical Fitness

Preparing the task analysis and developing the employee physical fitness component is the responsibility of the HSO, the occupational safety and health

Physical Performance Requirements — Fitness level benchmarks based upon recommended industry standards which firefighters must meet to be considered fit-for-duty.

committee, or a physical fitness subcommittee. Members of the subcommittee could include the following:

- The HSO
- Members of the organization's administration
- Representatives of the member organization
- Emergency response personnel
- The organization's physician
- A qualified/certified exercise physiologist

NOTE: The exercise physiologist provides the professional knowledge necessary to analyze the tasks in terms of physical exertion and can recommend the appropriate test criteria.

If the subcommittee is given the development responsibility, the first step is for committee members to perform the task analysis and develop a list of the basic services that the organization provides. These services may include but are not limited to the following:

- Structural fire fighting operations
- Wildland fire fighting operations
- Emergency medical services
- Light and heavy rescue operations
- Hazardous materials responses
- Training functions
- Building inspections and surveys

Next, committee members determine the types of tools and equipment that each service activity requires. The tasks must be performed while wearing the appropriate protective clothing, equipment, and respiratory protection. These physical tasks may include the following:

- Lifting an inert weight, such as an unconscious victim (**Figure 7.15**)
- Pulling a hoseline, both charged and uncharged (empty)
- Operating a hoseline and nozzle
- Climbing a ladder
- Climbing a flight of stairs in full protective clothing with SCBA
- Entering and operating in a confined space with hand tools (**Figure 7.16**)
- Pulling a ceiling with a pike pole

Once the list of tasks is complete, it can be categorized into general groups of similar activities, such as lifting, pulling, and climbing. A suitable physical fitness plan can be devised to meet the needs of each task. The physical fitness plan is not only used to improve the physical abilities and stamina of the current members but also provide preemployment testing criteria for candidates/applicants for the organization.

Physical Fitness Plan

NFPA® 1500 requires the fire and emergency services organization to establish and provide a **physical fitness plan** that meets the requirements of NFPA® 1583. This plan is designed to enable members to develop and maintain an

Physical Fitness Plan — Individualized or department-wide plan that firefighters can follow to maintain fitness-for-duty and improve their overall health and well-being.

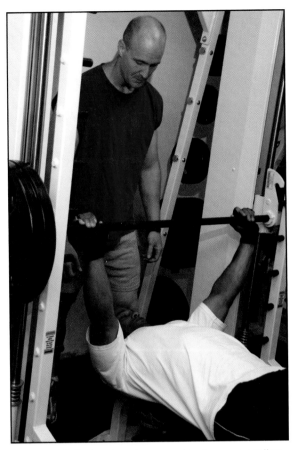

Figure 7.14 Professional personal trainers can tailor exercise programs to meet a firefighter's individual deficiencies based upon fitness-for-duty evaluations.

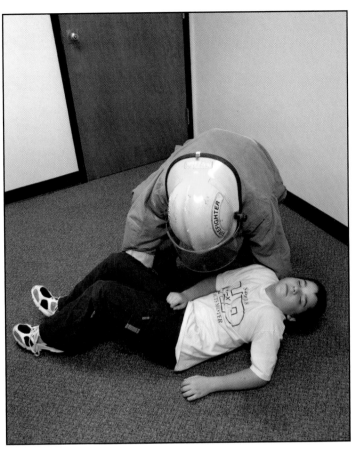

Figure 7.15 Lifting a nonresponsive victim has certain fitness requirements that a firefighter must meet in order to complete the task.

Figure 7.16 Entering a confined space to perform rescue operations is a unique skill set with unique fitness requirements.

appropriate level of fitness to safely perform their assigned functions. The maintenance of fitness levels shall be based on fitness standards determined by the organization's physician and may include a collaborative agreement between labor and management. These levels must reflect the member's assigned functions and activities and the severity of occupational injuries and illnesses associated with these activities. Results are compiled in a personnel file for each employee and maintained for analysis purposes.

Sprains and Strains[1]

In 2013, NFPA® reported that sprains, strains, and muscular pains accounted for 55 percent of all firefighter injuries during operations and nearly 60 percent of nonfireground injuries. Although these injuries are not career-ending or life-threatening, they do represent the injuries that take firefighters away from duties more frequently than all others.

Physical Rehabilitation Program — Physical fitness training program designed for firefighters who do not meet or no longer meet the physical performance requirements associated with their job functions.

All members should be required to participate in the physical fitness plan. They should be evaluated annually and certified to perform their assigned duties in emergency operations. Members who cannot meet the physical performance requirements should be required to participate in a **physical rehabilitation program** to assist them in meeting their designated levels. The HSO, physician, or physical fitness officer shall devise a set of exercises and schedules to assist employees in meeting their goals **(Table 7.2)**.

A physical fitness plan is positive, rehabilitating, and educational – it is *not* punitive. The goal of physical fitness is to improve the quality of life for all emergency service personnel and help them live a long, healthy life. Good physical fitness also improves the quality of services provided to the community and professional image of the organization. Adhering to a complete physical fitness plan helps to reduce the potential for fatigue, heart disease, stroke, shortness of breath, and stress.

Physical Performance Assessment — Series of exercises that are performed and evaluated before beginning a physical fitness plan in order to individualize the plan and establish a baseline for evaluating progress.

Before exercise can begin, a **physical performance assessment** (series of exercises) must be made of each individual's level of fitness to determine the correct exercise plan to meet the individual's needs **(Figure 7.17, p. 248)**. It also allows the officer or coordinator to establish a baseline for evaluating progress, set a realistic range of expectations or goals, and help the participant remain motivated. The individual's performance is scored and compared to a predetermined scale. Once the assessment is complete, a physical fitness plan can be developed for each individual based on age, need, and gender. The program coordinator will implement specific exercises using appropriate equipment to improve the individual's deficiencies.

Purchasing workout station equipment and placing it in a workout room in your station does not make a wellness program complete. There must be analysis, training, and follow-up components in any well-structured program.

Wellness Program

Wellness Program — Ongoing program that provides information, education, and counselling to fire service members on topics such as good nutrition, tobacco cessation, injury prevention, and substance abuse.

A comprehensive **wellness program** should address nutrition, health/fitness instruction, tobacco use and policies, and injury and illness prevention and rehabilitation. Promoting wellness means educating staff members about the

Table 7.2
Exercise Plan Comparison

Exercise Plans	Desired Result	Exercise Type
Flexibility	Improved mobility and range of motion in back and legs	• Posterior Thigh • Calf Stretch • Anterior Thigh • Inner Thigh • Iliotibial Band and Lateral Thigh • Soleus
Cardiovascular fitness	Strengthened heart muscles	• Weight-bearing exercises: — running — stair climbing — rope jumping • Non-weight-bearing exercises: — bicycling — rowing — swimming
Muscular fitness	Increased strength and endurance	• Weight training: — bar bells — leg presses — bench presses — dead lifts • Endurance training: — push-ups — dips — curls — squats — sit-ups — pull-ups
Body composition	Weight loss and reduction in body fat or mass	• Jogging • Swimming • Dancing • Cycling • Brisk walking • Aerobics

cause and effect of lifestyle choices on the body. With a thorough wellness program, members will have an opportunity to see the benefits of making the changes in their lifestyles.

Nutrition Information

Recent studies have linked poor diet to heart disease, cancer, diabetes, high blood pressure, high cholesterol, and other chronic diseases. It is estimated that two-thirds of the U.S. population is overweight and one-third of those are considered obese. As part of the employee wellness and fitness program, the HSO can provide members with training regarding the importance of good nutrition such as:

- Negative effects of certain foods **(Figure 7.18, p. 248)**

- Guidelines for a balanced diet

- Results of good nutrition

Figure 7.17 Exercise plans should be based upon firefighter skills. A skills assessment can be used to identify a firefighter's weaknesses in order to develop his or her exercise plan.

Figure 7.18 Firefighters should monitor their diets and be aware of the contents of the foods that they eat. All foods should be eaten in moderation, especially those foods with potentially adverse health effects.

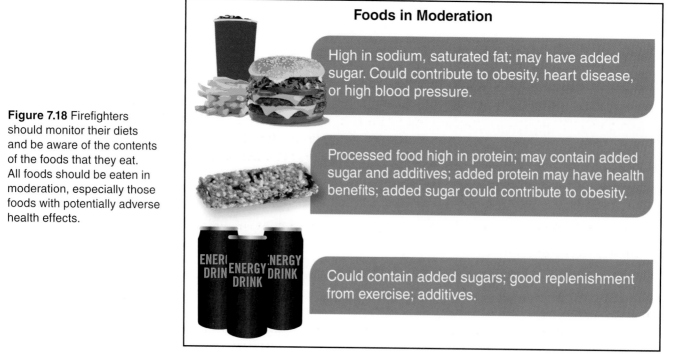

Foods in Moderation

High in sodium, saturated fat; may have added sugar. Could contribute to obesity, heart disease, or high blood pressure.

Processed food high in protein; may contain added sugar and additives; added protein may have health benefits; added sugar could contribute to obesity.

Could contain added sugars; good replenishment from exercise; additives.

- Recommended daily meal plans

- Safe and effective weight-control

An effective educational plan on nutrition can have the added bonus of altering the off-duty lifestyles of employees and their families. Information on nutritional issues can be obtained from the Centers for Disease Control, state/territorial/provincial or local health department, or the American Heart Association.

Obstructive Sleep Apnea (OSA)[2]

Shift workers, such as firefighters, are at a higher risk for Obstructive Sleep Apnea (OSA). OSA is an obstruction of an individual's airways during sleep. The body cannot provide sufficient oxygen to the brain, so the individual awakens frequently during sleep, which, in turn, interrupts the natural sleep cycle. Those individuals who suffer from OSA exhibit chronic daytime fatigue and lowered alertness. OSA is also connected to heart disease, hypertension, and diabetes.

Obesity is generally the cause of OSA. To complicate matters, studies show that healthy adults who get less than 7 hours of sleep per night have a higher risk of weight gain. As a result, those individuals who suffer from OSA and are not getting sufficient sleep will also find it more difficult to lose the weight needed to correct OSA. In addition, firefighters who do not practice good sleep habits increase their likelihood of weight gain, and as a result, the likelihood of developing OSA later in life.

Firefighters need to be vigilant about getting enough sleep (6 to 10 hours per 24 hours) as well as maintaining a healthy diet to avoid developing sleep apnea. HSOs should include information and training in the health and wellness program about good sleep and nutritional habits that help prevent OSA.

Health Fitness Instructor Training Program

NFPA® 1583 states that a fire and emergency services organization should have a **health and fitness coordinator (HFC)**. This person may be a member of the department or from an outside entity. This HFC must be qualified and meet the minimum requirements of NFPA® 1583. In addition, the HFC's responsibilities listed in NFPA® 1583 include but are not limited to the following:

- Coordinate with and provide guidance for the peer fitness trainers

- Serve as a liaison with the HSO and the department physician

- Supervise the fitness assessments and exercise program of the department

- Promote health education

Peer fitness trainers are an added element to the fitness program. Peer fitness trainers provide confidential one-on-one fitness assessments and individualized fitness programs **(Figure 7.19, p. 250)**. The IAFF, IAFC, and American Council on Exercise have developed a peer fitness training program as part of the *Fire Service Joint Labor Management Wellness-Fitness Initiative*. The HSO should ensure all recognized peer fitness trainers obtain this certification and recertify at the required two-year intervals.

Health and Fitness Coordinator (HFC) — Individual who, under the supervision of the fire department physician, is responsible for all physical fitness programs in the fire and emergency services organization.

Peer Fitness Trainer — Firefighter-certified fitness trainers who oversee fitness programs for firefighters as directed by the Health and Fitness Coordinator (HFC).

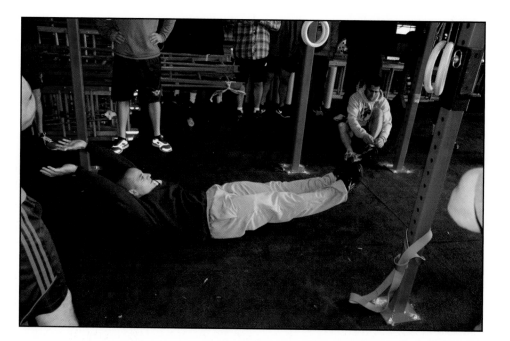

Figure 7.19 Peer fitness trainers are other firefighters who can either work one-on-one with their peers or lead fitness training classes.

NOTE: Some information in this section comes from the American Council on Exercise (ACE) from its website.

Tobacco Policy and Cessation Information

In order to create a healthy and smoke-free workplace, the fire department can approach the tobacco use and smoking problem from two directions. First, mandating that candidates be tobacco-free can be justified through existing documentation on the effects of tobacco use. Candidates can be required to remain tobacco-free during their employment. Many departments are implementing this preemployment criteria. Second, the department can provide tobacco and smoking-cessation training for current members. These programs can be part of the training cycle for all members or specific cessation classes for individuals. The basis is an education program that points out the hazards of smoking, the reasons for quitting, and the methods available for quitting **(Figure 7.20)**.

Based on the national mortality rate due to smoking, the United States fire service loses approximately 1,800 members per year. Firefighters are already at risk because they are exposed to the unburned products of combustion. According to the American Lung Association, smoking increases these hazards. Studies indicate that firefighters who smoke have a higher level of risk for heart and lung diseases than firefighters who do not smoke. Smoking also results in lowered lung capacity and shortness of breath. These results can impair the stamina of firefighters during emergency operations, such as wildland or high-rise incidents.

Injury and Illness Prevention

The prevention of injury and illness is a mainstay of the safety and health program. There must be written policies and procedures outlining safe work practices in all areas and facilities of the organization. For example, one of the wellness aspects of the operational setting is the requirement of decontamination of both equipment and skin at emergency incidents **(Figure 7.21)**. These

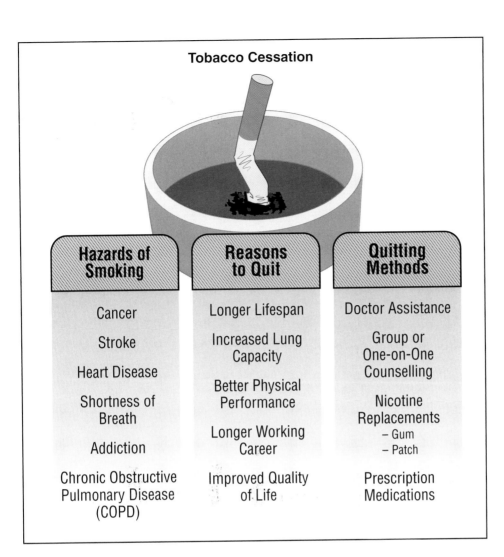

Tobacco Cessation

Hazards of Smoking	Reasons to Quit	Quitting Methods
Cancer	Longer Lifespan	Doctor Assistance
Stroke	Increased Lung Capacity	Group or One-on-One Counselling
Heart Disease	Better Physical Performance	Nicotine Replacements – Gum – Patch
Shortness of Breath	Longer Working Career	
Addiction	Improved Quality of Life	Prescription Medications
Chronic Obstructive Pulmonary Disease (COPD)		

Figure 7.20 A firefighter's lung capacity is crucial to his or her job performance. Smoking decreases lung capacity; therefore, firefighters should use whatever methods work for them to cease using tobacco.

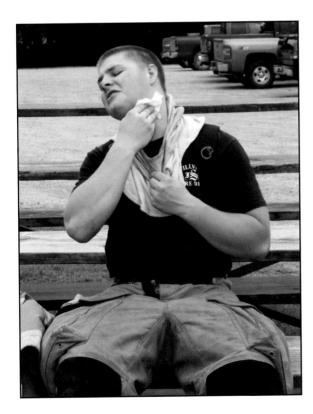

Figure 7.21 Using cleaning cloths to remove soot and smoke residue from skin immediately following emergency operations is a preventative measure against contracting cancer later in life.

procedures in combination with the cleaning and/or removal from service of contaminated protective clothing and equipment may reduce the risks of long-term illnesses, such as cancer.

The injury and illness prevention program should include research on local, state, and national statistics. The HSO should examine the root cause analysis, especially with significant occurrences, and identify the sequence of events that led to an injury or illness. The HSO should also evaluate safety audit reports, near-miss reports, and general safety practices of the department with a specific focus on preventing injuries and illnesses. This information can lead to training and education on preventive measures. HSOs are encouraged to remain up-to-date on the latest research on operational tactics so that they

Monetary Cost of Firefighter Injuries and Fatalities

Results vary wildly when trying to estimate the financial damage that fire injuries and fatalities cause. However, the financial hardship is significant. During the development of this manual, NFPA®'s most recently published research[3] collected data on the cost of fire through 2009. The data estimates that all civilian and firefighter deaths and injuries due to fire cost $31.7 billion in the United States just in 2011. NIST studies from 2004 estimated the cost of firefighter injuries alone at between $2.8 billion and $7.8 billion annually[4]. According to the USFA analysis of reports to NFIRS, 42 percent of all fire fighting injuries resulted in lost time (time away from active duty) for injured firefighters[5].

Costs associated with staffing, to fill in for the injured member(s), are the first costs incurred, followed by hospitalization and medical care payouts associated with these injuries. These studies, however, include analysis of hidden costs related to firefighter injuries and fatalities that include but are not limited to the following:

- Insurance claims
- Litigation expenses and legal fees
- Maintaining and replacing protective clothing and equipment
- Enhancement to prevention programs
- Investigation expenses
- Lost firefighter income
- Additional pay to replacement personnel (overtime)
- Necessary increases to funding to prevent repeat incidents
- Increases to training program costs
- Hiring, training, and other related costs

We cannot overestimate the hidden costs associated with injuries and fatalities, such as the difficulty in volunteer member retention and recruiting after an injury. In addition, officers/commanders may be less willing to take tactical stances that place firefighters at risk, resulting in higher property loss. Although safety officers should advocate for safety to reduce the personal hardship on firefighters and their families, safety officers should also be aware of the hardship to their organizations. Being a safety advocate is also beneficial to the long-term financial health of an organization as well as the long-term physical health of its membership.

are best informed to identify safety deficiencies during investigations and postincident analyses. See Chapter 9, Accident Investigation and Postincident Analysis, for more information.

Injury and Illness Rehabilitation

Data shows that injuries and illness can occur in emergency and nonemergency situations. In emergency situations, the potential for illness and injury does not end with the completion of the operation. Members can develop symptoms of heat exhaustion, fatigue, stress, smoke inhalation, or other illnesses immediately following an emergency or upon returning to quarters. In a nonemergency situation, injury and illness can occur in a fire department facility or while on a fire department apparatus.

Rehabilitation usually refers to specific operational functions at emergency incidents meant to return members to service. However, it also refers to the postincident assessment, treatment, care, and ongoing evaluation of members when the injury or illness requires physician-level care.

The fire and emergency services organization should establish a written policy and procedure for the rehabilitation process for members who have been injured or become ill. The fire department physician should work closely with the member to ensure a personalized rehabilitation program guides the member back to a full recovery and a return to duty.

Member Assistance Program (MAP)

Stress encountered by fire and emergency personnel can result in dependence on tobacco products, abuse of alcohol or drugs, domestic violence, depression, suicidal tendencies, or post-traumatic stress. In recognition of this fact, NFPA® 1500 mandates the establishment of a **member assistance program (MAP)** within the fire and emergency services organization. A MAP is essential to personnel health and wellness. Because it is difficult for the organization to provide the professional counseling services to meet these needs and ensure complete confidentiality, a member assistance program often includes outside contract counselors to provide the services. The HSO is responsible for ensuring prevention, education, and availability of program counselors. All officers must also be aware of the symptoms of alcoholism, drug abuse, and other types of abuse in order to provide direction and care as soon as possible.

Member Assistance Program (MAP) — Program to help employees and their families with work or personal problems.

Studies indicate the vast majority of those individuals who receive counseling return to full productive status within the workforce. Member assistance programs can also reduce the cost of prolonged medical care and lost-time benefits. In addition to fire and emergency service members, NFPA® 1500 requires assistance to immediate family members through the program. Finally, the use of member assistance programs can result in improved employee morale. Peer assistance may be useful to some firefighters and a supplement to the MAP, but it is not a replacement for professional counseling services.

Substance Abuse Assistance

While smoking can have a negative effect on the health of the individual firefighter, drug and alcohol abuse can have an even more widespread effect. Because drugs and alcohol impair judgment and slow reaction times, their impacts are not only on individuals but also on those around them, both uniformed and civilian. The United States Fire Administration (USFA) estimates that as many as 10 percent of the 1.1 million firefighters in the United States may be abusing drugs. To offset the potential danger of this type of abuse, the fire department must establish a written policy within the MAP. The HSO's duties in this area would involve the following:

- Developing and presenting education programs on alcohol and drug abuse
- Assisting the administration in developing a drug and alcohol policy
- Directing members to the MAP when necessary
- Ensuring a liaison between the MAP and the administration

NOTE: In states, provinces, or countries where marijuana is legal, testing for substance abuse may more frequently include marijuana testing.

Family Assistance

The MAP outlined in department policy should have the ability to provide a wide range of counseling services for both employees and their families. In addition to smoking-cessation and substance-abuse assistance, counseling services for domestic violence, child abuse, family issues, and financial management should be available. Success of the program depends on the quality of the services offered, the administration's support, the members' involvement, and the confidentiality of all services. The HSO should work to ensure that all of these elements are achieved.

Occupational Exposure to Atypically Stressful Events

Stress has always been a part of the emergency responder's life due to the high level of uncertainty, limited control over the work environment, and the psychological effect of repeated emergency calls **(Table 7.3)**. Add major events that exceed the normal level of stress and the ability of the body to cope, and critical stress develops. For this reason, a program to assist members with atypically stressful events should be developed and made available. According to NFPA® 1500, Chapter 12, recent research has challenged the benefit of what has been called Critical Incident Stress Management (CISM) or Critical Incident Stress Debriefing (CISD). In response to this research, NFPA® 1500 has placed the emphasis on members utilizing professional services from "licensed and certified specialists [who may] include psychiatrists, psychologist, and clinical social workers." The current edition of the standard also excludes the terms CISD and CISM from the whole of the document.

NFPA® 1500 defines atypically stressful events as:

- Mass casualty incidents
- Firefighter line-of-duty fatality
- Any other circumstance that falls outside the ordinary experience of its members

Accident Prevention Program

The HSO is ultimately responsible for the development, review, and supervision of the accident prevention program but may delegate this task. As part of this responsibility, the HSO is required to periodically review research, operations, procedures, equipment, and facilities, and recommend any changes in work practices and procedures to the authority having jurisdiction. The accident

Table 7.3
Warning Signs and Symptoms of Stress

Cognitive Symptoms
- Memory problems
- Inability to concentrate
- Poor judgment
- Dwelling on the negative
- Anxious thoughts
- Constant worrying

Physical Symptoms
- Diarrhea or constipation
- Nausea, dizziness
- Loss of sex drive
- Frequent colds
- Pain in the chest, shoulders, neck, or low back
- Stomach/abdominal pain
- Muscle tension, spasms, or nervous tics
- Unexplained rashes or skin irritations
- Sweaty palms
- Sweating when not physically active
- 'Butterflies' in stomach
- Indigestion
- Inability to sleep or excessive sleep
- Shortness of breath
- Holding breath
- Loss of energy

Emotional Symptoms
- Moodiness
- Irritability or short temper
- Agitation, inability to relax
- Feeling overwhelmed
- Feeling lonely and isolated
- Depression or general unhappiness

Behavioral Symptoms
- Eating more when you are not hungry
- Sleeping too much or too little
- Isolating yourself from others
- Procrastinating or neglecting responsibilities
- Using alcohol, cigarettes, or drugs to relax
- Nervous habits (nail biting, pacing)
- Feeling frustrated at having to wait for something
- Feeling restless
- Being easily confused
- Negative self-talk
- Feeling you can't cope
- Difficulty making decisions
- Having emotional outbursts
- Generally feeling upset
- Lack of sense of humor

or loss prevention program includes instruction of all personnel in safe work practices both in emergency and nonemergency operations. Fundamental to this program is an effective fire department driver/operator training and testing policy that covers both apparatus and staff vehicle operators.

Engineering Controls

According to the National Institute for Occupational Safety and Health (NIOSH), **engineering controls**:

> ... are used to remove a hazard or place a barrier between the worker and the hazard. Well-designed engineering controls can be highly effective in protecting workers and will typically be independent of worker interactions to provide this high level of protection. The initial cost of engineering controls can be higher than the cost of administrative controls or personal protective equipment, but over the longer term, operating costs are frequently lower, and in some instances, can provide a cost savings in other areas of the process.

Engineering Controls — Barrier to a hazard that is built into the design of a building, apparatus or piece of equipment, for example, fire doors, smoke evacuation systems, or sprinkler systems.

OSHA has a similar definition of engineering controls:

Engineering controls [control the hazard at its source], unlike other controls that generally focus on the employee exposed to the hazard. The basic concept behind engineering controls is that, to the extent feasible, the work environment and the job itself should be designed to eliminate hazards or reduce exposure to hazards.

Engineering controls can be simple in some cases. The OSHA engineering controls are based on the following principles:

- *If feasible, design the facility, equipment, or process to remove the hazard or substitute something that is not hazardous.*

- *If removal is not feasible, enclose the hazard to prevent exposure in normal operations.*

- *Where complete enclosure is not feasible, establish barriers or local ventilation to reduce exposure to the hazard in normal operations.*

Protective Clothing and Equipment Policies

The availability and use of protective clothing and equipment must be addressed in the department SOP/Gs. The HSO should evaluate the protective clothing and equipment and ensure that they meet the needs of the operational setting. This evaluation will include the limitations of the clothing and equipment, inspection, care and maintenance, cleaning and disinfecting, and replacement procedures. The HSO should also assess the use of the clothing and equipment to ensure personnel are properly following safety practices. The department SOP/Gs should include the type of protective clothing and equipment that should be worn or used in certain situations. The level of protection should meet or exceed the potential level of exposure.

Crew Resource Management (CRM)

A blue-ribbon committee of the International Association of Fire Chiefs studied a safety system that several industries and the U.S. military have adopted. The committee concluded that if the fire service adopted the system, the number of firefighter injuries and fatalities could be reduced. This comprehensive program is called *Crew Resource Management (CRM)*. The CRM program provides better teamwork, improved communication and problem solving, promotes team member input while preserving legal authority, and provides for proactive accident prevention. While there are many facets to the program, in general, it addresses leadership and followership.

Those officials in leadership positions are obligated to acquire and develop four critical leadership skills: authority, mentoring, conflict resolution, and mission analysis.

- **Authority** — involves the leader ensuring mission safety, fostering an environment of respectful communication, establishing tasks with clearly defined goals, and considering crew input.

- **Mentoring** — involves the leader demonstrating skills and techniques, demonstrating professional standards and best practices, verbalizing errors and limitations promptly, recommending solutions, monitoring and assessing crew performance, and motivating crew members.

- **Conflict resolution** — involves the leader identifying core conflict issues, encouraging diplomatic questioning of the actions/decisions of others, acknowledging differences of opinion.

- **Mission analysis** — involves the leader evaluating risk versus gain, identifying objectives, developing strategies and tactics to meet the identified objectives, implementing an action plan, expecting the unexpected, evaluating the effectiveness of the action plan, and devising alternative strategies.

Goal attainment and teamwork require people who can think and follow directions. In this context, followers are not to be viewed in a negative manner. To function safely and effectively, CRM requires team members (followers) to do the following:

- Respect authority.
- Be safe.
- Keep their fellow workers and leaders safe.
- Accept that authority goes with responsibility.
- Know the limits of their own authority.
- Desire to make the leader succeed.
- Possess good communication skills.
- Develop and maintain a positive learning attitude.
- Keep their egos in check.
- Demand clear assignments.
- Establish an assertiveness/authority balance.
- Accept direction and information as needed.
- Publicly acknowledge mistakes.
- Report status of work.
- Be flexible.

A paper describing the CRM program in detail is available from the International Association of Fire Chiefs (IAFC). It is also available through the IAFC website.

Safe Work Practices

Safe work practices are the responsibility of every member of the fire and emergency services organization. Each person has an obligation to monitor safety and work in the safest manner possible for the given circumstances. As the manager of the risk management program, the HSO is responsible for identifying and recommending safe work practices of the organization. This responsibility will involve interviewing or surveying members to identify what is working and what is placing them at risk. In addition, the HSO should observe a variety of work practices to identify potential risk or identify improvements to work practices. Recommendations can be made through the chain of command to modify, change, or eliminate work practices deemed unsatisfactory or unnecessarily risky.

Sleep Deprivation[2]

Individuals need between 6 and 10 hours of sleep per 24-hour period to function optimally. When we get less than 6 hours of sleep, we suffer from acute sleep loss, which can affect performance up until we have a good night's sleep.

More problematic for firefighters is chronic sleep loss. Chronic sleep loss is defined as getting fewer than 6 hours of sleep per day over a series of days. Chronic sleep loss decreases alertness, reaction time, decision-making ability, and motor function. It can also contribute to long-term depression and may be a contributing factor to heart disease, obesity, and diabetes. Sleep loss weakens the immune system as well, making individuals more susceptible to infection. Fatigue from chronic sleep loss may increase the risk for motor vehicle accidents, both during response and when returning from duty.

Firefighters are already a higher-risk group for injury and illness. Mismanagement of their sleep cycles can increase these risks. HSOs should ensure that policies based upon research for managing work shifts and sleep patterns while on shift are established. These policies may include establishing set work shifts, providing opportunities for naps while at the station, and recognizing firefighters' personal preferences on shift work (day or night). Consulting with firefighters' families and medical consultants is also recommended.

HSOs should also include training information on healthy sleep habits as part of the health and wellness program. Research shows that individuals with healthy lifestyles manage sleep deprivation better than those who are unhealthy.

Safety Audit — Comprehensive compliance review of all organizational components that could contribute to firefighter safety including policies, procedures, practices, inspection reports, and firefighter behaviors.

Normalization of Deviation — State of a safety culture in which acting against SOP/Gs becomes normal behavior rather than an exception.

Safety Audit Program

A **safety audit** program is a comprehensive evaluation of the fire and emergency service organization in how safety compliance is achieved. The safety audit should peel back the layers of the operational environment and evaluate every contributing organizational component that affects how operations are carried out. This audit will include consideration of policies, practices, and behaviors within the organization that can lead to a safety issue. The frequency of a safety audit will be determined by the authority having jurisdiction.

Normalization of Deviation is a way that safety can become compromised over time **(Figure 7.22)**. When deviating from SOP/Gs becomes the normal behavior rather than an exception, the value of the SOP/Gs becomes marginalized. When those procedures deal with safety, it is likely that the frequency of change means that safe practices are not being followed or constantly being added and removed from procedures. Constant change is as ineffective as a complete lack of change.

Safety Audit Planning

To be effective, safety audits must be well-planned. The sections that follow describe considerations the HSO should follow when preparing for safety audits.

Internal Versus External Audit

A safety audit can be an internal or external review depending on the needs of the organization and the complexity of the safety evaluation. The purpose

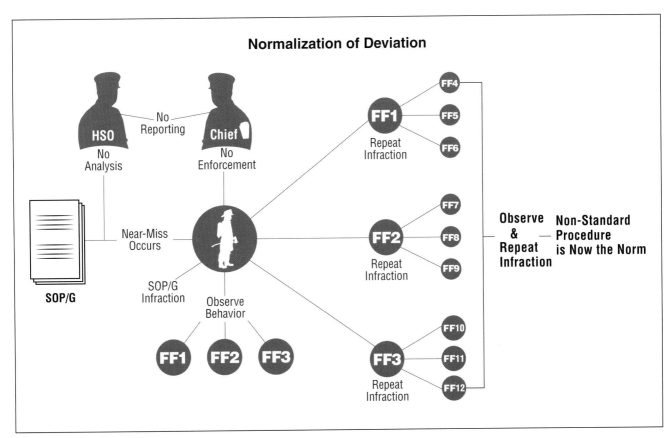

Normalization of Deviation

Figure 7.22 When breaking a rule or ignoring a rule (deviation) becomes common practice rather than an exception, deviation from standard operation procedures has been normalized and the department culture has changed. HSOs should be vigilant to make sure that infractions are investigated and documented and that SOPs are revised if needed.

Swiss Cheese Model of Defenses

In his book *Managing the Risks of Organizational Accidents*, James Reason describes "The Swiss Cheese Model of Defences [sic]", in which an accident occurs if errors go uncorrected and pass through the holes, or windows of opportunity. Reason describes two types of acts that relate to errors, *active failures* and *latent conditions*. Active failures are attributed to people and create immediate negative outcomes. Latent conditions are attributed to the organization and can go unchecked for long periods of time before the window of opportunity leads to an accident. The goal is to devise defenses that prevent the holes from aligning. Applying this theory to the safety audit, the HSO should look for active failures and latent conditions when evaluating the organization. Defensive measures can be recommended based on this theory.

of the audit will help guide this determination and should be clearly stated. Both types of audits have pros and cons that should be identified within an organization.

CAUTION
Personal bias or hidden agendas should be openly discussed and addressed in the planning phase to gain greater confidence and acceptance in the process.

Depth and Focus of the Audit

A safety audit can be defined in several ways, and all can be used at some point in time in an organization. A department should have a statement of purpose for each audit to help guide the depth and focus. An audit can include every aspect of an organization in a comprehensive evaluation of the policies, practices, and behaviors of personnel within the hierarchy structure. An audit can also be focused on one aspect or negative trend identified during an analysis of accidents or near-misses that involve – or potentially involve – injuries, fatalities, illnesses, and/or exposures.

Resources Needed for the Audit

The HSO should seek out available resources when planning an audit. First, the HSO can reach out to other fire and emergency services organizations to elicit safety audit procedures, forms, or general guidance. Second, the National Institute for Occupational Safety and Health (NIOSH) has the *Health Hazard Evaluation* program, which the HSO can request an evaluation of workplace health hazards. This evaluation can be incorporated into a comprehensive or focused audit. Third, the HSO can consult the American Chemical Society Committee on Chemical Safety, *Safety Audit/Inspection Manual* in planning an audit. This manual provides a good detail of what an audit is and should contain.

Finally, an OSHA inspection is not an audit but can lead to an audit or help define specific focal points in the next audit. What is important for the HSO to be knowledgeable of is that any employee or member of the organization can request an OSHA inspection for a serious hazard, but only a management representative can request an OSHA consultation. Federal or state/provincial OSHA regulations on inspections should be known for a specific jurisdiction, as they can vary.

Components of a Safety Audit

A safety audit should include an evaluation of the following components **(Figure 7.23)**:

- SOP/Gs
- Compliance with safety laws, codes, standards, and regulations
- Overall safety culture of the organization
- Record keeping of reports, inspections, and other documents related to the risk management and the occupational safety and health program
- Risk management
- Health maintenance program
- Accident prevention program
- Emergency vehicle safety program
- Infection control program
- Inspection program of facilities, apparatus, equipment, and protective clothing
- Training and education on safety and health topics
- Incident management

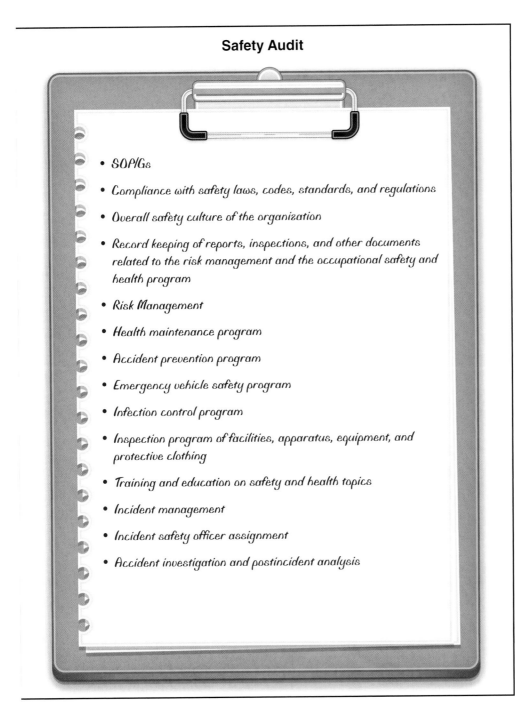

Safety Audit

- SOP/Gs
- Compliance with safety laws, codes, standards, and regulations
- Overall safety culture of the organization
- Record keeping of reports, inspections, and other documents related to the risk management and the occupational safety and health program
- Risk Management
- Health maintenance program
- Accident prevention program
- Emergency vehicle safety program
- Infection control program
- Inspection program of facilities, apparatus, equipment, and protective clothing
- Training and education on safety and health topics
- Incident management
- Incident safety officer assignment
- Accident investigation and postincident analysis

Figure 7.23 Safety audits should be comprehensive and cover all aspects of an organization's safety culture.

- Incident safety officer assignment
- Accident investigation and postincident analysis

Audit Template

A safety audit conducted by a third party will typically have its own template, checklist, and written submission guideline. The final submission report should be in a form that is mutually agreeable to both agencies. **Appendix C** provides an example of a safety audit template.

An internal safety audit template can be customized to the evaluation, but should have some general consistency. Checklists can be used during the process to ensure all required components are addressed, but it should not be the final report. One general template the HSO can follow is from the Center for Public Safety Excellence, Commission on Fire Accreditation International (CFAI), *Fire & Emergency Service Self-Assessment Manual.* Generally speaking, there are four main headings of the template - description, appraisal, plan, and references. This style of report is written in narrative form to describe a program, appraise the performance of a program, plan the future direction of the program, and list any references associated with the program.

Gap Analysis — Comparison between standards/regulations/ best practices and actual behaviors within the organization to determine where real world performance differs from best practice.

A **gap analysis** is another template the HSO can follow. In this approach, the HSO can utilize a standard, regulation, or best practice as a basis for analysis **(Figure 7.24)**. The HSO can then compare the standard, regulation, or best practice to the policies, practices, and behaviors in the organization and see where the gaps are. A gap analysis is also a written narrative report that is similar to the CFAI method. This approach can help modify programs and improve the overall safety in the workplace with immediate corrections and long-term planning.

The final written report should promote an understanding of each program or area of the organization being audited, explain the measurement or performance in an area, and set a historical record and reference for future audits and reports.

NOTE: The HSO should consult other fire and emergency service organizations for templates or general written report guidance. A search of the Internet can be a starting point for identifying publicly available documents.

Conducting the Audit

Conducting a safety audit will take time. It is not as simple as a facility inspection. The HSO will coordinate the audit with those individuals responsible

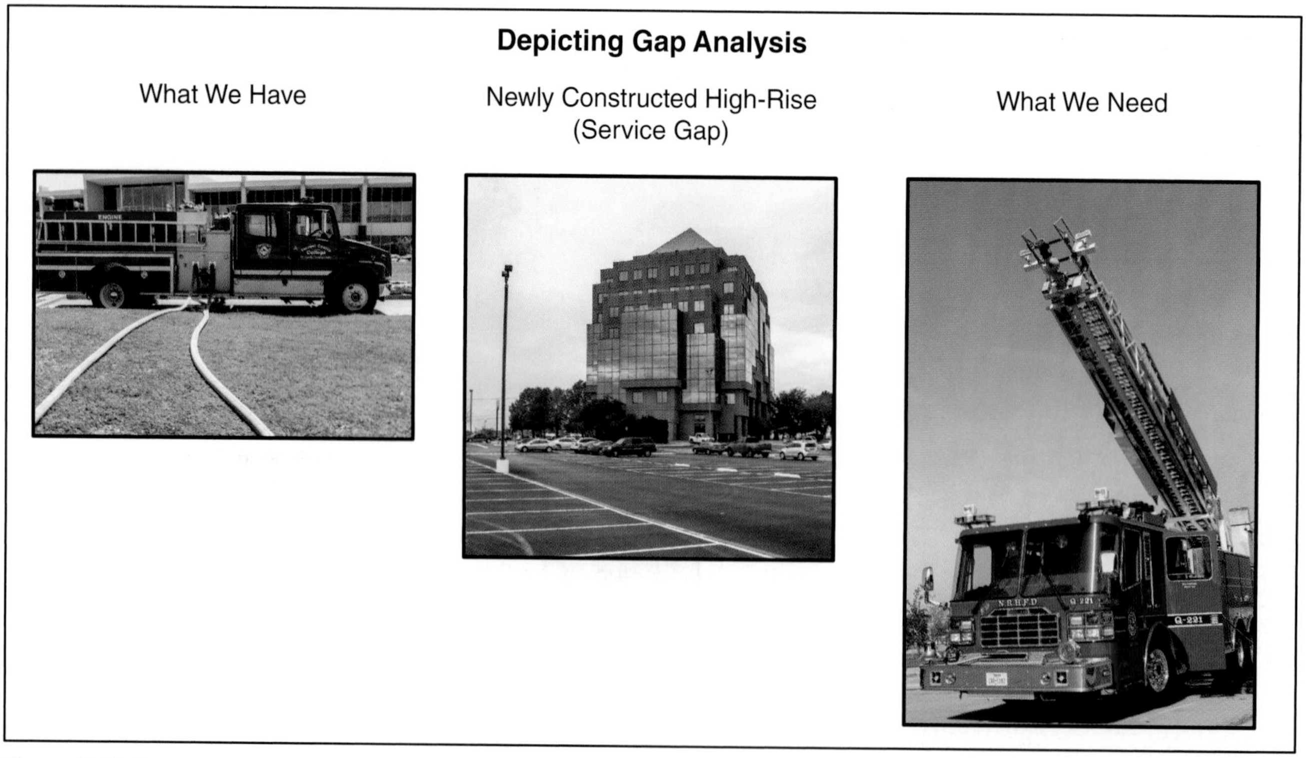
Depicting Gap Analysis
What We Have
Newly Constructed High-Rise
(Service Gap)
What We Need

Figure 7.24 Gap analysis compares what you have to what you need, in this case an aerial apparatus to reach higher floors on a new high-rise.

for its completion, but the following are some general guidelines that can be followed:

- **Review of SOP/Gs** — a safety audit should include a review of the SOP/G to ensure that the manual includes safety and health topics.

- **Review of the accepted practices** — a safety audit should review the accepted practices employed by the fire and emergency services organization. They should meet all applicable codes, standards, regulations, and laws. This review will require technical specialists to assist in those specific areas.

- **Review of personnel performance** — a safety audit should include an evaluation of how personnel are behaving with regards to safety. This evaluation should include observing the daily fire station routine, the emergency and nonemergency apparatus operations, and the handling of a variety of emergency and nonemergency incidents. In addition, interviews and discussions with personnel should be open, honest, and supported by the senior management **(Figure 7.25)**. The final report should outline the general safety behavior culture and not single out individuals.

- **Review of inspections** — a safety audit should take advantage of any inspection of a facility, apparatus, protective clothing, and/or equipment. Inspections should be assessed for frequency and completion compliance.

- **Review of defensive measures** — a safety audit should review the current defensive safety measures and assess their adequacy in preventing an accident.

Identifying Compliance and Violations

The safety audit should identify compliance and violations of any safety regulation, standard, or accepted practice. Safety audits are not to set blame or find fault, but should identify areas where the safety of personnel or the workplace can and should be improved. The culture of safety should be emphasized and the safety audit should be promoted as the opportunity to improve that culture.

Figure 7.25 Interviews informing personnel of evaluation results should be honest and have the support of senior management.

The final written safety audit should be forwarded through the chain of command to the fire chief. Communication of the final written report should be shared with the membership along with any actions that are to be taken.

Infection Control Program

From the perspective of management, nothing has had a greater impact on the fire service and emergency medical services (EMS) than Title 29 CFR 1910.1030 *Bloodborne Pathogens* and NFPA® 1581, *Standard on Fire Department Infection Control Program*. This OSHA regulation and NFPA® standard have changed the delivery of patient care provided by emergency medical service providers. These documents require fire and emergency medical services organizations to perform a risk assessment of their operations from the standpoint of personnel safety and health. This risk assessment covers both emergency and nonemergency duties and operations.

An exposure to a **communicable disease** can occur just as easily during the cleaning and decontamination of equipment at the fire station as it can during the delivery of patient care at the incident scene. A common philosophy that must spread throughout the fire and EMS community is that all patients must be treated with the use of universal precautions. The consequences of an exposure to a variety of communicable diseases can be devastating for the infected members, their families, the fire department, and the governmental jurisdiction. Fire and EMS personnel must place their safety first and foremost in each situation.

The OSHA **bloodborne pathogen** regulation applies to all occupational exposures to blood or other potentially infectious materials. An occupational exposure is defined as reasonably anticipated skin, eye, mucous membrane, or parenteral contact with blood or other potentially infectious materials that may result from the performance of an employee's duties. In order to develop, implement, and manage an effective infection control program, fire service administrative managers and the HSO should understand the regulations that govern infection control. The primary components of this OSHA regulation are as follows:

- Work practices **(Figure 7.26)**

- Development of an exposure control plan for members at risk

- Training and education in infection control

- Engineering controls **(Figure 7.27)**

- Protective clothing and equipment

- Housekeeping practices

- Hepatitis B vaccination

- Postexposure evaluation and follow-up

- Medical record keeping

The key to ensuring compliance with the regulation is the development of the **exposure control program** and the training of members about the process for preventing and controlling infection exposure. The organization should establish the position of infection (exposure) control officer who ensures that an adequate **infection control plan** is developed and that all members

Communicable Disease — Disease that is capable of being transmitted from one person to another.

Bloodborne Pathogens — Pathogenic microorganisms that are present in the human blood and can cause disease in humans. These pathogens include (but are not limited to) hepatitis B virus (HBV) and human immunodeficiency virus (HIV).

Exposure Control Program — Organizational program that provides resources, training, and equipment to firefighters in order to protect them from exposure to chemical and biological hazards in the workplace including hazardous materials, infectious diseases, and bloodborne pathogens.

Infection Control Plan — Policies and procedures managed as part of an exposure control program to protect members from contracting infections in the workplace; includes training on the plan and supervision of the plan.

Figure 7.26 OSHA regulations require reminders of safe work practices, such as hand washing, be a part of infection control and bloodborne pathogen protocols.

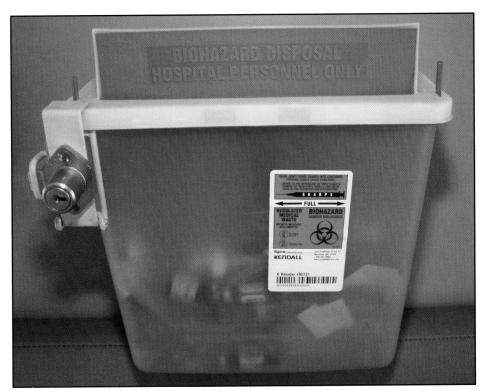

Figure 7.27 Sharps containers are an example of engineering controls. The container itself is designed to prevent contact with possibly contaminated medical equipment.

are trained and supervised in the plan. The HSO or another officer who has the knowledge, training, and skills to fulfill the required duties may fill this position in accordance with NFPA® 1581.

A written plan provides the necessary guidelines to ensure compliance and to ensure that personnel understand the infection control process. A successful program depends upon thorough training and education program and enforcement from command personnel. The written plan should provide information about each of the following:

- Potential exposure hazards
- Appropriate levels of protection to be worn or used
- Methods for caring for an exposure victim
- Procedures for reporting an exposure incident

Training shall occur when an individual is hired and then annually thereafter. Detailed contents for the training are found in Title 29 CFR 1910.1030.

Exposure reports must be maintained in a record-keeping system. Because some symptoms may not become apparent for many years following exposure, these records must be maintained for 30 years following termination of employment. These records are confidential and may only be released to the member or a designated representative. Records are also maintained for training that involves the proper use of protective clothing and equipment, exposure protection, post-exposure protocols, and disease modes of transmission as they relate to infectious diseases.

The Ryan White HIV/AIDS Treatment Extension Act of 2009, Part G – Notification of Possible Exposure to Infectious Diseases has had additional effect on the fire service. The act states that the infection control program should have a notification process from the receiving facility to the organization to the affected member(s). The notifications include the initial evaluation for the member, prophylactic treatment(s) recommended, and any post-exposure follow up requirements.

Infection Control Program Objectives and Components

According to NFPA® 1581, the goal is to identify and limit the exposure of members to infection during the performance of their assigned duties and within the fire department working and living environment. Infection control begins with a written plan that clearly explains its intent, benefits, and purposes. The plan must cover the standards of exposure control such as the following:

- Education and training requirements
- Vaccination requirements
- Documentation and record-keeping requirements
- Cleaning, decontamination, and disinfection of personnel and equipment
- Exposure control and reporting protocols

Infection Control Equipment and Facilities

The fire and emergency services organization must comply with all applicable laws, codes, standards, and regulations regarding infection control. Infection control equipment must be provided to all members and include all needed protective clothing in order to protect all skin surfaces, eyes, nose, mouth, and respiratory system **(Figure 7.28)**. Protective clothing and masks come in presealed kits for quick deployment during an emergency medical incident. These kits can be carried in personal fanny packs worn around the waist or in the apparatus EMS bag. Either way, these kits must be readily available at the patient location on every call; the kit cannot be used if left on the apparatus.

Engineering controls in the Infection Control Program include safety devices that protect a member from coming in contact with a sharp object. For example, intravenous needles have protective sheaths that allow a used needle to lock within its protection after use.

Most EMS equipment is disposable, but items such as backboards, cardiac monitors, oxygen cylinders, and EMS bags must be able to be cleaned and disinfected safely. Fire stations should have designated areas for the disinfecting of nondisposable equipment and clothing. Readily available splash protection, disinfecting solutions, a rinsing area, and drainage system must be provided **(Figure 7.29)**. In addition, if station wear/clothing becomes contaminated, the fire and emergency service organization must provide laundering facilities and/or outside services.

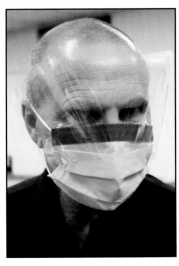

Figure 7.28 Infection control protective clothing should feature face pieces that cover the mouth, eyes, and nose.

Figure 7.29 Fire stations should have designated disinfecting areas that have appropriate cleaning agents, rinsing sinks, and drainage systems.

Infection Control Program Assessment and Revision

As with all other programs, the Infection Control Program needs to be assessed and revised on a regular basis. OSHA 29 CFR 1910.1030, *Bloodborne Pathogens*, uses the term exposure control plan and states that the program must be reviewed annually or as needed to remain up-to-date with the latest tasks and procedures of fire department members, the latest technology changes, and the latest safety devices. Any changes to the infection control program must be communicated to the membership and may require training prior to implementation.

Infection Control Officer Duties

The organization should establish the position of infection (exposure) control officer who ensures that an adequate infection control plan is developed and that all members are trained on the plan and supervised. The HSO or another officer who has the knowledge, training, and skills to fulfill the required duties may fill this position.

NFPA® 1581, Section 4.4, states the infection control officer shall be responsible for maintaining a liaison with the following:

- Fire department physician
- HSO
- Infection control representative at health care facilities
- Health care regulatory agencies

Additional responsibilities of the infection control officer as listed in NFPA® 1581, Section 4.4, include:

- Notification, verification, treatment, and medical follow-up of members after an infectious exposure
- Documentation of the exposure
- Examine compliance procedures and engineer controls to ensure effectiveness
- Shall serve on the occupational safety and health committee
- Shall be knowledgeable and cognizant of issues associated with bioterrorism pathogens and emerging infectious diseases.

Emergency Vehicle Safety Program

Although most people envision fire engines, or pumpers, when they think of fire department apparatus, pumpers make up only a portion of the modern fire department fleet. In addition to pumpers, fire departments may own and operate the following:

- Aerial ladders or elevating platforms
- Wildland fire apparatus
- Tankers/tenders
- Ambulances
- Heavy/medium/light rescue trucks
- Hazardous materials trucks

- Mobile command centers
- Aircraft rescue and fire fighting (ARFF) vehicles
- Marine vessels
- Fuel and supply trucks
- Staff cars
- Trailers
- Battalion/district chief's vehicles
- Incident Command/Command post vehicles

The HSO's responsibility is to ensure that each vehicle meets the needs for which it was purchased and the department's safety standards. The HSO is also responsible for ensuring that personnel are trained in the safe operation and care of the apparatus/vehicles. To assist with the realization of these goals, the safety officer must perform the following activities:

- Review vehicle specifications during the design and purchasing phase in order to make recommendations for safety-related changes.

- Ensure acceptance testing and periodic testing of the apparatus to verify that it meets the applicable standards **(Figure 7.30)**.

- Ensure safe operating practices.

- Investigate all vehicle incidents.

- Recognize and recommend corrections of unsafe practices.

- Provide guidelines for driver/operator training and certification programs.

Even though the trend in fire apparatus design has been toward increased safety, firefighter injuries and fatalities related to vehicle op-

Figure 7.30 Pumper testing is just one example of the periodic tests needed to ensure that all apparatus and equipment are functioning properly.

eration continue to occur. The HSO's duty is to work to prevent these types of injuries and fatalities through apparatus design standards, driver/operator training, and apparatus/vehicle safety policies.

All of the following continue to contribute to apparatus-related firefighter injuries:

- Lack of seat belt use
- Disabling safety warning devices in apparatus
- Backing apparatus without a spotter
- Unsafe apparatus operation under given conditions
- Vehicle modifications not performed or based upon manufacturer recommendations
- Repurposing of vehicles for unintended uses
- Mounting or dismounting the apparatus

Components of a Vehicle Safety Program

A vehicle safety program will include the following components:

- Driver/operator requirements and minimum qualifications that meet NFPA® 1002, *Standard for Fire Apparatus Driver/Operator Professional Qualifications*
- Driver/operator training program that meets NFPA® 1451, *Standard for a Fire Service Vehicle Operations Training Program*
- Vehicle inspections and maintenance that meet NFPA® 1911, *Standard for the Inspection, Maintenance, Testing, and Retirement of In-Service Automotive Fire Apparatus*
- Vehicle refurbishment requirements that meet NFPA® 1912, *Standard for Fire Apparatus Refurbishing*
- Roadway operations and apparatus placement guidelines
- Record-keeping requirements
- General roadway safe-driving practices, including both departmental and personal vehicles

In addition to apparatus response, volunteer firefighters frequently drive their personal vehicles to emergency scenes. As a result, most incidents of driving injuries and fatalities have involved firefighters' privately owned vehicles (POVs) rather than departmental vehicles or apparatus.

When designing a vehicle safety program, the HSO should ensure the most up-to-date laws, codes, standards, and regulations are used. Vehicle safety and highway operations are well-documented in the following resources:

- U.S. DOT, *Manual on Uniform Traffic Control Devices (MUTCD)*
- *Manual of Uniform Traffic Control Devices for Canada (MUTCDC)*
- U.S. DOT, *Traffic Incident Management Handbook (TIMS)*
- USFA FA-336, *Emergency Vehicle Safety Initiative*
- USFA FA-330, *Traffic Incident Management Systems*
- IAFC, *Guide to IAFC Model Policies and Procedures for Emergency Vehicle Safety*

- IAFF, *Best Practices for Emergency Vehicle and Roadway Operations Safety in the Emergency Services*
- National Fire Service Incident Management System Consortium, *Model Procedures Guide for Highway Incidents*
- NFPA® 1091, *Standard for Traffic Control Incident Management Professional Qualifications*

Apparatus Safety Policies

Apparatus safety policies should address all aspects of vehicle operation. Specific reference material will include the manufacturer's operation manual, local and state traffic laws, applicable NFPA® standards, and U.S. Department of Transportation regulations. The SOP/Gs must be clear with compliance and deviation consequences.

Necessary steps must be taken to ensure that fire department or jurisdictional legal representatives and risk manager review all SOP/Gs and policies regarding the operation of fire department vehicles/apparatus. The liability of operating fire department vehicles/apparatus on the roadway in a nonemergency mode is reason enough to prompt assistance. Legal representatives should review and approve SOP/Gs regarding response to incidents, licensing requirements, insurance requirements, use of personal vehicles, and operator certification. This review should include consulting with local and state law enforcement agencies that enforce traffic laws in the jurisdiction in which the department operates.

General Apparatus Safety

NFPA® 1500, Section 6.2.7.1, states: "Procedures for all responses shall emphasize that the safe arrival of fire apparatus to the incident scene is the first priority." Furthermore, NFPA® 1451, *Standard for a Fire and Emergency Service Vehicle Operations Training Program*, Chapter 8, states that while a driver/operator is directly responsible for the safe operation of the apparatus, a ranking officer is responsible for the actions of the driver/operator if an officer is present.

Policies governing the general safety of apparatus should promote a team or crew approach. All crew members riding on an apparatus should be involved in ensuring the safe operation of the apparatus. The HSO should advocate for full support of the Seat Belt Pledge as part of the safety culture of the department. This team approach is a good example of the concept of crew resource management that will be discussed in Chapter 13, Risk Management Principles.

Apparatus Safety Features

The safety features in the design of new fire apparatus continue to improve. Rollover and air bag protection systems are excellent safety features that are now available; however, they are not currently mandated.

NFPA® standards on apparatus design mandate computerized systems that sense when a person is seated and whether the seat belt is being worn. However, these automated safety features are only good when they are operating as designed. Investigations of accidents involving these new safety features have discovered that these systems are sometimes being intentionally deactivated or disabled. The HSO should be cognizant of these safety violations and include specific safety system checks with routine inspections and with the more detailed safety audit.

Apparatus Emissions Safety

Studies on the health hazards of vehicle exhaust have been directly correlated to cancer and cardiac problems. As a result, vehicle exhaust ventilation systems are recommended, and in some jurisdictions mandated, as a part of the facility design **(Figure 7.31)**. In addition, personnel and the HSO should examine vehicle operations for unnecessary exposure to vehicle exhaust (running vehicles in close proximity to open apparatus bay doors). New vehicle designs include exhaust extraction systems that significantly reduce exhaust emissions.

Figure 7.31 Vehicle exhaust systems are designed to keep apparatus bays free of carbon monoxide and other engine exhaust gases when apparatus engines are running in the bay.

Training and Certification

In order to develop an effective vehicle/apparatus safety program, the department has to provide a training program that encompasses driving and operating fire apparatus/vehicles. The National Safety Council's eight-hour defensive driving course is one recommended driver training course. The National Safety Council also offers an educational program specifically designed for fire and EMS driver/operators. The program should include instruction on department SOP/Gs relating to apparatus/vehicle operations (emergency and nonemergency) and response. In addition, the Volunteer Firemen's Insurance Services (VFIS) and many national insurance companies provide excellent driver training programs.

Apparatus equipped with engine, transmission, or driveline retarders require specific operator training. For further information on these systems, reference IFSTA's **Pumping and Aerial Apparatus Driver/Operator Handbook**.

Training on Traffic Laws

All apparatus driver/operators must be trained on the traffic laws of their state/province. In designing a training course, the HSO should communicate with local and state law enforcement agencies and the state/province Department or Division of Motor Vehicles office in his or her jurisdiction to ensure accurate information is provided to driver/operators.

Department policy on emergency vehicle operations must meet or exceed the state/province traffic laws. This training should include but not be limited to the following topics:

- Driver's license requirements
- Speed allowance when all warning devices are activated
- Intersections and stop signs
- Marked school zone
- Stopped school buses with red lights activated
- Railroad crossings
- Overtaking or passing another vehicle
- Right-of-way between emergency vehicles with all warning devices activated
- Highway driving
- Seat belt use

Training on Traffic Preemption Devices

Traffic preemption devices provide safer and more efficient emergency vehicle response at controlled intersections. The most commonly used devices have coded emitters typically affixed on or near the rooftop lightbar **(Figure 7.32, p. 274)**. The emitter sends an infrared signal to a receiver affixed near the traffic signal light – with one receiver for each direction of travel. The receiver then sends a signal to the intersection control box, signaling a request for right-of-way from a specific direction at that intersection. This right-of-way is a temporary change in the traffic signal, allowing the emergency vehicle to pass on a green light.

Traffic Preemption Device — Wireless system (coded emitter or GPS activated) on apparatus that can communicate with traffic signals to request right-of-way at intersections for emergency vehicles.

Figure 7.32 Some apparatus lightbars are equipped with traffic preemption emitters that control intersection traffic signals in order to provide a clear emergency response route for emergency apparatus.

New technology integrates this system with global positioning systems (GPS). The GPS preemption device works in a similar manner as described above. It also adds additional tracking information (vehicle speed and turn signal activation) for improved coordination at multiple intersections along an emergency response route.

Either preemption system – coded emitter or GPS – provides options for control priority between vehicle types and an audit tracking history. Traffic preemption is a jurisdictional system and must be coordinated between agencies that use it. Decisions must be made based upon which agency or vehicle type has priority when multiple vehicles approach the same intersection from different directions at the same time. This coordination typically involves law enforcement, fire department, private ambulance companies, and in some communities mass transit. Some intersection control systems are strictly first-come, first-served.

While the preemption systems provide a safer emergency response, some limitations must be included in a training and education program. First, apparatus-coded emitters have the option of having a screen placed over the front face so others cannot see when the emitter is activated. This screen decreases the distance the emitter can reach, thus reducing its effective range. Apparatus can overdrive the system, getting to the intersection before it has a chance to grant the right-of-way signal. Another issue with having a screen in place is that under normal driving conditions personnel can activate the emitter, thus abusing the system. This constant disruption of traffic creates traffic flow issues and frustration within the community.

Second, while vehicles or agencies can have priority over another vehicle or agency, none has priority over an activated crosswalk signal. Traffic signaling controls have timers. When a crosswalk signal is activated, the timer must continue to run, allowing the pedestrians to clear the intersection before right-of-way is granted to an emergency vehicle. Third, if right-of-way is not granted, there is no indication as to why. Emergency vehicle operators must be cognizant of the fact that not all intersections will grant a right-of-way when requested.

With these limitations, it is imperative that a training and education course includes reasons why right-of-way is not granted. When right-of-way is not granted, emergency vehicles must come to a complete stop at a red light or stop sign and ensure traffic is clear before proceeding. In addition, personnel should be trained on any preemption devices used in neighboring jurisdictions where automatic or mutual aid services are rendered.

Emergency Vehicle Operators Course

Members who are required to drive and operate a variety of fire department vehicles/apparatus must be properly trained in emergency and nonemergency conditions **(Figure 7.33)**. The **Emergency Vehicle Operator's Course (EVOC)** provides the medium for potential driver/operators and current driver/operators to be certified or recertified. Most state fire service training agencies offer this course, which coupled with the National Safety Council's Defensive Driving Course, is a total of 40 hours of education, training, and

Emergency Vehicle Operator's Course (EVOC) — Training that originated with the National Highway Traffic and Safety Administration in the U.S. The training certifies drivers of emergency vehicles; courses may vary depending upon response discipline and jurisdiction.

Figure 7.33 Proper driver/operator training should include driving tests along predetermined routes that include or simulate urban and rural driving conditions.

certification relating to the operation of fire department vehicles/apparatus. The fire department's training program should clearly outline the training, certification, and recertification requirements for the operation of vehicles/apparatus. This training and certification program can be based on NFPA® 1002. Personnel assigned to aircraft rescue and fire fighting apparatus must meet the requirements of NFPA® 1003, *Standard for Airport Fire Fighter Professional Qualifications*.

Automatic Vehicle Location Devices (AVL)

An **Automatic Vehicle Locator (AVL)** uses global positioning system (GPS) to transmit the location of an emergency vehicle to dispatch centers and networking enabled mobile devices (laptops, tablets, smartphones, and GPS devices). All departmental vehicles can be networked together so that members with mobile devices can monitor the movements of other departmental vehicles.

AVL can be used to enhance safety during response. Firefighters in responding vehicles can monitor one another's locations to avoid collisions at intersections. They may also be able to communicate impediments to response that other units will encounter.

AVL is also a safety accountability tool. In addition to GPS location, AVL devices keep a constant record of vehicular speed and direction of travel that is logged with time stamps and dates. This data can become part of investigative information about vehicle incidents or provide analysis and evaluation information of driver safety in the department.

Automatic Vehicle Locator (AVL) — Computer system onboard an apparatus that uses GPS coordinates to deliver and log real-time location and driving information (speed, direction of travel) about the apparatus over wireless networks.

Chapter Summary

To improve the safety, health, and wellness of fire and emergency responders, the organization must develop, implement, and manage a comprehensive safety and health program. The safety and health programs described above provide a holistic approach for the management and the membership to collectively integrate in everyday routines. The health maintenance program lays the groundwork for all employees during their tenure in the fire and emergency services. It begins with the basic medical and fitness evaluations and hopefully ends with the successful completion of a member's service. The accident prevention, safety audit, emergency vehicle safety, and infection control programs provide defensive safety measures and evaluation guidelines to further improve the safe working environment.

Review Questions

1. What are some guidelines for coordinating fire department safety and health programs? (pp. 227-241)

2. What are the components of a fire department health maintenance program? (pp. 242-254)

3. What components make up a fire department's accident prevention program? (pp. 254-257)

4. What processes should the health safety officer follow when conducting a safety audit within the fire and emergency service organization? (pp. 258-264)

5 What are some aspects of a jurisdictional infection control program? (pp. 264-268)

6. What are some aspects of an emergency vehicle safety program? (pp. 268-276)

Chapter 7 End Notes

1. Karter, Michael J. Jr.; Molis, Joseph L. "U.S. Firefighter Injuries – 2013," November, 2014: NFPA®

2. Elliot, Diane L. MD, FACP, FACSM and Kuehl, Kerry S. MD, Dr.PH, "The Effects of Sleep Deprivation on Fire Fighters and EMS Responders," June, 2007: International Association of Fire Chiefs (IAFC)

3. John R. Hall Jr. "The Total Cost of Fire in the United States", March 2014: NFPA®

4. "The Economic Consequences of Firefighter Injuries and Their Prevention. Final Report." TriData Corporation, a Division of System Planning Corporation, 2004 NIST: GCR 05-874

5. "Fire-Related Firefighter Injuries Reported to the National Fire Incident Reporting System (2010-2012)," *Topical Fire Report Series* Vol. 15, Issue 6: November, 2014: USFA

Refer to Appendix B: Learning Activity Answers in the back of this manual for suggested responses.

Purpose

Identifying the need for safety and health programs within an organization is an important responsibility of the health safety officer. For this activity, practice addressing various health and wellness problems with the appropriate safety and health programs.

Directions

1. Read each of the scenarios.

2. Create a list of the major safety and wellness problems presented in each scenario.

3. Based on your reading from the chapter, determine which safety and health program would appropriately address each situation (e.g., Medical Surveillance, Physical Fitness, Wellness, etc.).

4. Provide a brief description of what each program should consist of in order to address the problem(s). If applicable, list or describe any legal mandates, guidelines, or other resources that would provide the necessary framework for the program (e.g., NFPA® standards, federal guidelines, etc.).

Scenario 1

Your department has recently suffered two firefighter fatalities due to cardiac arrest. As HSO, you observe that a significant number of firefighters in your organization regularly consume foods that are high in fat and sodium. You are also aware that several firefighters use tobacco products when they are not on duty.

Safety and Wellness Problems:

Safety and Health Program:

Program Description:

Scenario 2

At a structural training evolution, a firefighter was injured because he wasn't wearing his helmet. During the evolution, the roof ladder was not secured properly and slid off the roof, striking the firefighter on the side of the head. He suffered a concussion and was off work for a significant period of time.

Safety and Wellness Problems:

Safety and Health Program:

Program Description:

7-1 (cont.)
Identify safety and health programs based on departmental needs.

LEARNING ACTIVITIES

Refer to Appendix B: Learning Activity Answers in the back of this manual for suggested responses.

Scenario 3

As HSO, you would like to evaluate overall safety compliance in your organization. You specifically have concerns about diesel exhaust exposure. You observe that apparatus are frequently left running outside of the bay, allowing exhaust to enter facility doors leading to the occupied part of the fire station. You also suspect that the garage lacks an effective ventilation system.

Safety and Wellness Problems:

Safety and Health Program:

Program Description:

Scenario 4

You have received a letter from the local Emergency Room Director stating that personnel from your department arrived covered in blood when they brought in victims. Additionally, a firefighter reports that she believes she was exposed to blood while assisting a victim in a car accident. She is unsure of the proper procedures for reporting this incident.

Safety and Wellness Problems:

Safety and Health Program:

Program Description:

Scenario 5

As HSO, you witnessed a driver/operator backing a fire apparatus without a spotter. When you confronted the personnel involved, he informed you that there are no procedures in place for the maneuver.

Safety and Wellness Problems:

Safety and Health Program:

Program Description:

Training Functions

Key Terms

NFPA® Job Performance Requirements

This chapter provides information that addresses the following job performance requirements of NFPA® 1521, *Standard for Fire Department Safety Officer Professional Qualifications (2015)*.

4.2.3	4.5.2
4.4.1	4.11.4
4.4.2	4.12.2

Training Functions

Learning Objectives

After reading this chapter, students will be able to:

1. Describe the role of the health safety officer in providing safety and health information to fire departments. (4.4.1)

2. Determine ways to ensure that medical advice is available to members of a jurisdiction. (4.11.4)

3. Explain the responsibilities of the health safety officer in training personnel on safety and health-related topics. (4.2.3, 4.4.2, 4.5.2, 4.12.2)

4. Learning Activity 8-1: Develop safety and health information for various training topics. (4.4.1)

Chapter 8
Training Functions

Case History

A firefighter with a combination fire department was performing the daily inspection of SCBA equipment. While conducting the inspection, a damaged SCBA was found and removed from service. The SCBA was placed in the station's maintenance area without being properly identified or tagged. The next day, another firefighter found the SCBA and returned it to service without properly inspecting the unit. During a fire, the SCBA malfunctioned and lost air pressure from the first stage regulator and a firefighter had to make an emergency exit from the structure. The air cylinder went from 3,000 psi to completely empty in approximately 10 seconds. The department had experienced similar instances that have been undocumented.

Upon investigating the near-miss, the department discovered that the SOP/G for removing equipment from service had been updated, but there was no record of the firefighters having been trained on the updated procedures. In addition, there was no tracking mechanism to discover when, or even if, the new procedure had been distributed to the firefighters. The current distribution method, adding the new page to SOP/G guides at the station, was not an effective means of informing the membership of procedures.

The department took steps to create training procedures that could be tracked in the department's database. Regular, mandated refresher courses on SOP/Gs were scheduled, and attendance records were kept. All departmental SOP/Gs were added to the department's database so that firefighters could access them more easily using newly purchased SOP/G management software.

In addition to creating the safety procedures for live-fire training evolutions described in Chapter 4, Standard Operating Procedures, NFPA® 1521, *Standard for Fire Department Safety Officer,* assigns the following responsibilities to the HSO regarding training and education:

1. Developing and distributing safety and health information to all department members

2. Implementing the training and education of department members on safety and health policies and procedures used by the AHJ

These responsibilities do not mean that the HSO must personally participate in all training operations or teach all safety-related classes. The HSO can create a systematic approach to training and education through delegation of authority to all officers, collaboration with the health and safety committee to develop training topics, and "train-the-trainer" programs.

16 Firefighter Life Safety Initiatives 1, 2, 3, and 5

The *16 Firefighter Life Safety Initiatives* were discussed in Chapter 1, Health Safety Officer Responsibilities. Initiatives 1, 2, 3, and 5 are pertinent to the HSO's responsibilities related to training responsibilities.

1. Define and advocate the need for a cultural change within the fire service relating to safety; incorporating leadership, management, supervision, accountability and personal responsibility.

2. Enhance the personal and organizational accountability for health and safety throughout the fire service.

3. Focus greater attention on the integration of risk management with incident management at all levels, including strategic, tactical, and planning responsibilities.

5. Develop and implement national standards for training, qualifications, and certification (including regular recertification) that are equally applicable to all firefighters based on the duties they are expected to perform.

Safety and Health Information

Safety and health information will cover a wide range of topics. The fire service is an all-hazards environment, and the safety and health information should include all aspects of this dynamic operational setting. The HSO should conduct research on all fire service-related safety and health topics in the development of a comprehensive training and education program. The risk management plan and the medical surveillance program are two prominent programs within the HSO's responsibility that will help guide the education and training program. At times, the HSO will need to think creatively to provide the best training. This creativity will involve discussing safety and health topics with others. Any information provided should remain on topic and be valuable to the membership.

Development of Safety and Health Information

The development of safety and health information should be based upon the following foundational information:

- **Legal mandates** — some safety and health information is mandated. For example, infection control procedures require initial and recurring training, per OSHA.

- **Data analysis** — research should be conducted to evaluate data on injuries, fatalities, occupational exposures, and illnesses. This information can show trends locally, at the state/provincial level, across the nation, or internationally.

- **Near-miss reporting** — near-miss reports should be incorporated into the educational program. Using real-world examples are a great way to promote discussions and improve learning.

- **Policy and procedure review** — regular reviews of policy and procedures should be included to determine current adequacy, effectiveness, and any gradual drift away from the SOP/G. Normalization of Deviation is a significant concern and should be assessed as needed.

- **NIOSH Fire Fighter Fatality Reports** — these reports provide valuable information on fatality incidents, possible causes, and contributing factors. In addition, these reports should be examined for lessons learned to assist in preventing similar tragic events.

- **Peer-reviewed journals** — peer-reviewed journal articles of research studies on firefighter health, wellness, and fitness have become more frequent. These studies can provide validated statistical data that are useful in the educational setting.

- **Professional organizations** — professional organizations specific to safety, health, and wellness are also a resource. These organizations do not have to be fire service-related, but they provide health information and certifications to personal trainers.

- **Regulatory and government agencies** — regulatory agencies provide legal mandates for worker and workplace safety. Government agencies can provide additional legal criteria. Both agencies may provide training, safety bulletin information, model procedure guides, and other guidance documents.

- **Other personnel** — the development of safety and health information will involve interacting with and discussing topics with technical specialists, the health and fitness coordinator, peer fitness trainers, and the occupational safety and health committee. These personnel can serve as subject matter experts on topic specific items.

NOTE: **Learning Activity 8**-1 provides an opportunity to practice developing safety and health information.

Distribution Methods

Safety and health information can be distributed in several ways. Some of the common distribution methods are but are not limited to **(Figure 8.1, p. 286)**:

- **Handouts** — this is simple and requires minimal resources.

- **Computer system** — email is an easy, nonintrusive method of distribution of materials. Documents and/or videos can be attached to email as supplementary material. In addition, organizational intranet sites can provide wide access to recorded sessions without having to mass-produce or copy materials. Some systems allow for read-and-sign acknowledgement that documents a member's participation in a training session.

- **Internet** — the use of information sources on the Internet can be useful. Programs can offer training modules and keep member participation logs for records. HSOs should explore these resources and determine the most appropriate ones for their department.

- **DVDs or other video materials** — these materials can be mass-produced or circulated between stations and crews. These media are good for in-house or in-classroom training.

- **Journal articles** — personnel can be referred to journal articles for specific topics.

- **Posters** — posters provide a good reminder of safety and health information.

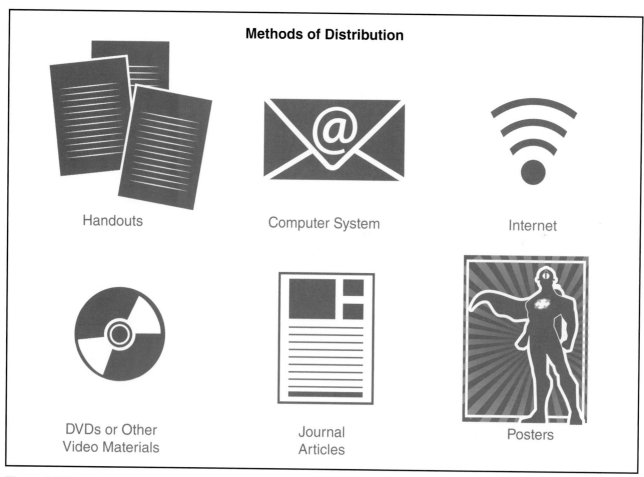

Methods of Distribution

Handouts

Computer System

Internet

DVDs or Other
Video Materials

Journal
Articles

Posters

Figure 8.1 The HSO is responsible for distributing health and safety information to organizational members using a variety of distribution methods.

The Internet is perhaps the most powerful tool to distribute information to your organization. It can connect your firefighters to outside safety programs online. It can also be the portal for promoting the safety message and culture of your organization both internally and externally. Posting to blogs, video sites, social media platforms, and web pages gets your message to the people you serve.

Although open access to the Internet is beneficial to individuals, it can be detrimental to organizations. As a result, organizations should take steps to control the content that it posts for public consumption and within the organization.

A few individuals with clearly defined responsibilities for posting to the web should oversee the Internet policy. These individuals should be the gatekeepers of the organization's public face on the web, though membership can be encouraged to provide web content to them **(Figure 8.2)**.

In addition to posting rights, most sites have easy-to-use permission systems that allow certain privileges and access to organizational members. For example, large public sites such as YouTube® or Facebook® allow the creation of private sites that are password protected on which the administrator can limit the viewership to only department members. As a possible advocate of the department and one of the organization's gatekeepers of safety information, the HSO should become familiar with these tools and recommend their use.

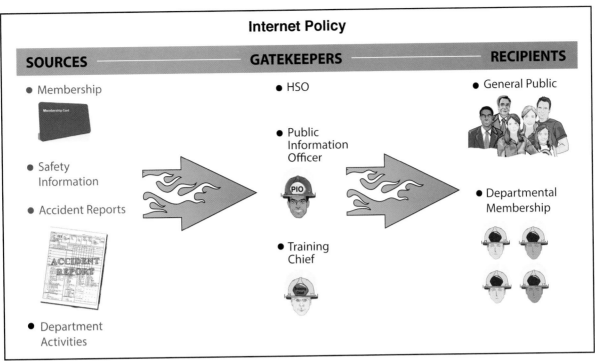

Figure 8.2 Organizations should have Internet policies in place to control information released to the public and to organizational members.

CAUTION
Information posted from the organization should be controlled.

Access to Medical Advice

The HSO is not responsible for the personal dispersion of medical advice but should ensure members have access to and receive the assistance they need. NFPA® 1500, *Standard on Fire Department Occupational Safety and Health Program,* states that members should have access to the fire department physician when needed. The fire department physician is probably the best point of contact for medical advice on topics ranging from general health to exposure to disease and occupational hazards. The fire department physician will be knowledgeable about items that directly relate to the member's service-related concerns.

However, some members may prefer to seek medical advice from their private physician. The choice to see a private physician is a personal decision and should always be allowed if requested. According to NFPA® 1582, *Standard on Comprehensive Occupational Medical Program for Fire Departments*, it is even permissible for a member's private physician to provide some aspects of the medical surveillance program.

Medical advice is not limited to the physical health of a member, but it also includes the psychological health. Any member seeking psychological counseling should be referred to the Member Assistance Program (MAP) or another licensed professional who is specifically trained in this area.

Training Personnel on Safety and Health

For firefighters, safety begins with their initial training. Not only should they learn how to do their job safely and efficiently, but they should also be guaranteed that the training environment is safe. To this end, the HSO's responsibility is to ensure that proper training in safety-related topics is provided and training procedures for unsafe conditions are reviewed **(Figure 8.3)**. The HSO should also be present at potentially hazardous training events whenever possible. The safety and health topics will mainly come from the risk management plan and medical surveillance program. Risks and hazards identified through the analysis process provide a foundation for training and education topics.

The HSO or incident safety officer should work closely with the administration, the training division, and the department's membership to ensure that the training program meets the safety needs of the department as well as federal, state, and provincial mandates. In addition to regulatory and policy driven training, safety and health training should be a cultural norm within the organization. Personnel should be encouraged to suggest new or improved safety and health components with any training class or exercise. The HSO and training staff should review all suggestions with appropriate professional advice obtained when needed to determine validity and any need to change a practice.

Figure 8.3 HSO's should ensure that training courses and classes include or begin with safety briefings.

Coordinating Training with Training Personnel

Training is intended to maintain and/or improve the education, knowledge, skills, abilities, and competencies of all department members. Training requirements must be outlined in a matrix that all members can understand and strive to complete. While the training division oversees the creation of a compliant training program, the HSO is responsible for ensuring the tasks and evolutions that are taught are based on best practices and industry standards that enhance firefighter safety. Training safety can be accomplished in a two-fold systematic approach.

First, the HSO reviews all training evolutions in comparison to the task analysis developed to set hiring standards. The training evolutions should conform to the operational tasks that members perform on a daily basis. The HSO then ensures that the tasks are performed in as safe a manner as possible. The HSO performs a review for each department standard, evolution, and practice.

For example, one task defined in the task analysis that is common to the fire service is the raising or deploying of a two-section extension ladder by one or two firefighters. The HSO would have the following responsibilities before the training:

- Review the method by which firefighters are trained to lift, carry, set, extend, and retract the ladder
- Evaluate the protective clothing and equipment worn when handling ladders
- Recommend changes to the training programs if necessary
- Consider the possibility of back injuries and other physical problems that can occur while lifting, extending, and carrying
- Consider potential environmental hazards associated with operating metal ladders

Second, the HSO provides the members of the training division with training in applicable national standards and safety-related topics. This training has an additional benefit of providing backup personnel for the HSO and provides a core of trained personnel to function as incident safety officers at major incidents. Training officers should have the knowledge to function as incident safety officers during training operations. This knowledge relieves the HSO of the need to be present during all training activities. The training officers should be able to:

- Recognize potential safety hazards
- Evaluate the need for proper infection control
- Understand and apply all vehicle operation laws
- Follow the procedures outlined in the safety and health program

Figure 8.4 When an HSO has health/safety officer and training duties, personnel should be informed of when the officer will be functioning in which capacity.

Not all fire departments can afford to have a staff member who functions solely as the HSO. When this situation occurs, a training officer may assume the HSO's duties. This assignment is a logical use of existing skills because training and education are primary functions of both positions. When the same person performs both functions, the HSO duties and training officer duties should be clearly delineated **(Figure 8.4)**. Supervisors and commanding officers must recognize the importance of the separation of duties and allow the individual to fulfill the assigned task of the respective position, especially during live-fire training exercises. NFPA® 1403, *Standard on Live Fire Training Evolutions,* mandates that the safety officer should not be assigned any conflicting tasks under these circumstances. The two functions should also be delineated during incident investigations and postincident analysis. As the HSO, the individual must be able to perform an analysis free from outside pressures that might occur when there is a conflict of interest.

To properly train emergency personnel for all potential hazards, entry-level and in-service training must be as realistic as possible. Therefore, the approach to safety on the training ground should mirror the approach to safety at a real-life incident. Mandatory safety procedures on the training ground can develop into safe habits during the rest of a firefighter's career.

A department's safety culture is reflected in how it trains. When safety is emphasized as a key component of successful training and is not compromised, safety lessons and safe techniques learned during training are much more likely to be repeated on the fireground.

Incorporating Safety Provisions

Safety provisions should be incorporated into training and education programs. First, the HSO should ensure that the organization has provided training, facilities, education, equipment, and clothing which meet the requirements of each member's position. In addition, the HSO should review all applicable NFPA® standards and OSHA regulations regarding mandated training, personal equipment, fit testing, and personal protective clothing, and ensure that the organization is in compliance with these standards and regulations.

Second, the HSO should ensure that the appropriate level of rehabilitation is provided at emergency and training events. Food and fluid replenishment should promote healthy choices to the membership **(Figure 8.5)**. This practice is also an example of how safety and health information can be incorporated and distributed to personnel.

Orange County Hydration Study[1]

In August of 2007, the Orange County, California fire department conducted a dehydration study during training with the assistance of outside experts who contributed to the county's wellness and fitness programs. The experts ran benchmark tests before training sessions began and monitored the firefighters' hydration and heat levels during two, 15-minute drills. They discovered that roughly 90 percent of the firefighters were dehydrated when they arrived at the training ground, before they had even begun training. During the drills, monitoring showed that 62 percent of the firefighters lost on average 3 pounds [1.5 kg] of water weight.

Although this was a small sample size, it is still significant information. Firefighters may not arrive at training with enough hydration. They may need to drink water when they arrive and then frequently throughout an all-day exercise or a series of drills. Over half of the firefighters in the study were significantly or seriously dehydrated after only 30 minutes of exertion. Firefighters are at a risk during training if rehabilitation is not part of the training procedures at a training facility or in an organization.

Symptoms of Dehydration

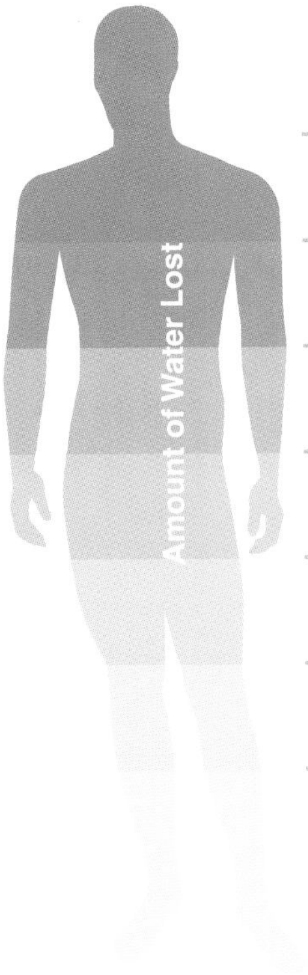

Amount of Water Lost

	Symptoms
1.5 L	Thirst
3 L	Sluggishness, fatigue, nausea, emotional instability
4 L	Clumsiness, headache, elevated body temperature, elevated pulse, elevated respiratory rate
5 L	Dizziness, slurred speech, weakness, confusion
6 L	Delirium, swollen tongue, circulatory problems, decreased blood volume, kidney failure
9 L	Inability to swallow, painful urination, cracked skin
12 L	Imminent death

Figure 8.5 Firefighters, HSOs, and training officers should monitor hydration levels during training evolutions and during emergency response.

Figure 8.6 No matter the evolution, simple or complex, time should be set aside for safety information such as correct lifting techniques.

Finally, the common adage that "Every day is a training day" should emanate throughout the organization. Training does not have to be a scheduled event that is only accomplished within a specified time frame. Every opportunity to review, teach, and incorporate safety into everyday activities should be encouraged **(Figure 8.6)**. This impromptu interaction will advance the professional development of all personnel and be invaluable to the prevention of injuries, fatalities, exposures, and illnesses that continue to affect personnel.

Meeting Operational Safety Goals

Operational safety goals, such as no training injuries, should be outlined in the department's SOP/Gs and ingrained within the culture. The risk management plan is one method of identifying risks and hazards that can reasonably be determined to exist. From this analysis, control measures with the use of the hierarchy of controls provide five concepts of risk reduction that can improve the working environment for personnel. See Chapter 5, Organizational Risk Management for detailed information on the five risk concepts.

A second method of identifying risks and hazards is a thorough training and education program. The HSO should research the safety and health aspects of every training and education program or class. This review will include independent safety and health classes or those classes that are included with other training topics. The intention is for the safety and health topics to directly correlate to the stated operational safety goals of the department. For example, if research shows that personnel have been injured while performing a similar task, the HSO should examine the root cause and recommend training and education to reduce the potential for recurrence.

Identifying Training Materials

The HSO may be the instructor of a safety and health training course or program. When the HSO is not the instructor, assistance from the training staff will need to be requested to achieve the needed training. The HSO or any individual instructor should not be expected to know all topics that will be provided. Cooperation must be developed between those best qualified to teach and those who are responsible for ensuring training is safe, supported, and promoted positively in the organization.

Training materials are available from a variety of sources. When HSOs also serve as instructors, they should work with the training division to identify appropriate materials. If HSOs must create their own teaching materials, they can, again, use training officers as a resource or review existing training materials and use them as a template for development. The HSO may also choose to contact the local public school system for guidance, attend a college course in education or teaching theory, or take an educational methodology course offered by a state/provincial fire training academy or the National Fire Academy.

NOTE: IFSTA's **Fire and Emergency Services Instructor** manual is also an excellent source for instructor-related curriculum development, lesson development, and resource/material use.

Performing Job Task Analysis for Safety Training

In Chapter 7, Safety and Health Programs, a job task analysis was described in terms of establishing requirements for physical fitness. Job task analysis can also be used to design appropriate training for personnel and trainees who must learn certain tasks to perform a job. In order to create a course or curriculum, the HSO or training staff must understand the tasks that will be taught as part of the training. Conducting a job task analysis is the best way for the HSO or training staff to understand what skills need to be included and taught in the course.

Each task is divided into steps that contribute to the correct completion of the task. In order to perform a task analysis, the HSO must first collect information on the specific tasks that compose the job. The HSO can use either formal or informal methods to collect information as follows (**Figure 8.7**):

- Formal methods
  - Carefully designed and executed surveys
  - Opinion polls
  - Checklists
  - Observations
  - Psychological profiles
  - Research analyses
  - Tests
- Informal methods
  - Conversations
  - Casual observations of activities and habits
  - Other unobtrusive measures

The information is then used to determine the steps that compose the task. The following four organizational methods can determine the order in which steps must be accomplished.

- **Sequential** — arranging tasks in order of operation

- **Cause and effect** — completing one action or determining the existence of a condition before deciding on the next appropriate action or step

- **Model-based** — model used for professional tasks when the steps for performing the tasks are vague or difficult to define

- **Cognitive** — critical decision-based model that focuses on the psychological processes that underlie the physical task

A sequential task analysis is the method that is used most frequently. In this method, the steps are arranged in sequence from first to last. The method may be used for a simple task (depicted in a linear fashion) or a complex task that may contain a combination of simple tasks, with some performed simultaneously.

Steps that are considered key points are used to create the teaching outline for the task. Some steps may require the student to make a decision before performing the step. Decisions may be based on safety concerns or cause-and-effect considerations. For instance, before raising a ground ladder, the student must determine whether overhead obstructions or electrical power lines are present.

Implementing Safety and Health Training

Safety and health procedures will often require classroom instruction and/or hands-on practice. Any new technology, equipment, apparatus, and the associated practices and procedures need to be provided in a training and education program prior to implementation. This **in-service training**, as it is sometimes called, should provide sufficient information on the proper use and limitations of the equipment as stated by the manufacturer **(Figure 8.8, p. 294)**. The manufacturer and/or sales representatives can be a useful resource for training support. The training session should also provide ample time for personnel to gain the needed hands-on practice to become proficient in the use of the tool, equipment, or vehicle before it is placed in service. Several training sessions may be needed for some topics.

Task Analysis

Formal | **Informal**

- **Surveys**
- **Opinion Polls**
- **Observations**
- **Profiles**
- **Research**
- **Tests**

- **Conversations**
- **Casual Observations**

Figure 8.7 Job task analysis requires both formally collected data and information recorded directly from casual observations and conversations.

In-Service Training — Formal or informal training received while on the job; in the fire service, this training generally occurs in-house at the station rather than at formal training facilities.

Figure 8.8 Firefighters should attend scheduled, in-service training on new equipment and apparatus.

Station personnel may provide instruction on other, less complicated procedures in-house. For example, new procedures on laundering of soiled clothing or regular nutritional recommendations will not require formal classroom training. These topics are best implemented as time allows without overwhelming the training schedule. In-house training can be promoted through the use of handouts, computer software program illustrations, and videos. In-house training allows the HSO and training staff to be creative in achieving the needed training with minimal resource allocation.

Few instructors are qualified to "teach it all." Rather, instructors tend to specialize in certain areas and become proficient in teaching knowledge and skills specific to their areas of experience and expertise. In addition to topic expertise, instructors must have credibility with the personnel being trained. Personnel perceive that instructors have credibility when they display technical proficiency and evidence of formal training and education and demonstrate instructional experience. Credibility is also indicated by rank, reputation, and respect among members. The HSO should coordinate with the training division on an appropriate pool of instructors qualified to teach safety and health topics.

Class Scheduling

In addition to selecting instructional personnel, the HSO will work with the training division to schedule training programs or courses. Providing a training schedule enables unit supervisors to assign personnel to training with minimal interference with or effect on daily duties. For volunteer fire personnel, for example, training schedules allow them to integrate required training with regular employment responsibilities and personal activities. Posted schedules provide training topics, dates, times, and locations (**Figure 8.9**). The organization may also post schedules to notify potential instructors of upcoming classes that are available for them to teach.

2014 COMPANY TRAINING SCHEDULE

	Instr.	Subject
JANUARY		
Monthly Subject:	C.O.	Infection Control SOP
Other:	A.T.O.	Annual Respirator Fit-Testing
HazMat:	A.T.O.	Hazmat TECH Annual Refresher Training
Officer's Class:	T.O.	Suspicious White Powder SOP
MultiCompany Drill:	T.O.	Suspicious White Powder Incident
Rescue Drill:	A.T.O.	Ice Rescue
EMS CEU:	T.O.	All Shifts: Infection Control Refresher
FEBRUARY		
Monthly Subject:	C.O.	Ch. 17, Loss Control (Essentials, 6th ed.)
	C.O.E.	Annual Respirator Refresher training
Driver Training:	A.T.O.	Autry Tech Driving Simulator [Refresher and New Driver Training]
Officer's Class:	T.O.	Administrative Policies & Procedures SOP
Rescue Drill:	T.O.	Confined Space Rescue
EMS CEU:	E.M.S.	A-Shift: Ryder- The Obese Patient
	E.M.S.	B-Shift: Compton- The Obese Patient
	E.M.S.	C-Shift: McDevitt- The Obese Patient
MARCH		
Monthly Subject:	C.O.	Ch. 18, Protecting Fire Scene Evidence (Essentials, 6th ed.)
Officer's Class:	T.O.	FF Safety & Health SOP
Other:	T.O.	Emergency Services Instructor Course (Prerequisite for Lieutenant) Dates: March 7-11, 2011
	T.O.	ERG & Hazardous Communication Annual Refresher
	P.F.I.	Quarterly Physical Fitness Review
HazMat:	A.T.O.	Quarterly HazMat Drill
EMS CEU:	E.M.S.	A-Shift: Palmer- Head Injuries
	E.M.S.	B-Shift: Gates- Head Injuries
	E.M.S.	C-Shift: Craig- Head Injuries
APRIL		
Monthly Subject:	C.O.	EFD Rules and Regulations Annual Refresher
Other:	C.O.	Hydrant Flowing
Driver Training:	A.T.O.	EVDT Course [Refresher and New Driver Training]
Officer's Class:	T.O.	Special Situations SOP
Rescue Drill:	T.O.	Grain Bin Rescue
EMS CEU:	E.M.S.	A-Shift: Copeland- Chest Trauma
	E.M.S.	B-Shift: Williams- Chest Trauma
	E.M.S.	C-Shift: Jenkins- Chest Trauma

Figure 8.9 Posted training schedules, whether online or on bulletin boards, allow firefighters to plan to attend training.

When developing training schedules, the HSO should consider the following factors that affect unit supervisors, personnel and instructors:

- **How will the training schedule affect other job activities?** — Personnel have responsibilities other than attending training: inspections, expected incident responses, special events, and annual leaves. Some responsibilities may have a higher priority to the organization at the moment than training, and the HSO must be aware of these other activities when creating the training schedule.

- **When are instructional resources (including instructors) most readily available?** —Organizations may share training resources, such as classrooms, driving courses, and the burn building. When this is the case, the HSO must make cooperative arrangements, consider weather that may cause cancellations and rescheduling, and coordinate timely arrival and departure of class participants. The HSO also has to consider instructor schedules and conflicting assignments. Instructors may not always be available for assignments at certain times of the day or week, and available instructors may not be qualified to teach certain topics in some programs.

- **What is the most appropriate time for training?** — When a training program must be taught outdoors, it is best to schedule training when the weather is suitable to the topic. Evenings and weekends may be the best time to schedule some training, especially for volunteer organizations.

- **How quickly must the training be completed?** — In some cases, an organization's administration may want a specific training program completed immediately in order to fulfill a regulatory requirement. To meet the need for immediate training, the HSO can coordinate a plan for program offerings in several time frames. This practice maximizes the times and opportunities for personnel to complete the training. In addition, the HSO can work with the training division to reprioritize other organizational activities and training programs where possible. For most training, programs may be scheduled over longer time periods and more frequently throughout the year so personnel can take advantage of required programs at their convenience.

The process of developing a training schedule is not always a simple one. Responding to all the factors mentioned is taxing. To simplify the task, the HSO and the training division can establish guidelines that outline steps that provide consistency to the planning or scheduling process. At times, the HSO may need to strongly advocate for certain safety and health training sessions, especially when other departmental activities, training, and duties are considered more valuable to the organization's administration **(Table 8.1)**.

Attendance

Attendance at training sessions may be voluntary or mandatory depending on organizational directives and legal mandates. The HSO is not responsible for

---

Table 8.1
Factors That May Affect Scheduling

Health of the Organizational Safety Culture

Training Requirements
— Local, State, and Government Mandates

Physical Resources
— Availability of Resources

Instructor Availability

Minimum Staffing Levels

Budgetary Considerations

Environmental Conditions
— Adverse Weather
— Temperature Extremes

---

mandating attendance or taking disciplinary action for those individuals who miss training. However, the HSO will make recommendations on whether classes should be defined as voluntary or mandatory. Attendance will need to be coordinated with the training division and shift supervisory personnel to ensure class details are clearly communicated. Deficient attendance at training should be handled through the normal personnel chain of command. Make-up sessions should be made available within a reasonable period of time. All attendance at training should be documented for record-keeping purposes.

Frequency and Tracking of Training

Departmental policy should define the frequency of training on safety and health topics. Generally, specific safety and health topics have annual training frequency, but this is not an absolute rule. All training and operational reviews should include safety and health topics. The HSO is responsible for defining appropriate topics for discussion that are included in other training. In addition, variations to standard frequency schedules will include training on new technologies and new procedures before they are implemented as standard practice.

Record keeping of all training should comply with NFPA® 1401, *Recommended Practice for Fire Service Training Reports and Records*. There are legal mandates for record keeping of training, retention schedules, and department needs that all must be met. The HSO should be familiar with the record-keeping requirements and ensure records are obtained and retained.

Training on Safe Work Practices

Included in the training program are specific training topics that should address safe work practices in the emergency and nonemergency operational setting. The training should prepare the membership with the necessary information to safely perform all required tasks. In order to accomplish this, the HSO must stay current on the latest safety topics, issues, injury reports, surveys, and audit reports **(Figure 8.10)**. When designing the training program and curriculum, the HSO should work closely with the training division and those individuals who may provide the instruction of material.

Figure 8.10 Ensuring safe work practices requires research and review of all pertinent documents, records, and publications.

Safe Practices at Emergency Operations

The organization's culture should promote safe practices at all emergency incidents. As previously mentioned, everyone has an obligation and responsibility for safe practices. Implementation of safety practices is the culmination of the training and education of personnel, the outfitting of personnel with protective clothing and equipment, the organizational SOP/Gs, and the safety culture of the organization. Some highlighted operational areas for safe work practices include but are not limited to:

- **Incident Management System (IMS)** — the IMS needs to be implemented with the first arriving unit and maintained throughout the incident operations. This practice promotes a coordinated approach with personnel working in teams to accomplish stated goals.

- **Incident Safety Officer (ISO)** — the ISO is responsible for monitoring all conditions, activities, and operations to ensure as safe an environment as possible. The assignment of the ISO is dependent on the size and complexity of the incident, type of incident, SOP/Gs, and legal mandates.

- **Accountability** — the Incident Commander must maintain accountability of all personnel operating at an incident at all times. Personnel must be formally given an assignment before entering the hazard area. Freelancing or self-assigning are a significant concern and must not be permitted.

- **Communications** — all personnel should follow the communications model for receiving and repeating orders. Proper radio etiquette must be followed. An SOP/G must also address emergency notifications and radio protocol for lost/downed personnel, and when/how a mayday is declared.

- **Incident operations** — all personnel must work toward the same incident action plan goals and objectives. All operational tasks should be conducted in a coordinated manner with the IC providing clear communications on team assignments and designated task objectives.

- **Special operations** — the fire service continues to expand operational services beyond fire suppression. In these operations, training and operational SOP/Gs must address the specific safety issues that personnel may encounter.

- **Rapid Intervention Crew (RIC)** — any incident with personnel operating in an **immediately dangerous to life and health (IDLH)** environment must have at least two RIC members stationed outside the IDLH environment. RIC must be prepared and equipped to take immediate rescue action **(Figure 8.11)**.

- **Personal protective clothing and equipment** — all personnel operating at an incident must have the knowledge of the proper use of all protective clothing and equipment. Each team should ensure all members within their team are properly outfitted and prepared for action.

- **Equipment and tools** — the use of equipment and tools require knowledge of their appropriate use and limitations. Users must wear appropriate PPE. The team supervisor should supervise equipment and tool use to monitor a broad perspective of the area and ensure safety.

Rapid Intervention Crew (RIC) — Two or more firefighters designated to perform firefighter rescue; they are stationed outside the hazard and must be standing by throughout the incident.

Immediately Dangerous to Life and Health (IDLH) — Description of any atmosphere that poses an immediate hazard to life or produces immediate irreversible, debilitating effects on health; represents concentrations above which respiratory protection should be required. Expressed in parts per million (ppm) or milligrams per cubic meter (mg/m3); companion measurement to the permissible exposure limit (PEL).

Figure 8.11 RIC teams should be present according to SOP/Gs at any training evolution with an IDLH environment.

- **Apparatus placement and operations** — all personnel operating an apparatus or on an incident scene must be knowledgeable about apparatus placement, traffic safety, and vehicle operations. Personnel must operate within a safe zone with appropriate protections in place **(Figure 8.12, p. 300)**.

- **Rehabilitation** — rest, replenishment, medical evaluation, and environmental relief should be provided at incidents and training exercises when appropriate.

Safe Practices at Nonemergency Operations

Safe practices at nonemergency operations, as well as during station duties, will include all those stated for emergency operations. Just because an incident is defined as a nonemergency incident does not mean complacency is acceptable. These incidents can, and do, result in injuries, fatalities, exposures, and illnesses. Personnel must remain vigilant to the hazards and risks of any operation. Safe practices at nonemergency incidents should receive the same consideration and alertness as emergency operations.

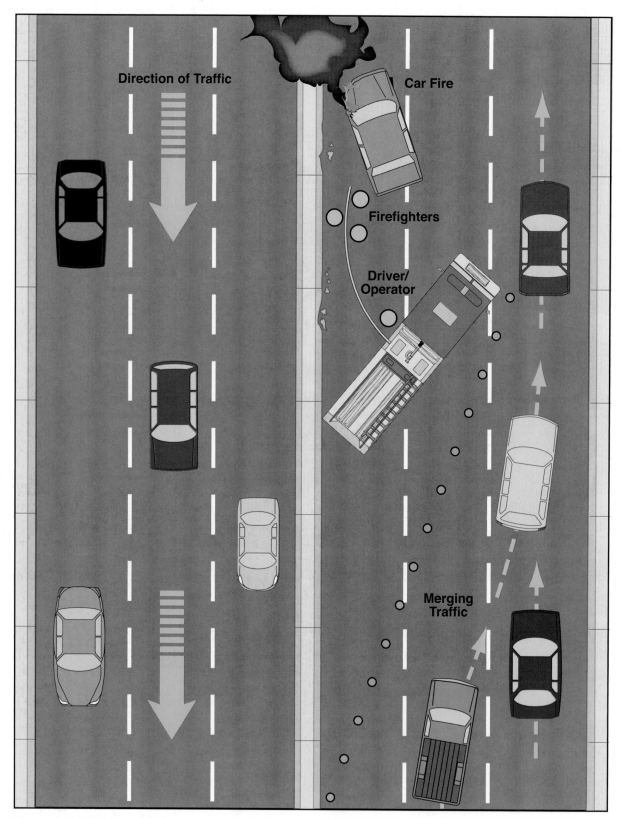

Figure 8.12 SOP/Gs should dictate safe practices for parking apparatus at roadway incidents.

Infection Control Training

NFPA® 1581, *Standard on Fire Department Infection Control Program*, Section 4.3.1 states that infection control training must be provided upon initial employment and annually thereafter. This training must meet all local protocols and regulations per state/provincial and federal jurisdictions, such as OSHA 29 CFR1910.1030 *Bloodborne Pathogens*. Infection control training should include the elements in NFPA® 1581, which are repeated here:

- Use of personal protective clothing and equipment
- SOP/Gs for safe work practices in infection control
- Methods of disposal of contaminated articles and medical waste
- Cleaning and decontamination
- Exposure management
- Medical follow-up

This list of infection control training items should be applied to all functions associated with fire department facilities, apparatus, and EMS operations. Personnel must also be educated on the disease causes and control measures against disease transmission **(Figure 8.13)**. The education program should include the effects of disease on an individual's health. The HSO, or infection control officer if assigned separately, must be cognizant of bioterrorism agents and newer infectious diseases that are becoming prevalent in modern society.

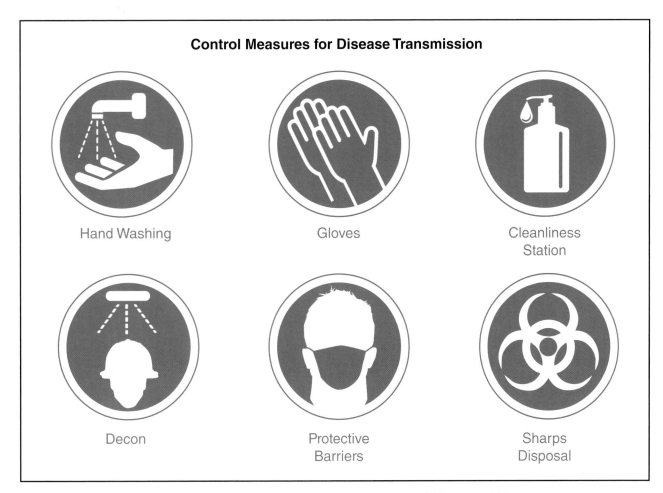

Control Measures for Disease Transmission

Hand Washing

Gloves

Cleanliness Station

Decon

Protective Barriers

Sharps Disposal

Figure 8.13 Training personnel on infection control measures is an important HSO responsibility.

Evaluating the Effectiveness of Training

Training programs must be evaluated in order to be successful. The training program's goals and objectives form the basis for evaluation and identify what the training program is to accomplish. The success of the program is determined by how well it achieves its goals and objectives.

Evaluating the training program includes determining the satisfaction of program recipients. Personnel participating in an *effective* training program appreciate the time they spend there and the information they learn. Likewise, participants are the first to recognize a training program that is ineffective or inappropriate and will express these concerns in evaluations.

The training program evaluation process should also include surveys of supervisory personnel, such as incident commanders, all officers, and program managers. These supervisory personnel work with the individuals who complete the training programs, and they should be aware of the skills and attitudes that these individuals now display on the job. Supervisory personnel can provide invaluable information about the successes and results of training programs.

If the training and education program was conducted to address a recurrent injury among personnel, then evaluating injury rates after the session is an important follow-up point. The effectiveness of a training program is also assessed from direct observation of personnel as they perform in the real world. This assessment is probably the most important and will answer the question: *Did the training transfer to practice?*

Chapter Summary

The fire and emergency service organization must promote safety in all aspects of training and operations. The HSO serves a prominent role in accomplishing this task. A comprehensive approach with the risk management plan and medical surveillance program that translates to the training and operational setting is vital to achieving the best safety environment possible. The HSO will work with all department members to identify unsafe conditions, alter the habits that may have caused them, and educate the membership in corrective actions. Positive outcomes can result with a cooperative team approach to safety that promotes accountability at all levels and encourages a culture of safe actions.

Review Questions

1. Where can a health safety officer find information on safety and health topics? (pp. 284-285)

2. How can the Internet be used to distribute safety and health information to fire department personnel? (pp. 285-287)

3. What ways can members get access to medical advice? (p. 287)

4. How can the health safety officer incorporate safety provisions into training and education programs? (pp. 290-291)

5. What sources could be used to identify training materials? (p. 292)

6. What methods are used for a job task analysis for safety training? (pp. 292-293)

7. How can the health safety officer implement safety and health training? (pp. 293-297)

8. What are some operational areas where safe work practices can be addressed in training? (pp. 297-300)

9. What are the elements of NFPA® 1581 that should be included in infection control training? (p. 301)

10. How can the health safety officer evaluate the effectiveness of departmental training programs? (p.302)

Chapter 8 End Notes

1. Contreras, Michael and Espinoza, Nancy, "Orange County Fire Authority Hydration Study", August, 2007.

Refer to Appendix B: Learning Activity Answers in the back of this manual for suggested responses.

Purpose

The Health Safety Officer is responsible for developing and distributing safety and health information to all department members. A crucial aspect of this responsibility is identifying all training topics that must be covered and developing appropriate safety briefings to communicate information and findings to personnel.

Directions

1. Choose **one** of the training topics listed below.

2. Identify sources for research on your chosen topic, and conduct the proper amount of research. For example, if you choose to develop a safety briefing on dehydration, sources for research could include the U.S. OSHA or U.S. Fire Administration websites. Remember to refer to your own jurisdiction's SOP/Gs.

3. Draft a **one-page memorandum** that provides essential information and evidence about the topic you have chosen and researched. Information should include a list of action items that address safety issues.

   NOTE: An example of a safety briefing memorandum on the awareness and importance of sleep has been provided in **Appendix B** at the back of the manual.

Training Topics

1. Develop a safety briefing that instructs personnel on proper lifting techniques.

2. Develop a safety briefing that addresses dehydration.

3. Develop a safety briefing that addresses the proper use of hearing protection.

4. Develop a safety briefing that discusses the value of a nutrition plan.

Root Cause Analysis: Accident Investigation and Postincident Analysis

Chapter Contents

Key Terms

NFPA® Job Performance Requirements

This chapter provides information that addresses the following job performance requirements of NFPA® 1521, *Standard for Fire Department Safety Officer Professional Qualifications (2015).*

4.1.2   4.6.4

4.6.1   4.7.1

4.6.2   4.7.4

4.6.3

Root Cause Analysis: Accident Investigation and Postincident Analysis

Learning Objectives

After reading this chapter, students will be able to:

1. Explain the health safety officer's role in gathering information for a safety and health investigation. (4.6.1)

2. Describe situations that would present a conflict of interest for the health safety officer. (4.1.2)

3. Describe the postincident analysis process as it relates to health safety officer duties. (4.6.3)

4. Explain the process of identifying the root cause of an accident. (4.6.1, 4.6.2, 4.6.4, 4.7.1, 4.7.4)

5. Describe the process of developing corrective action plans for a fire service organization. (4.6.1, 4.6.2, 4.6.4, 4.7.1, 4.7.4)

6. Learning Activity 9-1: Conduct a postincident analysis of a MVA incident where two responding firefighters were injured. (4.1.2, 4.6.1, 4.6.2, 4.6.3, 4.6.4, 4.7.1, 4.7.4)

Chapter 9
Root Cause Analysis: Accident Investigation and Postincident Analysis

Case History

In the summer of 2012, a local fire department was dispatched to a report of a wildland fire. The first due engine arrived on-scene, provided a brief size-up, and passed Command to the chief officer who was still en route. As personnel started a mobile attack on the left flank, the chief arrived and assumed incident command. Mutual aid engines arrived on scene and were assigned to the right flank of the fire.

During fire fighting operations, conditions became very smoky and visibility was limited. Two engine companies experienced a near-miss as they almost collided when they both reached the head of the fire. Fortunately, no one was injured and no equipment was damaged.

According to the ISO's postincident analysis, there were several contributing factors to the near-miss. The two trucks were from different jurisdictions and did not use the same communications protocols. In addition, one truck had been asked to go to a particular part of the fire but was in the wrong location. One vehicle was traveling faster than it should have been given the terrain and conditions.

The HSO reviewed the SOP/Gs for the department and compared them to the mutual aid agreement procedures. He discovered that local communications procedures had been updated but had not been reported to mutual aid units. He also discovered that the personnel on the truck that was in the wrong location was staffed with members who had not yet received the jurisdiction's wildland fire training. Finally, he discovered that there were no records on file for recertification driver training for the other engine. The root causes of the near-miss were the jurisdiction's inability to communicate mutual aid procedures and maintain records of training for assigned personnel.

NFPA® 1521, *Standard for Fire Department Safety Officer* Section 3, defines *accident* as "an unplanned occurrence, which results in a loss such as unintended injury, illness, death, property damage, or damage to the environment." To reduce the potential for accidents or to reduce the severity of accidents, the organization must develop and implement an accident investigation policy and procedure. The policy should define accidents, establish the authority for investigating each type of accident, and set a procedure for accident investigation. According to NFPA® 1500, *Standard on Fire Department Occupational Safety and Health Program,* investigations should not be limited to accidents but should also include job-related near-miss accidents, injuries and illnesses, fatalities, and exposures.

In NFPA® 1521, the overall responsibility for accident investigation belongs to the HSO. If an accident occurs where an ISO is assigned, the ISO is responsible for providing the HSO with a written accident report.

Too often, fire department investigations only seek to identify the person, if anyone, responsible for the accident. If accident investigations only serve to identify guilty parties, then fire department members may become less willing to support investigations because the investigations only result in disciplinary action, not improved safety. In addition, placing blame has little effect on preventing recurrences of the behavior or the injury. The only time a person should be named is when the individual was willfully ignoring procedure or has a history of unsafe behavior **(Figure 9.1)**.

A more appropriate approach to accident investigation is to pair the investigation with a root cause analysis. The investigation and analysis should seek to identify what policies, procedures, or cultural behaviors contributed

Figure 9.1 Placing blame is not the primary purpose of an accident investigation; getting to the root cause of the accident is.

to the accident being investigated. The investigation and subsequent analysis can be completed together and submitted in a single report or as separate independent reports.

Along with performing the accident investigation and root cause analysis, the HSO is responsible for ensuring health and safety considerations are included in a postincident analysis (PIA). The PIA is a review of incidents to assess actions and decisions taken to stabilize an incident. A SOP/G should define criteria for the PIA and the responsibilities of personnel in providing information and participating in the process.

The final step in a PIA or an accident investigation is to make corrective action recommendations and the appropriate implementation procedures based on the facts of the situation. Corrective actions should guide the organization and membership toward improvements in policy and practice as they relate to people, the department, and the apparatus and equipment used.

16 Firefighter Life Safety Initiatives #9

The *16 Firefighter Life Safety Initiatives* were discussed in Chapter 1, Health Safety Officer Responsibilities. Initiative number 9 is pertinent to the HSO's responsibilities related to accident investigation:

9. Thoroughly investigate all firefighter fatalities, injuries, and near misses.

Gathering Information

Gathering information for an investigation will begin with documenting the facts of the accident/occurrence. As the investigation leader, the HSO must determine if any conflicts of interest exist. Procedural adjustments should be made as necessary to eliminate any perception of conflict or bias. Some investigations will require technical expertise to provide a clearer understanding of policy, practice, or situational factors. The HSO should develop a resource or reference list of experts to assist when needed. The HSO must be knowledgeable in the necessary investigative information that is needed for a complete report. Refer to Chapter 3, Record Keeping and Data Analysis for specific safety investigation documentation needs and procedures.

During the information gathering process, the HSO becomes part of the **chain of custody** of the documents and **evidence (Figure 9.2, p. 312)**. The HSO may also conduct interviews that become evidence and part of the chain of custody. The HSO should ensure policy and procedures are followed during a criminal investigation. The HSO should understand the process of preserving evidence, but may not have preservation authority at the scene. HSOs should recognize that there may be a long delay before they have access to the evidence. However, HSOs may not need to see all of the evidence in order to complete their investigations.

Evidence — Information collected and analyzed by an investigator.

Chain of Custody — Continuous changes of possession of physical evidence that must be established in court to admit such material into evidence. In order for physical evidence to be admissible in court, there must be an evidence log of accountability that documents each change of possession from the evidence's discovery until it is presented in court.

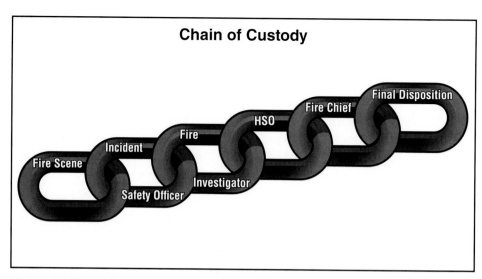

Figure 9.2 The HSO is part of the chain of custody for evidence and should follow all SOP/Gs for evidence handling and analysis.

These responsibilities are learned skills. The HSO should seek out training and education opportunities to gain the needed competency in fulfilling investigator duties. The HSO should explore resources and recommendations from the following parties:

- OSHA
- Local law enforcement
- Safety officer organizations
- Workers compensations carrier
- Risk management office
- Professional accident investigation organizations

In addition, the HSO must recognize those events that require external investigation assistance. Law enforcement, OSHA, USFA, Public Safety Officers' Benefits Program (PSOB), and public health notifications must be made as soon as possible to comply with legal investigative mandates. One additional consideration for assistance is from a neighboring jurisdiction or regional investigation teams. Having mutual aid agreements in place can expedite the process.

SOP/Gs should also address incident scene preservation and the securing of evidence. Investigations may involve external agencies, such as law enforcement, NIOSH and/or OSHA, and scene preservation of all evidence must be protected. The gathering of information should be expedited and accomplished as soon as possible after the event. Scene control and preservation should continue until all documentation and photographs are obtained and the investigation team has released the scene back to the fire department **(Figure 9.3)**. Using the departments' fire investigation personnel and equipment is a cost-effective approach to gathering information.

Conflicts of Interest

At times, conflicts of interest will exist with personnel that are involved in the investigation process, including the HSO. Potential conflicts should be recognized at the outset of an investigation. An SOP/G should define a

Figure 9.3 Security cordons, security fences, or security personnel may be used to keep a fire scene secure during a fire or accident investigation.

What This Means to You

The HSO at a municipal fire department faced a conflict of interest when he investigated an apparatus accident at his station. A new ladder platform apparatus was significantly damaged when it struck the front bay door header as it was being driven into the station.

The department's senior management had required that all new apparatus be placed at the downtown station where the accident occurred. The ladder apparatus had been driven in and out of the station countless times before the accident.

During the ensuing safety investigation, several reenactments were conducted using a duplicate ladder apparatus purchased at the same time as the damaged one. But none of the reenactments led to the ladder platform striking the front bay door header. No disciplinary or corrective actions were directed at the driver of the apparatus. Still, senior management insisted that someone be disciplined and held accountable for the costly accident.

The HSO determined that the accident was the result of the ladder platform being so close to bay door header. Measurements found the clearance between the ladder and the header were less than 1½ feet. This realization created an embarrassing situation for the senior management, which had insisted that the apparatus be placed in the station.

It also created a conflict of interest since there would have been negative consequences to the department's safety program if the driver had been disciplined for a senior management mistake. HSOs should understand that conflicts of interest may involve department members who were not directly part of the accident or injury investigation.

predetermined process for alternative assignments to handle the investigation or parts of the investigation. Conflict of interest may exist when the investigator:

- Is a witness.
- Is or was a part of the involved fire company.
- Has a relation to anyone in the investigation.
- May benefit from any disciplinary action against another, such as promotional opportunity after a demotion or separation of employment.
- Has been involved with a previous disciplinary action with anyone under investigation.
- Has a financial stake in the outcome.
- Is a part of the original Command team.

The consideration of a conflict of interest must go beyond the above listed items and include perception from within the department or in the public. When the perception of a conflict of interest exists, the findings of the investigation may come into question. The HSO should ensure all real and perceived conflicts are eliminated from the investigation. This responsibility may include removing oneself from the investigation, which will give credibility to the investigative process, the findings, and any recommendations made.

Technical Knowledge Research

Some investigations will require technical knowledge research and input. The HSO may need subject matter expert assistance from the following areas:

- **Manufacturers** — provide information on the proper operations and limitations of their product (apparatus, equipment, or clothing) in their user and operations manuals, which provide procedural steps for a particular apparatus or equipment.

- **Law enforcement personnel** — provide assistance with interviews, evidence, and general investigative procedures **(Figure 9.4)**. Accident investigation and re-creation require specialized training that law enforcement may possess. These re-creations may include computer-generated reenactments that can be valuable in understanding crash dynamics.

- **Fire behavior scientists** — provide models that can re-create a variety of situations, such as structure fires, wildland fires, wind-driven fires, flammable/combustible liquid fires, and explosions. Refer to Chapter 2, Safety and Health Laws, Codes, Regulations, and Standards for an organizational list.

- **Structural engineers** — provide technical information on the structural components of a building and possible failure explanations.

- **Forensic scientists** — provide laboratory and field examination that reveals and analyzes trace evidence, such as DNA, fingerprints, or apparatus damage not visible from simple observation.

- **Public health officials** — provide information specific to infectious disease and occupational illnesses.

- **Medical doctors or coroners** — provide specialized medical information or autopsy results.

Figure 9.4 Law enforcement officers often have information that is important to an accident investigation.

- **Bioterrorism specialists** — provide specialized information on the various agents and diseases associated with terrorism events.

- **Technical rescue specialists** — provide technical information specific to operations defined as technical rescue.

- **Hazardous materials specialists** — provide technical information specific to operations involving hazardous materials. This group also includes chemists that can provide specialized information on chemical actions and interactions.

- **Aviation Specialists** — provide technical expertise for accidents that involve aircraft.

Necessary Investigation Information

Accident investigations should be objective, impartial, and directed toward fact-finding, not fault-finding. The investigation process will include gathering pertinent information that directly leads to an understanding of what occurred. The HSO should consider all incident actions and organizational influences when determining the extent of information necessary to the investigation. Necessary investigative information will help identify the following workplace accident factors:

- The culture, habits, behavior, or condition that caused the accident (root cause)

- Previously unrecognized hazards

- Apparatus/equipment defects or design flaws

- Additional training needs

- Improvements needed in safety policies and procedures

- Evidence that could have a legal effect on an accident case

- Trends

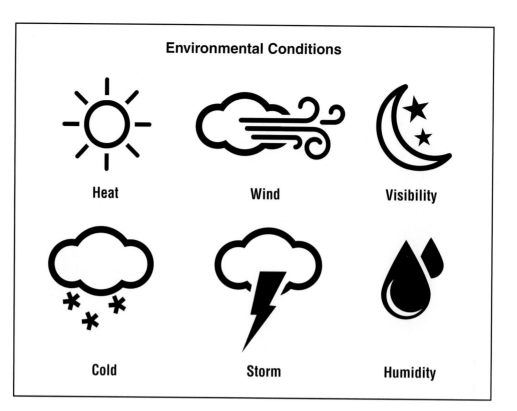

Figure 9.5 Environmental factors are an important piece of evidence to gather during an accident investigation.

Environmental Conditions

Heat   Wind   Visibility

Cold   Storm   Humidity

- Timeline
- Environmental factors **(Figure 9.5)**
- Communications
- Procedural inconsistencies

The investigation process will begin with the ISO gathering pertinent facts about the incident and notifying the HSO. The HSO will then coordinate the investigation process, which may include external agency involvement. Coordination considerations include but are not limited to the following:

- **Fire investigators** – certified fire investigators can provide guidance on procedures for conducting interviews, documenting and preserving evidence, and criminal investigation requirements **(Figure 9.6)**.

- **Law enforcement** — detectives can provide assistance and/or guidance on conducting interviews, documenting and preserving evidence, and criminal investigation requirements. If law enforcement is the lead investigative agency, such as with vehicular accidents, the HSO will serve as the liaison to ensure departmental investigative needs are met.

- **OSHA and NIOSH** — if the occurrence involves a significant injury or fatality, the HSO will ensure notifications are made. The HSO will serve as the liaison for external agency cooperation with the investigation.

Personnel Interviews

Department personnel involved in the accident/occurrence must be interviewed. While interviews should be conducted as early in the investigation as possible, consideration of the situation must be taken into account. Interviews may be delayed when personnel are being medically treated or when the emotional and psychological well-being of the personnel involved is a concern.

Figure 9.6 During an accident investigation at a scene, the HSO should coordinate with fire investigators who can provide guidance for evidence gathering.

Interviews should be conducted with individuals and not as a group. The HSO should ensure the department has an established SOP/G outlining interview participation and when that will occur. Conversations between witnesses should be limited when appropriate. An individual account of an event can change as time between the event and the interview increases and conversation between witnesses occurs. Written witness statements should be included in the early stages of the investigation. All interviews and documents should address and capture the relevant factors of what occurred and clarify confusing or conflicting information. Department policy should address when, and if, audio or video recordings are used during interviews. At a minimum, signed written statements should be obtained and filed in the report.

Evidence Documentation and Preservation

Documentation and preservation of evidence requires special handling and process procedures. The HSO should ensure a department policy addresses and outlines this process and the associated responsibilities. Documentation of evidence will include taking detailed photographs, accurate measurements, and scaled drawings and diagrams, along with a corresponding written description of the scene. The process of thoroughly documenting the scene and any associated evidence takes time to accomplish. The HSO should request assistance when needed, including official requests to law enforcement agencies.

General evidence documentation and preservation considerations include:

● Securing the scene, which may involve coordination with law enforcement

● Securing any involved apparatus or equipment

● Scene preservation, which should include removal of all persons from the immediate scene

Documentation — Written notes, audio/videotapes, printed forms, sketches and/or photographs that form a detailed record of the scene, evidence recovered, and actions taken during the search of the crime scene.

- Obtaining a **search warrant** when required
- Photographs and videos - this may include:
  - Surveillance video
  - On-board computers (black box)
  - Dashboard video
  - Automatic Vehicle Locator (AVL) data
  - Communication recordings
  - Training records
  - Drug and alcohol testing
- Evidence chain of custody procedures

Documents, photographs, videos, and investigative reports may become public records. Public records requests are common from the media and legal representatives. Local, state/provincial, and federal regulations must be followed in regards to releasing investigative documentation.

Policy and Procedure for Criminal Investigation

Any criminal investigation will involve law enforcement and jurisdictional prosecutors. If not already notified, the HSO must ensure immediate notification of the appropriate law enforcement agency having jurisdiction. The HSO should ensure a policy (SOP/G) is established that outlines the notification procedures, responsibilities of personnel, and the cooperation of department personnel. Legal representation of personnel (whether private, corporate, or union) and the organization should be outlined. The policy should also address guidelines on whether personnel remain in their regular duty assignment, are placed on an administrate leave status, or receive an alternate duty assignment during the investigative process. In most departments, this determination will be made in junction with the human resources department. Fire department personnel should make no presumptions of guilt during a criminal investigation. Personnel must wait for adjudication from the judicial system.

Postincident Analysis

The **postincident analysis (PIA)**, evaluation (PIE), or review (PIR) is essential to the successful and safe operations of the fire and emergency services. Properly developed and written, the PIA determines the strengths and weaknesses of the organization's response to the emergency. The PIA provides an opportunity for participants to objectively review the operation in a constructive manner. It provides a training tool as well as the basis for future planning for emergency responses. It also motivates change in policies and procedures that may be outdated or ineffectual in meeting the current needs of the response area **(Table 9.1)**.

The postincident analysis is a written document that is compiled by the IC, a designated member of the Incident Command or general staff, or a designated member not associated with the incident, such as a training officer. The department will determine the ultimate responsibility for the PIA. The HSO and ISO are responsible for ensuring all safety and health concerns are included in the PIA. **Learning Activity 9-1** provides an exercise for practicing writing PIAs.

Table 9.1
Postincident Analysis Components

Strategy and Tactics Analysis	Safety Issues
Interviews of witnesses and participants	Violations of SOP/Gs
News media photographs and video	Future training topics
Contents of the Incident Action Plan (IAP)	Poorly defined operational procedures
Communication logs and tapes	Unforeseen situations
Preincident site plans and inspections	Training deficiencies identified
Structural reports	
Owner/occupant statements	

The analysis is intended to focus on the activities of the participants, the elements of the emergency, and the decisions made that were intended to control the incident. The PIA is *not* intended to place blame or find fault with the participants, their decisions, or actions. It must not be used to punish any of the participants and must not have the perception of a fault-finding process. If the results of the PIA indicate that a postincident critique should be held, all participants and agencies should be involved in the critique.

Postincident Analysis or Critique

Some fire and emergency service organizations use the term *postincident analysis* as the written document and a meeting of the personnel involved to review the incident. However, for this manual, the term *postincident analysis* is used to define only the written evaluation of an operation. The term *postincident critique* defines the meeting of the personnel involved to discuss the *postincident analysis* findings.

Health and Safety Components of a Postincident Analysis

The PIA is an opportunity for the HSO to identify, analyze, and correct any problems or deficiencies discovered during an incident. The final written report should include additional information pertaining to the following:

- Use of protective clothing
- The personnel accountability system
- Rehabilitation operations
- Hazardous conditions
- Other issues relating to the safety of personnel at the incident

The HSO should look for what went right and/or what improvements can be made in operational procedures. One way to determine what these items are is for the HSO to have discussions with personnel present at the incident. Health and safety considerations exist at all levels of the operation, so discussions should include command staff, crew members, and the ISO (if assigned).

Rehabilitation Procedures

Any fire department activity, whether it is an event or training exercise, needs a designated **rehabilitation** area for members and a designated **Responder Rehabilitation Manager (Figure 9.7)**. As part of postincident analysis review, the HSO should review the postincident analysis report and ensure that the organization's rehabilitation procedures were followed. In order to make that determination, HSOs must know about rehabilitation best practices.

Rehabilitation of members may be a formal or informal process. An informal rehabilitation is one that is used for a minor event or training exercise. These events are typically less than 30 minutes in duration and do not involve labor-intensive activities. Informal rehabilitation is the responsibility of the IC or company officer operating at the event.

Rehabilitation Terminology

Rehabilitation is a broad term that often includes procedures as simple as providing water during short training sessions or as complex as providing medical surveillance and scheduling work shifts at large incidents. Because the definition of rehabilitation is so broad, some departments use specific terminology, such as *replenishment*, to differentiate formal rehab from informal rehab. Replenishment might refer to having a refreshment station during training, while rehabilitation might refer to more complex incidents and require a designated officer to oversee that incident function **(Figure 9.8)**. When writing rehabilitation procedures, the HSO may want to consider using similar language to ensure that all responders understand the procedures for formal rehabilitation and do not confuse these procedures with the requirements of short-term incidents or training.

A formal rehabilitation area is typically established at events that are in extreme climates or involve labor-intensive activities. Rehabilitation best practices are ever-evolving, and the time extent of the incident may not be a good indicator for formal rehabilitation. Formal rehabilitation areas should provide a means for responders to get out of the environment (such as air-conditioned or heated vehicles), have rehydration and nutrition supplies readily available, and include a standard medical evaluation process. During the SOP/G development or revision process, the HSO needs to ensure the following rehabilitation elements are included:

- **The criteria for establishing a rehabilitation area** — not all events or training exercises need a formal rehabilitation area established. The SOP/G should provide decision criteria for establishing a formal or informal rehabilitation area.

Figure 9.7 Rehab areas at emergency scenes should have a designated rehabilitation manager to oversee rehab and check firefighters in and out. *Courtesy of Bob Esposito.*

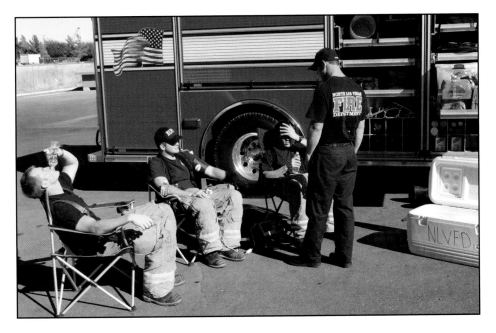

Figure 9.8 Some organizations use the term *replenishment* to describe very basic rehab consisting of an area to rest and rehydrate without the other, more formal aspects of rehabilitation.

- **Who is responsible for establishing a rehabilitation area** — this may be the IC, ISO, or training officer. Rehabilitation of responders is a function within the Medical Unit. Depending on the size of the incident and the expansion of the ICS structure, a Responder Rehabilitation Manager may be assigned. The SOP/G should address the process of expanding the ICS structure with position responsibilities defined.

- **Location of the rehabilitation area** — some departments have the ability to provide vehicles outfitted specifically for rehabilitation. Other departments must get creative and adapt to their situation. Either way, the process for establishing the location of a formal rehabilitation area should be written into the SOP/G. Once a formal rehabilitation area is established, the location must be communicated to all units operating at the event or training exercise.

- **Rehabilitation Manager Responsibilities** — the Responder Rehabilitation Manager will be responsible for maintaining personnel accountability, documentation of any medical evaluation data, and any decontamination activities of personnel. The Rehabilitation Manager will also make staffing requests to the IC for additional assistance when needed.

- **Rehabilitation rehydration and nutrition** — the HSO should carefully research and recommend that proper rehydration and nutrition are provided to members. Simply supplying fast food is not acceptable to meeting the health and wellness of members who are expected to function at a high physical fitness level. At a minimum, drinking water should be carried on every front-line apparatus and command vehicle **(Figure 9.9)**. Sports drinks should be carefully evaluated before use. Some drinks have high levels of sugar or other ingredients that may cause nausea and stomach cramps **(Figure 9.10)**. Any nutrition supplied at the scene must be easily digestible and a source of energy.

- **Medical evaluation** — once a formal rehabilitation area is established, a process of evaluating all members operating at the event or training exercise must be included **(Figure 9.11)**. The SOP/G should state what the medical evaluation includes and a decision matrix for when members are cleared to return to work, are held in the rehabilitation area, or are transported to a medical facility for further evaluation and treatment. The HSO should research medical evaluation and decision matrix criteria and make recommendations for inclusion in SOP/Gs.

- **Restroom and washing facilities** — some departments have rehabilitation or command apparatus with restroom and washing facilities included. The departments that do not have these mobile facilities need to have a standard process of securing restroom and washing facilities. Responders are expected to be hydrated prior to, and rehydrate during and after events. The HSO should work to ensure an SOP/G provides guidance on this often-overlooked element.

Review of SOP/Gs Based Upon Postincident Analysis

The postincident analysis is an opportunity to review all relevant SOP/Gs associated with an operation. In addition, it provides an assessment on the performance of the IC, decisions made, communications, and strategy and tactics employed. This assessment can be a useful training tool for those members who function as ICs. The review should determine if SOP/Gs were followed or if a deviation occurred. If a deviation occurred, it should be determined why. These reasons can include intentional or unintentional deviations, or gradual drifts that have gone unchecked over a period of time. Either way, the review should include an assessment of the adequacy and effectiveness of the SOP/Gs. The final report should state whether the SOP/Gs met the operational needs of the department or include recommendation for corrective actions, if necessary.

Figure 9.9 Drinking water should be carried on all front-line apparatus.

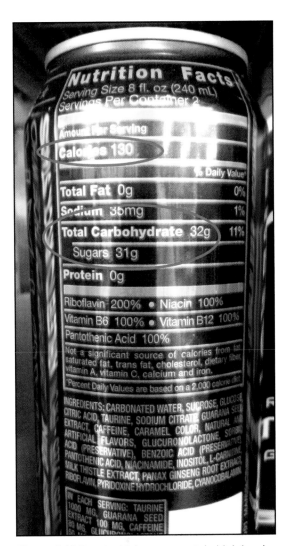

Figure 9.10 Sports drinks may contain high levels of added sugar and should be used sparingly.

Figure 9.11 Medical evaluations when joining an emergency or returning to an emergency are rehab functions.

Corrective Actions Based on the Incident

Corrective actions identified in a PIA should address critical needs to improve the safety and health of personnel during incident operations. The complexity and special circumstances of each incident must be taken into consideration on a case-by-case basis. The HSO should recognize that not all incident circumstances can or need to be addressed in the department policy and procedures manual. Some operational flexibility is needed to accomplish incident stabilization in a dynamic all-hazards environment. With this in mind, the HSO should understand that unsafe acts with no consequences may be perceived as acceptable, which reinforces the unsafe act and may lead personnel to taking additional risk that result in an accident. This practice may create drift from policy in subsequent emergency operations.

Revision of SOP/Gs Based Upon Postincident Analysis

When the postincident analysis is complete, the final written report will describe any needed changes to the department policy and procedures manual. This process should involve a careful consideration of existing SOP/Gs versus the recommended revisions. The HSO should evaluate the following questions:

- What is the basis for the recommendation?
- What research is available to support the recommendation?
- What training is needed?
- What unintended consequences may result?
- What is the financial effect on the organization?
- What is the effect on personnel?

If changes are recommended and accepted to the policy and procedures manual, they must be communicated to all personnel. Training (didactic and/or psychomotor) should be included with all procedural revisions.

Identifying the Root Cause of the Accident

A **root cause** analysis is an investigative tool to determine why something happened. This process may seem straightforward on a first impression, but it is more complicated than that. A **root cause analysis** should be approached in a comprehensive manner with an in-depth search beyond the obvious immediate actions and outcomes **(Figure 9.12)**. With a first impression, it may

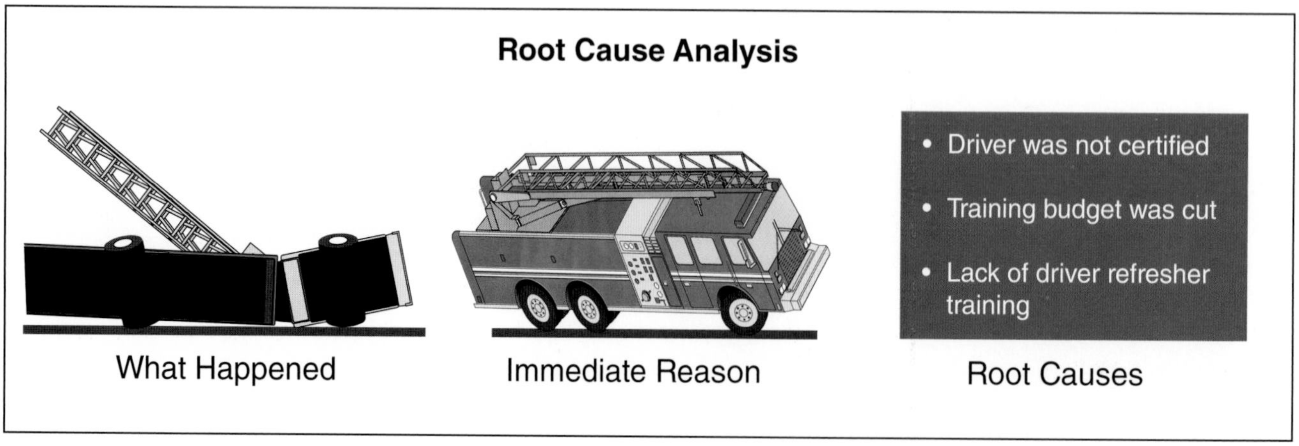

Root Cause — The cultural and attitudinal reasons that led to the circumstances or behavior surrounding an accident, injury, fatality, illness, exposure, or near-miss.

Root Cause Analysis — Investigative tool used to go beyond the immediate facts to discover what cultural attitudes or behaviors contributed to an accident, injury, fatality, illness, exposure, or near-miss.

Root Cause Analysis

What Happened   Immediate Reason   Root Causes

- Driver was not certified
- Training budget was cut
- Lack of driver refresher training

Figure 9.12 Root cause analysis does not end when the immediate reason for an accident is identified.

be easy to label a root cause(s) as human error, human caused, or a failure of human action. However, this assumption is short-sighted and does not provide a good understanding of what really happened and why. The root cause analysis exists to determine not only obvious factors that immediately preceded the occurrence, but also the undetected problem(s) that existed prior and influenced the outcome.

Every organization's risk management plan should include a root cause analysis process. The goal of a root cause analysis is to prevent future occurrences of a comparable nature or recurrences of the past, not find fault. A SOP/G will need to define the root cause analysis process, when it will be utilized, and any assigned responsibilities in the process. At a minimum, a root cause analysis should be conducted for the following occurrences:

- Accidents
- Near-misses
- Injuries
- Fatalities
- Occupational illnesses
- Occupational exposures
- Any other incident with special circumstances, as defined by the department

According to NFPA® 1521, the HSO is responsible for the overall investigation process that includes a root cause analysis. Depending on the complexity or severity of the accident/occurrence, a root cause analysis may lead to more than one (sometimes numerous) influential factor(s) or cause(s). Once the influential factors or potential causes are identified, it is time to delve into the accident/occurrence and peel apart the layers of conditions and actions that have occurred over time. The root cause analysis extends as far back in time as necessary to understand what potentially led to the negative outcome **(Figure 9.13, p. 326)**. While it may be relatively easy to determine the human actions during the investigation, it will be more difficult to determine what, if any, organizational factors or long-term underlying conditions had influence on any incident action(s) or lack of action. These immediate factors and underlying organizational conditions were described as *active failures* and *latent conditions* in Chapter 7, Safety and Health Programs. Additionally, the HSO should assess the organization's defense mechanisms/layers and look for strengths and weaknesses during the analysis.

The HSO should not get lost in all the negative findings – positive ones exist as well. It is just as important to determine and make known the positive findings from a root cause analysis. Lessons learned should include both. During the investigation, the HSO should also realize that investigations only provide an after-the-fact viewpoint. This **hindsight bias** is a significant consideration when making a judgment. Judgment can be influenced, knowingly or unknowingly, when the situation, actions, and outcome of an occurrence are already known.

Hindsight Bias — Tendency during investigations to see events as more predictable than they actually were or to judge events differently based upon the outcome of the event rather than the behavior that transpired.

Root Cause History

NOW

Firefighter suffers health problems after overhaul; not wearing respiratory protection.

1 YEAR AGO

Company Officer tells Firefighter as a recruit that SOP/Gs for overhaul do not require respiratory protection.

3 YEARS AGO

New standards say respiratory protection must be worn during overhaul; SOP/Gs are neither reviewed nor changed.

10 YEARS AGO

SOP/Gs written stating that it is acceptable to remove respiratory protection before overhaul.

Figure 9.13 A thorough root cause analysis should examine the decisions that led to an accident no matter how far back the HSO has to look in the organization's records.

Hindsight Bias

Hindsight bias is a concept from psychological research in the 1970s. Baruch Fischoff and Ruth Beyth authored, "'I Knew It Would Happen': Remembered Probabilities of Once-Future Things" in the journal *Organizational Behavior and Human Performance*. The article states that judgment of an event is different when viewed from foresight as opposed to hindsight because in hindsight there is a tendency to see the events as more predictable than they actually were. Credit must also be given to Amos Tversky and Daniel Kahneman for their work on psychological theory that influenced and preceded the specific study of hindsight bias. Readings from these authors and others will provide a richer understanding of the concepts and theories surrounding and including hindsight bias.

Judgment of an event in hindsight almost always includes information that was not known before or during the event. Fishcoff's study showed that judgments about behaviors were harsher if the outcomes from those behaviors were bad rather than good. For example, a near-miss *could* have resulted in a firefighter fatality, but since it did not, we tend to judge the behavior that led to the near-miss less harshly because we know the firefighter lived. Given the same behaviors, if the firefighter had died, the incident would be scrutinized more closely even though the behaviors at both incidents were the same.

During an investigation, the HSO should be cognizant of hindsight bias when rendering judgment and recommendations because the outcome is already known. If the outcome were positive rather than negative, would the same judgment and recommendations be made about the actions and conditions that existed? Did some other defense mechanism catch the action before leading to a negative outcome? These are important questions for the HSO to consider when conducting a root cause analysis.

Due to the complexity of a root cause analysis, the utilization of a computer software program and investigative training may help the HSO complete the process. Software programs can streamline the process by bringing multiple analysis or investigative facets together into a central point of entry. As stated with accident investigations, root cause analysis involves skills that are learned. The HSO should explore computer software and training options that meet the department's needs. Costs associated with computer software and training can be a significant consideration. The HSO should search for a cost-effective option, which may be a single-department or a multijurisdictional approach in which several departments share the financial responsibility and resources.

Research Sources for Root Cause Analysis

The HSO is encouraged to seek a wide-ranging source of research material with regards to human error and root cause analysis. An excellent starting point is with noted authors, such as Eric Hollnagel, Jens Rasmussen, James Reason, Karl Weick, and David Woods. The basis for root cause analysis and human performance in this chapter comes from the conceptualizations of these authors and others. In addition, readings on safety in the workplace can be found from Rhona Flin, Robert Helmreich, Todd LaPorte, Karlene Roberts, Gene Rochlin, and Eduardo Salas. These authors discuss the influence of crew resource management and the functions of high reliability organizations in the pursuit of reducing errors and accidents in critical situations.

Gathering Facts about the Incident

Fact gathering will begin with the ISO, if assigned. The ISO should sub.nit a written report to the HSO on any safety and health issues identified during an incident. This process follows the same guideline of a PIA report. The HSO, as the investigator, will confirm the facts and conduct any follow-up interviews that are needed.

When gathering facts, the HSO will focus on the human performance aspect, the choice of equipment used, the performance and use of the equipment, and environmental factors that may have influenced the outcome of an incident. Incident facts are just one part of the root cause analysis, but an important part.

In this process, the HSO will work with the ISO (if assigned), the IC, company officers, and any other members who are witnesses to the occurrence. Written statements, interviews, photographs or hand-written diagrams of the scene, and a review of the sequence of events will be a part of the process. In addition, the HSO may work with law enforcement, OSHA investigators, risk management personnel, or the fire department physician during the process.

Five Whys Analysis

Sakichi Toyoda, founder of the Toyota Motor Company, is credited with creating a system for root cause analysis consisting of asking "why" five times. The purpose of the exercise is to force the accident investigator to think beyond the immediate cause of an accident to its origins in human behavior, safety deficiencies, or inadequate equipment or procedures.

Here is an example of applying the five whys to an accident investigation.

What occurred: A firefighter was injured in an apparatus accident.

1. Why did the firefighter get injured? — The firefighter was not wearing his seat belt.

2. Why was the firefighter not wearing his seat belt? — None of the other firefighters in the truck wore their seat belts.

3. Why was no one wearing a seat belt? — Seat belt safety is not enforced by the truck's company officer.

4. Why doesn't the company officer enforce seat belt safety? — Seat belt safety is not emphasized as important in the department's safety culture or training.

5. Why is seat belt safety not part of the safety culture or training? — It has not become a part of the accepted culture because no accident-related injuries have been reported for an extended period of time.

The practice of asking why repeatedly in this example allows the investigator to delve deeper into the real reason that the firefighter was injured. In fact, if necessary, the investigator could continue to ask why in this case. *Why are accident-related injuries so infrequently reported?* This method is a simple technique that any HSO can use to seek out the root cause of an accident **(Figure 9.14)**.

5 Whys

SITUATION

FIREFIGHTER INJURED IN AN ACCIDENT

1. *Why?* .... Not wearing a seatbelt

2. *Why?* .... No one on the truck wears seatbelts.

3. *Why?* .... CO does not enforce seatbelt rules.

4. *Why?* .... Lack of seatbelts use has never been an issue and is not taught.

5. *Why?* .... No reported accidents over an extended period of time.

Figure 9.14 A simple technique for conducting a root cause analysis is to ask why something occurred five times, moving closer to the likely root cause every time.

Human Performance

The HSO should explore human performance, human error, and human factors as a line of research. Although a detailed discussion on these topics goes beyond the scope of this manual, the fact remains that humans are an integral part of how the fire service system works. The performance of humans interacting in a complex fire service system can lead to wrong determinations of what caused an accident or occurrence. The human element must be viewed as the starting point of the investigation. What should follow is a detailed evaluation of how the complex system influenced the human performance.

When evaluating human performance during an investigation, the HSO should be aware that this is just the beginning of the process, not the end. Human performance is a crucial element to the fact-finding process, but not the finish line. The ISO and HSO will collectively evaluate the positive and negative human performance factors that influence the outcome. Human factors that often contribute to accidents have been classified into the following three broad categories:

- **Improper attitude** — Includes any of a number of behaviors as outlined in **Table 9.2**. Readjusting any of these attitudes or personality traits through counseling, training, or discipline can lead to accident reduction.

Table 9.2
Human Factors

Improper Attitude	Lack of Knowledge or Skill	Physically Unsuited
Willful disregard	Insufficient knowledge	Hearing or vision problems
Recklessness	Misunderstanding	Over or under weight
Laziness	Indecision	Illness
Disloyalty	Inexperience	Allergies
Uncooperativeness	Poor training	Fatigue
Fearfulness	Failure to recognize potential hazards	Slow reactions
Oversensitivity		Disabilities
Egotism		Intoxication
Jealousy		Physical limitations
Impatience		
Obsession		
Absentmindedness		
Excitability		
Inconsideration		
Intolerence		

- **Lack of knowledge or skill** — Includes any deficiencies on firefighters' ability as outlined in **Table 9.2**.

- **Physically unsuited** — Includes any of a number physical limitations as outlined in **Table 9.2**. Correcting these physical limitations can often reduce accident rates. If they cannot be corrected, personnel should not be assigned to tasks in which their limitations might create a hazard or be potentially dangerous to themselves or others.

Choice of Equipment

The choice of equipment used for a specific task should meet the predetermined criteria of its intended use. This consideration includes examining the circumstances of the situation and the task being performed. Remember, the HSO is judging this decision after-the-fact. If it is determined a deviation of equipment choice occurred, it must be followed up with why an alternate choice was made. There may be a legitimate deviation justification after consideration of all the incident, environmental, and situational factors get included. When conducting the root cause analysis on equipment choice, the HSO should also research the purchase decision of the equipment. Was the right purchasing decision made to accomplish a specific task?

Performance and Use of Equipment

Along with evaluating the choice of the equipment, equipment performance and use must be considered. The HSO should determine if the equipment performed as designed. If not, further investigation into why it malfunctioned should be conducted. Are there maintenance issues, extended life use concerns, or other problems? Proper use of the equipment must also be evaluated. If the equipment was not used properly, further investigation should examine why a deviation occurred. Was the person trained on the use of a particular piece of equipment? These are just a few of the considerations and questions the HSO should explore.

Environmental Factors

Environmental factors will include the weather conditions and topography at the time of the incident. The environment can have a significant impact on human and equipment performance and should not be overlooked. The HSO should record the time of day and weather data that includes the temperature, humidity, and wind, along with any storm activity in the area at a minimum. The operational topography or landscape should also be detailed and photographed, if possible.

Identifying Deviations from SOP/Gs

When conducting the root cause analysis, all applicable SOP/Gs for the incident should be included in the evaluation in order to determine if any deviation occurred. When a deviation or deviations are identified, further analysis is needed. Are the deviation(s) intentional or unintentional? Are the deviation(s) drifts from standard practice that have crept into practice? Interviews with personnel should be included to obtain decision-making thoughts. The HSO should consider the adequacy and effectiveness of the SOP/G(s), and if needed, make corrective action recommendations. As stated earlier, not all minute procedures require a written SOP/G. Some deviations or drifts may require minor performance modifications and not elaborate solutions.

What This Means to You

As the HSO in your department, you are asked to look into an accident involving a fire engine pulling into a fire station. A fire engine crew had moved to another district to cover another station's run area while that crew attended a mandatory training session. The 3-person crew consisted of a captain, a driver/operator, and a firefighter. The fire engine had an enclosed cab with four seating positions, two forward-facing and two rear-facing. This fire engine had a 50-foot aerial ladder and a preplumbed waterway attached. The fire engine was equipped with headphones and an open intercom system that all personnel use.

As the crew arrived at their destination, they awaited the opening of the apparatus bay doors so that they could proceed into the apparatus bay. As the fire engine entered the apparatus bay door, the aerial ladder section struck the top of the bay door. The fire engine was temporarily wedged in the doorway opening. The crew immediately notified dispatch to place it out of service. The captain proceeded into the station to begin the unpleasant process of notifying the shift commander.

During your initial fact-gathering phase, you learn that this fire engine is too tall for the older station to which it was temporarily assigned. The damage to the station is minimal; however, the aerial ladder portion of the apparatus is damaged beyond repair and must be completely replaced.

Corrective Action Plans

Corrective actions plans will address items that are determined to be deficient for one reason or another. Corrective actions plans should not be used as a quick fix or a hasty reaction to an issue. These plans need to be well-thought-out. The HSO should ask and contemplate what unintended consequences may result from the corrective actions. Some corrective action items will be clear and easily rationalized, while others may be more difficult to process. The plan should focus on items that, when corrected, will prevent a future recurrence of an accident or incident that leads to injury, death, illness, or exposure.

Corrective Action Recommendations

After completing the analysis and determining the root cause of the accident, injury, job-related illness, or health exposure, the HSO should identify a solution or solutions to resolve the problem. The HSO should not approach the process of making recommendations in isolation. The HSO should reach out to other members for assistance or to the occupational safety and health committee. The HSO will then write a report outlining the problem, the investigation process, and one or more recommended solutions. Solutions to problems fall anywhere on the continuum of one solution to multiple solutions. In some cases, contingency recommendations should be developed.

Recommendations should be based on a comprehensive assessment. The use of an algorithm or decision matrix may help identify the root cause and the associated corrective action recommendations. The goal should be to address risk and not assign blame. The HSO should explore the algorithms or decision matrices available on the Internet.

The HSO should not hesitate to recommend a wellness program as a solution when it is evident that physical and/or psychological stress was the root cause of the injury or fatality. An effective program will help reduce needless loss of life if it promotes proper nutrition, physical fitness, periodic medical evaluations, ceasing tobacco use, and stress relief and control.

Corrective Action Plan Development

Each organization must determine how corrective action plans will be developed. At a minimum, a corrective action plan will include **(Figure 9.15)**:

- A statement detailing the issue(s) or deficiencies that need correction. This determination will come from the root cause analysis. The HSO should be careful in wording the issue, so as to not assign fault to a person or team.

- Each corrective action should be assigned to a person or division within the organization. This task can include training, SOP/G modification, and/or performance improvement plans. Some training may be available from outside entities with expertise in the applicable area. With this assignment, the organization should define what success is in achieving a stated goal. This determination will also involve a continuous evaluation or monitoring process of any corrective actions.

- Each corrective action should have a time frame for realistic achievement of goals. The time frame will be defined on a case-by-case basis and should not be a one-size-fits-all approach.

The following procedural considerations provide a baseline for the corrective action plan development:

- Use a team of personnel, such as the occupational safety and health committee, to develop the plan

- Have a process to review SOP/Gs to determine if modifications need to be made

- Have a process to review accident reports to determine if policy, procedure, training, and practice need to be modified

- Have a process to review injuries, fatalities, illnesses, and exposure to determine if policy, procedure, training, and practice need to be modified

- Have a process to review near-miss reports and trends for lessons

- Have a process to observe current practice to evaluate the need for systemic change

- Include a time frame for implementation of changes

- Include directions for what training is needed

- Have a process for how the plan will be disseminated throughout the organization

Figure 9.15 Corrective actions require thorough documentation, an authority to act on them, and clear guidelines defining the time frame for the actions to take effect.

Chapter Summary

Improvement within the fire and emergency services organization is a constant process. This process includes the evaluation of current practices, established policies and procedures, and applied operational strategies and tactics. Accident investigations, postincident analyses, and root cause analyses are critical assessments that must be conducted in a comprehensive manner and with a neutral mindset. The HSO is the safety and health advocate in the department promoting a safety culture. Unfortunately, at times, the HSO must serve as the investigator into negative occurrences. The positive and negative lessons must be determined and accepted if the department intends to continually improve workplace safety.

Review Questions

1. What is the health safety officer's relationship to evidence during the information gathering process of an investigation? (pp. 311-312)

2. What types of situations would result in a conflict of interest during a departmental investigation? (pp. 312-314)

3. Where can the health safety officer go to find subject matter knowledge and expertise when conducting an investigation? (pp. 314-315)

4. What general guidelines should the health safety officer follow when conducting personnel interviews? (pp. 316-317)

5. What considerations should the health safety officer take when documenting and preserving evidence for an investigation? (pp. 317-318)

6. What items should be addressed in departmental policies and procedures for a criminal investigation? (p. 318)

7. Why is the postincident analysis essential to successful and safe departmental operations? (pp. 318-320)

8. What rehabilitation elements should the health safety officer include during the SOP/G development or revision process? (pp. 320-322)

9. What should the health safety officer take into account when reviewing SOP/Gs, identifying corrective actions, and revising SOP/Gs once the postincident analysis is complete? (pp. 322-324)

10. What is a root cause analysis? (pp. 324-327)

11. Which factors should the health safety officer focus on when gathering facts about an incident? (pp. 328-331)

12. What factors should the health safety officer consider when identifying deviations from departmental SOP/Gs? (pp. 331-332)

13. What are some baseline considerations the health safety officer should follow when developing a corrective action plan? (pp. 332-333)

9-1
Conduct a postincident analysis of a MVA incident where two responding firefighters were injured.

Refer to Appendix B: Learning Activity Answers in the back of this manual for suggested responses.

Purpose

The health safety officer is the safety and health advocate for the fire department, the individual responsible for promoting a culture of safety. At times, however, the HSO must also serve as the investigator of accidents, injuries and illnesses, fatalities, and exposures. Postincident analyses and root cause analyses are critical tools the HSO must use as part of these investigations, and those assessments must be conducted in a comprehensive manner and with a neutral mindset.

Directions

1. Read the scenario.

2. Review the MVA incident from **Learning Activity 5-1**.

3. Read **Employee Accident Reports 1 and 2** (provided on the following pages) of the firefighter injuries that occurred during the MVA.

4. Conduct a full postincident analysis of the incident. As you work:

   a. Determine what other information you will need in order to fully perform your analysis.

   b. List possible root causes for the firefighter injuries.

   c. List other documentation or procedures that would be required to fully investigate the incidents and to perform a root cause analysis.

   d. List any procedures that would reinforce the health and safety component of the postincident analysis.

5. Write a short memorandum reviewing the incident and the two injuries. The memo should include the information listed in the step above: possible root causes for the firefighter injuries, any additional documentation or procedures that would be required to complete the postincident analysis and root cause analysis, and any procedures that would support the health and safety component of your analysis.

   NOTE: As you work, also consider and note any possible conflicts of interest.

Scenario

You are the new safety officer for the St. Florian Fire Department. One of your first tasks is to review injury reports for the last year. You notice that two firefighters were injured at a MVA in 2014 and decide to investigate further.

Upon further inquiry of the incident, you determine that Firefighter Ramirez suffered a broken ankle at the accident and was out of work for four months. She is now back on duty. Firefighter Wheeler suffered a concussion, a strained neck, and a torn rotator cuff. After an initial four-month rehabilitation period, it was determined that he required rotator cuff surgery. He is still out on medical leave and it is unclear if Firefighter Wheeler will regain enough strength in his shoulder to return to active duty.

LEARNING ACTIVITIES

9-1 (cont.)

Conduct a postincident analysis of a MVA incident where two responding firefighters were injured.

Refer to Appendix B: Learning Activity Answers in the back of this manual for suggested responses.

In order to determine the root cause(s) of these two injuries, you look for a postincident analysis. It appears a complete postincident analysis was never filed, so you decide to conduct one of your own and pull the original employee accident reports.

Employee Accident Report 1

St. Florian Fire Department
Employee Accident Report

Date: **February 1, 2015**	Date of Accident: **January 20, 2014** Time of Accident: **1645 hrs. approx.**
Accident Classification: **X** Injury Illness Fatality	Incident/Accident Location: **1234 Washington Avenue**
Employee Name: **Ramirez**	Incident Number: **15-011283**
Employee Assignment Location: Shift: A **X** B C	Employee Rank/Classification: **Firefighter**
Employee Age: **32** Gender: Female **X** Male	
Weather at Time of Accident: **Windy, cold, freezing rain**	Temperature at Time of Accident: **33°F (0.5 °C)**
Scene Conditions at Time of Accident: **ICY**	
Incident Commander: **Battalion Chief Peters**	Shift Commander: **Same**
Safety Officer: **Captain McLelland**	EMS Unit(s): **PA 101**
Motorized Equipment Involved in Accident: **None**	
Personal Protective Equipment: **Bunker gear, boots, gloves, helmet, ANSI approved reflective vest.**	

Refer to Appendix B: Learning Activity Answers in the back of this manual for suggested responses.

Narrative 1. How did the accident occur? **Firefighter Ramirez was carrying a hydraulic extrication tool from Engine 1 to the site of the collision (about 20m away). Due to icy conditions, she slipped and injured her ankle.**
Narrative 2. Why did the accident occur? **Icy/slippery terrain. Also, Firefighter Ramirez should not have attempted to carry the heavy tool in such treacherous conditions by herself.**
Narrative 3. What could be done to reduce exposure risk for future accidents? **Consider adding ice cleats to standard issue gear in winter.** **Increase training in winter conditions.**
Name of Witnesses: **J. Andersen, B. Ward, D. Singh**

Signature of employee: Date:	Signature of Employee Supervisor: Date:
Name of person filling out report **Captain McLelland**	

LEARNING ACTIVITIES

Conduct a postincident analysis of a MVA incident where two responding firefighters were injured.

9-1 (cont.)

Refer to Appendix B: Learning Activity Answers in the back of this manual for suggested responses.

Employee Accident Report 2

St. Florian Fire Department
Employee Accident Report

Date: **February 1, 2015**	Date of Accident: **January 20, 2014** Time of Accident: **1655 hrs. approx.**
Accident Classification: **X** Injury Illness Fatality	Incident/Accident Location: **1234** **Washington Avenue**
Employee Name: **Wheeler**	Incident Number: **15-011284**
Employee Assignment Location: Shift: A **X** B C	Employee Rank/Classification: **Firefighter**
Employee Age: **32** Gender: Female Male **X**	
Weather at Time of Accident: **Windy, cold, freezing rain**	Temperature at Time of Accident: **33°F** **(0.5 °C)**
Scene Conditions at Time of Accident: **ICY**	
Incident Commander: **Battalion Chief Peters**	Shift Commander: **Same**
Safety Officer: **Captain McLelland**	EMS Unit(s): **PA 101**
Motorized Equipment Involved in Accident: **Vehicle's front passenger airbag**	
Personal Protective Equipment: **Bunker gear, boots, gloves, helmet, ANSI approved reflective vest.**	

9-1 (cont.)
Conduct a postincident analysis of a MVA incident where two responding firefighters were injured.

LEARNING ACTIVITIES

Refer to Appendix B: Learning Activity Answers in the back of this manual for suggested responses.

Narrative 1. How did the accident occur?
Firefighter Wheeler was attempting to remove a child from a car seat. The child was fastened into a car seat in the rear passenger seat. Firefighter Wheeler was leaning in the window of the front passenger seat and attempting to disengage the car seat's straps when the front passenger airbag activated. Firefighter Wheeler was forcefully struck on the right shoulder and right side of the head, causing injuries to his head, neck, and shoulder.
Narrative 2. Why did the accident occur?
Unexpected airbag activation.
Narrative 3. What could be done to reduce exposure risk for future accidents?
Periodic training on airbag deployment.
Name of Witnesses: **J. Andersen, B. Ward, D. Singh**

Signature of employee:	Signature of Employee Supervisor:
Date:	Date:
Name of person filling out report **Captain McLelland**	

Facilities Inspection

Chapter Contents

Key Terms

NFPA® Job Performance Requirements

This chapter provides information that addresses the following job performance requirements of NFPA® 1521, *Standard for Fire Department Safety Officer Professional Qualifications (2015).*

4.9.2

Facilities Inspection

Learning Objectives

After reading this chapter, students will be able to:

1. Describe the process of conducting a fire department health and safety facility inspection. (4.9.2)

2. Identify processes for addressing violations that may be found during a facility inspection. (4.9.2)

3. Learning Activity 10-1: Conduct a mock health and safety inspection for a fire department facility. (4.9.2)

Chapter 10
Facilities Inspection

Case History

All workers, including fire and emergency service personnel, are entitled to working conditions that do not pose a risk of causing them serious harm. While working conditions on the fireground and other emergency scenes are difficult at best to control, the primary workplace, our fire stations and associated service facilities, should be both safe and healthful environments. Proper design, maintenance, and inspections of these facilities will assure a level of safety and comfort.

Some years ago, in the early morning hours, a career fire department crew was awakened in their station to respond to a call. Upon awakening, the Captain noticed a strange odor and began investigating. Almost immediately, his eyes began to tear. He recognized the smell as smoke that could originate in a malfunctioning boiler. The fire station's fire alarm system had not activated and the station was not equipped with a carbon monoxide detector or sprinklers.

He immediately woke the other members of the crew who had not responded to the original call and were still in their sleeping quarters. The firefighters shut down the apparent defective boiler and opened the overhead doors and windows in the firehouse to ventilate the carbon monoxide-laden smoke. The company members were transported to the hospital and tested for high CO levels in their blood, treated, and released.

As was reported, the irony of this event was that this department donated and installed smoke and CO detectors throughout its community; however, its own station was not equipped with a CO detector. If an emergency alarm had not awoken the Captain and one of his crews, the detrimental health effects could have been more severe or they could have died.

To ensure the health and safety of our personnel, all fire stations and associated facilities should be equipped with working fire alarm systems, CO detectors, and sprinkler systems. Facility inspections are excellent opportunities to check for and test these detectors and systems.

All fire and emergency services facilities require regular inspection and maintenance to prevent deterioration and unsafe working conditions. Some facilities are built with the intention of lasting 50 years or longer. With this in mind, the HSO's responsibility is to ensure a SOP/G is in place that defines the process, schedule, and responsibilities associated with inspections and maintenance of facilities. Risk assessment at a facility is the ultimate goal of any inspection. When conducting an inspection, the HSO can use the same risk evaluation procedures described in Chapter 5, Organizational Risk Management regarding risk identification or in Chapter 6, Operational Risk Management regarding preincident planning.

All inspections, in some way, have a safety and health objective for the workplace and the worker, which is why the HSO coordinates the facility inspection process. Each inspection may have a specific purpose. The HSO should ensure the completion of all inspections; however, responsibilities for performing the inspections will differ across departments and be dependent on the reason(s) for an inspection. For the HSO, the focus is to ensure all violations or corrective actions are addressed to improve workplace safety. Some organizations require or are required by law to have a safety and health committee member be present at the annual facility inspection. A standardized checklist helps ensure consistency over time and should be included in the SOP/G specific to the inspection type.

16 Firefighter Life Safety Initiatives 8 and 15

The *16 Firefighter Life Safety Initiatives* were discussed in Chapter 1, Health Safety Officer Responsibilities. Initiatives 8 and 15 are pertinent to the HSO's responsibilities related to facilities inspection:

8. Utilize available technology wherever it can produce higher levels of health and safety.

15. Advocacy must be strengthened for the enforcement of codes and the installation of home fire sprinklers.

Conducting the Inspection

Facility inspections can be an informal or formal process. The informal inspection occurs daily, or as personnel report to a facility such as volunteers or reserve personnel. Daily personnel rotations, shift changes, or reporting times for daily assignments are good opportunities to observe the facility's general condition **(Figure 10.1)**. In addition, as personnel are leaving shift, the opportunity exists to communicate information on what occurred during their tour of duty and any unresolved issues. **Learning Activity 10-1** provides an opportunity to practice conducting an inspection.

Formal inspections will occur as defined by the department, NFPA®, and legal mandates. At a minimum, NFPA® 1500, *Standard on Fire Department Occupational Safety and Health Program*, requires monthly safety and health inspections, and annual fire and life safety code inspections. The SOP/G should clearly state the responsibility of each type of inspection. One method of scheduling facility inspections could be as follows:

- **Daily** — performed informally by the assigned crew to address minor issues and/or report more significant maintenance issues.

- **Weekly** — performed formally by the assigned crew with a standard checklist to be documented and forwarded for retention. Weekly inspections will continue to address minor issues, with more significant maintenance issues forwarded through the chain of command.

- **Monthly** — performed formally by the assigned crew and/or battalion chief with a standardized checklist to be documented and forwarded on

Figure 10.1 Daily inspections are meant to identify problems, such as this leak from an apparatus, before they become larger issues.

for retention. The monthly inspection must comply with NFPA® 1500 and include safety and health issues or facility considerations.

- **Quarterly/Semi-annually** — performed formally to meet state OSHA regulatory requirements on certain facilities.

- **Annually** — performed formally by the fire chief, fire prevention bureau, HSO, organizational/third-party risk management personnel, insurance carrier, or other designated official. The annual inspection must comply with NFPA® 1500 and all local, state/provincial, and federal fire and life safety code regulations.

- **Post-damage** — performed formally after a significant natural or man-made event. Tornados, earthquakes, thunderstorms, floods, and terrorism can produce not only the obvious damaging forces, but some of them are capable of producing multiple damaging forces. After a significant event, the HSO will coordinate facility inspections with fire department personnel, facility maintenance personnel, building code inspectors, and/or engineers. Personnel performing special inspections will document any suspected structural or property damage resulting from an event.

- **Upon request** — inspections can also include those requested by OSHA, EPA, FEMA, or the jurisdiction's risk management office. These inspections may include items not normally inspected during other inspections. Again, the HSO will be the liaison to coordinate the inspections and gather documents requiring corrective actions.

The local jurisdiction should have an adopted fire code and life safety code. If not, NFPA® 1500 provides guidance for code compliance determination. Determining compliance is one of the primary goals of the annual inspection. During the inspection, specific items must be evaluated including:

- **Carbon monoxide and smoke detectors** — NFPA® 1500 requires carbon monoxide and smoke detectors to be present and functioning as designed. Smoke detector alarms must sound throughout the building when activated.

- **Air quality testing** — OSHA does not have air quality requirements, but recommends that indoor air quality should be assessed for carbon monoxide, dust and pollutants, and temperature and humidity **(Figure 10.2)**. There is no single air quality test, but separate measurements can provide a partial picture of a structure's air quality. Solutions to air quality complaints will typically focus on the HVAC system, general building maintenance, and plumbing leaks. The HSO should consult with an industrial hygienist if problems are suspected.

- **Proper separation of living and working areas** — vehicle exhaust is a known carcinogenic. Separation between vehicular areas and all other work or living areas must be evaluated to ensure continued indoor air quality.

Figure 10.2 OSHA compliance requires that the air quality within apparatus bays be checked during inspections and verified to be within acceptable limits.

NIOSH recommends vehicular exhaust exposure be reduced to the lowest possible level.

- **Noise level testing** — should be conducted in accordance with 29 CFR 1910.95 *Occupational Noise Exposure.*

- **Quick access fire pole safety** — should be evaluated to ensure safety around the floor opening and the landing area for department personnel and station visitors.

- **Operational readiness** — includes generators, fuel storage and dispensing, automatic appliance shutoffs, air compressor testing, emergency eye wash stations, lighting, elevators, and communications systems.

When conducting an inspection, the HSO should be organized, systematic, and methodical. By developing a systematic method that fits their needs, HSOs can follow the same format for every inspection. Repetition helps avoid mistakes and will assist in keeping the HSO on track during the inspection. When approaching the facility, it is a good idea for the HSO to note the general condition of the grounds, exterior, and notable issues. In addition, the inspection should include an awareness of personnel actions and behavior towards safety that can include compliance with the process. The HSO will then proceed to meet with the facility personnel and begin the standard inspection process.

Preparation for OSHA Inspections

HSOs can expect OSHA inspectors to be thorough and diligent in their inspections. States/provinces where OSHA is not the authority may have similarly stringent inspection procedures. HSOs should seek out checklists developed in their jurisdictions for OSHA or state/provincial inspections. They should also review the areas where OSHA finds the highest number of violations and try to correct these areas before OSHA arrives.

Checklists for OSHA inspections are lengthy, usually twenty to thirty pages. **Table 10.1, p. 348** shows the major topic areas for these inspections. A detailed list of questions about the topic follows each heading. The lists will vary depending upon the state requirements. Most of these topics are in some way applicable to fire and emergency services facilities and should be reviewed in preparation for OSHA inspections.

In addition to knowing the preparation checklist, HSOs should research the current listing from OSHA about the most commonly cited standards. At the time of this writing, the top ten OSHA standards for which OSHA cited violations were:

1. Fall Protection — 1926.501
2. Hazard Communication — 1910.1200
3. Scaffolding — 1926.451
4. Respiratory Protection — 1910.134
5. Powered Industrial Trucks — 1910.178
6. Lockout/Tagout — 1910.147
7. Ladders — 1926.1053
8. Electrical, Wiring Methods — 1910.305
9. Machine Guarding — 1910.212
10. Electrical, General Requirements — 1910.303

Table 10.1
Topic Areas for OSHA Inspections

Abrasive wheel equipment grinders
Chemical exposures
Compressors and compressed air
Compressed gas and cylinders
Confined spaces
Cranes and hoists
Electrical safety
Elevated surfaces
Emergency action plan
Environmental controls
Ergonomics
Exit or egress
Exit doors
Fire Protection
Flammable and Combustible Materials
Floor and wall openings
General work environment
Hand tools and equipment
Hazard communication
Hearing conservation
Infection control
Industrial trucks – forklifts
Injury and illness prevention program
Lockout/tagout procedures
Machine guarding
Materials handling
Medical services and first aid
Personal protective equipment and clothing
Piping systems
Posting
Portable ladders
Portable (power-operated) tools and equipment
Record keeping
Safety committees
Spray finishing operations
Stairs and stairways
Tire inflation
Transporting employees and materials
Ventilation for indoor air quality
Video display terminals
Walkways
Welding, cutting, and brazing

Cross-Contamination — In terms of health safety, any spread of a harmful contaminant into an environment in which the contaminant should not normally be found

Common Hazards

When conducting an inspection, personnel should be cognizant of common hazards that fall into two main categories: health and physical hazards. Health and physical hazards require corrective actions as a preventive measure to ensure workplace safety. The design of the facility should address these hazards, but personnel should also check for them during daily activities at the facility. Ergonomics is an additional area of concern to ensure that the facility's design does not place the worker in jeopardy of an injury.

The HSO should also ensure that the inspection process addresses work areas with specific hazards, such as shop areas, maintenance facilities, and mechanical rooms. These areas have a specific function that can create significant health and physical hazards. Therefore, these areas may require unannounced visits to ensure compliance with the various laws, codes, and regulations that exist to protect the worker.

Health Hazards

Health hazards exist in all areas of fire and emergency services facilities. **Cross-contamination** between the different areas of the station is a concern that should be addressed with good work practices. Exposure protection policies should be in place to protect you from contracting an illness. The HSO should ensure the following areas are inspected, kept clean and orderly, and that all needed corrective actions are addressed in a timely manner:

- Designated cleaning and disinfecting areas
- Laundry facilities
- Restrooms
- Kitchens
- Sleeping quarters (including bedding)
- Living/dining/office areas (including chairs and carpeting)
- Exercise rooms
- Training rooms or facilities
- Apparatus bay
- Storage areas
- Upper floor weight limitations
- Fuel storage
- Workroom machinery safety components
- Staircase railings
- Boiler rooms
- General hazardous materials use and storage
- Safety signage **(Figure 10.3)**
- Common areas
- EMS patient walk-in areas

Physical Hazards

Physical hazards should be addressed in the design phase of a facility. In the design phase, the HSO should ensure the facility creates a safe workplace for the specific use or purpose. If physical hazards were not addressed in the building phase because of the building's age, the HSO should document this and make a recommendation for corrective actions to mitigate possible risks. Some common physical hazards that personnel should be aware of include:

Figure 10.4 Basic housekeeping is key to maintaining a safe and healthy work place.

- Slips, trips, and falls (includes keeping walkways clear of ice or snow)
- Basic housekeeping **(Figure 10.4)**
- Illumination
- Air quality (exhaust/asbestos/mold)
- Noise pollution
- Electrical safety (grounding and extension cords, power tools)

Ergonomics

Ergonomics is the applied science of equipment and workplace design intended to maximize productivity by reducing operator fatigue and discomfort. The HSO must be aware of ergonomics and how it relates to both station design and operational hazards. **Ergonomic risk factors,** also called *ergonomic stressors* and *ergonomic factors*, can contribute to **musculoskeletal disorders (MSDs)**. MSDs are injuries and disorders of the muscles, nerves, tendons, ligaments, joints, cartilage, and spinal discs. MSD hazards are physical work activities and/or conditions in which ergonomic risk factors are present that are reasonable likely to cause or contribute to an MSD injury. Ergonomic risk factors that pose a biomedical stress to the worker include the following (**Figure 10.5**):

- Force (forceful exertions, including dynamic motions)
- Repetition
- Awkward positions
- Static postures
- Contact stress
- Vibration
- Temperature extremes, both hot and cold

MSDs do not include injuries caused by slips, trips, falls, or other similar accidents. Examples of MSDs include the following:

- Carpal tunnel syndrome
- Rotator cuff syndrome
- De Quervain's disease (afflicts the tendons in the thumb)
- Trigger finger
- Tarsal tunnel syndrome
- Sciatica
- Epicondylitis (tennis elbow)
- Tendinitis

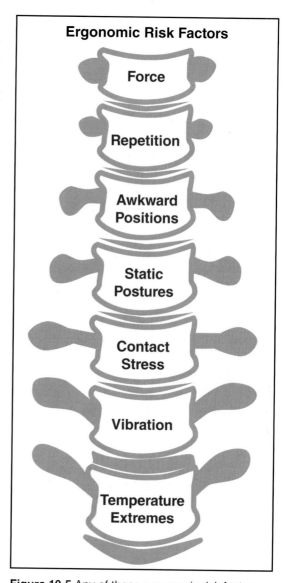

Figure 10.5 Any of these ergonomic risk factors could cause personnel to develop musculoskeletal disorders over time.

- Raynaud's phenomenon or disease (afflicts fingers and toes after hot or cold exposure)
- Carpet layer's knee
- Herniated spinal disc
- Low back pain

To address these MSDs and the resulting injuries, the HSO should develop an ergonomics program that includes the following six elements:

- Management leadership and employee participation
- Hazard information and reporting
- Job hazard analysis and control
- Training
- MSD management
- Program evaluation

Figure 10.6 Ergonomic inspections are intended to point out improvements to the work environment that pose a lower risk for MSDs, such as lowering the height of these shelves for easier access.

Generally, the HSO must consider issues such as workstations, tools, facilities, equipment, materials, and processes. A great starting point for the HSO is to explore the resources from OSHA and NIOSH on musculoskeletal disorders. In addition to observing the various rooms and equipment, HSOs may also want to spend some time during inspections discussing working conditions with the facility staff. These informal conversations could reveal chronic pain or health difficulties employees have, which could indicate MSD issues at the facility.

Engineering controls are the most effective means of eliminating MSDs before they occur. Third-party organizations with expertise in ergonomics are often best suited to evaluate existing facilities and facilities under construction. During facility construction or renovation phases, potential hazards created by storage height, equipment access, or office design can be addressed. Buildings built before ergonomics was a design consideration should be documented and assessed for possible ergonomic improvements **(Figure 10.6)**. Administrative policy and training can address process or operational issues, such as proper lifting techniques.

Necessary Resources and Equipment

In general, the fire prevention staff can determine the resources and equipment needed for conducting facility inspections **(Figure 10.7, p. 352)**. The following general list of items may be helpful for the HSO, but should not be considered all-inclusive:

- Laptop or tablet computer
- Flashlight
- Cellular phone

Figure 10.7 When performing inspections, the HSO needs to bring the proper tools, and most importantly the proper forms and writing utensils.

- Pen
- Clipboard
- Digital camera
- Refrigerator temperature gauge
- Noise level measuring device
- Electrical ground tester
- Fire and life safety code manual
- Safety and health inspection checklist
- Inspection form to document violations and track corrections

The HSO should wear clothing that is appropriate to the facility. In an office setting, the HSO should be in standard uniform and work attire. However, when inspecting a facility, such as a maintenance shop or storage area, the HSO may need coveralls, gloves, and head, eye, and ear protection.

Coordination with Facility Personnel or Contractors

The HSO is responsible for ensuring coordination of safety and health components of facility inspections. This responsibility will include coordinating the schedules of the fire prevention staff and operational personnel. The HSO does not necessarily need to be present for the inspection, but department responsibilities will differ across organizations. Similar coordination will occur with any external agency inspection, such as OSHA, EPA, and/or the organization's risk manager.

Safety Precautions

Safety precautions should be similar with any kind of inspection process. The HSO should meet with the facility supervisor prior to commencing the inspection. The HSO should be cognizant of the facility operation and not interfere with the work. The HSO should pay attention to apparatus in motion, equipment in use, and the movement of personnel as they continue their normal work routine. Protective clothing, eye and ear protection, dust mask, and/or gloves may be needed depending on the location. The attire should meet the conditions of the facility. In addition, as with any fire and emergency services organization operation, the person conducting the inspection should be accompanied by another individual. This individual may be another inspector or personnel from the facility.

Recognizing Violations

Fire department personnel have an obligation to ensure their workplace is safe. As such, personnel should be vigilant of their surroundings and report building or fire code violations and any safety and health hazards through their chain of command. Prompt reporting and documentation of violations promotes an efficient repair or correction process. Personnel must immediately address serious and life-threatening hazards by cordoning off an area and posting signage to warn others of the hazard. Documentation should also immediately follow so the organization can take corrective actions to correct a hazardous condition as quickly as possible.

Recognizing violations in the monthly or annual inspection requires personnel to look for specific problems. Assistance from the fire prevention inspectors, building safety inspectors, or risk management personnel provides a trained professional to identify violations not typically known to firefighters or staff.

Fire and life safety code adoption is a jurisdictional preference. The HSO must be knowledgeable of the current adopted code. If a code has not been formally adopted, the HSO may request permission from the fire chief to use the most current applicable code or regulation in conducting or coordinating facility inspections.

Documenting Violations

Any violation of a code, standard, or regulation should be documented and promptly reported. Documentation may be done on a computer form or a hard copy handwritten form. Regardless of how violations are documented, standard forms should be developed and utilized. The form should include, at a minimum, the following:

- Address of facility
- Name of facility
- Date of inspection
- Name of inspector
- Type of inspection (monthly, annual, special)
- Compliance violation reference
- Compliance violation description (narrative)
- Date of reinspection, if necessary
- Signature of both the facility representative and the inspector

A copy of the inspection form should be made available to the facility supervisor, station personnel, and the fire administrative staff. Original copies should be filed in accordance with department policy and retained as required by law. Historical documentation of facility issues provides data in assessing facility design, consideration of renovations or replacement, and long-term costs associated with each facility.

Correcting and Closing Violations

Fire and building code violations will periodically occur in the normal life span of a fire station or fire department facility. The department must take all code violations seriously. Enforcement within a department/jurisdiction must have the support of the command staff. The department is the example for the community and must demonstrate its ability to comply with the adopted codes.

The responsibility of making code violation corrections will depend on the violation's type and complexity. Some violations will require immediate correction, though all violations should be corrected as quickly as possible. The HSO, facility maintenance personnel, station personnel, or third-party vendors may be involved in correcting violations. However, some violations or facility conditions may require extended periods for compliance. This process can occur when the corrective action has a significant financial consideration or requires architectural or engineering design plans. The HSO should ensure these extended corrections are included in the next budget approval cycle if emergency approval is not granted. Additionally, the inspection process itself should be reviewed and audited for effectiveness.

Chapter Summary

Facility inspections are an essential component of a workplace safety program. The purpose of this program is prevention. Workplace injuries are preventable with a comprehensive program addressing the specific work area, hazards associated with each facility, and a department-mandated inspection and corrective action process. All members informally participate in this process. Some members, including the HSO, participate in the formal process of ensuring all fire and emergency service organizational facilities are safe for the workers and any visitors.

Review Questions

1. What methods can the health safety officer use to schedule facility inspections? (pp. 344-346)

2. What specific items must be evaluated during inspections of the department facility? (pp. 346-347)

3. What are the categories of common hazards that could be found at fire and emergency services facilities? (pp. 348-349)

4. How can the health safety officer use the science of ergonomics to improve conditions in a facility? (pp. 350-351)

5. What safety precautions should the health safety officer take while conducting inspections? (p. 353)

6. What information should be included in documentation addressing code violations? (pp. 353-354)

7. What factors should the health safety officer consider when correcting and closing code violations? (p. 354)

LEARNING ACTIVITIES

10-1

Conduct a mock health and safety inspection for a fire department facility.

Refer to Appendix B: Learning Activity Answers in the back of this manual for suggested responses.

Purpose

All fire and emergency services facilities require regular inspection and maintenance to prevent deterioration and unsafe working conditions. The HSO's responsibility is to ensure a SOP/G is in place that defines the process, schedule, and responsibilities associated with inspections and maintenance of facilities.

Directions

1. Review Chapter 9 NFPA® 1500, *Standard on Fire Department Occupational Safety and Health Program*.

2. Contact a neighboring fire fighting facility and request permission to conduct a mock health and safety inspection at that facility as a training exercise.

    NOTE: It is not suggested that you use your usual/home facility as it can be difficult to see the familiar with fresh, critical eyes.

3. Your home facility or station should have health and safety inspection checklists for week, monthly, and/or annual inspections. Request appropriate permission to access one of these forms for a training exercise.

    NOTE: Each facility or jurisdiction may have a slightly different form.

4. Review the form before your arranged visit to the neighboring facility.

5. At the arranged time, visit the facility. Specific items to be evaluated include:

    a. Carbon monoxide and smoke detectors

    b. Air quality testing

    c. Proper separation of living and working areas

    d. Noise level testing

    e. Quick access fire pole safety

    f. Operational readiness

6. Also consider:

    a. Health hazards

    b. Physical hazards

    c. Ergonomics

    d. Necessary resources and equipment

    e. Safety precautions

7. Take detailed notes of your findings during your inspection.

8. Note any instances where the facility does not meet requirements or any violations.

Refer to Appendix B: Learning Activity Answers in the back of this manual for suggested responses.

9. Check with your department supervisor, instructor, or training officer to determine if the checklist has been filled out correctly.

10. After "grading" your checklist, share your findings with a fellow safety officer or ranking supervisor at the chosen facility. Make recommendations for correcting and closing any noted violations. You may want to choose a specific method — a written memo, a copy of your inspection checklist, etc. — for sharing the information.

Apparatus, Equipment, and Protective Clothing

Chapter Contents

Key Terms

NFPA® Job Performance Requirements

This chapter provides information that addresses the following job performance requirements of NFPA® 1521, *Standard for Fire Department Safety Officer Professional Qualifications (2015)*.

4.8.1	4.8.4
4.8.2	4.8.5
4.8.3	4.8.6

Apparatus, Equipment, and Protective Clothing

Learning Objectives

After reading this chapter, students will be able to:

1. Describe apparatus, equipment, and protective clothing specifications as they relate to health safety officer responsibilities. (4.8.1, 4.8.2)

2. Identify the elements that comprise departmental apparatus and equipment service testing. (4.8.3, 4.8.4, 4.8.5)

3. Explain the components of a departmental protective clothing and equipment program. (4.8.6)

4. Learning Activity 11-1: Review department specs regarding structural fire fighting boots. (4.8.1, 4.8.2, 4.8.6)

Chapter 11
Apparatus, Equipment, and Protective Clothing

Case History

An engine company responded to the scene of a fire in a 2-story residence. The residence showed black smoke coming from a corner room on the second story with no indications of fire on the ground floor. An interior attack team, with RIC in place, entered through the front door and began advancing hoseline up the interior stairs while outside crew coordinated ventilation to ensure the interior crew's safety.

When the interior crew located the fire, the nozzle operator began to apply water. Visibility was low. Shortly after beginning the attack, the firefighters lost all pressure in their hoseline. The nozzle operator quickly signaled an evacuation to his crew, and the firefighters escaped safely. The driver/operator supplying the hoseline changed to a different intake on the apparatus and was able to reestablish pressure and allow the team to reenter the structure and extinguish the fire.

During the investigation, the firefighters discovered that the rear intake that had initially been used failed because of a faulty switch. The HSO who was assigned to review the postincident analysis reviewed the testing and maintenance records for the pump to see if there was anything out of the ordinary in the service history. He discovered that the apparatus had been taken out of service earlier that year because of intake problems with the pump. When it was returned to the station, the testing records showed no evidence of the pump's being tested upon return from the manufacturer.

The HSO investigated further and found that the root cause for the equipment failure might be a notable lack of regularity in the testing procedures at the station. The HSO recommended a refresher training for the station personnel on the department's testing procedures and also suggested more streamlined methods for reporting when testing had taken place.

The responsibility for determining apparatus, equipment, and protective clothing needs and specifications will differ among fire and emergency services organizations. Some departments may accomplish this task by committee, while other departments may assign this responsibility to an administrative officer. Regardless of how this responsibility is delegated, the HSO should assist in the process of determining the needs and specifications with a focus on ensuring safety and health recommendations correlate to compliance standards and the risk management plan.

Injury prevention is a goal of apparatus, equipment, and protective clothing purchasing and maintenance programs. In order to promote injury prevention, the HSO is responsible for researching new technologies, ensuring compliance with standards, and verifying that a testing and inspection program is ongoing and correctly documented. Improvements in apparatus, equipment, and protective clothing design continue to steadily progress, but injuries and fatalities associated with these items also continue. The HSO serves a significant advocacy role in the process to eliminate injuries and fatalities associated with the apparatus, equipment, and protective clothing that is used.

16 Firefighter Life Safety Initiatives 8, 10, and 16

The *16 Firefighter Life Safety Initiatives* were discussed in Chapter 1, Health Safety Officer Responsibilities. Initiatives 8, 10, and 16 are pertinent to the HSO's responsibilities related to apparatus and equipment programs:

8. Utilize available technology wherever it can produce higher levels of health and safety.

10. Grant programs should support the implementation of safe practices and/or mandate safe practices as an eligibility requirement.

16. Safety must be a primary consideration in the design of apparatus and equipment.

Apparatus, Equipment, and Protective Clothing Specifications

Apparatus, equipment, and protective clothing are expensive to purchase and must be maintained in an operational readiness condition during their service life. This process requires a team approach to the different aspects of specifying, purchasing, and maintaining all of these items within the department. The HSO is responsible for ensuring the following:

- Apparatus, equipment, and protective clothing comply with current standards at the time of purchase.

- Personnel are properly trained in the operation and use of these items **(Figure 11.1)**.

- Inspection and specification records are maintained.

Short- and long-term planning for equipment needs and compliance is essential to the safety and health of all emergency responders. Research into the current standards and regulations should be conducted as follows:

- Regularly as a part of the risk management plan

- Prior to the purchase of these items

- Annually evaluate continued compliance

While HSOs may not have the final decision regarding what new apparatus, equipment, or protective clothing to purchase, they do have a responsibility to inform decision makers about compliance issues and requirements for maintaining equipment. Any new research or innovation in design that could improve firefighter safety should be communicated as well. When appropriate the HSO should make recommendations as appropriate to decision makers as an advocate for firefighters having the best tools possible to keep them safe. **Learning Activity 11-1** provides an exercise for assessing departmental equipment and making recommendations.

Figure 11.1 Personnel should be provided training on all of the equipment that they will use.

Researching New Technology and Requirements

The HSO should stay current with technology and requirements. At times, this research may be done when a purchase is approved and a detailed specification sheet is needed. Researching new technology and requirements takes time. This section highlights some of the common areas used when researching new technology and requirements for apparatus, equipment, and protective clothing.

Current State of Technology

Standards, laws, and regulations are revised on a cyclical basis and are often changed to keep pace with new technologies. For example, older apparatus were not equipped with seatbelt sensors, but any prospective new apparatus must have this technology, according to current standards. HSOs should stay current regarding new technologies in order to evaluate changes to apparatus, equipment, and protective clothing and advise department staff as to how each new technology will make the department safer. The following are methods for keeping up-to-date on fire service technology:

Figure 11.2 Fire service organizations and the events that they sponsor offer opportunities to learn about the latest fire service technology and fire fighting techniques.

- Reading industry journals
- Attending conferences and trade shows
- Joining national and state fire service organizations **(Figure 11.2)**
- Networking and communicating with other fire and emergency professionals

NFPA® Standards

NFPA® standards and guides are typically updated on a five-year cycle. NFPA®technical committees work through a validation process to ensure all standards and guides are revised in order to provide the best guidance and protection criteria for fire and emergency service workers. Each NFPA® standard will provide details that pertain to a specific item and outline minimum criteria for manufacturers to meet. The HSO should ensure either current copies of NFPA® standards and guides are kept on file or electronic access is available.

Manufacturer Information

Manufacturers of apparatus, equipment, and protective clothing must meet current standards and regulations in the design or refurbishment process. Fire and emergency services organizations can open a *request for qualifications* and/or a *request for proposal* to obtain written documentation from manufacturers on the specifications they can meet and the costs associated with the item out for bid. Departments can then make a decision that best meets their needs and complies with all legal mandates of the process. HSOs should take care to differentiate between manufacturer information for specifications and information intended to promote products.

Departmental Inspection and Maintenance Records

Inspection and maintenance records of apparatus, equipment, and protective clothing provide a good insight into the dependability and serviceability of these items. Examining these records will reveal any issues that exist with current items or what benefits have been seen with different apparatus, equipment, or protective clothing. These records can provide some of the most useful data, especially with regards to the performance of the item over time.

Current Departmental Specifications

Each organization must determine what its apparatus, equipment, and protective clothing specifications will be based upon department needs and compliance deficiencies. This evaluation should correspond to the risk management plan. This evaluation, or *gap analysis*, helps determine what specifications are needed. Standards and regulations provide the minimum specification requirement, but organizations can apply more stringent requirements. Because of the financial consideration of these items, some departments may only revise current department specifications when a purchase is planned. Detailed specifications can then be written with the most current standard requirements.

Identifying Departmental Needs

Departmental needs must directly correlate to the risk management plan and to the identified fire and emergency services needed in the community. A comprehensive assessment of service delivery demands associated with a strategic planning or accreditation process provides valuable data for justifying new apparatus, equipment, and/or protective clothing purchases. This review can include all current and projected additional service demands in the future. These items require long-term budget planning and may require approval in a five-year or ten-year **capital improvement program (CIP)** budget **(Figure 11.3)**.

Capital Improvement Program (CIP) — 5 to 10 year program intended to identify large equipment purchases or project expenses, schedule their purchase, and identify the needed funding sources.

The service delivery demands are not the only consideration for departmental needs. The risk management plan identifies safety and health assessments of the overall workplace, including people, practices, and equipment. Effectively meeting the service demands of the community requires that the workplace be safe and support the mission. The HSO should continually review how the workplace environment helps or hinders the operational mission. When a deficiency is found, the HSO will assist in the process by researching solutions and making recommendations. Additionally, apparatus, equipment, and protective clothing have a recommended service life. Proving obsolescence can be a justification for a new purchase.

Assessing Specifications

The best way to assess apparatus, equipment, and protective clothing specifications is to research the current standards applicable to each of these items. The HSO should, at a minimum, consult the current standards and guidelines from:

- NFPA®
- ANSI
- ASTM
- OSHA
- EPA
- U.S. Department of Transportation
- Transportation Canada

Other important ways to assess specifications is to examine:

- **Historical records** – the historical records will provide the HSO with the initial cost, life-time cost, maintenance records, and any major repairs or refurbishment costs.

- **Surveys of other jurisdictions** – this information will provide the HSO with compatibility issues, manufacturer satisfaction, and long-term cost estimates.

- **Reviews of manufacturer business histories** — this should include a performance review of the business histories of various manufacturers and the vendors representing them.

- **Product comparison** — this should include examining the characteristics, availability of support and parts, and warranties. Trade shows offer a good opportunity to meet with manufacturers to discuss their products and standards.

- **Product evaluation** — this should include hands-on training and use for a specified period of time. Personnel should thoroughly test the product and provide an evaluation or grading. This evaluation should include regular consultation with the department's fleet maintenance technician.

Possible Funding for Capital Improvements

Property Taxes Trust Funds Fundraising Events

Grants/Gifts Fees Income Taxes

Bond Sales Enterprise Funds Sales Taxes

Special Purpose Tax Levy

Figure 11.3 Money for capital improvements can come from a variety of sources.

The sections that follow provide information about NFPA® standards that include requirements for apparatus specifications. For information on standards for personal protective clothing and equipment, see Chapter 2, Safety and Health Laws, Codes, Regulations, and Standards.

NFPA® 414 Requirements

The Federal Aviation Administration (FAA) enforces regulations that describe the minimum requirements for crash fire rescue apparatus based on the NFPA® 414, *Standard for Aircraft Rescue and Fire-Fighting Vehicle*. For example, the HSO should ensure the vehicle meets the minimum standard for the field of vision, cab interior, body, and safety requirements **(Figure 11.4)**. These vehicles have varying water carrying capacities, which directly relate to the performance parameters stated in the standard. In addition, this standard addresses the specialization of this apparatus and details the testing requirements that must be conducted.

NFPA® 1901 Requirements

NFPA® 1901, *Standard for Automotive Fire Apparatus,* defines all mandatory components that ensure that the fire apparatus meets applicable federal, state, and provincial motor vehicle laws and codes once construction is complete. The following apparatus requirements are included in this standard:

- Pumper fire apparatus
- Initial attack fire apparatus
- Mobile water supply fire apparatus
- Aerial fire apparatus
- Quint fire apparatus
- Special service fire apparatus
- Mobile foam fire apparatus

The standard outlines the basic components of each type of apparatus. Apparatus components include, but are not limited to, the following:

- General requirements: personnel protection, controls, instructions, stability, performance, roadability, serviceability, and predelivery testing
- Fire pump
- Aerial device
- Water tank
- Hose capacity and storage
- Equipment and tool storage **(Figure 11.5)**
- Foam proportioning system and foam tank
- Chassis, power plant, and electrical systems

NFPA® 1901, Appendix B guides the purchaser in providing the manufacturer with pertinent information on apparatus needs. This information enables the manufacturer to prepare a bid and a complete description of the apparatus it proposes to construct.

Figure 11.4 The field of view from the cab of an ARFF apparatus should meet or exceed minimum standards.

Figure 11.5 Apparatus standards have specific requirements for equipment and tool storage compartments.

NFPA® 1906 Requirements

Wildland fire apparatus consists of a vehicle with a pump, water tank, limited hose capacity, and equipment **(Figure 11.6, p. 368)**. Apparatus covered in NFPA® 1906, *Standard for Wildland Fire Apparatus*, have a pump size ranging from 20 gpm to 250 gpm (80 to 1000 L/min) and a minimum water tank capacity of 125 gallons (500 L). Fire apparatus designed to NFPA® 1906 requirements include built-to-specification apparatus or pump/tank packages capable of slipping onto a commercial vehicle chassis or into the beds of pickup trucks. Because of the popularity of Class A foam, the standard also addresses compressed air foam systems (CAFS).

The standard addresses both roadability and performance because wildland fire fighting apparatus must be able to operate on both hard surface roads and rugged terrain. Wildland fire apparatus must meet all requirements of the standard while stationary on a grade of 20 percent in any direction. Gross vehicle weight is another important consideration in the design of wildland fire fighting apparatus. The chassis must be designed to carry the load for

Figure 11.6 Wildland apparatus should meet hose capacity, tank and pump requirements based upon applicable standards.

which it is intended. In addition, the design must take into consideration the off-road environment in which the vehicle operates. If the vehicle is too heavy or has poor weight distribution, it can become stuck in soft terrain or be subject to overturning.

NFPA® 1911 Requirements

According to NFPA® 1911, *Standard for the Inspection, Maintenance, Testing, and Retirement of In-Service Automotive Fire Apparatus*, a pumper should be given a service test at least once a year or whenever it has undergone extensive pump or power train repair. These service tests are necessary to ensure that the pumper performs as it should and to check for defects that otherwise might go unnoticed until too late. These service tests include the following:

- Engine speed check
- Priming device tests
- Vacuum test
- Pumping test
- Overload test
- Pressure control test
- Gauge and flowmeter test
- Tank-to-pump flow rate test
- Internal intake pressure relief valve test (if so equipped)

NFPA® 1912 Requirements

NFPA® 1912, *Standard for Fire Apparatus Refurbishing*, provides specific criteria for fire apparatus refurbishment. Refurbishment does not mean that minimum standards are ignored or reduced. Many of the performance criteria referenced in NFPA® 1901 and 1906 must be met. In addition, equipment, such as hose and ladders, must also meet the requirements of their respective standards.

NFPA® 1914 Requirements

NFPA® 1914, *Standard for Testing Fire Department Aerial Devices*, provides the standard testing criteria and procedures for aerial devices on aerial apparatus. Service testing for an aerial device ensures that the device offers a minimum degree of safety under continued use. The test requirements in NFPA® 1914 specify the frequency of the tests and the procedures to be used. Annual tests consist of visual inspections, operational tests, and load tests. These tests are also conducted following the use of the aerial device under unusual conditions; exposure to excessive heat, stresses, or loads; or any use that exceeds the manufacturer's recommended operating procedures. Complete inspection and testing of the aerial device, including nondestructive testing, must be conducted at least every five years. **Nondestructive testing (NDT)** must also be conducted when other service tests indicate there is a potential problem with the aerial device. Detailed service test information is contained in the NFPA® standards and in IFSTA's **Pumping and Aerial Apparatus Driver/ Operator Handbook**.

NFPA® 1917 Requirements

NFPA® 1917, *Standard for Automotive Ambulances*, addresses ambulances used in fire and emergency services organizations. In addition to NFPA® 1917, the design and construction of ambulances may need to meet appropriate design criteria, such as the United States General Services Administration (GSA) Federal Specifications for the Star-of-Life Ambulance or KKK-A-1822D (current edition) specifications. These design criteria ensure that the following components are incorporated into the construction of the vehicle:

- Steering
- Braking
- Seating capacity
- Patient care compartment
- Wa rning lights
- Electrical system
- Emergency medical care equipment
- Infection control
- Other components

The fire department must ensure that the vehicle is inspected before use and that regular preventive maintenance is performed as per the manufacturer's guidelines. Inspections may also be required annually by state regulatory agencies that have ambulance service oversight responsibilit

Ensuring Code Compliance

Once the above research and evaluations are completed, the HSO must compare this information to the detailed specification sheet. Gaps or deficiencies should be identified and corrected prior to proceeding with a purchase. If a new code or standard is due for release, it may be prudent to wait on a purchase to ensure long-term compliance with standards and regulations. Codes may not be revised or released in the same cycle with updates to national standards. In addition, codes may exceed standards based upon jurisdictional needs. HSOs should remain informed about the codes that are coming up for revision in their jurisdictions and any new codes that are scheduled for adoption. In addition, they should monitor the standards' revision cycles in case new standards need to be adopted as codes in the jurisdiction.

Ensuring Training on Equipment

The HSO is responsible for ensuring training is developed and provided to all personnel who will operate or use any apparatus, equipment, or protective clothing. This process will require the HSO to work with the Training Division and possibly fleet maintenance personnel. All apparatus, equipment, and/or protective clothing must be phased in through an in-service process allowing all personnel the opportunity to be trained. This process may require the manufacturer to assist in initial training of personnel. Depending on the product, training sessions may need to be provided to all personnel. These sessions include but are not limited to the following:

- Normal operational use **(Figure 11.7)**
- Product limitations
- Basic maintenance
- System checks
- Cleaning and disinfecting procedures
- Testing requirements and procedures
- Safety systems
- Override operations
- Field troubleshooting
- Fit testing

All in-service training must be documented and retained per legal requirement. The HSO may not be responsible for conducting the in-service training, but is required to ensure its completion with appropriate record keeping.

Developing New Recommendations

The HSO plays an integral part in the design and review of new specifications. Any planned purchase of new apparatus, equipment, or protective clothing provides an excellent opportunity to examine improved safety features that may have been unavailable in the past. The HSO should promote these safety features with research and data supporting the recommendation. This data may be from new standards, but it could also come from historical data of current apparatus, equipment, and protective clothing. Historical data can also be obtained from other fire departments. The HSO should ensure the department adequately forecasts future needs and maximizes the usefulness of the item purchased. Standards provide the minimum criteria for design, but the department can decide to exceed these recommendations. Compatibility needs must be identified from within the department and with neighboring departments. The basis for these recommendations should already be referenced in the risk management plan.

Figure 11.7 In-service training should instruct personnel on the proper adjustments of equipment for normal operational use.

Revising Existing Specifications

Existing specifications are typically revised on an as-needed basis. Apparatus, equipment, and protective clothing are usually purchased infrequently, so repeated specification revisions are not needed. Frequent revisions may cause confusion in proper use and conflicting operational processes. The HSO should encourage developing a specification revision cycle that coincides with code or standard revision and major purchases.

Apparatus and Equipment Service Testing

Fire apparatus is tested and certified immediately following its construction – and before the purchaser accepts it – to ensure that it performs in the manner for which it was designed. Once it is placed into service, it is tested at least annually to ensure that it will continue to perform properly under emergency conditions. An organized system of apparatus testing, plus regular maintenance, is the best assurance that apparatus will perform within design limitations. Furthermore, the insurance industry, such as the Insurance Services Office (ISO) or state authorized rating service, requires that apparatus be tested in order for the community to receive full credit. This testing, in turn, affects the insurance rates in the jurisdiction.

Apparatus tests can be grouped into two basic categories: preservice tests and service tests. **Preservice tests** are conducted before the apparatus is placed into service. Usually, the department operational personnel are not involved in preservice tests, but these tests may involve fleet maintenance personnel. However, the personnel should have a basic understanding of the preservice tests in order to appreciate and understand the service tests. Preservice tests include:

Preservice Tests — Tests performed on fire pumps or aerial devices before they are placed into service; these tests consist of manufacturers' tests, certification tests, and acceptance tests.

- Manufacturer's tests
- Road test and hydrostatic test
- Pump certification tests
- Acceptance tests

Service tests are conducted on at least an annual basis while the apparatus is in service. Department personnel, and specifically driver/operators, may be required to perform these tests or at least assist fleet maintenance personnel who are doing them (**Figures 11.8 a and b**).

Apparatus and Equipment Testing Requirements

Generally speaking, apparatus are tested in the preservice phase, annually while in service, and periodically after a major repair. Annual service tests of apparatus will include pump testing to determine the percentage of full capacity the fire pump can reach. Periodic testing may include a mixture of the above mentioned testing, and is dependent on the repair extent or refurbishment level. The HSO is responsible for verifying that the tests are being conducted and that documentation of testing is retained. Part of this verification includes ensuring that testing complies with the NFPA® standards described in the sections included below.

In addition, equipment carried on apparatus should be tested according to various regulations and standards. While HSOs must verify this testing as well, NFPA® 1521, *Standard for Fire Department Safety Officer*, does not require them to have direct knowledge of all of these standards.

Equipment testing is typically conducted annually or after a major repair and includes:

- **Ladder testing** — this includes ground and aerial ladder testing and inspection. A third-party vendor usually conducts and certifies ladder testing.

- **SCBA testing** — includes testing regulator function and ensuring all components are in proper working order. Certified technicians, who may be department personnel or a third-party vendor, must conduct this testing.

- **SCUBA regulator and cylinder testing** — includes testing regulator function and ensuring all components are in proper working order.

- **SCBA air compressor testing** — typically air compressors require quarterly air quality testing that a certified agency must analyze.

- **Fit testing** — this involves specific fitting and testing of SCBA and CBRNE masks to the specific user. This testing requires a calibrated machine and trained staff, but certified technicians are not required to be present. In addition, studies have shown that the facepiece is the weakest part of protective clothing and equipment. Technicians should closely examine facepieces for indications of early failure potential.

- **Hose testing** — includes all fire hose on front-line and reserve apparatus as well as all stored hose that is ready for use. Department personnel or a third-party vendor may conduct this testing (**Figure 11.9, p. 374**).

- **Protective clothing and equipment testing** — annual testing is required to determine the integrity of the clothing layers.

Annual Pumper Service Tests

Engine Speed Test

Vacuum Test

Gauge and Flowmeter

Pumping Test

Pressure Control

Tank-to-Pump Flow

a

Examples of Annual Tests for Aerial Devices

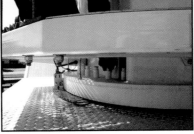

b

Figures 11.8 a and b Annual apparatus service tests and their documentation identify apparatus that are in need of repair or that need to be removed from service.

Figure 11.9 Periodic hose testing of front-line hose and stored hose helps to ensure that damaged hose that might fail during emergency response is removed from service.

Annual Evaluation Plan

The fire and emergency services organization should annually evaluate all apparatus and equipment currently in use. This evaluation will help the organization establish an action plan to address and correct any existing safety issues or deficiencies. Previous evaluations can be compared to current evaluations and set the stage for a long-term plan estimate on when and which apparatus to replace. Each organization will have differing front-line and reserve service

Equipment Standards and Regulations

The following NFPA® standards and U.S. governmental regulations address the testing, the protective clothing, and equipment included in the above list:

- NFPA® 1404, *Standard for Fire Service Respiratory Protection Training*
- NFPA® 1500, *Standard on Fire Department Occupational Health Program*
- NFPA® 1851, *Standard on Selection, Care, and Maintenance of Protective Ensembles for Structural Fire Fighting and Proximity Fire Fighting*
- NFPA® 1852, *Standard on Selection, Care, and Maintenance of Open-Circuit Self-Contained Breathing Apparatus (SCBA)*
- NFPA® 1932, *Standard on Use, Maintenance, and Service Testing of In-Service Fire Department Ground Ladders*
- NFPA® 1962, *Standard for the Care, Use, Inspection, Service Testing, and Replacement of Fire Hose, Couplings, Nozzles, and Fire Hose Appliances*
- NFPA® 1971, *Standard on Protective Ensembles for Structural Fire Fighting and Proximity Fire Fighting*
- NFPA® 1989, *Standard on Breathing Air Quality for Emergency Services Respiratory Protection*
- OSHA 29 CFR 1910.134 *Respiratory Protection*
- U.S. DOT 49 CFR 108.205 *General Requirements for Requalification of Specification Cylinders*

life expectancies. However, many organizations have realized this expectancy can change during economic downturns. The HSO should take the lead role to ensure that this action plan is developed and implemented.

Plan Development

Implementing an annual evaluation plan creates a consistent assessment of the organization's apparatus, equipment, and protective clothing. This evaluation process should include all project managers and maintenance personnel with specific responsibility within this scope. Typically, apparatus, equipment, and protective clothing require long-range planning for the initial purchase or replacement. The annual evaluation is a part of this long-term organizational planning, but it allows for more frequent assessment and provides the historical records necessary for long-range planning. The responsibility for the plan development may vary across organizations. However, the HSO should ensure it is completed and included in the organization's long-range planning process. For more information on developing a plan, refer to development strategies of the organizational risk management plan in Chapter 5, Organizational Risk Management.

Criteria for Refurbishment, Repair, or Retirement

While most of the above listed standards and laws regulate the manufacture of new emergency apparatus, NFPA® 1912 describes the minimum requirements for refurbishing apparatus. Recognizing that small career and volunteer fire departments may not be able to afford a complete overhaul of an aging apparatus, NFPA® created two options for refurbishment. The first option, termed a Level I refurbishment, describes the requirements for the assembly of a new apparatus using the following new components **(Figure 11.10, p. 376)**:

- Chassis frame
- Driving and crew compartments
- Front axle
- Steering and suspension components

NOTE: The remainder of the apparatus may be constructed from new or existing components, such as a pump, aerial device, hose bed, tool compartments, and rear axle.

Level II refurbishment consists of new components added to the existing apparatus chassis. The new components, such as front axle, engine, or crew compartment, must meet or exceed the requirements for the original manufacture of the apparatus.

The standard also requires that all safety requirements of NFPA® 1901 and 1906 are included on either Level I or II refurbishments. The department will need to assess the feasibility of refurbishment versus replacement. An evaluation of the costs, expected life span, safety feature compliance, and operational needs will influence the decision to refurbish or replace. Since options exist, these decisions require a careful evaluation to meet operational needs and community expectations.

Attempting to build apparatus without professional design help can lead to illegal and unsafe results. Fatalities and injuries have occurred as a result of vehicle rollovers of homemade water tenders (tankers), which

Figure 11.10 A Level I refurbishment requires the new assembly of specific apparatus components.

were often former flammable liquid carriers. Consult an apparatus design professional before attempting to modify any vehicle for fire fighting operations.

Protective Clothing and Equipment Program

Along with training and good judgment, personal protective clothing and equipment protect firefighters from hazards faced during emergency operations. Personal protective clothing and equipment is designed to allow personnel to enter into an environment that is immediately dangerous to life or health (IDLH). However, protective clothing and equipment does not provide complete protection to each hazard, nor does one type of protective clothing protect personnel from all types of hazards. Protective clothing and equipment is designed to protect personnel from specific types of hazards or in specific types of situations.

As the types and variety of hazards has increased over the past 50 years, the protective clothing and equipment industry has attempted to develop equipment with increased levels of protection **(Figure 11.11 a and b)**. At the same time, NFPA® committees responsible for protective clothing and equipment design criteria continue to require higher levels of protection. Technological advances in heat resistant and fire retardant fabrics developed by the aerospace industry were adopted and applied to protective clothing; for example, lightweight fabrics that could reduce the weight of

Figure 11.11 a and b Personal protective clothing and equipment has changed over time to meet higher and higher levels of protection. As technology advances, so does the protection it offers to firefighters.

clothing while increasing the level of thermal protection. Protective clothing and equipment weight is a critical factor because medical research and field experience have shown that physiological stress due to equipment weight can have an effect on cardiovascular incidents among fire service personnel.

According to NFPA® 1521, the HSO must verify that a program is in place to inspect, repair, and maintain protective clothing and equipment. To meet this responsibility, the HSO must be familiar with the manufacturer's specifications for all of the protective clothing and equipment used in the organization. SOP/Gs for the use and selection of the protective clothing and equipment should, in turn, reflect the manufacturer's recommended usage and the limitations of the protective clothing and equipment based upon their specifications and testing.

While HSOs are not required to perform any of these tasks, they must have a working knowledge of the program's requirements in order to verify its effectiveness. The sections that follow explain key components of a protective equipment and clothing program that the HSO should be able to recognize.

Clothing and Equipment Selection

Because no single type of protective clothing and equipment will protect against every hazard, the equipment should be carefully selected. The HSO plays a vital role in helping the organization purchase and issue protective clothing and equipment. On a scene, incident commanders and company officers will select appropriate protective clothing and equipment for the firefighters at the incident according to SOP/Gs. At hazardous materials incidents, identification of the chemicals involved or released are an additional consideration for protective clothing and equipment selection. In either case, the selection should be in keeping with the manufacturer's described level of protection.

Personal protective equipment must meet certain design standards, including the following:

- NFPA® standards **(Table 11.1)**
- OSHA federal regulations
- State OSHA regulations, such as CalOSHA (California)
- National Institute for Occupational Safety and Health/Mine Safety and Health Administration (NIOSH/MSHA)

Other sources for design criteria include both certification and professional organizations:

- American National Standards Institute (ANSI) certification for the intended use
- UL and ULC
- Southern Area Fire Equipment Research (SAFER)
- Fire Industry Equipment Research Organization (FIERO)
- Safety Equipment Institute (SEI)

Clothing and Equipment Care and Maintenance

NFPA® 1851, *Standard on Selection, Care, and Maintenance of Protective Ensembles for Structural Fire Fighting and Proximity Fire Fighting*, provides requirements for care and maintenance of protective clothing and equipment. From a safety standpoint, equipment that is clean and in serviceable condition continues to perform its intended function – protecting personnel. From an economic standpoint, proper care and maintenance ensures that the original cost/benefit ratio used to specify the equipment is met. Care and maintenance is the responsibility of both the administration and all person-

Table 11.1
NFPA® Standards To Meet Specific Hazards and Responses

Response Type	Specific Hazard	NFPA® Standard
Medical	Contaminated or low-oxygen atmospheres	NFPA® 1981, *Standard on Open-Circuit Self-Contained Breathing Apparatus (SCBA) for Emergency Services*, 2007
	Chemical, Biological, Radiological, or Nuclear	NFPA® 1994, *Standard on Protective Ensembles for First Responders to CBRN Terrorism Incidents*, 2007
	Biological contamination	NFPA® ® 1999, *Standard on Protective Clothing for Emergency Medical Operations*, 2008
Structural	Heat, flame, sharp objects	NFPA® 1971, *Standard on Protective Ensembles for Structural Fire Fighting and Proximity Fire Fighting*, 2007
	Contaminated or low-oxygen atmospheres	NFPA® 1981, *Standard on Open-Circuit Self-Contained Breathing Apparatus (SCBA) for Emergency Services*, 2007
	Disorientation and unconsciousness	NFPA® 1982, *Standard on Personal Alert Safety Systems (PASS)*, 2007
	Contaminated or low-oxygen atmospheres	NFPA® 1989, *Standard on Breathing Air Quality for Emergency Services Respiratory Protection*, 2008
	Chemical, Biological, Radiological, or Nuclear	NFPA® 1994, *Standard on Protective Ensembles for First Responders to CBRN Terrorism Incidents*, 2007
Wildland	Heat, flame, burning embers, and sharp objects	NFPA® 1977, *Standard on Protective Clothing and Equipment for Wildland Fire Fighting*, 2005
Hazardous Materials	Contaminated or low-oxygen atmospheres	NFPA® 1981, *Standard on Open-Circuit Self-Contained Breathing Apparatus (SCBA) for Emergency Services*, 2007
	Contaminated or low-oxygen atmospheres	NFPA® 1989, *Standard on Breathing Air Quality for Emergency Services Respiratory Protection*, 2008
	Contact with dangerous or hazardous vapors or gases	NFPA® 1991, *Standard on Vapor-Protective Ensembles for Hazardous Materials Emergencies*, 2005

Continued

Table 11.1 *(Concluded)*

Response Type	Specific Hazard	NFPA® Standard
Hazardous Materials *(Concluded)*	Contact with dangerous or hazardous liquids or powders	NFPA® 1992, *Standard on Liquid Splash-Protective Ensembles and Clothing for Hazardous Materials Emergencies*, 2005
	Chemical, Biological, Radiological, or Nuclear	NFPA® 1994, *Standard on Protective Ensembles for First Responders to CBRN Terrorism Incidents*, 2007
Water Rescue	Falls, under currents, swift water, and extrication	NFPA® 1983, *Standard on Life Safety Rope and Equipment for Emergency Services*, 2006
Industrial	Heat, flame, sharp objects	NFPA® 1971, *Standard on Protective Ensembles for Structural Fire Fighting and Proximity Fire Fighting*, 2007
Proximity	Heat, flame, and sharp objects	NFPA® 1971, *Standard on Protective Ensembles for Structural Fire Fighting and Proximity Fire Fighting*, 2007
	Contaminated or low-oxygen atmospheres	NFPA® 1981, *Standard on Open-Circuit Self-Contained Breathing Apparatus (SCBA) for Emergency Services*, 2007
	Contaminated or low-oxygen atmospheres	NFPA® 1989, *Standard on Breathing Air Quality for Emergency Services Respiratory Protection*, 2008
Urban Search and Rescue(USAR)	Sharp objects	NFPA® 1951, *Standard on Protective Ensembles for Technical Rescue Incidents*, 2007
	Contaminated or low-oxygen atmospheres	NFPA® 1981, *Standard on Open-Circuit Self-Contained Breathing Apparatus (SCBA) for Emergency Services*, 2007
	Fall prevention and extrication	NFPA® 1983, *Standard on Life Safety Rope and Equipment for Emergency Services*, 2006
	Contaminated or low-oxygen atmospheres	NFPA® 1989, *Standard on Breathing Air Quality for Emergency Services Respiratory Protection*, 2008
Special Duty	None	NFPA® 1951, *Standard on Protective Ensembles for Technical Rescue Incidents*, 2007

nel. The administration provides the materials, establishes the procedures for care and maintenance, and may contract with vendors to provide maintenance. Personnel clean and report any maintenance needs for the protective clothing and equipment.

Traditionally, dirty or soot-covered protective clothing was considered a mark of pride and indication of a firefighter's dedication. Today firefighters are more aware that the by-products of combustion – smoke, soot, and other contaminates – are hazardous to their health.

Protective clothing and equipment worn during fire fighting operations most likely will become contaminated with toxic gases and particulates. Recent studies have identified specific hazardous gases and particulates which firefighters are exposed, to that cause serious health problems, including numerous types of cancer. The following hazardous gases and particulate matter are among those that have been identified (**Table 11.2**):

- Carbon monoxide (CO)
- Benzene
- Hydrogen cyanide (HCN)
- Formaldehyde
- Hydrogen chloride
- Acrolein
- Nitrogen oxides
- Sulphur dioxide
- Ammonia
- Polycyclic aromatic hydrocarbons (PAHs)
- Asbestos
- Arsenic

Table 11.2 Health Effects of CO and HCN Exposure	
CO-Carbon Monoxide	**HCN Cyanide**
Short-Term Exposure	**Low Concentration**
Headache Dizziness Vomiting Nausea Unconsciousness	Eye Irritation Headache Confusion Nausea Vomiting Coma (in some cases) Fatality (in some cases)
Long-Term Exposure	**High Concentration**
Cardiovascular Disease Possible mental health problems	Immediate central nervous system, cardiovascular, and respiratory distress leading to death within minutes.

Figure 11.12 Contaminated protective clothing and equipment should be cleaned in an area of the station dedicated to decontamination.

These gases and particulates can contaminate structural fire fighting gear during fire suppression or overhaul activities. Many of these toxins and particulates are not visibly detectable, and many of them have no odor. Protective clothing contaminated with these toxins decreases protective effectiveness, possibly leading to a lower flammability potential. Therefore, every effort must be made to clean and decontaminate protective clothing after each use and on a regular basis.

Personnel should always follow the cleaning and care instructions of the protective clothing manufacturer and the department's policies. Protective clothing should be cleaned following each exposure to smoke or contaminated atmospheres. Water and a mild detergent is used to clean the outer shell of the coat and trousers, including the cuffs and collar, boots, hood, gloves, and helmet shell and neck shroud. The helmet head band and chin strap should be cleaned as needed in a similar fashion. Special cleaning will be required to decontaminate protective clothing and equipment exposed to hazardous materials, such as chemical or biological waste. Personnel must adhere to the following cleaning and care procedures:

- Never use bleach or a product containing bleach on protective clothing.
- Clean protective clothing and equipment in the designated cleaning area.
- Remove liners from shells and wash separately.
- Clean contaminated protective clothing and equipment in the designated Decon Sink **(Figure 11.12)**.
- Keep protective clothing and equipment in the assigned storage area.
- Wash protective clothing and equipment in a designated washer that is not used for sheets and towels.
- Do not clean protective clothing at home.
- Dry protective clothing in a designated dryer or by hanging on a drying rack.
- Do not store protective clothing in direct sunlight to dry (ultraviolet light will degrade the fabric).

NOTE: Protective clothing and equipment should not be stored in apparatus bays if at all possible. If this location is the only option, a separation of some kind around the protective clothing and equipment is recommended to protect it from diesel exhaust particulates.

To follow these procedures properly, each fire and emergency responder should have two sets of protective clothing, which is not economically possible for some departments. Therefore, it may be necessary to clean equipment at the end of a work shift or only after multiple exposures. It is not good policy to wear another person's protective clothing since this practice could potentially cause cross-contamination of the clothing and the wearers.

Cancer Tied to Protective Clothing Contamination[1]

Cancer research has shown a correlation between fire fighting and increased cancer rates among firefighters. Although these cancers may not become symptomatic until retirement age or after the firefighter has left active duty, the source of the cancer appears to be exposure to contaminants common to most structural fires. Many common practices, such as taking bunker gear home after incidents in personal vehicles, increase exposure levels and could contribute to cancer development later in life.

Figure 11.13, p. 384, shows the increased risks that firefighters have for contracting various kinds of cancer. While it has been known for some time that inhaling products of combustion causes cancer, new research shows that many of these cancers are contracted through the skin. The skin is the largest organ in the body and is highly absorbent, especially the face, neck, throat, and groin areas. For every 5 degree increase in body temperature, the skins' absorption potential increases by 400 percent.

Hoods are the most permeable piece of protective clothing that firefighters wear. Hoods are always necessary to protect exposed skin from heat; however, if they are not properly decontaminated and cleaned, soot from the hood is likely to be absorbed through the skin and cause delayed health effects.

HSOs can collect and compile data on fire fighting and its cancer-causing effects from many available support networks. The Fire Fighter Cancer Support Network includes the following list of preventative measures:

- Use SCBA from initial attack all the way through overhaul.

- Include gross field decon of protective clothing and equipment at all incidents, removing as much soot and particulate as possible.

- Use wet wipes or baby wipes to remove as much soot as possible from all exposed skin while still at the scene.

- Change and wash your clothes immediately after a fire.

- Shower thoroughly after a fire.

- Clean bunker gear, gloves, hood, and helmet immediately after each fire.

- Do not take contaminated protective clothing home in your vehicle.

- Do not store protective clothing in your personal vehicle.

- Keep bunker gear out of living and sleeping quarters.

A designated equipment maintenance person can do simple maintenance, such as the replacement of a helmet chinstrap. However, repair technicians must perform most maintenance and repairs with the proper tools and approved repair parts. This practice is especially true for respiratory protec-

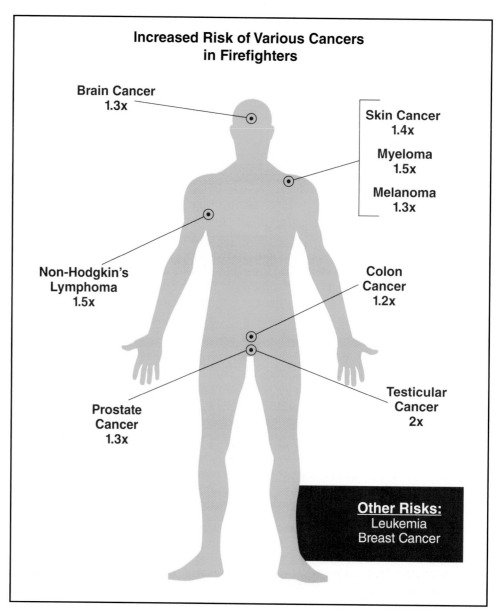

Increased Risk of Various Cancers in Firefighters

Brain Cancer
1.3x

Skin Cancer
1.4x

Myeloma
1.5x

Melanoma
1.3x

Non-Hodgkin's
Lymphoma
1.5x

Colon
Cancer
1.2x

Prostate
Cancer
1.3x

Testicular
Cancer
2x

Other Risks:
Leukemia
Breast Cancer

Figure 11.13 Because of their exposure to carcinogens contained in combustion byproducts, firefighters may be at a higher risk for various types of cancer.

tion equipment. Technicians who are trained and certified in the repair of SCBAs and SARs are the only ones who should repair them. These units must be tested following maintenance and prior to being placed back in service.

Personnel should never modify any piece of protective clothing or equipment. Manufacturers test and certify each piece to perform in its original condition. Modifications will nullify any warranty and can alter the performance of the item. If additional pockets or attachment points are needed, then they should be specified when new protective clothing or equipment is ordered.

Clothing and Equipment Storage

All protective clothing must be stored properly in well-ventilated lockers in or adjacent to the apparatus room **(Figure 11.14)**. These items should never be stored or taken into the living quarters of the station. Ventilation is necessary

Figure 11.14 Lockers for storing protective clothing should be well-ventilated.

to keep clothing that is damp from mildewing and molding and to allow the atmosphere to dilute any contamination.

Some organizations allow or require protective clothing to be taken home for off-duty response. To prevent exposure to contaminants, only protective clothing that has been cleaned should be transported in personal vehicles. Personnel must ensure all items are stored in a location and manner as to not cause contamination of personal property. In addition, all protective clothing and equipment must be stored in a manner to prevent theft.

Periodic Inspection and Evaluation

Protective clothing and equipment must be inspected and tested in accordance with NFPA® 1851 or the appropriate NFPA® standard based on the type of protection. There are four occasions on which protective clothing and equipment are inspected:

- When accepted by the department
- On a regular basis
- On a formal schedule
- Following repairs

Newly purchased protective clothing and equipment is inspected when it is delivered to the department. This initial inspection is necessary to ensure that the item is complete and meets the original specifications. New equipment is assigned an inventory control number at this time and an individual record is started on the equipment.

Personnel should inspect in-service clothing and equipment at the beginning of each work shift. Regular inspections ensure that the ensembles are ready for immediate use, that all items work properly, and that any required repairs are noted and reported. Following the inspection, the protective equipment is placed on or next to the apparatus.

Formal inspections are more thorough than the regular ones. Formal inspections should take place annually and coincide with a periodic cleaning

Figure 11.15 Every aspect of protective clothing should be checked for its condition during clothing inspections.

and preventive maintenance of the protective clothing or equipment. The formal inspection should include the following:

- Checking the date the clothing or equipment was manufactured
- Checking the condition of the clothing **(Figure 11.15)**:
  — Stitching
  — Seams
  — Buttons
  — Clasps
  — Hook and pile fasteners
  — Zippers
  — Retroreflective trim
  — Leather/vinyl trim
- Looking for unauthorized alterations or modifications
- Looking for cleanliness
- Checking for correct size on the wearer

Chapter Summary

Citizens expect the fire and emergency services organization to arrive quickly at an incident and be able to take action without delay. Safe and serviceable apparatus, equipment, and protective clothing are critical for the organization to meet its mission and citizen's expectations. Organizations should review their equipment specifications regularly and follow inspection and testing procedures based upon national standards and industry best practices to ensure a state of readiness. The analysis, testing, and inspection processes may involve any number of personnel performing research and evaluation to ensure regulatory compliance. HSOs are responsible for verifying that inspections and testing are taking place and that safety and health components are addressed in the program.

Review Questions

1. What resources can the health safety officer use to research new technology and requirements for apparatus, equipment, and protective clothing? (pp. 363-364)

2. What sources should the health safety officer consult or examine when assessing apparatus, equipment, and protective clothing specifications? (p. 365)

3. What are the most important items the health safety officer should gather from the various NFPA® requirements pertaining to apparatus and equipment testing? (pp. 366-369)

4. What areas should be included when the health safety officer provides apparatus, equipment, and protective clothing training? (p. 370)

5. What does equipment testing typically include? (p. 372)

6. What items should the health safety officer consider when developing and implementing an annual evaluation plan for a fire service organization? (pp. 374-376)

7. What items should the health safety officer take into account when establishing clothing and equipment care and maintenance guidelines for a department? (pp. 378-384)

8. What should the formal inspection of protective clothing and equipment include? (pp. 385-386)

Chapter 11 End Notes

1. "Taking Action Against Cancer in the Fire Service," Firefighter Cancer Support Network, August, 2013

Refer to Appendix B: Learning Activity Answers in the back of this manual for suggested responses.

Purpose

Safe and serviceable apparatus, equipment, and protective clothing are critical for the organization to meet its mission and citizen expectations. The health safety officer should review equipment and clothing specifications regularly and follow inspection and testing procedures based upon national standards and industry best practices to ensure a state of readiness.

Directions

1. At your department, review the manufacturer's specifications for the structural fire fighting boots your department currently uses. Take special note of the footwear's tread depth specs and other designs for slip resistance. Also be sure to note the hazard class or classes for which the boots are rated.

   NOTE: If your department does not have manufacturer's documents on file, you should be able to find them via an internet search or seek assistance from a ranking officer.

2. If equipment is on hand at your station, inspect at least three pairs of your department's fire fighting boots. Examine a larger sample, if available. Again, take note of tread depth and slip resistance.

3. Review NFPA® 1971, *Standard on Protective Ensembles for Structural Fire Fighting and Proximity Fire Fighting.* Note the tread depth and minimum Coefficient of Friction (COF) requirements set forth by the standard.

   NOTE: During your research, also be sure to consult the American National Standards Institute (ANSI) for additional information.

4. In a brief paragraph, summarize the manufacturer's specs for your department's structural fire fighting boots. If boots were available at your station, also summarize your findings based on the physical inspection of the boots.

5. Determine if the currently used boots meet departmental specs and the requirements of NFPA® 1971.

6. Seek out your department's vendor(s) for structural fire fighting protective clothing and equipment. Determine if new products or developments exist that could impact your department's footwear needs or requirements. Note any new relevant technology or products in your summary.

Reports and Recommendations

Chapter Contents

Key Terms

NFPA® Job Performance Requirements

This chapter provides information that addresses the following job performance requirements of NFPA® 1521, *Standard for Fire Department Safety Officer Professional Qualifications (2015)*.

4.3.2	4.11.1
4.4.2	4.11.3
4.7.4	

Reports and Recommendations

Learning Objectives

After reading this chapter, students will be able to:

1. Describe the process of writing safety and health reports. (4.3.2)

2. Identify types of safety and health reports. (4.3.2, 4.4.2, 4.7.4)

3. Explain the health safety officer's role in providing recommendations to reduce accidents, injuries, and loss. (4.11.1, 4.11.3)

4. Learning Activity 12-1: Write a memorandum recommending changes to PPE specifications. (4.11.1, 4.11.3)

Chapter 12
Reports and Recommendations

Case History

As one of its strategic goals, a large metropolitan fire department established a number of strategic initiatives to improve the quality of service that the department provided to the public. Among these initiatives was an acknowledgement that healthy, physically fit firefighters who train and perform safely were much more likely to meet public demand and have long careers in the department.

As a result, a health safety officer position was established and the HSO's responsibilities were outlined in the strategic plan. The HSO would manage the various health and fitness programs, educate firefighters on health and safety practices and requirements, and collect data on safety hazards and their impacts on operations. Acting as a liaison, the HSO would regularly make recommendations to reduce or eliminate safety hazards. The HSO would also lead an Occupational Health and Fitness advisory committee to evaluate the health and safety plan and programs on an ongoing basis. The committee would make further recommendations about new programs and the effectiveness of existing programs.

Working together, the HSO and committee evaluated the current state of the department's health and safety programs. They revised many programs, placing more emphasis on education. They recommended fitness incentives for firefighters and safety-related additions to preincident plans. Finally, they established a peer fitness trainer program and took over responsibility for evaluating the trainers on an annual basis. The department's administration accepted their recommendations, all of which greatly improved the overall health of their personnel over the next five years according to collected data.

As part of their responsibilities, HSOs are required to submit formal reports and recommendations on health and safety related issues to the fire chief and/or the organizational administration. These reports are generated from departmental records, research data, the occupational safety and health committee, accident investigations, near-misses, and postincident analyses. These reports and recommendations are the culmination of the day-to-day work the HSO performs, and they reflect the organization's performance and any inconsistencies between policy and practice. They are also one of the best opportunities for the HSO to inform and document organizational leadership about safety and health issues. This chapter explains the types of reports that are required and provides introductory information about creating them. HSOs who feel that they need training on writing should seek out programs that are tailored toward that topic, possibly at local community or junior colleges.

Reports

The HSO is required to develop regular reports on SOP/G compliance, training program compliance, and fire department accidents, occupational injuries, deaths, and exposures. This information must be compiled and analyzed to produce recommendations. These reports should meet the following criteria **(Figure 12.1)**:

- Be submitted to the fire chief on a set schedule, such as semiannually

- Provide a comparison between the department's records and national fire and industry safety and health data

- Help to determine trends that may be developing

- Be based on department audits, incident reports, surveys, accident reports, injury reports, inspection reports, and other pertinent department information

Besides memos and e-mails, reports constitute the bulk of the writing that department officers produce. Some reports are simple forms that are completed with specific information concerning an incident or event. Additionally, some recommendations may be included in memos or e-mails. While memos and e-mails can be actionable items in and of themselves, they generally do not contain the kind of broad analysis and research that guide agency-wide decision-making. Formal reports are more like essays, written in narrative, paragraph form and require greater thought and organization than forms, memos, or e-mails. Writing formal reports requires work and skill. Some of these writing skills are as follows:

- **Legibility** — text must be printed or typed rather than in script.

- **Research** — text must be based upon factual information.

- **Clarity** — concise wording that is grammatically correct and error-free.

- **Accuracy** — times, addresses, names, quantities, and events must be correct.

- **Completeness** — all available information must be included.

- **Objectivity** — text must express facts and not opinions; it cannot be subjective.

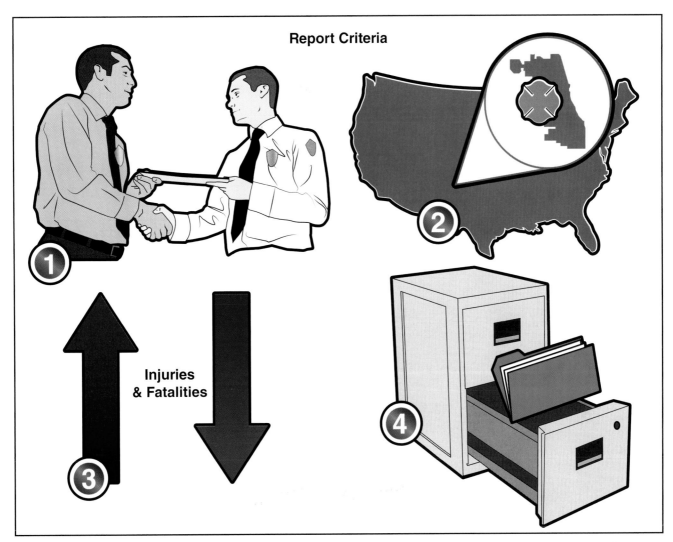

Report Criteria

Injuries & Fatalities

Figure 12.1 An HSO's reports need to be delivered on time and on schedule, reflect comparisons to fire industry safety data, identify trends, and be included in the department's record-keeping system.

Reports help decision-makers create or modify existing policy based upon accurate information. Narrative reports may have different functions or reasons for being written. Types of narrative reports include the following **(Table 12.1, p. 396)**:

- **Justification** — focuses on why a certain course of action was taken or should have been taken. This type of report could be used for a budget request, purchase recommendation, or after-action report. The report begins with the situation, problem, or case study and then provides the solution to the problem and the steps taken (or should have been taken) to gain the solution.

- **Recommendation** — states the problem, policy, practice, and proposed best solution.

- **Progress** — provides an overview of the current status of a project. It is chronological in nature, beginning with a description of the project and proceeding through the individual steps to the current point or the actual completion. The audience should be able to visualize the project development by reading the report. Progress reports are usually required in long-term projects, such as the development of a health and fitness program.

Table 12.1
Types of Narrative Reports

Justification	Recommendation	Progress	Progress and Justification	Description
Purpose:	*Purpose:*	*Purpose:*	*Purpose:*	*Purpose:*
Explain why a certain course of action is best suited to solve a particular problem.	Describe a problem and offer a solution.	Provide an overview of the current status of a project.	Explain the importance of continuing particular projects or programs with or without recommended changes.	Describe a program or policy in detail in order to inform the audience about the topic.
Useful for:	*Useful for:*	*Useful for:*	*Useful for:*	*Useful for:*
• Budget requests • Purchase recommendations • After-action reports	• SOP/G revisions • Postincident Analysis	• Program evaluations • Periodic status updates • Project tracking and accountability	• Defending and improving ongoing programs • Acknowledging needed changes in projects or programs	• Apparatus specifications • Policy implementation • Program implementation • Training

- **Progress and justification** — combines the two forms into one by providing justification for the project, describing the steps to complete the project, and including justification for any changes in the project development.

- **Description** — describes a process, project, or item that gives the audience a detailed image of the subject. This format could be used to describe a new apparatus design or each of the steps necessary to implement a rapid intervention crew policy.

With the purpose and format determined, the topic is then thoroughly researched. HSOs assemble background data from previous reports, personal experience, interviews, analysis, and other documents. Include source citations in the form of footnotes and endnotes to provide credibility and direct the audience to the original material.

The writing process takes time and should not be completed in one sitting. The process for writing reports includes (**Figure 12.2**):

- **Know your audience** — knowing who you are writing a report to will drive what to include in the report and the writing style used.

- **Determine the format of the report** — formal written reports require structure. At a minimum, include a title page, introduction, background, body, recommendations, and a conclusion or summary. An executive summary may also be included to provide a brief review of the key points. Write in the first person using active voice. Do not include opinions or subjective information. Keep it concise with factual, accurate, and objective information.

- **Develop a draft** — this process involves getting the basic information on paper. During draft writing, do not worry about perfection – get the information written.

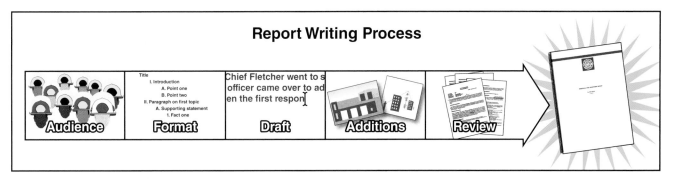

Figure 12.2 Following an established writing process helps to ensure a professional end product that is free of errors, easy to understand, and effective in its message.

- **Develop and include pictures and exhibits** — illustrations, graphics, diagrams, and photographs in a report are useful additions to present information briefly and concisely.

- **Review and edit** — this is an ongoing process of reading the report for grammar and spelling, verifying facts, documenting references, and revising the report. Again, this is a process and time needs to be devoted to it. Have other individuals proofread it. Make sure they understand the content and concur with the writing style and structure.

- **Develop the final report** — after reviewing, editing, and having others proofread your report, develop your final report. Let the report sit for a day or two, and then review it again. Did you address the reason for the report? Finally, ensure the final report is what you want to submit.

Any written report you submit is a direct reflection on you. Take the time to investigate and research the facts, read or collect testimony from witnesses and on-scene personnel, find appropriate reference material, proofread for grammar and spelling, and edit, edit, edit. Getting an extra set of eyes – or two – to proofread the report helps ensure it is logical and complete. These reports could be used at any time in legal proceedings or be discoverable as public record. The Freedom of Information Act (FOIA) allows for a public record request on any record on file. The quality of the report will lend credibility both to you as the author and the information in the report.

CAUTION
All report documents, both final and in-process, may be requested under public records laws.

Report on SOP/G Compliance

SOP/Gs should be reviewed and assessed for continued adequacy and applicability. The HSO and the occupational safety and health committee should develop a schedule for these reviews. The review schedule should include assessment of the topics listed below regarding occupational health and safety. Other fire department divisions will review the same SOP/Gs based upon criteria important to their divisions. The report should also include the consequences of noncompliance.

According to NFPA® 1500, *Standard on Fire Department Occupational Safety and Health Program,* the SOP/Gs reviewed should include, but are not limited to, the following topics:

- **Risk management** — such as rehabilitation protocols, communication procedures **(Figure 12.3)**

- **Training and education** — such as frequency of training, recertification requirements

- **Accident prevention** — such as accident reporting procedures

- **Records management** — such as retention and security procedures

- **Accident and equipment** — such as equipment use procedures, equipment inspection record programs

- **Facility and equipment inspections** — such as daily, monthly, annual, and OSHA or state labor inspection procedures

- **Health maintenance** — such as physical assessment procedures, fitness-for-duty records and reporting

- **Infection control** — such as exposure procedures, bloodborne pathogens procedures

Figure 12.3 Established communication procedures that are familiar to all personnel and mutual aid units are an excellent risk management tool at emergency scenes. *Courtesy of Ed Kirtley.*

Adequacy of Current SOP/Gs

In the SOP/G compliance report, the HSO will include information on the adequacy of current SOP/Gs. SOP/Gs must address all accepted practices and associated procedures that are expected to be followed. Flexibility of guidelines in the SOP/Gs should be included where appropriate. Any gaps between SOP/Gs and practices/procedures must be included in the report. When considering the adequacy of SOP/Gs, the HSO should assess whether a normalization of deviation has occurred. These deviations can indicate needed changes to personnel behavior or a need for updating a policy. Either way, deviations from SOP/Gs should receive special attention in the compliance report.

NOTE: Refer to Chapter 7, Safety and Health Programs, for more information on normalization of deviation.

Effectiveness of Current SOP/Gs

An additional component of the SOP/G compliance report is information on the effectiveness of current SOP/Gs. SOP/Gs are effective if they address risk management concerns and provide needed guidance to personnel in accomplishing operational effectiveness. Concerns will be identified during an analysis of all injuries, deaths, illnesses, exposures, accidents, and near-misses. In addition to this analysis, the HSO will report on whether the SOP/Gs provide the needed guidance for some standardization of operations while maintaining flexibility when needed. In essence, the HSO conducts a gap analysis on what SOP/Gs address and where deficiencies exist and revisions are needed.

Report on Training Program Compliance

As a system of checks and balances with training, the HSO will report on training program compliance with regards to safety and health, and include any deficiencies or improvement recommendations. This report should outline how well the organization achieved mandatory safety and health training, and the inclusion of safety and health topics in all other training. Mandatory training may include, but is not limited to, the following:

- Annual OSHA refresher training, including respiratory protection training **(Figure 12.4)**
- Infection control and prevention
- Bloodborne pathogen training
- Annual HIPAA compliance
- OSHA Hazard Communication

Figure 12.4 Annual refresher training on respiratory protection use is an OSHA requirement in many U.S. states.

- New apparatus, equipment, and/or protective clothing in-service
- New or revised operating procedures

Report on Accidents, Occupational Injuries, Illnesses, Deaths, and Exposures

The HSO is responsible for producing a regularly occurring report to the fire chief that outlines any department accidents, occupational injuries, illnesses, deaths, and exposures. The report provides a comparison between the department's records and national fire and industry safety and health data. This report helps to determine trends that may be developing. However, national data may be dated, incomplete, and unreliable. The report should be based on department audits, incident reports, surveys, accident reports, injury reports, inspection reports, and other pertinent department information.

In addition, the report should contain comparison data on similar occurrences in the local, regional, state, and national setting. Some fire departments use comparison data between themselves and other similarly sized and structured departments. Analyzing accidents from different locations may provide valuable lessons learned that can be incorporated locally. Once an issue or trend is identified, recommendations for risk control measures must be identified and communicated in the report **(Figure 12.5)**. Chapter 3, Record Keeping and Data Analysis, explains further information about report writing.

Reporting on department accidents, occupational injuries, illnesses, deaths, and exposures will require review of accident investigations and reporting on the root cause findings that resulted. The HSO must report facts and not allow bias or personal opinions to influence the report. The HSO is responsible for providing recommendations to prevent similar future events from occurring, not recommending disciplinary action. Ethical considerations can also be used to help create change. Simply put, doing the right thing can go a long way to convince organization members that change is necessary.

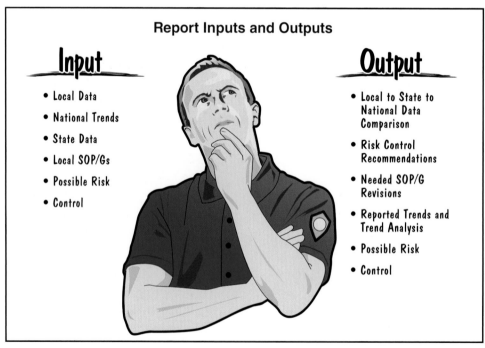

Report Inputs and Outputs

Input
- Local Data
- National Trends
- State Data
- Local SOP/Gs
- Possible Risk
- Control

Output
- Local to State to National Data Comparison
- Risk Control Recommendations
- Needed SOP/G Revisions
- Reported Trends and Trend Analysis
- Possible Risk
- Control

Figure 12.5 Reports on occupational injuries, illnesses, and fatalities should begin with strong local, regional, and national research and result in calls to action for needed revisions, trends to attend to, and control measures to implement.

Current Local and National Fire Service Trends

HSOs should examine local and national reports for any developing trends. Granted, some data will be dated, but this should not be cause for exclusion. All accidents, near-misses, injuries, deaths, illnesses, and exposures reports provide valuable clues and lessons to improve departmental practices, training, and culture. The HSO should gather these reports, discern critical information, and include a summary in the written report.

Comparison with Identified Trends

After the HSO gathers local and national trend data, a comparison of the identified trends with departmental data should follow. This comparison should illustrate if the department has similar accidents or near-misses as found in the trends. Some trends will be localized to a department or jurisdiction, while other trends may have national significance that alters standards, best practices, or training manuals. The HSO has the most impact at the local department level by recommending changes before they become trends.

Prevention or Mitigation Recommendations

Following the trend analysis and comparison, the HSO, with assistance from the occupational safety and health committee, should identify prevention or mitigation recommendations. This process should include a root cause analysis of departmental incidents and accident reports. Prevention and mitigation recommendations should be directed at improving processes, practices, or the culture, not assigning blame to individuals.

Recommendations for Change

Developing recommendations for change is based on research, the need to correct an unsafe practice or procedure, and new evidence-based technologies and methods. Compiling this information with additional hazard identification and control measures helps the HSO and the occupational safety and health committee generate recommendations to reduce accidents, injuries, and loss. Recommendations for change should include specific assignments with names, time frames for compliance, and schedules for follow-up reports.

Recommendations from the Accident Prevention Program

Recommendations based upon the accident prevention program should be developed to reduce workplace risk as much as possible. Recommendations may be preventive or reactive measures based on a specific operation and any reports of accidents, injuries, or incidents. As an HSO, consider the following when developing recommendations:

- **Laws, codes, regulations, and standards** — recommendations should address any deficiencies in compliance. Refer to Chapter 2, Safety and Health Laws, Codes, Regulations, and Standards for a detailed discussion on laws, codes, regulations, and standards.

- **Training** — recommendations in training should include curriculum updates, ergonomic issues identified from injury reports, rehab, and preburn inspections.

- **Accident or incident injury investigation** — may include recommendations to prevent or reduce the chance of a repeated incident based on investigations. The investigation may include input from a supplemental **accident review board (ARB)** that is comprised of various representatives from the greater organization.

- **Treatment and transport of an injured department member** — may include recommendations to revise SOP/Gs regarding the treatment, transportation, and medical facility options for any injured department member.

- **Driver/Operator** — may include recommendations for SOP/Gs, certifying courses, and recertifying criteria.

- **Safety audits** — recommendations should address any deficiency in workplace practice, procedure, or legal mandate compliance.

- **Postincident analysis** — recommendations based on deficiencies or preventative measures necessary to improve safety based upon firefighter performance during incidents.

While these items highlight the HSO responsibility, consideration should also be given to company officer, Command staff, and junior officer training and refresher training. As attrition occurs in a department, training should be in place to prepare those members for moving up to the next level of responsibility. Additionally, training and certification of specialty positions should be assessed for compliance with local SOP/Gs and NFPA® standards.

Accident Review Boards

In some jurisdictions, an accident review board (ARB) is convened on a regular basis to review all vehicular accidents involving departmental vehicles or personnel. These reviews occur after the immediate accident investigation has concluded. The board members will vary among jurisdiction, but they could include the following:

- Battalion Chief

- Company officers not involved in the accident

- Jurisdictional safety officer or risk manager

- Members of the training division

The purpose of the board is to provide accountability and quality assurance of the investigation process. This team can forward determinations of preventable/nonpreventable events with or without contributing factors.

During board hearings, those individuals involved in the accident and investigation will have an opportunity to present their account of events to the board and answer any questions that the board may have. This testimony is typically internal to the organization, but considerations for confidentiality should be included in SOP/Gs for the board proceedings.

Upon the completion of its review, the board presents its findings to the fire chief and has a number of responsibilities:

- Determine whether accidents were preventable

- Verify that investigations were thorough and impartial

- Determine causative factors relating to the accident that may have been missed
- Make recommendations to prevent future accidents

Some jurisdictions also grant the board the right to suggest corrective actions for units or individuals involved. These actions could include mandated retraining or disciplinary action. Disciplinary action is not the intention of ARB review; however, when the individuals involved in the accident have a history of SOP/G infractions, some boards are allowed to be specific in their disciplinary recommendations.

Reports from the ARB become a part of departmental records. The fire chief has the enforcement responsibility to either follow the boards' recommendations or take other action. The board may review reports from earlier meetings and accidents to help inform future decisions.

Recommendations from the Occupational Safety and Health Committee

The occupational safety and health committee serves an advisory role when making recommendations to the fire chief. The HSO's responsibility is to guide the committee in its decision-making process and report its recommendations to the fire chief or appropriate authority. Disciplinary action is one issue that is not an objective of the committee. The activities and issues that are addressed must be within the committee's scope. The committee's intent is to conduct research, develop recommendations, and study and review matters pertaining to occupational health and safety within the department.

Improvements to Safety and Health Programs

Improvements to safety and health programs are an ongoing process. The HSO serves as the main point of contact for all safety and health programs and any improvement recommendations. These recommendations should be based on research and not the latest fad. The HSO must be able to justify improvements and explain why they are needed. Showing how an existing program is deficient or obsolete will help the membership understand the importance of any change. Getting personnel to accept the change is essential for the success of any program.

Changes in Equipment, Procedures, and Methods

After all the data analysis of accidents, near-misses, injuries, deaths, illnesses, and exposures is completed, the written recommendation report should include any needed changes in equipment, procedures, and practices. The recommendations may come from safety audits, accident reports, and/or root cause analysis reports. The HSO should examine all of the above-mentioned information to determine if equipment, procedures, and/or methods of operations are trending toward an unsafe condition. The goal in making changes is to improve the safe working environment for all personnel. **Learning Activity 12-1** provides an exercise to create recommendations for changes in equipment.

Chapter Summary

A vital component of a safety and health program is ensuring communication with department personnel. The HSO should regularly submit reports and recommendations to keep administrators informed. This information is critical to the short- and long-term planning and decision-making process. Departmental policies, operations, and programs require a review to ensure continued adequacy, effectiveness, and compliance. The HSO evaluates all of this information with a specific focus on the safety and health of the workplace and the membership. Research and trend analysis are important components in this review process and can lead to improvement recommendations.

Review Questions

1. What criteria should the health safety officer consider when developing reports for a fire service organization? (p. 394)

2. What topics should be included in departmental reports on SOP/Gs and training programs? (pp. 397-399)

3. What items should be included in a departmental report on accidents, occupational injuries, illnesses, deaths, and exposures? (pp. 400-401)

4. What is the health safety officer's role in providing recommendations to reduce accidents, injuries, and loss in a department? (pp. 401-403)

12-1
Write a memorandum recommending changes to PPE specifications.

 LEARNING ACTIVITIES

Refer to Appendix B: Learning Activity Answers in the back of this manual for suggested responses.

Purpose

The responsibility for determining apparatus, equipment, and protective clothing needs and specifications will differ among fire and emergency services organizations. However, the health safety officer should assist in the process and ensure that safety and health recommendations correlate to compliance standards and the risk management plan.

Directions

1. Read the scenario.

2. Using your findings from the research performed in **Learning Activity 11-1** and the information taken from the scenario, write a brief memorandum recommending that your department upgrade its structural fire fighting boots to footwear that has superior tread and traction. Your memo should include:

- The number and type of injuries sustained by firefighters due to slick conditions

- Types of structural fire fighting boots currently approved for use by your department

   NOTE: This information should include the tread depth and slip resistance based on the physical inspection you performed for **Learning Activity 11-1**.

- Rationale for changing the type of footwear currently used (include all pertinent research taken from national standards, vendor information, etc.)

- A recommendation to upgrade the type of footwear based on your research

Scenario

As your department's new health safety officer, you have reviewed firefighter injuries for the last five years. You have determined that a high number of injuries – some 55% during this five-year-period – have involved firefighters slipping or falling on slick terrain. You have also just reviewed your department's current specifications regarding structural fire fighting boots, have performed a physical inspection of the tread on the boots, and have compared your findings to national standards. As a result of your research, you have decided to recommend that the department upgrade its structural fire fighting boots to footwear that has superior tread and traction.

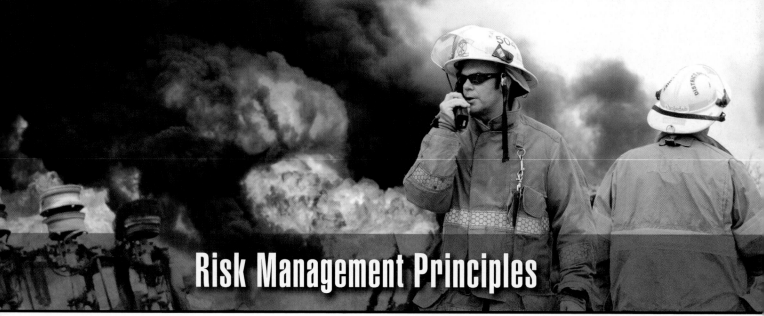

Risk Management Principles

Photo courtesy of Chris Mickal, District Chief, New Orleans (LA) Fire Department.

Chapter Contents

chapter 13

Key Terms

NFPA® Job Performance Requirements

This chapter provides information that addresses the following job performance requirements of NFPA® 1521, *Standard for Fire Department Safety Officer Professional Qualifications (2015)*.

5.2.1	5.2.6	5.5.2
5.2.2	5.2.9	5.7.1
5.2.3	5.2.10	5.7.2
5.2.4	5.3.6	
5.2.5	5.4.2	

Risk Management Principles

Learning Objectives

After reading this chapter, students will be able to:

1. Describe recognized safety practices that should be implemented as part of an overall risk management framework. (5.2.1, 5.2.2, 5.2.4, 5.2.5, 5.2.6, 5.2.9, 5.2.10, 5.3.6, 5.4.2, 5.5.2, 5.7.1, 5.7.2)

2. Identify methods used by the incident safety officer for assessing and managing risks. (5.2.2, 5.2.4, 5.2.10)

3. Describe characteristics of equipment and technology as they relate to firefighter safety and health. (5.2.1, 5.3.6)

4. Explain common incident protocols and procedures. (5.2.1, 5.2.3, 5.2.4, 5.2.5, 5.2.6, 5.2.9, 5.2.10)

5. Learning Activity 13-1: Analyze fire department operations for adherence to risk management principles and practices. [5.2.2, 5.2.4, 5.2.5, 5.2.6, 5.2.7, 5.2.8, 5.2.9, 5.2.10, 5.4.2, 5.5.2]

Chapter 13
Risk Management Principles

Photo courtesy of Chris Mickal, District Chief, New Orleans (LA) Fire Department.

Case History

In 2011, record snowfall around the headwaters of the Missouri River in the Rocky Mountains of Montana and Wyoming coupled with above average spring rainfall resulted in catastrophic flooding in several Midwestern states. One river community in Iowa was at or above flood stage for 105 days during the event, pushing its levee system to its limits, destroying homes, and damaging critical infrastructure. The event was managed using the NIMS model, utilizing all appropriate ICS forms and functional branch assignments to help with planning, implementing, and documenting the incident.

The incident safety officer for the flood event was responsible for conducting risk management analysis for all operational sections of the response. These sections included the fire department, law enforcement, public works, National Guard, private contractors, U.S. Army Corp of Engineers, and civil engineers working in the field.

The citizens and flood workers were faced with the ever-present threat of a catastrophic failure of the river levee system that would flood a large portion of the city, affecting a population of over 60,000 people. Other challenges faced by the incident safety officer included:

- Communications
- Worker accountability
- Protective clothing and equipment issues (visibility and personal flotation devices)
- Long operational work periods
- Environmental hazards
- Sink holes
- Streets collapsing

Daily work was comprised of reviewing the Medical Plan (ICS 206 form), analyzing the operational plan (ICS 215 form) for potential safety concerns, developing an Incident Action Plan Safety Analysis (ICS 215A form), and preparing a daily Safety Message/Plan (ICS 208 form). The ISO also closely monitored and analyzed the daily weather forecasts to identify potential hazardous conditions for flood workers.

Weather and environmental conditions were major concerns during the entirety of the incident for several reasons. Primarily, any precipitation locally or upstream could cause catastrophic failure of the saturated levee system surrounding the community and place civilians and flood workers in grave danger. Secondly, workers needed to be protected from the elements (sunscreen, bug spray, hydration). Heat-related emergencies were a key concern during July and August as temperatures and humidity levels rose to dangerous levels.

Case History *(cont.)*

The potential for workers operating in and near contaminated flood waters prompted the action of ensuring all personnel had up-to-date tetanus and hepatitis vaccinations. Procedures had to be established for the use of personal flotation devices, hip-wader boots, and decontamination when exposed to flood water.

In addition to physical dangers that flood workers faced, the mental health of all workers was also a concern for the incident safety officer. Every day brought new dangers and challenges, which created high levels of atypical work-related stress. Both Command staff and field workers were required to take time away from the disaster, and counselors were available for all workers.

By the time the flood waters had receded, the city had incurred over 7 million dollars in infrastructure damage, nearly 100 homes damaged or destroyed, and thousands of worker hours logged with no serious injuries. The flood event demonstrated that applying solid risk management principles and using the NIMS model, including a unified command structure, trained personnel could successfully manage a complex, long-term natural disaster.

Risk management principles provide a comprehensive approach to fire and emergency services operational safety. This chapter outlines safety principles and practices that directly address risks and hazards confronting the fire and emergency services organization. This inherently risky work requires a myriad of protective actions and practices to make emergency operations as safe as possible. All firefighters accept risk to a certain extent, but safety is priority number one. The risk management principles focus our attention on how we accept risk. Generally, this focus involves identifying the risks of a situation and creating a plan that limits responder exposure to risks. This risk/benefit assessment provides a guideline of rules for Incident Commanders (IC), tactical-level management supervisors, and the Incident Safety Officer (ISO) to consider. Sometimes this guideline will mean that the risk is unacceptable and the action plan is limited to those tasks that can be safely performed, such as following a defensive strategy at a structure fire where no lives or property are deemed savable. Risk management principles and practices must continually adapt to the dynamic all-hazards interaction between responders, operations, and risk.

Recognized Safety Practices

The ten practices listed in this section are a part of the overall risk management framework to improve workplace safety (**Figure 13.1**). They include:

- Hierarchy of controls
- Incident Management Systems (IMS)
- Incident Action Plans (IAPs) and SOP/Gs
- Personnel accountability systems
- Appropriate protective clothing and equipment, including respiratory protection

16 Firefighter Life Safety Initiatives 3, 4, 11, and 12

The *16 Firefighter Life Safety Initiatives* were discussed in Chapter 1, Health Safety Officer Responsibilities. Initiatives 3, 4, 11, and 12 are pertinent to the ISO's understanding of risk management:

3. Focus greater attention on the integration of risk management with incident management at all levels, including strategic, tactical, and planning responsibilities.

4. All firefighters must be empowered to stop unsafe practices.

11. National standards for emergency response policies and procedures should be developed and championed.

12. National protocols for response to violent incidents should be developed and championed.

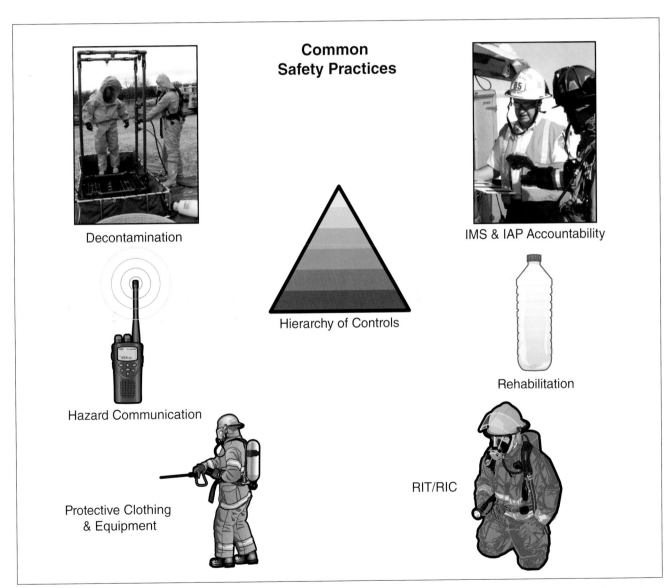

Figure 13.1 Many safety practices are widely recognized across departments, regions, and the nation as being universally useful at all emergency response scenes.

- Effective emergency communications
- Hazards communicated to all responders at the scene
- Rapid intervention crews (RIC) in place
- Decontamination at all incidents
- Rehabilitation at all incidents

Many of these practices relate to the quality of control efforts. These practices may also address how well task and incident risks are managed, how well established practices succeed at improving the incident environment, or how well established practices are implemented. These practices must have top management and membership support. Policies, practices, and risk management control measures must be implemented by everyone – and not just written on paper. All of the components of the risk management plan and all of the safety practices implemented by an organization and its membership create a line of defense. The goal is for these defensive layers to prevent actions or sets of actions that could lead to a bad outcome. **Learning Activity 13-1** in combination with the information in this chapter provides you with a scenario intended to make you consider safety practices and principles at incident scenes.

Every member of the fire and emergency services organization has an obligation and responsibility to see that safety practices are utilized all of the time. This responsibility is the first line of defense against injuries, fatalities, illnesses, and exposures. The ISO is the last line of defense.

Following the Hierarchy of Controls

The concept of the hierarchy of controls can be referenced to the National Institute for Occupational Safety and Health (NIOSH). NIOSH has ranked the five control measures from most effective to least effective in controlling risks and hazards as follows:

1. Elimination
2. Substitution
3. Engineering controls
4. Administrative controls
5. Personal protective clothing and equipment

The elimination or substitution of a hazard can happen, but it is often unrealistic, especially for the fire and emergency services organization. Engineering controls (covered in Chapter 7, Safety and Health Programs) create a separation between responders and hazards.

Administrative controls and personal protective clothing and equipment are the final two measures. According to NFPA® 1026, *Standard for Incident Management Personnel Professional Qualifications*, the hierarchy of controls is requisite knowledge for the ISO regarding the evaluation of incident safety practices.

Using an Incident Management System (IMS)

Each organization needs to have a policy in place outlining how incidents will be managed. It is commonplace to use the phrases incident management system (IMS) and incident command system (ICS) interchangeably; however, personnel should understand that there is a difference between them. The incident management system is an overall strategy for achieving a coordinated incident management outcome. According to the National Incident Management System (NIMS) (2008, p. 5), "Incident management refers to how incidents are managed across all homeland security activities, including prevention, protection, response, mitigation, and recovery." The NIMS document outlines the core components of incident management, which include:

- Preparedness
- Communications and information management
- Resource management
- Command and management
- Ongoing management and maintenance

The ICS is one component of the overall IMS. ICS is the operational element that provides a framework for maintaining control of personnel assignments and actions while promoting a coordinated effort in which all members are working toward the same goals.

Following an Incident Action Plan (IAP) and Local SOP/Gs

All incidents should have an **incident action plan (IAP)**. Some IAPs are written, especially at large incidents. IAPs at smaller incidents are usually verbally communicated to responders on the incident scene or may consist of a simple tactical worksheet. Written IAPs are required for incidents with multiple operational periods or those involving hazardous materials. The plan should reflect the following priorities:

1. Ensuring personnel safety and survival
2. Rescuing or evacuating endangered occupants **(Figure 13.2)**
3. Eliminating the hazard
4. Conducting loss control
5. Protecting the environment

All incident personnel must function within the IAP. Tactical-level management supervisors should follow SOP/Gs, and incident personnel should direct every action toward achieving the goals and objectives specified in the plan. When all members (from the IC to the lowest ranking member of the team) understand their positions, roles, and functions in the ICS, the system can serve to safely, effectively, and efficiently use resources to accomplish the IAP.

> **Incident Action Plan (IAP)** — Written or unwritten plan for the disposition of an incident; contains the overall strategic goals, tactical objectives, and support requirements for a given operational period during an incident. All incidents require an action plan.

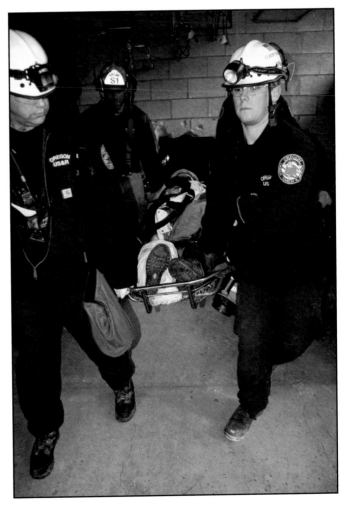

Figure 13.2 IAPs should have written plans for rescuing or evacuating possible victims.

Maintaining a Personnel Accountability System

Each organization must adopt an existing **personnel accountability system** or develop its own system of accountability that identifies and tracks all personnel working at an incident. The organization should standardize the system so that it is used at every incident. All personnel must be trained on the system and participate in it when operating at an emergency incident **(Figure 13.3)**. Each department should communicate its accountability system with mutual and automatic aid partners so that all crews have working knowledge of the system. The system must also account for those individuals who respond to the scene in vehicles other than emergency response apparatus, including staff vehicles and personally owned vehicles (POVs). The current trend is a move toward interoperability among departments.

Accountability is vital in the event of a change in the status of the emergency incident. At a structure fire, that change might be the extension of the fire through a concealed space, the rapid increase in the volume of fire due to the ignition of a flammable or combustible liquid, or a rapid fire development situation. The IC must know who is at the incident, where each person is located, and under which specific tactical function or supervisor they are working **(Figure 13.4)**. For example, SCBAs can malfunction or run out of air; and firefighters can get lost in structures. Without having an accountability system, it is impossible to determine who and how many firefighters may be trapped inside a structure or injured. Too many firefighters have died because they were not discovered missing until it was too late.

Tactical-level unit supervisors are responsible for keeping track of the members of their unit. When operating in the hot zone, the units should be within visible range of each other. When the atmosphere is obscured, they should be in contact using other means (voice or touch). When broadcasting a personnel accountability report to the IC, the tactical-level supervisor must clearly state who they are accounting for in the report. Departmental SOP/Gs must define how and when this communication is to occur.

Figure 13.3 All personnel must check into the accountability system at emergency scenes. *Courtesy of Ron Jeffers.*

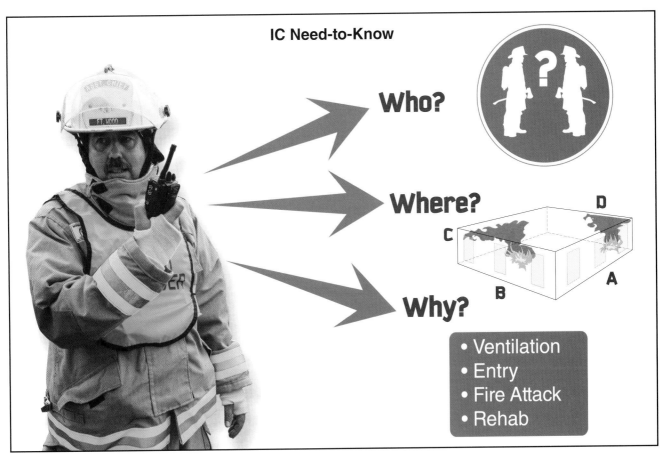

Figure 13.4 The IC should be kept informed about who is active at the scene, where they are active, and why they have been assigned to that location.

The system should indicate the following:

- Individuals assigned to each apparatus crew or staff position
- Names of people responding individually, such as staff personnel and volunteers
- Time of arrival
- Assigned duty or unit
- Time of release from the scene

The ISO is responsible for ensuring that the system is in place and that all members are in compliance. The ISO must have the authority to enforce the use of the system and correct any violations. Working through the IC, the ISO may enforce the accountability system and advise the IC of any deficiencies.

Ensuring the Use of Appropriate Protective Clothing and Equipment

Because the environment inside burning buildings is potentially hostile – even lethal – firefighters must wear the protective clothing and respiratory protection provided them. Firefighters are at risk even when working outside the structure. Even though the use of personal protective clothing and equipment does not guarantee safety, wearing them correctly and conscientiously will reduce the chances of serious injury, chronic illness, or death.

Departments should adopt and strictly enforce SOP/Gs requiring the use of appropriate protective clothing and equipment and respiratory protection during overhaul. During overhaul operations, firefighters can be exposed to a variety of hazards, including numerous toxic gases. Because the health effects of some of these gases are delayed – sometimes for years – it is easy for firefighters to be lulled into a false sense of security.

Air Monitoring Research[1]

The Office of the State Fire Marshal in Oregon conducted a research study on air monitoring and air quality during overhaul operations. Officials evaluated thirty-eight structure fires of varying types over an 8-month period. At each fire, they monitored air quality during the overhaul stage of the fire and made comparisons between the levels of carbon monoxide (CO) and other toxic gases. In addition, they collected data on the levels of all harmful gases at regular time intervals during overhaul, salvage, and scene investigation to determine how long gases remain harmful following a fire and how much gas is in the atmosphere during this time period.

Officials discovered that the following chemical concentrations in the air during overhaul exceeded the NIOSH Immediately Dangerous to Life and Health (IDLH) levels:

- Nitrogen dioxide (NO2)
- Acrolein
- Carbon monoxide (CO)
- Arsenic
- Mercury

Officials also discovered that these and many other chemical concentrations exceeded Oregon's state OSHA requirements and NIOSH requirements for Short Term Exposure Limits (STEL), including:

- Nitrogen dioxide (NO2)
- Hydrogen chloride (HCl)
- Carbon monoxide (CO)

These discoveries corroborated other national studies. In addition, they established that testing only for CO, which is often an accepted practice in SOP/Gs, is not a good indicator of the overall safety of air concentrations during overhaul. For example, officials discovered no correlation between low levels of CO and low levels of other toxic gases. According to this study, testing only for CO is not an adequate test to declare a site safe for work without respiratory protection.

This study and others similar to it indicate that firefighters and other responders working in a scene from overhaul through the investigation process need to be wearing respiratory equipment while they work -- full SCBA, if indicated through air monitoring. In addition, someone trained on the equipment and wearing SCBA should perform air monitoring of the scene as soon after knockdown of the fire as possible and before investigators later enter the scene. The testing should cover as wide a range of airborne contaminants as possible. The results of the testing should be used to determine the level of respiratory protection needed when firefighters begin to overhaul the scene or conduct investigations.

Maintaining Good Communications

To effectively communicate with the IC and other emergency scene officers, the ISO must have good interpersonal communication skills. The ISO must be able to articulate and express thoughts clearly, concisely, and calmly during stressful situations.

The ISO communicates at an incident scene through radio or face-to-face interactions. The ISO must be prepared to use the radio system, including the department's approved clear-text message system. When possible, face-to-face communication is the most effective type of communication because it reduces the possibility for misunderstandings, produces immediate responses, and adds the benefits of nonverbal aspects of communications (facial expressions and gestures).

The ISO should also be aware of common barriers to communications **(Figure 13.5 a and b, p. 418)**:

- Distance
- Physical barriers
- Interference
- Ambient noise
- Communication system overload
- Task saturation or enhanced span of control

The ISO should advise the IC of any problems occurring with the communications at the scene. At larger incidents, these issues may be communicated to the Comms Section.

Reporting Hazards Immediately

All responders should be empowered to communicate safety hazards immediately through the chain of command at any time. When safety hazards are located, the ISO must immediately communicate this fact to IC. If an unsafe hazard or activity is potentially life-threatening, the ISO must then exercise his/her authority to stop the activity or direct firefighters to work around the hazard. The ISO must, at the same time, be aware of the unity of command and that contradictory commands can lead to other problems. When other problems occur, the ISO has to depend on his or her credibility and the working relationship that he or she has developed with fire fighting personnel to solve them.

Ensuring Rapid Intervention Is Available

NFPA® 1500, *Standard on Fire Department Occupational Safety and Health Program,* and OSHA regulations require a rapid intervention crew (RIC) whenever firefighters are in the hazard zone inside a burning building. At large or unusual events where there are multiple points of entry into the hazard zone, the IC has the option to assign multiple RICs. In every case, at least two fully equipped firefighters must be standing by outside the hazard zone prepared to initiate a rescue of the interior crew, if necessary. Firefighter safety/survival may depend on rapid intervention following a partial building collapse, a lost or disoriented firefighter running low on air, or a firefighter suffering a medical emergency in the hazard zone.

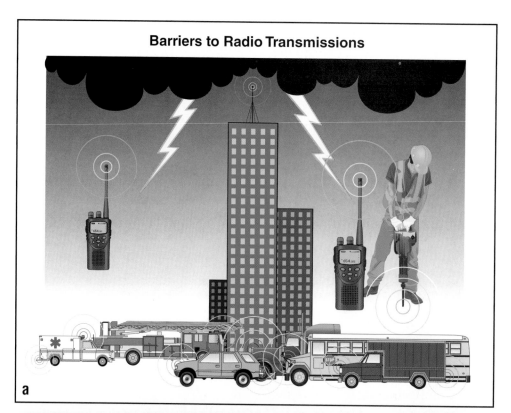

Barriers to Radio Transmissions

Figure 13.5 a and b Barriers to radio communications may come from the environment surrounding the emergency or from the noise associated with emergency activities. *(b) Courtesy of Ron Moore and McKinney Tx Fire Department.*

Rescuing a downed firefighter takes time and effort. In recognition of the complexity of finding and removing a downed firefighter, some fire and emergency services organizations have SOP/Gs directing the dispatch of additional units, specifically RICs. The ISO should evaluate the operation and the assignment of RIC to ensure compliance with NFPA®, OSHA, and departmental policy **(Figure 13.6)**. The ISO should make recommendations to the IC if improvements can be made or personnel available for RIC is inadequate (see info box).

Figure 13.6 The ISO should monitor RIC activity and ensure that the crews are in place and have everything they need to respond if necessary.

RIC Rescue Research[2]

In 2001, the Phoenix Fire Department and the Seattle Fire Department conducted independent studies of the effectiveness of RIC teams at structure fires where firefighters inside the structure required rescue. They were surprised at the results and that the two studies corroborated one another without any collaboration among the researchers.

Both studies revealed that it took on average eleven firefighters entering a structure to find and retrieve a downed firefighter within an acceptable amount of time to ensure the firefighter's survival. At large buildings, the search and rescue from RIC teams could take as long as 20 minutes.

These studies included structure fires of various sizes, so the number of firefighters needed for rescue at single residences is lower than the eleven or more firefighters needed at large buildings. The most important conclusion to be drawn from these studies is that RIC teams can be effective, but only if they are staffed in sufficient numbers for the incident. For example, at fires in large structures, these studies recommend that no firefighters enter the structure for interior attack or search and rescue unless there are at least a dozen firefighters outside who can conduct a search, if necessary. This number will be lower at smaller fires, but should always be sufficient to the requirements of the incident.

Rapid intervention search is high risk and not always guaranteed to be successful. It is better to make as accurate and informed a size-up as possible before sending crews into a compromised structure. Interior crews should also be well-trained, stay together, and follow all appropriate safety protocols. They are more likely to successfully evacuate from a bad situation as a group than to be found individually in a secondary search.

Ensuring the Presence of Decontamination

Decontamination is typically associated with hazardous materials incidents. However, structural and/or aircraft fire suppression activities also require decontamination of personal protective clothing and equipment. The ISO must ensure steps are taken early in the incident to have personnel and resources readily available for decontamination. Decontamination at structural fire scenes may include:

- Rinsing protective clothing and equipment
- Immediate doffing of equipment after overhaul.
- Total removal of protective clothing and equipment before mounting apparatus to return to the station.
- Cleaning exposed skin at the scene **(Figure 13.7)**.

Providing Rehabilitation at All Incidents

Emergency scene operations place a great deal of physical stress on responders. Therefore, rehabilitation areas are necessary to provide a place where personnel can rest, relax, rehydrate, take nourishment, and have their vital signs monitored by medical personnel. Rehabilitation areas, also known as *rehab*, are located in the cold zone and are generally incorporated with the on-scene medical facilities. The administration's responsibility is to establish procedures for rehab at emergency incidents and to fund the items needed for the site. Water or fluid containers, folding cots, warming tents, and water mist systems are just a few of the items generally associated with rehab areas **(Figure 13.8)**. Interagency agreements with local transit or school districts can be written to include climate-controlled buses on call for responders' use.

The level of rehabilitation will be consistent with the size and scope of the incident. It is not unheard of to need cots or warming tents at some incidents. For example, a 4-hour hazmat incident during a snowstorm would require it. A similar incident during the summer heat would require some means of reducing body temperatures.

Rehabilitation is not just a site, however. It is also the awareness of the need for rehab that is the responsibility of all operational personnel. Supervisors must monitor the physical condition of their subordinates and send them to rehab before they become too fatigued. Members should be sent to rehab before their condition deteriorates to the point of affecting the safety of other members. Responders must monitor their own condition and report the need for rehab to their supervisor. In practice, rehab may take two forms. The first form involves resting, removing wet or damp protective clothing and equipment, cooling down or warming up as needed, and drinking fluids. The second form involves medical rehab that includes medical monitoring, treatment of injuries, rehydration, and/or transportation.

A general rule for structure fires or incidents that require the use of SCBA is to send personnel to rehab when they have used two (2) 30-minute air bottles or one (1) 60-minutes air bottle. Other factors, such as weather conditions, type of work, or fire behavior, will affect this estimate. For a detailed look at rehabilitation, see the U.S. Fire Administration's *Emergency Incident Rehabilitation* (FA-314) manual.

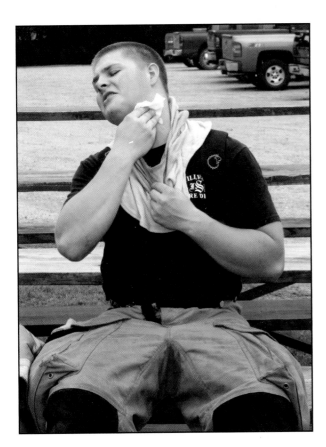

Figure 13.7 Using moist towelettes to remove soot from skin immediately following each incident is one preventative measure against contracting cancer later in life.

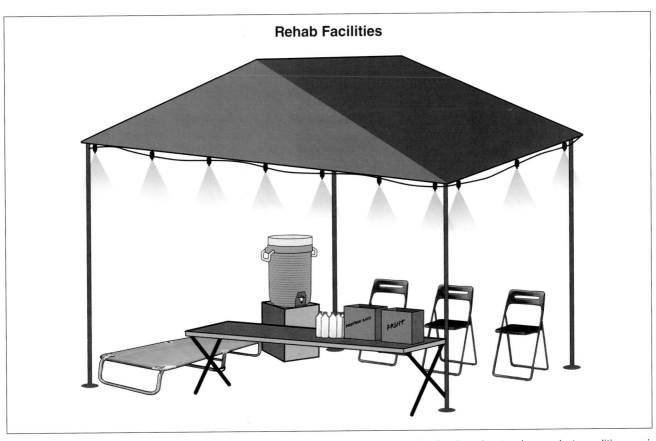

Rehab Facilities

Figure 13.8 Rehabilitation stations should provide protection from the sun, healthy food, and water. In very hot conditions, mist sprayers can be used to provide additional cooling.

ISO Risk Management Assessment

A risk management assessment essentially covers every aspect of incident operations. The ISO must have the experience and training to quickly identify and stop any safety-related issue. The ISO must maintain the big picture of the incident while monitoring each division or group operating on the scene. The strategy and tactics employed on an incident must first and foremost consider personnel safety as the number one priority. In order to do this, the ISO should utilize a recognized risk management framework during an incident assessment. The sections that follow describe a number of risk assessment methods that have been developed to help firefighters make informed strategic decisions at incidents.

Risk Management Framework

Fire and emergency services responders are expected to take calculated risks to provide for life safety, incident stabilization, and property conservation. Calculated risks mean that we do not blindly go into a situation, but rather we gather information through size-up and determine what level of risk is acceptable for the given situation.

All of the following sections provide differing considerations with regards to safety and risk/benefit analysis. The ISO should be familiar with all of them and apply the concept that best fits the situation. The ISO may find that one approach fits the need of the situation, but at other times a multifaceted approach may be needed.

10 Rules of Engagement for Structural Fire Fighting

In 2001, the International Association of Fire Chiefs (IAFC) developed a model policy called *The 10 Rules of Engagement for Structural Fire Fighting*. The policy was developed to help ensure that all firefighters return home safely. The *10 Rules* are as follows:

- **Acceptability of Risk**

  1. No building or property is worth the life of a firefighter.

  2. All interior fire fighting involves an inherent risk.

  3. Some risk is acceptable, in a measured and controlled manner.

  4. No level of risk is acceptable where there is no potential to save lives or savable property.

  5. Firefighters shall not be committed to interior offensive fire fighting operations in abandoned or derelict buildings.

- **Risk Assessment**

  6. All feasible measures shall be taken to limit or avoid risks through risk assessment by a qualified officer.

  7. It is the responsibility of the Incident Commander to evaluate the level of risk in every situation.

  8. Risk assessment is a continuous process for the entire duration of each incident.

  9. If conditions change and risk increases, change strategy and tactics.

  10. No building or property is worth the life of a fire fighter.

In *The 10 Rules of Engagement for Structural Fire Fighting*, the prohibition for committing an interior attack in an abandoned or derelict building can generate a great deal of discussion. For instance, because a structure is unoccupied, vacant, abandoned, or derelict does not mean that there is not a life safety hazard present. These types of structures may contain homeless people, demolition or construction workers, or security personnel. One approach is to consider all structures as occupied until proven otherwise. Of course, once you have committed personnel to an interior attack, the structure is very much occupied.

NFPA® Rules of Engagement

In addition to *The 10 Rules of Engagement for Structural Fire Fighting* from the IAFC, the NFPA® has *Rules of Engagement* for consideration. They are **(Figure 13.9)**:

1. We will risk our lives a lot, in a calculated manner, to save SAVABLE LIVES.

2. We will risk our lives a LITTLE, in a calculated manner, to save SAVABLE property.

3. We WILL NOT risk our lives at all for a building or lives that are already lost.

Risk Management Criteria

Each fire and emergency services organization should define risk management criteria for those members either making command decisions or assessing decisions, such as the ISO. When an incident occurs, the IC and the ISO must ensure that strategic and tactical decisions do not place personnel at an unacceptable risk. Risk management criteria should be in conjunction with the above stated risk/benefit analysis and include consideration of the following:

- Incident hazards
- Imminent hazards
- Laws, codes, regulations, or standards
- Facility operations
- Building construction
- Fire dynamics and smoke characteristics
- Hazardous energy sources
- Traffic hazards
- Limited personnel
- Inadequately trained personnel

NOTE: For more information on these hazards, see Chapter 14, Incident Hazard Recognition.

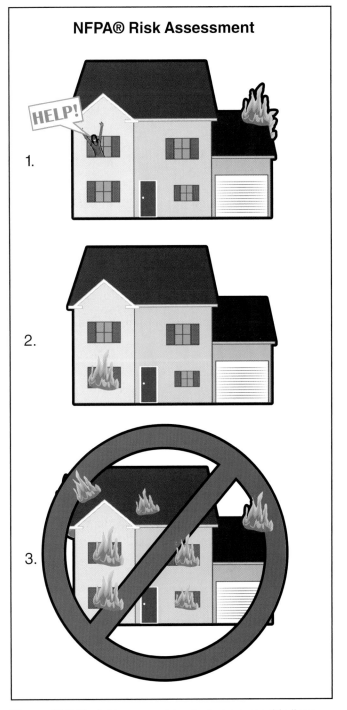

NFPA® Risk Assessment

Figure 13.9 Firefighters may risk a lot to save savable lives, risk less to save savable property, and take no risks to save lives or property which are already lost.

Safety and Health Equipment and Technology

The equipment and technology provided to emergency responders offer critical layers of defense against the hazards as they perform their jobs. ISOs must know what these items are in their department and their proper use in differing situations. Some equipment, such as cribbing, while not directly related to safety, is essential to creating a safe operating environment. The equipment and technology is only a good defense if it is appropriate for the situation, personnel are trained to use it, and personnel use it correctly.

Fireground Operational Safety Equipment

The ISO is responsible for monitoring conditions during fire suppression operations. Any hazardous condition must be reported to the IC so strategic and tactical considerations can be evaluated and altered, if necessary. The ISO must immediately act on any imminent hazard. This responsibility includes monitoring personnel for proper use of protective clothing, SCBA, equipment and tools, accountability system, and air monitoring.

Fire Protective Clothing

Fire protective clothing provides a durable outer shell and layers for thermal and vapor protection. Modern fire protective clothing is often advanced enough to prevent not just damage from heat but also the sensation of being hot. Firefighters should consider aspects of situational awareness other than simply "feeling hot" to assess whether an environment is potentially life-threatening. Observing fire behavior or monitoring air supply during interior attack may be better indicators of hazards.

Fire protective clothing provides a limited vapor or toxic gas protection for the skin. The outer shell provides limited protection against abrasion and struck-by injuries. The ISO must recognize the potential for these types of injuries and contamination and ensure personnel are properly protected. The ISO should also ensure the IC incorporates decontamination at the scene.

Breathing Apparatus

Both the IC and the personnel entering an immediately dangerous to life and health (IDLH) environment should enforce the organization's air management policy. At structure fires or hazardous vapor leaks, the IC must evaluate the size and complexity of the structure's interior to determine the amount of time required to exit the structure from the **point of no return**. The point of no return is the point at which air in the SCBA will last only long enough to exit a hazardous atmosphere **(Figure 13.10)**. This calculation will determine maximum amount of time that can be spent working in the IDLH area.

Thermal Imagers

Thermal imagers are quickly becoming a priority safety tool in all aspects of emergency operations. Entry/attack crews use thermal imagers to maneuver through a smoky, zero visibility environment to quickly locate the seat of the fire. Search and rescue crews and rapid intervention crews use the thermal imager to quickly find and remove victims or a downed firefighter. Thermal imagers can also be used to locate hidden fires. Technology is also available

Point of No Return — Point at which air in the SCBA will last only long enough to exit a hazardous atmosphere.

Thermal Imager — Electronic device that forms images using infrared radiation. *Also known as* Thermal Imaging Camera.

Figure 13.10 Firefighters should recognize the point of no return – the distance into the building at which they do not have enough air to exit the building, if needed.

for these images to be displayed on a television screen for the IC. The IC can track the crew's movement and the conditions being encountered. The thermal imager's versatile use – whether hand-held or helmet-mounted – provides the needed visibility for improved safety and efficiency of fire suppression activities.

Global Positioning System (GPS)

Global positioning system (GPS) technology is often used as a safety device at search and rescue and wildland incidents and is becoming more common at structural fires. GPS mounted on the SCBA or carried by a firefighter provides accurate information to the IC to monitor the location and movement of a firefighter or a team of firefighters. This technology can reduce the search time in the event of a downed or lost firefighter. The IC can either direct the rapid intervention crew to a downed firefighter's location or direct a lost firefighter to the nearest exit.

Accountability Devices

Various systems, such as the tag system, SCBA system, and barcode readers, are available for tracking individuals at the emergency incident. Other electronic systems are also being used to track individuals remotely.

Accountability Tags. Personnel can be equipped with a personal identification tag **(Figure 13.11, p. 426)**. Upon entering the outer perimeter, emergency responders leave their tags at a given location or with a designated person. Tags can be attached to a control board or personnel identification chart for quick reference **(Figure 13.12, p. 427)**. Upon leaving the incident perimeter, the emergency responders collect their tags. This system enables officers to know exactly who is operating at the incident scene.

SCBA tags. SCBA tags are used in search and rescue and hazardous materials operations but less frequently at structure fires. Each SCBA is provided with a tag containing the name of the user and the air pressure in the SCBA air tank.

Global Positioning System (GPS) — System for determining position on the earth's surface by calculating the difference in time for the signal from a number of satellites to reach a receiver on the ground.

Figure 13.11 All personnel should have identification tags that can be turned in at the accountability station. *Coutrtesy of Ron Jeffers.*

Upon entering a hazardous area or the hot zone, personnel give their tags to a designated entry officer, if this person is available. This officer records time of entry and expected time of exit and performs a brief check to ensure that all protective equipment is properly worn, used, and activated, including the personal alert safety system (PASS) device. Responders leaving the danger area retrieve their tags so that the control officer knows who is safely outside and who is still inside the hazardous area.

Barcode readers. Some organizations have adopted barcode readers for tracking personnel at emergency incident scenes. Similar to the inventory control devices that retail outlets use, the system involves the assignment of a unique barcode number to each member of the organization. When that person arrives at the incident, the barcode is scanned into a computer, which registers the presence of the individual at the scene. When the person leaves the scene, the barcode is scanned a second time and the person's name is removed from the site. Depending on local policies, the barcode may be attached to the helmet, protective clothing, or other equipment that is permanently assigned to each organization member. It may also be on a personal identification card.

Electronic accountability system. The electronic accountability system is a new system designed to meet both accountability requirements and provide notification in the event a firefighter is trapped or injured. Based on radio

Figure 13.12 Boards for attaching identification tags are common tools used for tracking accountability. *Courtesy of Ron Jeffers.*

transmissions, the master unit located at the incident command post tracks the units worn by firefighters. If a wearer stops moving for an extended period or activates the remote unit, an alarm is transmitted to the control panel.

Common Tools

While monitoring fire suppression activities, the ISO must also monitor what tools firefighters are using and if they are being carried and used properly. The ISO should evaluate the use of the following tools:

- **Fire hose** — Evaluation questions:
    - Is the hose size appropriate for fire conditions?
    - Are enough personnel working on a hose line?
    - Is the nozzle appropriate?
    - Are hose stream operations working counterproductively?
    - Is the hose stream pointing into a ventilation hole?
    - Is the extinguishment method appropriate?

— Are supply hose lines protected from vehicular traffic **(Figure 13.13)**?

— Is there a confirmed secondary water supply?

- **Ground ladders** — Evaluation questions:

  — Are ladders placed in a good location and away from power lines?

  — When personnel are working on the ladder, is it being anchored by another firefighter? Are at least two ladders placed on opposite sides of the roof during roof operations?

  — Has the IC communicated the location of ground ladders to all personnel on scene?

- **Aerial ladders** — Evaluation questions:

  — Are aerial apparatus placed in a good location?

  — Are personnel working on the ladder or in the platform wearing a helmet, safety belt, and SCBA (or integrated breathing system) **(Figure 13.14, p. 430)**?

  — Are aerial operations away from any power lines?

  — Are master streams being employed while crews are still working inside a structure?

- **Cutting tools** — Evaluation questions:

  — Are axes or chainsaws being used safely?

  — Are ventilation holes being cut in the right location?

- **Ventilation fans** — Evaluation questions:

  — Are fans placed in the right location?

  — Are fans used in coordination with fire suppression activities?

Monitoring Equipment

Air monitoring at structural fires commonly includes the measurement of toxic gas levels inside a structure. After fire suppression activities are concluded, overhaul becomes the primary activity. Taking this action does not mean air quality is safe without an SCBA. Air monitoring should be completed and the air quality determined to be safe before personnel are allowed to remove their SCBA or non-suppression individuals are allowed to enter a fire-damaged area. **Multigas detectors** should be used to detect the presence of toxic gases after all structure fires **(Figure 13.15, p. 431)**.

Multigas Detector — Personal device that checks air quality against a wide range of harmful gases.

Hazardous Materials Operations Safety Equipment

Almost every incident response has the potential for hazardous materials involvement. Early detection in the incident size-up is critical to safe and appropriate strategic and tactical decisions. The IC and ISO should ensure that proper protective clothing and equipment is used. The level of protection must meet the level and type of hazard present. Hazardous materials technicians or technical specialists should research and determine the level of personal protection needed for a specific substance. Additional consideration should be given to the task of the responder making entry and the route of possible

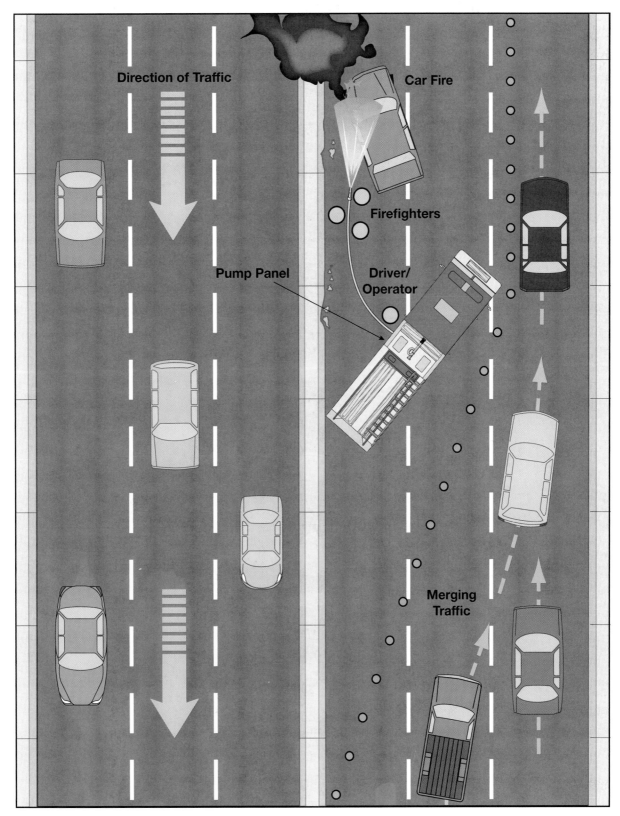

Figure 13.13 Supply hose should always be protected from traffic to prevent damage to the hose and protect the hose operators and pump operators from harm.

Level A Protection — Highest level of skin, respiratory, and eye protection available, as specified by the U.S. Environmental Protection Agency (EPA); consists of positive-pressure self-contained breathing apparatus, totally encapsulating chemical-protective suit, inner and outer gloves, and chemical-resistant boots.

Level B Protection — Personal protective equipment that affords the highest level of respiratory protection, but a lesser level of skin protection; consists of positive-pressure self-contained breathing apparatus, hooded chemical-protective suit, inner and outer gloves, and chemical-resistant boots.

Level C Protection — Personal protective equipment that affords a lesser level of respiratory and skin protection than levels A or B; consists of full-face or half-mask APR, hooded chemical-resistant suit, inner and outer gloves, and chemical-resistant boots.

Level D Protection — Personal protective equipment that affords the lowest level of respiratory and skin protection; consists of coveralls, gloves, and chemical-resistant boots or shoes.

exposure of the hazard. OSHA, 29 CFR 1910.120, Appendix B categorizes the level of protective clothing and equipment as Level A, B, C, and D as follows **(Figure 13.16 a-d):**

- **Level A protection** is a fully encapsulated suit that provides the highest level of protection against chemical absorption and inhalation.

- **Level B protection** is a non-encapsulated chemical resistant suit. It provides maximum respiratory protection as with Level A, but a lesser skin protection capability.

- **Level C protection** is a non-encapsulated chemical splash suit. The respiratory system is permitted to be protected with an air purifying respirator. This level of protection provides lesser skin and respiratory protection than Level A and B suits.

- **Level D protection** is a limited protection ensemble, such as structural fire fighting gear.

Figure 13.14 Firefighters working in an aerial platform should be wearing safety belts and have the same protective equipment as interior firefighters.

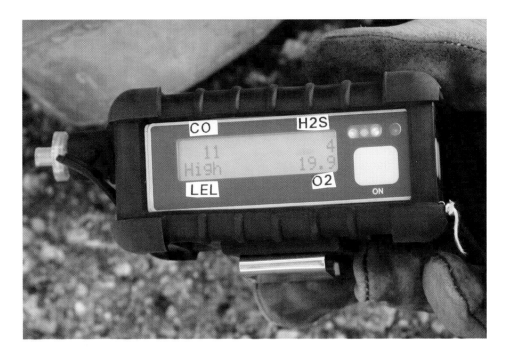

Figure 13.15 Multigas detectors show firefighters the levels of toxic gases and also show how much oxygen has been displaced by other gases.

Figure 13.16 a-d OSHA describes four levels of personal protection against hazardous materials.

The NFPA® provides standard criteria to the manufacturing of ensembles worn for chemical, biological, radiological, and nuclear (CBRN) events. The NFPA® classification system (Class 1-4) is different but comparable to OSHA's as follows:

● Class 1 ensemble is defined in NFPA® 1991, *Standard on Vapor-Protective Ensembles for Hazardous Materials Emergencies,* and meets the OSHA Level A requirement.

- Class 2 ensemble is defined in NFPA® 1994, *Standard on Protective Ensembles for First Responders to CBRN Terrorism Incidents,* and meets the OSHA Level B requirement.

- Class 3 ensemble is defined in NFPA® 1994 and meets the OSHA Level C requirement.

- Class 4 ensemble is defined in NFPA® 1994 and meets the OSHA Level C requirement.

The following four sections will address basic information on chemical, biological, and radiological protective clothing and air monitoring equipment. For more detailed information, the ISO should seek out training and education from local, state, and federal agencies.

Chemical Protective Clothing

Chemical protective clothing (CPC) is required when skin and respiratory system protection is needed at the highest level. Chemicals are in every community and every household. They are on our roadways and railways. The potential for an incident is significant. When a hazardous materials incident involving chemicals occurs, the level of exposure, chemical concentration, length of exposure, and type of work will determine the level of protection needed **(Figure 13.17 a and b)**. Commonly encountered chemicals in communities include:

- Ammonia
- Chlorine
- Sulfuric acid
- Hydrochloric acid
- Pesticides
- Insecticides

The use of chemical agents in terrorist attacks is also a concern for fire and emergency services organizations. Chemical agents will have a distinguishable odor or taste and are able to penetrate the skin. Symptoms of exposure

Figure 13.17 a and b The level of CPC worn depends upon the chemicals involved, level of exposure, length of exposure, chemical concentrations, and type of work performed. *(a) Courtesy of U.S. Air Force photo by Airman 1st Class Jason Epley, (b) Courtesy of U.S. Air Force Photo by Senior Airman Taylor Marr.*

are typically seen immediately. Chemical agents can be in the form of a liquid, solid, or gas and include some of the following:

- **Nerve agents** — Sarin and VX
- **Blister agents** — also known as vesicants, are mustard agents
- **Blood agents** — hydrogen cyanide and arsine

The purpose of chemical protective clothing and equipment is to shield or isolate individuals from the chemical hazards that may be encountered. Design and testing standards generally recognize two types of CPC: liquid-splash protective clothing and vapor-protective clothing.

CPC is made from a variety of different materials, none of which protects against all types of chemicals. Each material provides protection against certain chemicals or products, but only limited or no protection against others. The manufacturer of a particular ensemble must provide a Chemical Compatibility Chart or Chemical Resistance Guide describing for which chemicals the suit was designed. Selection of appropriate CPC depends on the specific chemical and the specific tasks that the wearer intends to perform.

Biological Protective Clothing

Biological protective clothing is also required when skin and respiratory system protection is needed at the highest level. The use of biological agents in terrorist attacks is the primary consideration with exposure potential. Biological agents can be in the form of liquid or solid particles and include some of the following **(Figure 13.18)**:

- **Bacteria** — anthrax, cholera, and the plague
- **Viral** — smallpox and Ebola
- **Toxins** — ricin

Biological agents will not have an odor or taste and do not penetrate the skin. Symptoms of exposure are typically delayed, so detection of an exposure is more difficult than a chemical exposure. Biological protective clothing selection must meet the OSHA 29 CFR 1910.120, Appendix B regulation.

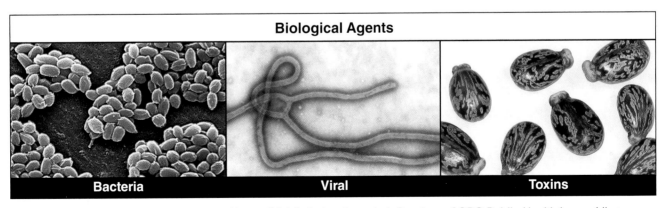

Figure 13.18 Biological agents can be liquid or solid, inhaled, or ingested. *Courtesy of CDC Public Health Image Library.*

Radiological Protection

Radiological protection depends on the form of radiation present. They are **(Figure 13.19)**:

- **Alpha (ά) particles** — create the least exposure risk. Alpha particles can be easily blocked, but inhalation or ingestion can be particularly damaging to tissues.

- **Beta (β) particles** — are stronger than Alpha particles, but can be blocked by material such as a sheet of aluminum. Direct exposure can cause burns and can be ingested or inhaled. Exposure to beta particles can be lethal in some cases.

- **Gamma (γ) rays** — are comparable to an X-ray. They penetrate more than Alpha or Beta particles but have less damaging effects. They require higher levels of shielding for protection.

- **X-rays (X)** — are electromagnetic radiation that requires higher levels of shielding for protection. The chances of encountering them at a hazardous materials incident are remote, so they are much less of a threat than Alpha, Beta, and Gamma radiation. They are produced primarily at low levels by machines in controlled environments.

Each form of radiation requires different exposure time, distance, and shielding protection considerations. Terrorist attacks may involve the use of explosive devices containing radiological materials. Commonly referred to as a *dirty bomb*, these devices not only have the damaging explosive effects but also inflict radiation exposure to victims. The presence of radiation may not be known until detected by a monitoring device such as a Geiger counter.

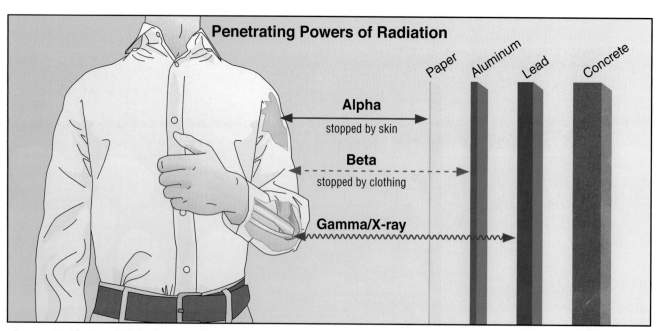

Source: *Modified from U.S. Environmental Protection Agency*

Figure 13.19 Radiation penetrates at different levels depending upon the type. Certain materials can block different types of radiation. Ensuring that skin is not exposed is very important when dealing with radiation.

Air Monitoring Technology

OSHA requires air monitoring at hazardous materials incidents before personnel are permitted into a hazard zone. There are different types of air monitoring equipment available that will detect specific gases. Air monitoring equipment is not a one-size-fits-all technology. Some monitors will only detect a single gas, while others may read four gases. Radiological monitoring can be done with a hand-held monitor or by personnel wearing a detection tag or badge. Air monitoring equipment must be calibrated to ensure accurate readings on an incident. Common detectable gases associated with hazardous materials incidents include:

- Oxygen levels
- Flammable/Combustible gases and vapors
- Toxic gases

Technical Rescue Safety Equipment

Technical rescue involves a special skill set to solve numerous types of incidents. Personnel can be trained and certified to the awareness, operations, and technician level. As personnel move from one level of training to the next, more technical or complex skills are added to the rescuers abilities. NFPA® 1670, *Standard on Operations and Training for Technical Search and Rescue Incidents,* defines technical rescue as those incidents involving the following:

- Rope (low- and high-angle rescues) **(Figure 13.20)**
- Structural collapse
- Confined space
- Vehicle
- Water (watercraft, dive, ice, surf, surface, swift water, and flood operations) **(Figure 13.21, p. 436)**
- Wilderness
- Trench **(Figure 13.22, p. 436)**
- Machinery
- Cave
- Mine and tunnel
- Tower
- Animal

Figure 13.20 High-angle rope rescue is one example of a technical rescue skill that requires the presence of a rescue qualified ISO.

Confined Space Safety

Any permit-required confined space entry must meet OSHA 29 CFR 1910.146, *Permit-Required Confined Spaces.* Before any entry can be made, all task assignments must be made including the ISO, or **Technical Safety Officer (TSO)**. Any rescue person entering a permit-required confined space must have completed required entry training within the last year, regardless of technical rescue certification level (OSHA requirement).

> **Technical Safety Officer (TSO)** — Individual assigned to function as the safety officer at technical rescue or hazardous materials incidents; assigned at the request of an incident safety officer to ensure the proper level of experience based upon incident type and conditions.

Figure 13.21 Water rescuers wear drysuits or wetsuits, flotation devices, and other specialized equipment.

Figure 13.22 Trench rescue introduces stability hazards, fall hazards, and air quality hazards during operations.

At the scene, the personnel preparing for entry into the confined space must complete the permitting process. The entry permit functions both as permission to enter the confined space and a checklist of safety precautions that should be in place. Permits usually require the following:

- Air monitoring must be completed to assess the level of hazardous atmospheres and periodically checked throughout the incident **(Figure 13.23)**.

- Forced ventilation must ensure a clean working environment.

- Personnel must be dressed in protective clothing and equipment that is appropriate to the conditions present.

- A proper breathing air system must be utilized based on air monitoring readings and potential confined space hazards **(Figure 13.24 a and b)**.

- Personnel should also be attached to a communication system or have intrinsically safe portable radios.

- Lockout/tagout procedures are followed to mitigate energy or engulfment hazards.

Figure 13.23 Air monitoring during confined space rescue is essential to ensure rescuer safety.

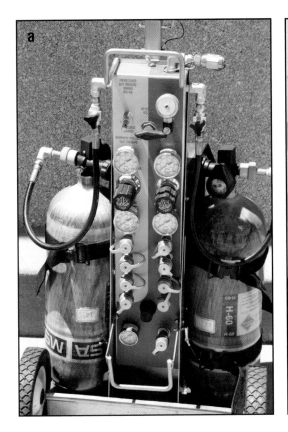

Figures 13.24 a and b SCBA is often too large to be safely used in confined spaces. Air breathing systems staffed from outside the confined space are an alternative to providing respiratory protection to rescuers.

Rigging and Hoisting Tools and Procedures

While detailing the specifics of rigging and hoisting in a technical rescue event, the ISO should employ a TSO trained to the level of the technical operation – awareness, operations, and technician. Each level has a degree of requisite knowledge and ability of complexity that personnel must be proficient in performing, including the ISO. Rigging and hoisting tools include all of the hardware (tripod, ropes, harnesses, carabiners, pulleys, anchors, and ladder racks) to create a haul system **(Figure 13.25)**. The type of haul system will be dependent on the weight of the load and the angle of the slope. Prior to any rescue operation commencing, a TSO should check the haul system(s) to ensure proper set up. All haul system operations require specific communication terminology – such as "on belay" – so all members are in sync with the operation **(Figure 13.26)**. The ISO should monitor for proper procedural compliance and recommend corrective action to the IC when needed.

Excavation and Construction Equipment

NFPA® standards or OSHA regulations do not specifically address the excavation equipment that technical rescue personnel may use. Excavation equipment may be needed for below ground rescues where victim removal from a surface operation is not possible. When a rescue requires excavation of earthen materials, fire and emergency services organizations will typically rely on and request assistance from public works department personnel or private companies that have trained and experienced operators.

When conducting a rescue that requires excavation, rescue personnel and ISO must ensure compliance with the following standards and regulations:

- NFPA® 1006, *Standard for Technical Rescuer Professional Qualifications*

- NFPA® 1026, *Standard for Incident Management Personnel Professional Qualifications*

Figure 13.25 Haul systems should be constructed using the correct rope hardware. Only qualified personnel should be allowed to build haul systems.

Figure 13.26 Belay lines are safeties that should have personnel assigned to them. Belay lines can be used to catch a falling load if there is a problem with the primary haul line.

- NFPA® 1951, *Standard on Protective Ensembles for Technical Rescue Incidents*
- OSHA 29 CFR 1926.650, Subpart P, *Excavations*

Cribbing and Shoring Equipment

Almost all rescue operations require the use of **cribbing** and **shoring** to stabilize heavy objects **(Figure 13.27, p. 440)**. Cribbing generally refers to creating a base to stabilize an object in conjunction with a lifting or raising operation of some type, as in the case of vehicle extrication activities. Shoring typically refers to the stabilization of objects that are in danger of collapse (or a secondary collapse), such as a trench cave-in. Stabilization is important when either the victim or rescuers are in a potentially dangerous environment. The TSO will be responsible for ensuring stabilization safety in conjunction with the ISO.

Cutting and Extrication Equipment

Cutting tools are perhaps the most diversified of the tool groups. However, some cutting tools are designed to cut only specific types of materials. Cutting tools should not be used to cut material that they were not designed to cut; doing so can damage the tool and endanger the operator. The ISO should have a general understanding of cutting and extrication equipment safety. The TSO will be able to provide a more technical review of the safe selection and use of these types of equipment during technical rescue operations.

Water Rescue Equipment

The selection and proper use of appropriate protective clothing and equipment is critical to the successful execution of a water-based rescue. Environmental forces and conditions that can change quickly and in unpredictable ways make water-based rescues particularly hazardous for both victims and rescuers. While water-based rescues often require similar protective clothing and equipment as land-based operations, there are additional protective clothing and equipment requirements, such as flotation devices and swim aids that

Cribbing — Lengths of solid wood or plastic, usually 4- X 4-inches (100 mm by 100 mm) or larger, used to stabilize vehicles and collapsed buildings during extrication incidents.

Shoring — General term used for lengths of timber, screw jacks, hydraulic and pneumatic jacks, and other devices that can be used as temporary support for formwork or structural components or used to hold sheeting against trench walls. Individual supports are called shores, cross braces, and struts. Commonly used in conjunction with cribbing.

Figure 13.27 Cribs are used to stabilize heavy objects after lifting tools have raised the objects to the desired height.

technical rescuers must consider. Protective clothing and equipment used for water-based rescues must conform to the standards identified in NFPA® 1952, *Standard on Surface Water Operations Protective Clothing and Equipment,* or AHJ requirements.

Unlike land-based operations where it may be acceptable to use structural fire fighting helmets for head protection, rescuers engaged in water-based operations should use helmets specifically designed for use in the water. Helmets for water rescue are designed to minimize drag when moving through the water. Given the forces that may be present during a water-based rescue, these helmets must have an effective strap system to ensure that they remain in place throughout the operation. In addition, water should easily drain from the helmet, and the amount of water that the helmet and its components can absorb should be limited. A significant amount of heat loss can occur in the head and neck area; when appropriate, a wetsuit cap or hood should be included in the protective clothing and equipment to provide thermal insulation.

A **wetsuit** is a type of protective outerwear used during water-based rescue operations. The wetsuit is so named because water is introduced into the space between the suit and the rescuer's skin. The rescuer's body heat warms the water, which, when combined with the thickness of the suit, provides a layer of thermal insulation for the rescuer. Wetsuits are produced in many different configurations and thicknesses that can be tailored to match expected local conditions. Wetsuits also provide limited impact protection to areas of the body that the suit covers.

A **drysuit** is another type of protective outerwear used for water-based rescues. In contrast to a wetsuit, when using a drysuit, the areas of the body enclosed in the suit remain dry despite immersion in water. Drysuits use gaskets to create watertight seals around areas where the user's body exits the suit, such as the wrists, ankles, or neck. Some drysuits, particularly those used in ice rescue situations, have integrated insulation to keep the users warm during cold weather or cold water operations. Other drysuits allow the user to wear undergarments that meet environmental conditions or personal preference. Drysuits are also available that protect rescuers from contaminants in water, such as chemicals, sewage, or other harmful materials.

In addition to protecting the hand from physical injury, gloves worn during water-based rescue operations should provide a measure of thermal insulation. Rescuers with cold hands may have difficulty accomplishing tasks requiring manual dexterity, and cold hands are more susceptible to injury. Shore-based rescuers who are using life-safety ropes in support of water rescue operations should use gloves designed for rope rescue work. Drysuits designed for ice or cold water rescue may have integrated gloves.

Footwear used during operations in or on the water should be designed to provide both support and protection to the feet and ankles. The ability for water to drain from the footwear is an important consideration. Water should drain easily from the footwear. For example, structural fire fighting boots should not be worn into water because they can fill with water and pull the wearer down. Additionally, footwear used during water-based rescues should provide an appropriate level of thermal insulation. Some drysuits used in water and ice rescue applications have integrated footwear, while others require donning external footwear.

Wetsuit — Protective outerwear worn during water-based rescue operations; water permeable: allows water between the garment and the rescuer's skin to provide thermal insulation.

Drysuit — Protective outerwear worn during water-based rescue operations; provides an impermeable barrier between the wearer and the surrounding water. May be used in ice rescue or as protection from contaminants in water.

///////////////////////

WARNING!
Structural fire fighting boots can fill with water and cause the wearer to sink.

Flotation devices assist rescuers and victims to stay afloat. The **personal flotation device (PFD)** is the most important of these devices in the water-based rescue arena. All personnel operating within 10 feet (3 m) of the water's edge, entering the water, or riding in waterborne craft must wear a U. S. Coast Guard or Transport Canada approved PFD **(Figure 13.28)**.

The United States Coast Guard has identified five categories of PFDs based on intended use. The standard outlined in NFPA® 1952 calls for personnel engaged in water rescue operations to use a Type V vest with at least 22 pounds of buoyancy. Certain Type III/V PFDs are also specifically designed for water rescue applications. Because of the importance of the PFD staying in position on the user's body, the vest should be sized to the individual rescuer or be adjustable to create a close fit. PFDs used for water rescue applications should have attachment points for accessories, such as knives, lights, signal whistles, and tow tethers.

Swimming aids are used to help rescuers move through the water with greater speed and efficiency. Swim fins that strap to the feet and rescue boards that provide buoyancy in the water are both examples of swimming aids.

Figure 13.28 Personal flotation devices (PFDs) should be worn whenever rescuers or firefighters are working in, on, or near bodies of water.

Environmental Hazards During Operations

Extreme weather conditions must be monitored as they can adversely affect personnel, resulting in shorter work periods and increased rotation. Some complex operations can extend for long periods of time, requiring operational periods and complete crew rotations. The ISO must monitor these effects and make recommendations to the IC when needed.

Long Work Shifts

Incidents lasting days, weeks, or months require special consideration of work shifts. Consideration must be given to the type of work being performed and the weather conditions. Personnel must be provided adequate work/rest periods to prevent fatigue and overexertion: the longer the work shift, the greater the chance for injury. Forecasting resource needs along with changes in incident scope will help define needed work shifts. The IC, ISO, and planning staff should look for ways to reduce worker fatigue with the following:

- **Limit work shifts depending on conditions** — some work shifts may only last 4 hours, while others may last 12 hours.

- **Alternate assignments** — personnel should be assigned to varying responsibilities between work shifts. Personnel should rotate from complex to less complex assignments to reduce fatigue and stress.

- **Rehabilitation** — ensure personnel are given breaks during their assigned work shift to rehydrate, get nutritional replenishment, be medically evaluated, and rest.

- **Day/Night shift rotations** — when operations are ongoing 24-hours a day, there should be a clear policy on whether personnel rotate between day and night shift assignments. The ISO should advise the IC on the necessary rest periods for personnel who are rotating onto a night shift from a day shift or vice versa. Research guiding these decisions is ongoing. Departments should explore the use of day/night shift rotations with the department physician or other medical professionals who can provide research-based recommendations.

There is not a one-size-fits-all approach to managing long work shifts. Fire and emergency services organizations must have a system to monitor personnel for adverse physiological effects during extended operations. Work shifts should be altered as needed to appropriately manage responder fatigue.

Hearing Protection

Policies should be established that require the use of hearing protection when operating equipment or riding on apparatus. These policies may be required to meet or exceed OSHA 29 CFR 1910.95 *Occupational Noise Exposure*.

Hearing protection usually includes earplugs, earmuffs, or two-way communication systems that include earphones **(Figure 13.29, p. 444)**. Noise cancelling earmuffs can reduce the noise of operating equipment while still permitting some hearing of voice communications. Protective hoods or helmet earflaps can provide a limited amount of protection at fire-related incidents. Driver/operators with pumping responsibilities should wear earmuffs or earplugs at a minimum, and when available should wear earphones with two-way communications to monitor fire suppression activities and needs. The ISO should monitor the use of hearing protection during operations to ensure personnel are properly protected.

Heat and Cold Stress Safety

The ISO should be cognizant of the effects of weather on personnel. Extreme heat and cold conditions can quickly dehydrate personnel. Personnel in full fire suppression protective clothing and equipment can become overheated

Hearing Protection

Figure 13.29 There are a variety of styles of hearing protection. Regardless of the protection available, wearing hearing protection should be advocated when appropriate. *(a) Courtesy of Alan Braun.*

during hot and/or humid conditions. During extreme cold conditions, full fire suppression protective clothing and equipment only provides limited protection. Personnel must be monitored for hypothermia and frostbite exposure. The ISO is responsible for ensuring that the IC has established rehabilitation at an appropriate location. The rehabilitation manager should evaluate the weather conditions and consider moving personnel out of the elements when necessary. For more information on rehabilitation, refer to U.S. Fire Administration's *Emergency Incident Rehabilitation* (FA-314) manual.

Visibility

The lack of visibility and other protective measures can lead to firefighters being struck by motor vehicles while working on or near roadways. New visibility studies have recommended ways to mark apparatus with warning lights and reflective tape. At the same time, NFPA® has established the requirement

Figure 13.30 Crews functioning at vehicle incidents or on roadways should don reflective vests over their protective clothing to increase their visibility. *Courtesy of Bob Esposito.*

for minimum reflective trim on protective clothing and equipment. Furthermore, the U.S. Department of Transportation has established requirements for emergency scene warning signs, traffic cones, and the use of ANSI-approved fluorescent breakaway vests during highway emergencies **(Figure 13.30)**.

While the department or agency must supply the reflective trim, apparatus marking, and signage, each member is responsible for wearing and using them. Supervisors must ensure that personnel don the fluorescent vests, place signage as required, and keep the reflective trim on their protective clothing and equipment clean and repaired. In addition to personal and supervisory compliance with visibility safety requirements, the ISO is responsible for monitoring this compliance and recommending improvements as necessary.

Standards for Highway Safety Vests

The OSHA vest rule (23CFR634) does not require 5-point breakaway vests. The minimum requirement in OSHA is an ANSI 107 class 2 vest. The 5-point breakaway vests are ANSI 207 class 2 vest. MUTCD also only requires a 107 vest. NFPA® 1901, *Standard for Automotive Fire Apparatus*, requires a 207 compliant vest for any apparatus purchased after Jan 1, 2009.

Vehicle Work Zone Safety

Traffic-related injuries and fatalities for fire and emergency service personnel, including law enforcement, is a significant concern. To address this concern, fire and emergency service responders must ensure the establishment of a vehicle work safety zone for any incident on, or adjacent to, a roadway. The goal of this zone is to provide a protective area where responders can work to stabilize an incident. Several professional organizations provide guidance on how to achieve a vehicle safety zone. These organizations have similar criteria in their documents and represent labor and management audiences. The organizations include, but are not limited to:

- **The U.S. Department of Transportation (DOT)** — published the *Manual on Uniform Traffic Control Devices* (MUTCD). The MUTCD is the guiding standard for all transportation and public safety agencies across the United

States for all roadway signage and traffic control devices. States have also adopted their own supplements MUTCD manual. In addition, the U.S. DOT has published the *Traffic Incident Management Handbook* that covers federal programs and best practices.

- **Canadian Ministries of Transportation** — each Canadian province regulates traffic management requirements. Each province has a document similar to the *Manual of Uniform Traffic Control Devices (MUTCD)*.

- **American Association of State Highway and Transportation Officials (AASHTO)** — established the National Traffic Incident Management Coalition (NTIMC) that brings public safety and transportation officials together to improve traffic incident management best practice recommendations.

- **National Fire Protection Association® (NFPA®)** — several NFPA® standards address the reflective and retroreflective requirements, lighting, and equipment requirements for apparatus and protective clothing. NFPA® 1091, *Standard for Traffic Control Incident Management Professional Qualifications*, is a proposed standard with an estimated publish date in 2015.

- **U.S. Fire Administration (USFA)** — the USFA has published several documents on traffic safety, including the *Emergency Vehicle Safety Initiative* (FA-336), *Emergency Vehicle Visibility and Conspicuity Study* (FA-323), and *Traffic Incident Management Systems* (FA-330).

- **International Association of Fire Chiefs (IAFC)** — the IAFC has published the *Guide to IAFC Model Policies and Procedures for Emergency Vehicle Safety*. The IAFC partnered with the U.S. Department of Homeland Security and the U.S. Fire Administration to produce this best practice guide.

- **International Association of Fire Fighters (IAFF)** — the IAFF has published a manual in cooperation with the U.S. Department of Homeland Security and the U.S. Fire Administration on best practices, *Best Practices for Emergency Vehicle and Roadway Operations Safety in the Emergency Services*.

The following five topics cover items that have improved responder safety in recent years. The ISO should ensure these safety features comply with all applicable regulations and standards during incidents on or adjacent to roadways.

Rescue Clothing/Applicable Protective Clothing and Equipment for Extrication and Fire Suppression

Each emergency scene where extrication and fire suppression activities occur must be assessed for appropriate protective clothing and equipment selection and use. Extrication can take on different forms between vehicle accidents, structural collapse, and machinery entrapment. Not all extrication operations require full fire suppression protective clothing. The level of risk and hazards present, tools used, and the type of extrication performed must be assessed to determine the proper level of protection. The ISO will assess this decision, monitor activities, and recommend improvements as needed.

Similarly, fire suppression activities must be assessed within different fire agency disciplines. Fire suppression activities with structural and vehicular response, wildland, marine, industrial, and aircraft fire fighting have specific protective clothing and equipment standards that must be met. The critical incident safety assessment ensures proper protective clothing and equipment is selected, worn, and continued to be worn appropriately throughout the incident stabilization process. This process includes safety considerations during the salvage and overhaul stages and fire investigations.

Compliant Markings for Both Apparatus and Protective Clothing and Equipment

Compliant markings for apparatus and protective clothing and equipment includes specific colors and reflective and retroreflective effectiveness. To improve the visibility of emergency vehicles when they are at an incident, NFPA® requires the application of retroreflective trim on the vehicle body to meet ASTM D 4956, *Standard Specification for Retroreflective Sheeting for Traffic Control*, Type I, Class 1, or Class 3. The **retroreflective trim** must extend across at least 25 percent of the front of the vehicle and 50 percent of the sides and rear. The trim must be a minimum of 4 inches (100 mm) in width. The retroreflective trim should also be applied to the inside of cab doors so it will be visible when open at night **(Figure 13.31)**.

Retroreflective Trim — Surfaces such as those used on road signs, emergency vehicle markings, or safety vests which are designed to reflect light along multiple planes at once, giving the surface the appearance of illumination.

NFPA® standards address the varying criteria for the different kinds of protective clothing and equipment, which includes reflective trim. The ISO should assess personnel operating on an incident to ensure protective clothing and equipment reflective trim is in good condition. If not, the ISO should make a note and follow up after the incident to recommend repair or replacement of protective clothing and equipment. Responders must realize that structural fire fighting gear and/ or EMS pants do not meet the required visibility standards when operating at traffic incidents. Traffic safety vests must be worn in compliance with applicable standards. NFPA® requires one traffic safety vest for each seating position on the apparatus. The ISO must ensure all personnel operating on a traffic incident is wearing an approved safety vest or take immediate action to correct the deficiency.

Figure 13.31 Reflective trim is not intended just for the exterior of fire apparatus. The interior of the doors should also contain reflective trim to make it more apparent to drivers that the door is open and someone may be exiting the vehicle.

Temporary Traffic Control Devices

The MUTCD and NFPA® provide requirements for **temporary traffic control devices**: traffic signs, cones, flags, and lighting used at traffic incidents. Traffic signs can warn motorists when they are approaching an accident scene. Traffic warning signs include permanently installed or portable changeable message signs or temporary signs that are erected on a metal frame. Cones or channeling devices are used to guide traffic around a work zone. These devices should clearly indicate where motorists should drive. The distance between devices will be dependent on the number of devices available, but the MUTCD recommends optimal spacing for different speed limits: difference between cones should be half the speed limit **(Figure 13.32)**. Flags are not typically used on accident scenes, but can be employed if specifically assigned to a person to give additional visual cues to motorists.

Proper lighting at traffic work safety zones is critical for alerting motorists. However, personnel must be aware of the potential for glare that impedes the vision of motorists. NFPA® 1901 recommends two modes of warning lights – one for response and one for blocking traffic. The design of the apparatus can incorporate which lights are illuminated with the parking brake on and off. To reduce the glare impact on motorists, emergency vehicle operators must ensure their headlights, preemption lights, fog lights, or other flashing white lights are turned off when the apparatus is parked. Spot lights or emergency scene lights should never point in the direction of approaching motorists **(Figure 13.33)**.

Patient Protection

The placement of apparatus at traffic incidents requires consideration of apparatus type(s) and operational needs, vehicle speeds, and the environment. Larger apparatus not utilized at a traffic scene should be placed at the transition area where motorists enter a safety zone. These apparatus create a diversion and provide protection for the work safety zone **(Figure 13.34, p. 450)**. The transition area is where lane reduction measures are implemented. When rescue vehicles and ambulances arrive on the scene, they should be positioned within the work safety zone and not placed in the transition zone. Personnel deploying equipment from rescue vehicles and ambulances to assist patients will be protected in the work safety zone. Additionally, patients being treated on backboards or gurneys are vulnerable and must be protected. The movement of patients must be coordinated with other emergency personnel so situational awareness of scene safety is maximized. Patients being loaded into ambulances should never be exposed to vehicular traffic from the rear.

WARNING!
Drivers on the roadways are unpredictable. Control measures should be in place, but are not a guarantee of drivers' compliance with traffic control devices.

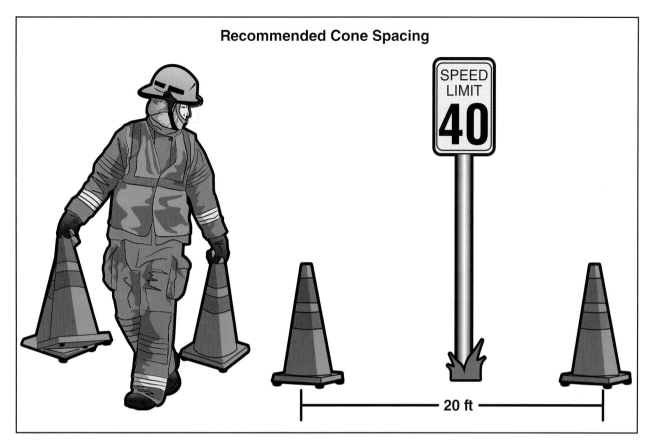

Recommended Cone Spacing

SPEED LIMIT 40

20 ft

Figure 13.32 A good guideline for placing cones to divert traffic is to place cones at intervals equal to one half of the posted speed limit.

Common Incident Protocols and Procedures

Incident risk management principles in the form of protocols and procedures provide a framework for managing the incident in a consistent manner that all personnel are familiar with. The safety of all personnel assigned in any fire and emergency services operation is the guiding purpose of incident protocols and procedures. The ICS structure, IMS, emergency radio communications, and personnel accountability must be implemented with training of personnel and incorporated into the operational setting of the organization.

Incident Command Structure (ICS)

The incident command structure is a nationally accepted framework for managing emergency incidents. This structure begins with the IC. The IC has overall responsibility for all incident operations, including the expansion or reduction of the ICS. Within this structure are the command staff (ISO, PIO, and Liaison Officers) and the general staff (Operations, Planning, Logistics, and Administration/Finance). See Chapter 6, Operational Risk Management, for an explanation on each of these positions.

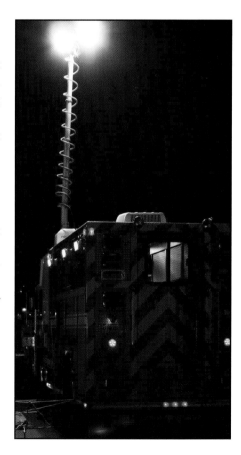

Figure 13.33 Scene lighting should illuminate the emergency scene, not oncoming traffic. Spotlights should not point in the direction of approaching drivers.

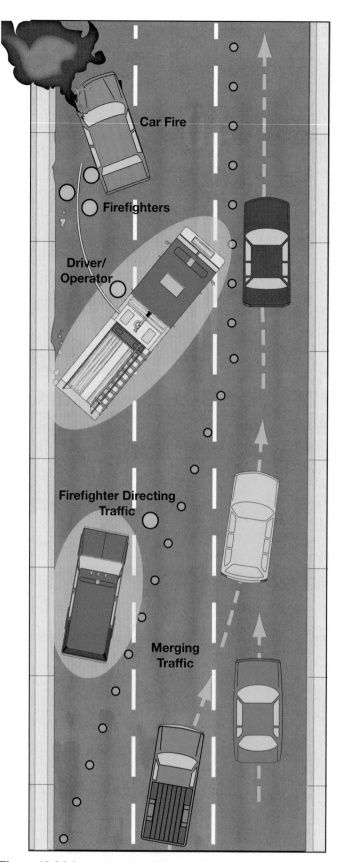

Figure 13.34 Apparatus should be positioned at the scene to protect the incident and firefighters working the incident. Farther upstream, other vehicles may be used to begin diverting traffic well before drivers approach the incident scene.

Role of the Incident Commander (IC)

At any incident or training exercise, the IC is responsible for setting the strategy and assigning and directing the tactics used to meet that strategy. The IC uses the ICS to manage the incident, ensure the safety of all personnel, account for all personnel present and their location, and delegate assignments as needed. As the incident expands in size and complexity the IC will expand the ICS structure, including assigning an ISO. The IC is responsible for briefing the ISO on the operation and the incident action plan. The ISO needs to quickly review the incident action plan and confirm the use of personnel accountability, rapid intervention placement, radio frequencies, and rehab needs. In large, extended incidents, the incident briefing will be between the off-going and on-coming ISOs. This briefing will be in addition to any planning meeting briefings.

Incident Command Post (ICP)

The IC is responsible for establishing and communicating the location of the **incident command post (ICP) (Figure 13.35)**. For smaller operations, the command post should be in a relatively close position to the incident where the IC can have direct visualization of the operation. In larger incidents, the command post may be located in an area or a facility away from the incident. Personnel at the command post should be limited to the command and general staff officers. The command staff (ISO, Public Information Officer, and Liaison Officer) will typically check in at the command post, obtain a briefing, and then function away from the command post. This process reduces the noise and distractions that can occur at the command post. Tactical-level supervisors will not be at the command post. Instead they will be positioned at a division or group location supervising a specific area.

> **Incident Command Post (ICP)** — Location at which the Incident Commander and command staff direct, order, and control resources at an incident; may be co-located with the incident base.

Possible Command Posts

Figure 13.35 The Incident Command Post could simply be the IC's vehicle at smaller incidents. A more formal command post is usually needed at larger or more complex incidents. *Second Photo Courtesy of Ron Jeffers.*

Role of the ISO

Through continual risk assessment, the ISO evaluates and suggests effective safety enhancements that provide a successful outcome of the incident while ensuring the safety of the members operating at the incident. In this role, the ISO must not circumvent the ICS chain of command. The only time the ISO intervenes at the tactical level is to stop an unsafe act or prevent an injury. All other suggestions on operations must be communicated to the IC.

As the ISO, evaluates the incident, the strategies and tactics employed, and the available resources to achieve a successful outcome, he or she should forecast additional needs. This review will include requesting **Assistant Incident Safety Officers (AISOs)** or TSOs. The ISO must conduct a risk management assessment and be able to recognize when assistance is needed. The technical ability of the ISO must meet the technical nature of the operation or a TSO must be assigned to assist or assume safety officer duties.

Other duties of the ISO, as outlined in NFPA® 1521, *Standard for Fire Department Safety Officer Professional Qualifications,* include the following:

- Ensure that incident scene rehabilitation is established.
- Monitor the scene and report the status of conditions, hazards, and risks to the incident commander.
- Ensure that a personnel accountability system is being used.
- Ensure that all personnel understand the IAP.
- Provide the IC with a risk assessment of the IAP.
- Ensure a plan for the treatment and transport of any ill or injured member is in place, and ensure appropriate medical facilities are identified.
- Suggest safety zones, collapse zones, a hot zone, and other designated hazard areas.
- Evaluate motor vehicle traffic hazards.
- Monitor radio transmissions to ensure proper and effective communications.
- Identify the need for additional AISOs.
- Evaluate hazards associated with helicopter landings.

Assistant Incident Safety Officer (AISO) — Individual(s) who reports to the Incident Safety Officer and assist with monitoring hazards and safe operations for designated portions of the operation at large or complex incidents.

Tactical-level supervisors must be aware that the ISO does not perform the same function. While both the tactical-level supervisor and the ISO report to the IC, they serve two different purposes. If serving as a Division Supervisor, the tactical-level supervisor will remain in a single location that funnels personnel in and out of the operational area. On the other hand, the ISO must be able to move freely around the incident scene and monitor operations to ensure the safety of all personnel.

Incident Management System (IMS)

As stated earlier in this chapter, the incident management system (IMS) is broader in scope than the ICS. All personnel should receive training in the ICS and IMS. ICS 100 and 200 level training can be accomplished online and is recommended for all emergency responders. ICS 300 is more advanced and expands upon the information learned in the 100 and 200 level courses. ICS 300 is typically recommended for personnel who have company officer responsibilities or function as a Division/Group supervisor. ICS 400 is the most advanced level of training and includes multi-agency coordination of complex incidents. ICS 400 is typically recommended for personnel who have chief officer or emergency operation center responsibilities. In addition to ICS 100-400 level training, the ISO should have completed the FEMA Independent Study courses of IS-700.a, *National Incident Management System (NIMS): An Introduction*, and IS-800.b, *National Response Framework: an Introduction*.

At an event where operational periods are defined and required, the ISO is responsible for completing the following:

- Complete a written general safety message on ICS form 201, *Incident Briefing*
- Approve and sign ICS form 206, *Medical Plan*
- Complete ICS form 208 (optional), *Safety Message/Plan*
- Complete ICS form 214, *Activity Log*
- Be involved with completing ICS form 215, *Operational Planning Worksheet*
- Complete ICS form 215A, *Incident Action Plan Safety Analysis*

Radio Protocols and Transmission Procedures

Fire departments throughout North America have a variety of protocols for transmitting a radio signal for an emergency during an incident. Although the terminology may differ, the terms can be divided into two categories:

1. **MAYDAY protocol** — the broadcast of a MAYDAY indicates an emergency situation in which a firefighter is in trouble, such as **(Figure 13.36)**:
    - Firefighter in low air alarm and disoriented or unsure of location
    - SCBA failure
    - Firefighter trapped, entangled, or unable to free self within approximately one minute
    - Finding a firefighter in distress
    - At the discretion of Command

2. Emergency Traffic protocol — the broadcast of emergency traffic is used when there is an increased hazard to all personnel, such as a potential structural collapse, indication of an extreme fire condition (flashover), or a shift to defensive strategy and the need to evacuate the structure from an IDLH area.

In both cases, all nonessential radio traffic ceases or is shifted to another radio channel. In the case of a MAYDAY, RIC resources are committed to the incident while other personnel continue to perform their duties.

Recognized Personnel Accountability Protocols

All personnel assigned at an incident or training exercise must be accounted for. In addition to knowing who is present, the location of personnel must be tracked. According to NFPA® 1500, fire and emergency services organizations must establish, implement, and utilize a personnel accountability system. Whether a department develops its own system or utilizes a commercially available system, personnel accountability must be done. Commonly used systems include nametags, metal clasps, or computer-based programs. The IC is responsible for implementing personnel accountability, but may assign an accountability officer to assist with the function. The ISO must ensure the accountability system is used on every incident and that it accurately tracks all personnel.

Chapter Summary

Risk management principles include the practices, technologies, and protocols used during incident operations to ensure the safety of personnel assigned to an operation. The ISO is the checks and balance to ensure personnel are following accepted safe practices. The ISO must recognize the complexity and technical nature of an operation and ensure Assistant Incident Safety Officers and/or Technical Safety Officers are appropriately assigned when needed.

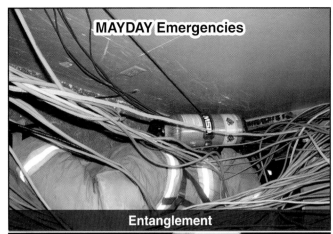

Figure 13.36 MAYDAY emergencies include entanglement, SCBA failure, distress, and disorientation. In these situations, firefighters should be trained to remain as calm as possible and follow MAYDAY protocols.

Review Questions

1. What safety practices have been recognized as part of the overall risk management framework for improving workplace safety? (pp. 410-412)

2. What priorities should be reflected in a fire department's incident action plan (IAP)? (p. 413)

3. What is the incident safety officer's role in maintaining personnel accountability? (pp. 414-415)

4. What barriers to communications should the Incident Safety Officer be aware of? (p. 417)

5. How can the incident safety officer ensure rehabilitation is provided for personnel at all incidents? (pp. 420-421)

6. What are *The 10 Rules of Engagement for Structural Fire Fighting* as developed by the International Association of Fire Chiefs (IAFC)? (pp. 422-423)

7. What elements should the incident safety officer consider when defining criteria for incident risk management? (p. 423)

8. What types of tools and equipment should the incident safety officer monitor when being used on the fireground? (pp. 424-428)

9. What types of safety equipment should the incident safety officer monitor when being used at hazardous materials operations? (pp. 428-435)

10. What types of safety equipment should the incident safety officer monitor when being used at technical rescue incidents? (pp. 435-442)

11. How can the incident safety officer help mitigate environmental hazards during operations? (pp. 442-445)

12. What precautions can the incident safety officer take to ensure safe work zones at a traffic incident? (pp. 445-449)

13. What is the incident safety officer's role in the incident command structure? (pp. 449-452)

14. What are the incident safety officer's responsibilities in the incident management system (IMS)? (p. 452)

15. What are the common categories of radio protocols in North America? (pp. 452-453)

Chapter 13 End Notes

1. Regional Hazardous Materials Team HM09-Tualatin Valley Fire & Rescue, "A Study on Chemicals found in the Overhaul Phase of Structure Fires using Advanced Portable Air Monitoring available for Chemical Speciation,", Office of the State Fire Marshal, Oregon, February 25, 2011.

2. "Can rapid intervention save fire fighters?" IAFC Health and Safety Bulletin, December 01, 2004

13-1
Analyze fire department operations for adherence to risk management principles and practices.

LEARNING ACTIVITIES

Refer to Appendix B: Learning Activity Answers in the back of this manual for suggested responses.

Purpose

One of the primary responsibilities of the incident safety officer is to demonstrate a thorough understanding of risk management principles as they relate to emergency incidents. But a simple knowledge of these principles is not enough; the ISO must also be able to guide, manage, and assess all responding personnel as they perform actions and make decisions in environments that are fast-moving, hazardous, and constantly evolving.

Directions

1. Based on your study of the risk management principles found in the chapter, carefully analyze the **Rhoads Building Scenario** and its timeline.

2. Take note of all personnel activities, decisions, and locations. You do not need to focus at this point on incident hazards or scene conditions (Incident Hazard Recognition will be covered in Chapter 14). Only consider the movements, actions, and decisions of the firefighter personnel and commanding officers, including that of the incident safety officer.

3. After analyzing the scenario, create a chart of **pros** and **cons** to assess how well the St. Florian Fire Department performed in terms of **risk management principles**. Use the following questions to assist in the creation of your chart:

   ● How well did the department follow the safety practices outlined in the manual chapter as part of the overall risk management framework? (pp. 410-412)

   ● What were the specific problems created as a result of the fire department's actions, if any?

   ● What did the fire department do correctly during the operations?

   ● What could or should have been done differently to strengthen the department's risk management framework, if anything?

Rhoads Building Scenario

9:26 a.m. — The St. Florian Fire Department receives a call reporting the collapse of a five-story apartment structure known as the Rhoads Building on the west side of town. For the past week, the area has been receiving heavy snowfalls, averaging accumulations of 2 inches (50 mm) a day. The snow has created dangerous conditions all over town, but particularly to the west where many of the streets are narrow and full of dead-ends and potholes.

Built in 1943, the Rhoads Building is a condemned structure that's well known for sheltering numerous squatters and homeless people. The structure sits on a large, weedy lot bordered by four narrow streets, and without address markings it's difficult to tell which side of the building is the front entrance.

13-1 (cont.)
Analyze fire department operations for adherence to risk management principles and practices.

Refer to Appendix B: Learning Activity Answers in the back of this manual for suggested responses.

The caller has reported that the heavy snow was the apparent reason for the collapse. Also, a 55-gallon barrel had been seen inside the structure and was apparently being used to contain a fire. Not only did the caller witness the building's collapse, but he also witnessed a fire begin to build at the center of the structure where the barrel tipped over.

9:39 a.m. — The fire department arrives at the collapsed structure with a total of nine personnel:

- One Engine Company of three responders
- One Ladder Company of four responders
- A battalion chief serving as Incident Commander
- You are serving as Incident Safety Officer.

Upon arrival, you and the IC observe that a good portion of the Rhoads Building has "pancake"-collapsed under the weight of the snow. You also observe that the reported fire has broken through the center of the building, the flames reaching heights of up to 50 feet (15 m) and producing thick, black columns of smoke. There are no victims immediately visible in the rubble. The IC assigns the Ladder Company to position the aerial apparatus along the southwest corner of the structure's Alpha side. The IC also orders you to assist the Ladder Company in backing up the aerial apparatus. Meanwhile, the IC takes two personnel from the Engine Company to the building's Charlie and Delta sides to continue size-up. The Engine Company's driver-operator parks the pumping apparatus on the Alpha side's southeast corner and awaits orders.

9:47 a.m. — While attempting to record personnel positions for accountability, you hear a command from the IC on your radio, but the communication is too garbled to understand. You ask for a repeat of the command but receive no response. The Engine Company driver-operator offers to walk around back to retrieve the IC, but you tell him to assist as spotter for the repositioning of the aerial apparatus, which is having a hard time in the snowy, constricted street, especially with so many power lines crossing overhead.

9:49 a.m. — The IC returns to the Alpha side of the structure alone, having ordered the two Engine Company responders to stay around back, make entry, and search for survivors. He reports that victims may be trapped at the rear of the structure and orders you to make a call for Mutual Aid from a neighboring county department. Meanwhile, the Ladder Company has successfully repositioned the apparatus and is awaiting further orders. The IC directs the Ladder Company to begin an indirect attack on the fire from the Bravo side using an elevated master stream.

9:51 a.m. — You make the call for Mutual Aid and receive a response that one additional Ladder Company of four firefighters will be responding. You then notify the IC that the incident is large enough to require a written incident action plan, but the IC informs you there is no time for a written plan. He orders all commands to be verbally communicated. You decide the IC is wrong and that it would be best to proceed without the IC's permission and develop

Refer to Appendix B: Learning Activity Answers in the back of this manual for suggested responses.

a written tactical worksheet to keep the incident focused and organized. The IC informs you he is going back around to the rear of the building – which he is now referring to as "the Alpha side" – to assist the two responders in their search. He directs you to monitor the progress of the Ladder Company's indirect attack on the fire.

9:53 a.m. — While developing your tactical worksheet, you note that because the building is in such disrepair, the front entrance is not obvious and confusion has set in over which side is Alpha. You also document the earlier problem with the radio communication. After taking a few more notes on observed safety hazards, you join the Ladder Company and assist in the attack operations. The fire inside the structure appears to intensify.

10:17 a.m. —During the fire attack, you hear a muddled transmission on your radio and realize the IC is communicating actively with Mutual Aid, who has just arrived at the rear of the Rhoads Building on the opposite street. You walk to the rear of the structure and see that the IC has already allocated two respective teams of Mutual Aid – the first assisting with victim search, the second standing by as RIC for the search operation. At this point you realize that more than ten responders are now on scene and that you do not have accurate accountability.

Incident Hazard Recognition

Chapter Contents

chapter 14

Key Terms

This chapter provides information that addresses the following job performance requirements of NFPA® 1521, *Standard for Fire Department Safety Officer Professional Qualifications (2015)*.

5.2.4	**5.3.3**
5.2.7	**5.3.4**
5.2.8	**5.3.5**
5.2.13	**5.3.6**
5.3.2	

Learning Objectives

After reading this chapter, students will be able to:

1. Describe environmental and physiological hazards that may be encountered at emergency incidents. (5.2.4, 5.2.7)

2. Explain hazards associated with structure fire development. (5.2.4, 5.2.7, 5.3.2, 5.3.4)

3. Determine hazards associated with building construction and structural features. (5.2.4, 5.2.7, 5.3.2, 5.3.3, 5.3.6)

4. Identify utilities and energy sources that may affect the safety and health of fire personnel. (5.2.4, 5.2.7, 5.2.13, 5.3.2)

5. Explain hazards associated with wildland and vegetation fire development. (5.2.4, 5.2.7, 5.3.5)

6. Recognize hazards fire personnel may face during vehicle incident response. (5.2.4, 5.2.7, 5.2.8)

7. Identify potential hazards present during apparatus placement at an emergency incident. (5.2.4, 5.2.7, 5.2.8)

8. Learning Activity 14-1: Practice identifying hazards at an emergency operation. (5.2.4, 5.2.7, 5.2.8, 5.2.13, 5.3.2, 5.3.3, 5.3.4, 5.3.6)

Chapter 14
Incident Hazard Recognition

Case History

On July 6, 1994, fourteen firefighters died while battling a wildland fire. On July 2, lightning ignited a single tree, which evolved into a small wildland fire. At the time, there were larger wildland and forest fires in the area. The entire region was suffering through a major drought with frequent "Red Flag" weather warnings. The terrain around the lightning strike fire was mountainous and very steep.

On July 4, a team of seven United States Forestry Service (USFS) and Bureau of Land Management (BLM) firefighters arrived below and decided to wait to attack the fire until the next morning as the hike would be difficult and take 2 ½ hours to complete. At this time, the fire was only three to four acres in size.

The next day, July 5, the seven firefighters and a BLM Incident Commander hiked to the fire to begin their attack. The IC recognized the hazards and ordered a helispot constructed (Helicopter Landing Area). Eight more firefighters from Montana parachuted into the fire to assist with the attack. The fifteen firefighters continued to construct a fire line until night fall by which time the fire covered an area of fifty acres.

On July 6, more Red Flag Warnings were issued that forecast shifting winds accompanying a cold front. The firefighters started to construct a fireline early that day and were joined by ten Hot Shot firefighters from Oregon who had arrived by helicopter that afternoon. By 1:00 p.m., the fire had expanded to 150 acres and was burning erratically, with spotting across firelines and tree torching. Around 3:00 p.m., ten more Hot Shot firefighters from Oregon arrived at another helispot and immediately began downhill fireline construction. At 3:20 p.m., the cold front moved through the area with strong winds to 45 mph (70 kph). The fire activity increased to blowup proportions. Driven by strong winds, fueled by dry vegetation, and intensified by the steep terrain, the fire spotted below the firefighters and raced uphill. The fire moved at 20 mph (30 kph) with flame lengths of 300 feet (100 m). All of the firefighters on that slope ran for their lives uphill, upwind in unforgiving terrain. By 4:30 p.m., fourteen of the firefighters had lost their lives.

The firefighters were highly trained and Type-1 qualified. In this situation, it is unclear whether the firefighters could have predicted the fire's behavior. One thing is clear: understanding of fire behavior and scene hazards must be continually taught, reviewed, and updated so that firefighters can make the safest decisions possible at a fire scene. Situational awareness, available fuels, weather conditions, and topography are all important considerations at a wildland fire scene.

Each type of incident will have hazards that must be identified during size-up and throughout the incident operation. The ISO's key responsibility is to recognize incident hazards and make corrective recommendations to prevent injuries to responders. The ISO must check in with the IC and, after receiving a briefing, conduct an independent 360-degree assessment of the incident. The ISO must note the condition of the emergency, the potential hazards to personnel, and the deployment of resources. At structural fires, the ISO notes the type of construction in order to visualize the fuel or fire loading and identify potential structural weak points. The ISO needs to determine where the fire is located, what is burning, what is the phase or stage of the fire, and what is the potential direction of fire spread. By reading the smoke, the ISO can judge the types of fuel or fuels involved and the progress of the fire. In order to be effective in the assessment of hazards, the ISO must have the requisite knowledge and skill in all areas of the fire and emergency services organizations' operations. This knowledge and skill is obtained from education, training, and experience. This chapter identifies hazards associated with physiological and environmental conditions, fire conditions, building construction, wildland and vegetation, utilities, and vehicles and apparatus. **Learning Activity 14-1** provides an opportunity to apply the information in this chapter to an incident scenario.

16 Firefighter Life Safety Initiatives 2

The *16 Firefighter Life Safety Initiatives* were discussed in Chapter 1, Health Safety Officer Responsibilities. Initiative 2 is pertinent to the ISO's understanding of incident hazard recognition:

2. Enhance the personal and organizational accountability for health and safety throughout the fire service.

Environmental and Physiological Hazards

Fire and emergency services operations are inherently hazardous and can require high physical demands from firefighters. They must carry out their tactical objectives in toxic environments with limited workspace while wearing heavy protective clothing and equipment. The physical demands on firefighters are intensified when physiological and environmental hazards are factored in. The weather, extreme heat and cold temperatures, cardiac strain, noise, and long work shifts place additional stress on the human body. Incident Commanders, tactical-level supervisors, and the ISO must monitor personnel to ensure they are functioning within their physical capabilities.

Weather Conditions

Weather conditions can have an adverse effect on all types of operations and can affect the health and stamina of fire crews. The ISO must be able to monitor changes in weather conditions and notify the IC of potential hazards. Adverse weather conditions include storms, high humidity and temperatures, freezing rain, snow, extreme cold temperatures, and high wind.

Personnel with potential ISO responsibilities should monitor daily weather forecasts and be alert to inclement weather statements. Personnel should pair the forecasts with actual real-time conditions and understand how it may affect emergency operations. During operations, the ISO can request the dispatch/telecommunication center to contact the local weather service office for updated weather conditions or use cellular or wireless devices if they are available at the scene. Adverse weather can also reduce the operational capacity of equipment and apparatus. The ISO should monitor the weather-related conditions described in the sections that follow for adverse consequences during operations.

Ice

Ice is not always visible, it makes advancing attack or supply hoselines, performing vertical ventilation, and doing forcible entry difficult. Hoses, ladders, and apparatus can become ice-covered, causing slipping hazards. Ice and snow accumulation on a structure can cause ground ladders to slip or move, and accumulation on power lines can cause them to sag or fail. When parking apparatus, personnel should assess the area to reduce the chance of sliding on icy roadways.

Snow

Snow creates some of the same difficulties as ice. It can obscure tripping hazards, obstacles, and/or unstable structural features, such as skylights on a roof under its surface.

Rain

Rain and fog can reduce your ability to see the entire scene. It can make metal surfaces slippery and it can freeze on equipment and apparatus as the temperature drops.

Humidity

High humidity can cause smoke to remain close to the ground, obscuring visibility of the building. It can also affect personnel, causing them to tire quickly, raising body core temperature, and making them become dehydrated through perspiration loss.

Wind

High winds can create dangerous fire behavior changes in all types of fire suppression operations. Winds as slow as 10 mph (15 kph) can be deadly if personnel are not alert to the rapidly changing conditions. The ISO must continuously monitor wind velocity and direction to ensure personnel and hose streams are not placed in a windward position. Generally, wind speeds greater than 20 mph (30 kph) will reduce aerial ladder load capacity. The ISO should ensure the aerial ladder operations are within the manufacturer guidelines.

Storms and Other Conditions

Lightning is a significant concern for all personnel operating at emergency events. All aerial ladder operations must be curtailed and personnel should take all possible precautions to ensure their safety. Storms can cause downed power lines and trees that can block access to an area, especially during hurricane or severe thunderstorms. Hail can damage apparatus and injure personnel. Flash flooding or rapidly flowing water can sweep away vehicles and people, even with minimal depth. Visibility reducing situations (dust storms, fog, and blizzards) can create driving and scene operation hazards. The ISO must ensure personnel are operating within a safe zone with proper traffic control implemented.

Heat and Cold Stress

Both hot and cold environments can fatigue personnel (**Figure 14.1**). The ISO is responsible for monitoring resource and personnel availability and make recommendations to the IC when needed.

In extremely hot climates, personnel may rapidly succumb to heat stress and require rehabilitation earlier and more frequently than normal. They may also become dehydrated, requiring additional fluids and medical care. Extreme cold temperatures can cause skin and clothing to stick to metal tools and equipment, cause frost bite injuries, and reduce stamina. Hoselines, pumps, and water supplies can freeze, causing a loss in water supply or pressure. Hose, tools, and equipment can be damaged or become inoperable.

Hot or Humid Conditions

Hot and/or humid conditions can overheat apparatus during pumping operations. The ISO should communicate with apparatus pump operators to ensure early detection of operability issues. The ISO should also ensure the IC has a rapidly deployable backup plan with alternate apparatus, especially during interior fire suppression activities. Personnel operating at a scene with high intensity activity must be provided proper work/rest periods and follow the recommendations in NFPA® 1584, *Standard on the Rehabilitation Process for Members During Emergency Operations and Training Exercises*. Personnel must also be monitored when operating at traffic scenes or other activities where radiated heat from road and concrete surfaces significantly increases heat-related illness potential.

Cold Conditions

Cold weather can freeze fire hoses and couplings and create icy conditions in areas where water is being applied during fire suppression activities. The ISO must monitor for the development of hazardous conditions and communicate them to the IC. The ISO must monitor personnel for signs of hypothermia and/or frostbite and ensure rehabilitation provides relief from the elements.

Cardiac Arrest

Cardiac-related events at emergency incidents are a leading cause of firefighter illness and death. Annually, the NFPA® publishes a firefighter fatality report in which cardiac and cardiac-related issues continue to be leading causes of firefighter fatalities. Research is beginning to show these fatalities can occur at the scene or after personnel have returned to service. The physical demands required in many operational settings are extremely high. Not all personnel are prepared to meet this physical demand. Some firefighters may have hidden, undiagnosed cardiac disease that may precipitate into sudden cardiac arrest.

NOAA's National Weather Service Heat Index

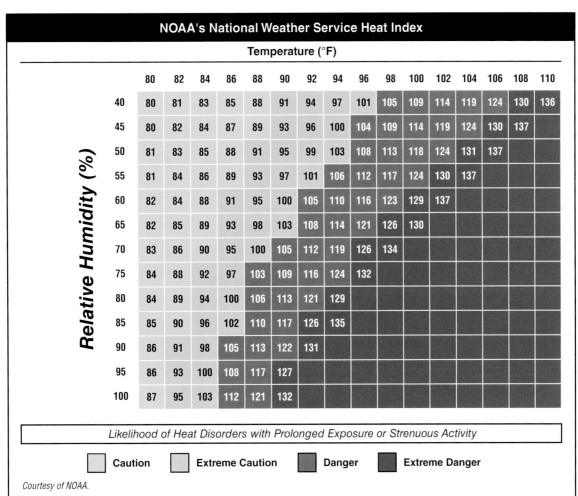

Temperature (°F)

Relative Humidity (%)	80	82	84	86	88	90	92	94	96	98	100	102	104	106	108	110
40	80	81	83	85	88	91	94	97	101	105	109	114	119	124	130	136
45	80	82	84	87	89	93	96	100	104	109	114	119	124	130	137	
50	81	83	85	88	91	95	99	103	108	113	118	124	131	137		
55	81	84	86	89	93	97	101	106	112	117	124	130	137			
60	82	84	88	91	95	100	105	110	116	123	129	137				
65	82	85	89	93	98	103	108	114	121	126	130					
70	83	86	90	95	100	105	112	119	126	134						
75	84	88	92	97	103	109	116	124	132							
80	84	89	94	100	106	113	121	129								
85	85	90	96	102	110	117	126	135								
90	86	91	98	105	113	122	131									
95	86	93	100	108	117	127										
100	87	95	103	112	121	132										

Likelihood of Heat Disorders with Prolonged Exposure or Strenuous Activity

☐ Caution   ☐ Extreme Caution   ■ Danger   ■ Extreme Danger

Courtesy of NOAA.

Figure 14.1 The heat index and wind chill indicate how ambient temperatures feel to responders. Wind chill and heat stress are fatiguing to personnel.

Wind Chill Chart

Temperature (°F)

WIND SPEED (mph) \ Calm	40	35	30	25	20	15	10	5	0	-5	-10	-15	-20	-25	-30	-35	-40	-45
5	36	31	25	19	13	7	1	-5	-11	-16	-22	-28	-34	-40	-46	-52	-57	-63
10	34	27	21	15	9	3	-4	-10	-16	-22	-28	-35	-41	-47	-53	-59	-66	-72
15	32	25	19	13	6	0	-7	-13	-19	-26	-32	-39	-45	-51	-58	-64	-71	-77
20	30	24	17	11	4	-2	-9	-15	-22	-29	-35	-42	-48	-55	-61	-68	-74	-81
25	29	23	16	9	3	-4	-11	-17	-24	-31	-37	-44	-51	-58	-64	-71	-78	-84
30	28	22	15	8	1	-5	-12	-19	-26	-33	-39	-46	-53	-60	-67	-73	-80	-87
35	28	21	14	7	0	-7	-14	-21	-27	-34	-41	-48	-55	-62	-69	-76	-82	-89
40	27	20	13	6	-1	-8	-15	-22	-29	-36	-43	-50	-57	-64	-71	-78	-84	-91
45	26	19	12	5	-2	-9	-16	-23	-30	-37	-44	-51	-58	-65	-72	-79	-86	-93
50	26	19	12	4	-3	-10	-17	-24	-31	-38	-45	-52	-60	-67	-74	-81	-88	-95
55	25	18	11	4	-3	-11	-18	-25	-32	-39	-46	-54	-61	-68	-75	-82	-89	-97
60	25	17	10	3	-4	-11	-19	-26	-33	-40	-48	-55	-62	-69	-76	-84	-91	-98

Frostbite occurs in 15 minutes or less

Courtesy of NOAA

It is critical that medical surveillance monitoring and proper rehabilitation is established at emergency and planned events. The importance of rehabilitation services at the scene cannot be overemphasized. All operations personnel should be cleared from the medical evaluation and rehabilitation area prior to being reassigned or returned to available status. Early detection of a possible cardiac event is critical to saving lives.

Noise

Emergency incidents have several sources of noise that can adversely affect personnel. Apparatus, generators, equipment, and radio communications add to the noise level. Repeated exposure to high levels of noise is known to cause permanent hearing loss. The safety and health program in fire and emergency services departments should address awareness of high noise situations and preventive hearing protection options. The ISO should evaluate noise levels and the hearing protection provided for their personnel. Recommendations should be made to the IC if unsafe noise conditions exist so modifications and corrections can be made. High noise levels can also lead to a condition called *tunnel hearing*. Tunnel hearing can cause people to concentrate so closely on one task that they lose their sense of situational awareness. The IC, other operational supervisors, and the ISO must maintain acute situational awareness during any incident by listening to other personnel, asking questions about the operation, and monitoring any incident changes. The IC and other personnel should be alerted if there is any indication that personnel safety is or will become compromised.

Extended Work Shifts

Extended work shifts can cause fatigue and stress in responders. As the work shift gets longer, the chance of injury becomes greater. Personnel can lose track of time and not realize how long they have been actively involved in an operation. Longer shifts equate to lessened situational awareness, which increases the risk of injury. The ISO must monitor operation activities, weather conditions, and personnel performance to ensure work shift length does not endanger personnel. For operations that last more than a day, the Incident Command team must determine the appropriate rotation schedule of personnel. See Chapter 13, Risk Management Principles, for ways to manage long work shifts.

Structure Fire Development and Hazards

Research shows that fires go through four distinct stages: incipient, growth, fully developed, and decay. Fires may move through these stages in order (fuel-controlled fires) or reach the decay stage and rekindle and begin to grow again (ventilation-controlled fires). Actual conditions can vary widely within a building made up of multiple compartments. For instance, the compartment of origin may be in the fully developed stage, while adjacent compartments may be in the growth stage. In another example, an attic or void space may be ventilation-limited while adjacent compartments are in the growth or fully developed stage. ISOs should assume that an entire structure is the compartment that fire is affecting rather than just the compartment of origin. Open interior doors, hallways, and stairwells connecting rooms extend the possible growth potential of a fire beyond its compartment of origin.

At a fire scene, the stages of fire development are a guide for what *could* occur during the fire but are not a pattern of what *will* occur every time. ISOs should assess the changing hazards and fire conditions at the incident rather than assume that the fire will follow the same pattern identified in laboratory tests.

Factors That Affect Compartmental Fire Development

Compartmental fire development, or that which occurs in a limited area, will have numerous influencing factors in how rapidly a fire can develop and spread. Compartment fires can be considered to be room and content fires, but construction features can differ greatly between occupancy types. Factors affecting the development of compartment fires include but are not limited to:

- Fuel type
- Availability and location of additional fuels
- Compartment volume and ceiling height
- Ventilation
- Thermal properties of the compartment
- Ambient conditions
- Fuel load

All personnel operating on a fire scene should evaluate these factors to ensure safe and efficient suppression methods are employed. The ISO should forecast fire spread based on fire department suppression efforts and conduct an ongoing assessment of hazards as they relate to the stages of fire growth. For instance, hoseline placement and size, ventilation, coordination of effort, and flow rate should be monitored for desired effect. Any unusual fire behavior, fire spread beyond the compartment of origin, or the potential for hidden fires should be communicated to the Incident Commander.

Fuel Type

The type of fuel involved in combustion affects the **heat release rate (HRR)**. Fires involving Class B and C fuels will eventually spread to the building contents and structure, resulting in a primarily Class A-fueled fire.

In a compartment fire, surface-to-mass ratio is one of the most fundamental Class A fuel characteristics influencing fire development. Combustible materials with high **surface-to-mass ratios** are much more easily ignited and will burn more quickly than the same substance with less surface area.

Fires involving Class B flammable/combustible liquids will be influenced by the surface area and type of fuel involved. A liquid fuel spill will increase that liquid's surface-to-volume ratio, generating more flammable vapors than the same liquid in an open container **(Figure 14.2, p. 468)**. The increase of vapor due to the spill will also allow more of the fuel to ignite, resulting in greater heat over a shorter period of time.

Structure fires involving single types of fuels are rare. Modern homes and businesses are largely filled with contents made from petroleum-based materials (plastics or synthetic fabrics). These fuels have a higher heat of combustion and produce higher HRRs than wood alone. Burning synthetic fuels produces products of combustion that contain large quantities of solid and liquid particulates and unburned gases.

Heat Release Rate (HRR) — Total amount of heat produced or released to the atmosphere from the convective-lift phase of a fire, per unit mass of fuel consumed per unit time, expressed in kilowatts or British Thermal Units (BtU).

Surface-To-Mass Ratio — Ratio of the surface area of the fuel to the mass of the fuel.

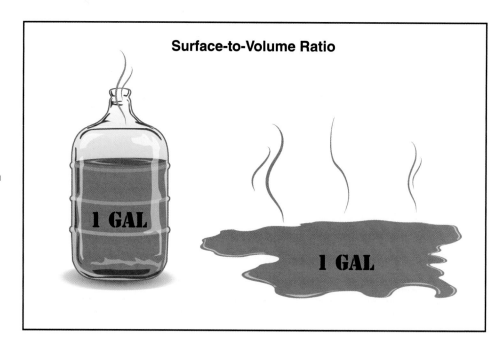

Figure 14.2 Just like with solids, an increase in a liquid's surface area correlates to the generation of more flammable vapors.

A compartment fire that results from a flammable/combustible gas leak may begin with a rapid ignition of the gas and an explosion. If the fuel source is not controlled, it will continue to burn at the point of release, extending to adjacent combustibles. Shutting off the fuel source or controlling the leak will reduce or eliminate the Class B fuel, but the resulting Class A fire will continue to burn until extinguished.

Availability and Location of Additional Fuel

Factors that influence the availability and location of additional fuels include the building configuration, construction materials, contents, and proximity of the initial fire to these exposed fuel sources. Building configuration is the layout of the structure, including:

- Number of stories above or below grade
- Compartmentation
- Floor plan
- Openings between floors
- Continuous voids or concealed spaces
- Barriers to fire spread

Each of these elements may contribute to either fire spread or containment. For instance, an open floor plan space may contain furnishings that provide fuel sources on all sides of a point of ignition. Conversely, a compartmentalized configuration may have fire-rated barriers, such as walls, ceilings, and doors, separating fuel sources and limiting fire development to an individual compartment **(Figure 14.3 a and b)**.

In buildings where the construction materials are flammable, the materials themselves add to the structure's fuel load. For example, in wood-frame buildings, the structure itself is a source of fuel. The orientation of these fuels as well as their surface-to-mass ratio will also influence the rate and intensity of fire spread. Plywood, for instance, consists of several thin layers of wood

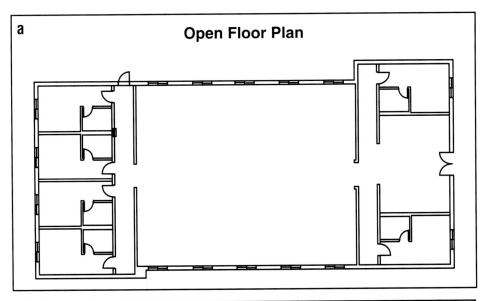

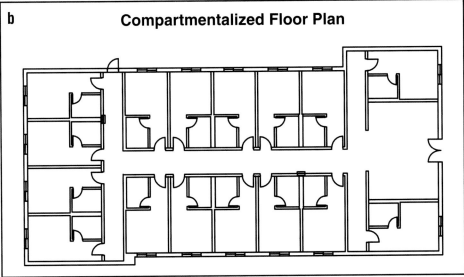

Figures 14.3 a and b Open floor plans have fewer compartments and as a result, fewer barriers to fire spread.

veneer laminated together while alternating the direction of grains with each layer until the desired thickness and strength is achieved. Plywood is easily ignited, even while level and horizontal, because it has a high surface-to-mass ratio. As the material continues to burn, the adhesive bond of each layer is weakened and results in delaminating. The surface-to mass-ratio increases, resulting in rapid consumption of the material.

If this same sheet of plywood were to be oriented in a vertical position, it would burn even faster because the growing fire would heat the material above it and cause pyrolysis more quickly. In addition to structural members, combustible interior finishes, such as wood paneling, carpets, and carpet padding, can be a significant factor influencing fire spread.

The contents of a structure are often the most readily available fuel source, significantly influencing fire development in a compartment fire. When contents rapidly release a large amount of heat, both the intensity of the fire and speed of development will be increased. For example, synthetic furnishings,

Figure 14.4 Polyurethane foam has a high surface-to-mass ratio and will continue to burn after it has liquefied.

Pyrolize — Description of the process of a solid beginning to emit gases due to heat exposure.

such as polyurethane foam, will begin to **pyrolize** rapidly under fire conditions, even when they are located some distance from the origin of the fire. The chemical makeup of the foam and its high surface-to-mass ratio speed the process of fire development. Polyurethane foam will liquefy and continue to burn **(Figure 14.4)**.

The proximity and continuity of contents and structural fuels also influence fire development. Fuels located in the upper level of adjacent compartments will pyrolize more quickly from the effect of the hot gas layer. Continuous fuels, such as combustible interior finishes, will rapidly spread the fire from compartment to compartment. Similarly, the location of the fire within the building will influence fire development. When the fire is located low in the building, such as in the basement or on the first floor, convected heat currents will cause vertical extension through atriums, unprotected stairways, vertical shafts, and concealed spaces. Fires originating on upper levels generally extend downward much more slowly following the fuel path or as a result of structural collapse.

The ISO must consider the presence of modern construction and furnishings. Residential structures built after 1990 burn hotter, faster, and produce more smoke with flammable properties than traditional or legacy construction. The greater use of synthetic materials in home furnishings in residential homes, regardless of age, also contributes to this growth rate. This increase in fire development speed requires that fire fighting tactics, ventilation and extinguishment, must be well coordinated with little margin for error. Poorly coordinated tactics can harm firefighters.

Compartment Volume and Ceiling Height

All other factors being equal, a fire in a large compartment will develop more slowly than one in a small compartment. Slower fire development is due to the greater volume of air and the increased distance radiated heat must travel from the fire to the contents that must be heated. However, a large volume of air will support the development of a larger fire before the lack of ventilation becomes the limiting factor.

A high ceiling can also make determining the extent of fire development more difficult. In structures with high ceilings, a large volume of hot smoke and fire gases can accumulate at the ceiling level, while conditions at floor level remain relatively unchanged. Firefighters may mistake floor level conditions for the actual state of fire development. If the large hot gas layer ignites, the situation becomes immediately hazardous.

Ventilation

Ventilation in a compartment significantly influences how fire develops and spreads within the space. Pre-existing ventilation is the actual and potential ventilation of a structure based on structural openings, construction type, and building ventilation systems. For the most part, all buildings have the potential to exchange air inside the structure with the air outside the structure. In some cases, this exchange is due to constructed openings, such as windows, doors, and passive ventilation devices as well as leakage through cracks and other gaps in construction. In other cases, this air exchange is primarily through the heating, ventilating, and air conditioning (HVAC) system.

Room or compartment fires take two forms: **fuel-controlled** and **ventilation-controlled**. When sufficient oxygen is available, the characteristics and configuration of the fuel control fire development. Under these conditions, the fire is said to be fuel-controlled. For example, a small fire that is confined to a noncombustible waste basket in a large, well-ventilated room will self-extinguish when all the fuel is consumed no matter how much air remains in the room **(Figure 14.5)**.

Fuel-Controlled — A fire with adequate oxygen in which the heat release rate and growth rate are determined by the characteristics of the fuel, such as quantity and geometry. (NFPA® 921)

Ventilation-Controlled — Fire with limited ventilation in which the heat release rate or growth is limited by the amount of oxygen available to the fire. (NFPA® 921)

Figure 14.5 Small fires in well-ventilated rooms will self-extinguish when the fuel is exhausted. Small fires near a wall, like this one, may ignite exposed walls.

When the available air supply begins to limit fire development in a compartment fire, the fire is said to be ventilation-controlled **(Figures 14.6 a and b)**. The characteristics of the fuel and fuel load in today's typical fires will cause fires to quickly become ventilation-controlled. When a fire becomes ventilation-controlled, the available air supply will determine the speed and extent of fire development and the direction of fire travel. Fire will have a tendency to grow in the direction of ventilation openings, such as failed windows and doors, because of the introduction of fresh air.

When considering fire development, personnel should consider potential openings that could change the ventilation profile under fire conditions. Under fire conditions, windows can fail or doors can be left open, increasing ventilation into the compartment. Bi-direction flow paths, sometimes created by the task of ventilation, can be deadly to firefighters and civilians inside the structure. Wind conditions at structure fires can influence the direction of airflow.

Changes in ventilation can alter the ventilation flow path, create rapid fire development, and place firefighters in extreme danger. When the fire becomes ventilation-controlled, the fire's HRR will decrease. Control the air, control the fire. The ISO should watch operations to ensure ventilation activities are coordinated to maximize the ventilation benefit. If windows or doors fail at this time, the sudden introduction of fresh air creates a rapid increase in the HRR. This rapid increase will also occur when firefighters open a door or window to ventilate the room, enter for fire attack, or perform search and rescue.

Figure 14.6 a and b A ventilation-controlled fire has consumed all available oxygen in the compartment. If there is still sufficient heat and fuel for a fire, the fire could reignite if provided more oxygen. *Courtesy of Dan Madrzykowski, NIST.*

Thermal Properties of the Compartment

The thermal properties of the compartment can contribute to rapid fire development **(Figure 14.7)**. The thermal properties can also make extinguishment more difficult and reignition possible. Thermal properties of a compartment include:

- **Insulation** — contains heat within the compartment, causing a localized increase in the temperature and fire growth

- **Heat reflectivity** — increases fire spread through the transfer of radiant heat from wall surfaces to adjacent fuel sources

- **Retention** — maintains temperature by slowly absorbing and releasing large amounts of heat

Ambient Conditions

Ambient conditions, such as high humidity and cold temperatures, can slow the natural movement of smoke. Strong winds place additional pressure on one side of a structure and force both smoke and fire out the opposite side. If a window fails or a door is opened on the windward side of a structure, fire intensity and spread can increase significantly, creating a "blowtorch" effect **(Figure 14.8)**. During fire suppression activities, wind direction and velocity can prevent or assist in ventilation activities. Even in moderate winds (10-25 mph [15-25 kph]), the ISO's responsibility is to forecast the failure of building components on the windward side of the structure and keep the IC appraised.

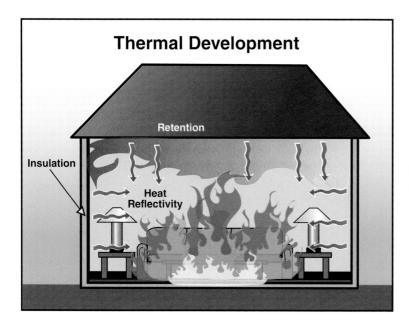

Figure 14.7 A compartment's thermal properties contribute to the accumulation of heat.

Figure 14.8 When a window fails, a new source of oxygen is suddenly available to the fire. The fire can rapidly move toward and consume this oxygen, creating a "blowtorch" effect. *Courtesy of Mike Wieder.*

Cold temperatures can cause smoke to appear white and give a false impression of the interior conditions based upon the color of smoke. Atmospheric air pressure can also cause smoke to remain close to the ground, obscuring visibility during size-up.

NOTE: While ambient temperature and humidity outside the structure can have an effect on the ignitability of many types of fuels, these factors are less significant inside a compartment.

Fuel Load

The total quantity of combustible contents of a building, space, or fire area is referred to as the **fuel load** (some documents may use the term fire load) **(Figure 14.9)**. The fuel load includes all furnishings, merchandise, interior finish, and structural components of the structure. At a scene, you will only be able to estimate the fuel load based upon your knowledge and experience. For example, a concrete block structure containing stored steel pipe will have a much smaller fuel load than a wood-frame structure used for storing flammable liquids. Your knowledge of building construction and occupancy types will be essential to determining fuel loads. Building fuel loads impact firefighter safety when offensive tactics are insufficient for large fuel loads, placing firefighters in dangerous positions. ISOs should inform the IC of excessive fuel loads if the IC is unaware.

> **Fuel Load** — The total quantity of combustible contents of a building, space, or fire area, including interior finish and trim, expressed in heat units of the equivalent weight in wood.

Figure 14.9 Big box stores have a high fuel load, and the normally safe contents present a wide variety of hazards during a fire or other emergency. *Courtesy of Ron Moore, McKinney (TX) Fire Department.*

Incipient Stage

The incipient stage starts with ignition. At this point, the fire is small and confined to the material (fuel) first ignited.

Once combustion begins, development of an incipient fire is largely dependent on the characteristics and configuration of the fuel involved (fuel-controlled fire). Air in the compartment provides adequate oxygen to continue fire development:

- During this initial phase of fire development, radiant heat warms the adjacent fuel and continues the process of pyrolysis. A plume of hot gases and flame rises from the fire and mixes with the cooler air in the room.

- As this plume reaches the ceiling, hot gases begin to spread horizontally across the ceiling in what firefighters have historically called *mushrooming*. However, in scientific or engineering terms, it is referred to as a **ceiling jet**. **(Figure 14.10)**

- Hot gases in contact with the surfaces of the compartment and its contents transfer heat to other materials. This complex process of heat transfer begins to increase the overall temperature in the room.

In this early stage of fire development, the fire has not yet significantly influenced the environment within the compartment. The temperature, while increasing, is only slightly above ambient and the concentration of products of combustion is low. During the incipient phase, occupants can safely escape from the compartment and the fire could be safely extinguished with a portable extinguisher or small hoseline. The transition from incipient to growth stage can occur quite quickly (in some cases in seconds), depending on the type and configuration of fuel involved.

Ceiling Jet — Horizontal movement of a layer of hot gases and combustion by-products from the center point of the plume, when the vertical development of the rising plume is redirected by a horizontal surface such as a ceiling.

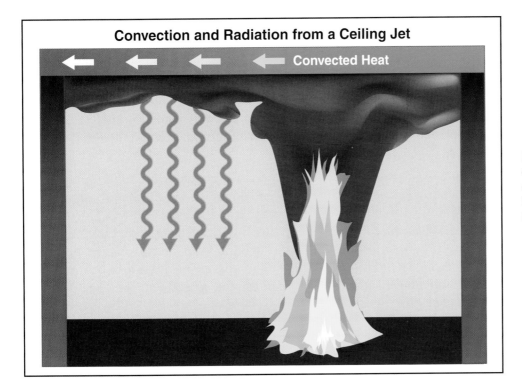

Convection and Radiation from a Ceiling Jet

← ← ← ← **Convected Heat**

Figure 14.10 A ceiling jet convects heat through the ceiling, which in turn radiates heat back down toward the room some distance away.

Growth Stage

As the fire transitions from incipient to growth stage, it begins to influence the environment within the compartment and has grown large enough for the compartment configuration and amount of ventilation to influence it. The first effect is the amount of air that is entrained into the plume. In a structure fire, the location of the fuel package in relation to the compartment walls affects the amount of air that is entrained and therefore, the amount of cooling that takes place. Unconfined fires draw air from all sides and the entrainment of air cools the plume of hot gases, reducing flame length and vertical extension:

- Fuel packages in the middle of the room can entrain air from all sides.
- Fires in fuel packages near walls can only entrain air from three sides.
- Fires in fuel packages in corners can only entrain air from two sides.

Therefore, when the fuel package is not in the middle of the room, the combustion zone (the area where sufficient air is available to feed the fire) expands vertically. The expanded combustion zone increases both the temperatures in the developing hot gas layer at ceiling level and the speed of the ceiling jet. In addition, heated surfaces around the fire radiate heat back toward the burning fuel, which further increases the speed of fire development.

Thermal Layering

The **thermal layering of gases**, sometimes referred to as *heat stratification* and *thermal balance*, is the tendency of gases to form into layers according to temperature. Generally, the hottest gases tend to be in the upper layer, while the cooler gases form the lower layers. Radiation from the hot gas layer also acts to heat the interior surfaces of the compartment and its contents. Changes in ventilation and flow path can significantly alter the thermal layering.

When a fire develops in a compartment, heated products of combustion and entrained air become hotter than the surrounding air and rise to the ceiling in a plume. When these hot gases reach the ceiling, they spread horizontally through the compartment. The gases continue to spread until they reach the compartment walls. As combustion continues, the depth of the gas layer begins to increase. The difference between hot smoke and the cooler air below causes them to separate into two distinct thermal layers.

As the volume and temperature of the hot gas layer increases, so does the pressure. Like water, gas will expand when heated. Higher pressure in this layer causes the hot gas layer to spread downward within the compartment and laterally through any openings, such as doors or windows. The thermal layer fills the room from the top down within the compartment and out through any openings, such as doors or windows. Once through an opening, the thermal layer will try to rise. The temperature and rate of heat transfer will dictate how fast the layer will move and spread out from the compartment of origin.

The pressure of the cool gas layer is lower, resulting in inward movement of air from outside the compartment at the bottom as the hot gases exit through the top of the opening. Pressure is higher in the hotter gas layer near the ceiling, forcing smoke out through openings. The interface of the hot and cooler gas layers at the opening is commonly referred to as the **neutral plane** because the pressure is neutral where the layers meet **(Figure 14.11)**. The neutral plane only exists at openings where hot gases are exiting and cooler air is entering the compartment. It may also be visible in hallways between the point of ventilation and room fire.

Thermal Layering (of Gases) — Outcome of combustion in a confined space in which gases tend to form into layers, according to temperature, with the hottest gases found at the ceiling and the coolest gases at floor level.

Neutral Plane — Level at a compartment opening where the difference in pressure exerted by expansion and buoyancy of hot smoke flowing out of the opening and the inward pressure of cooler, ambient temperature air flowing in through the opening is equal.

Figure 14.11 The neutral plane indicates the interface between cooler gases and hotter gases. The neutral plane will lower as the fire burns the available fuel in the compartment. *Courtesy of the National Institute of Standards and Technology.*

Pyrolysis — Thermal or chemical decomposition of a solid material by heating, generally resulting in the lowered ignition temperature of the material; the pre-ignition combustion phase of burning during which heat energy is absorbed by the fuel, which in turn gives off flammable tars, pitches, and gases; often precedes combustion.

During the development of a compartment fire, **pyrolysis** of exposed fuels can produce combustible gases, which can gather at locations in the layer some distance away from the fire plume **(Figure 14.12, p. 478)**. These pockets of gas may undergo piloted ignition from the transfer of heat energy directly from the fire plume itself or ignition as a result of having reached their auto-ignition temperature **(Table 14.1, p. 478)**.

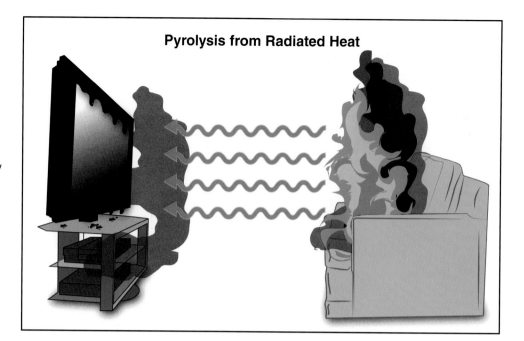

Figure 14.12 Radiated heat from a fire can pyrolize nearby materials.

	Table 14.1 Pyrolysis Zones	
	Temperature	**Chemical Changes**
Stage 1	Less than 392°F (200°C)	Moisture is released as the wood begins to dry; combustible and noncombustible materials are released into the atmosphere, although there is insufficient heat to ignite them.
Stage 2	392° — 536°F (200°— 280°C)	The majority of the moisture has been released, charring has begun, and the primary compound being released is carbon monoxide. Ignition has yet to occur.
Stage 3	536° — 932°F (280°— 500°C)	Rapid pyrolysis takes place; combustible compounds are released, ignition can occur, and charcoal is formed by the burning process.
Stage 4	Greater than 932°F (500°C)	Free burning exists as the wood material is converted to flammable gases.

Source: Adapted from NFPA® *Fire Protection Handbook*, 19th edition, Volume II, pages 8-35 and 36.

Whenever possible, maintain or raise the level of the hot gas layer above the floor to provide a more tenable environment for firefighters and trapped occupants. Use effective fire control and ventilation tactics to raise the position of the hot gas layer.

Isolated Flames

As the fire moves through the growth stage and becomes ventilation-controlled, **isolated flames** may be observed moving through the hot gas layer. Combustion of these hot gases indicates that portions of the hot gas layer are within their flammable range and there is sufficient temperature to result in ignition. As these hot gases circulate to the outer edges of the plume, they find sufficient oxygen to ignite. This phenomenon is frequently observed prior to more substantial involvement of flammable products of combustion in the hot gas layer.

Rapid Transition

Rapid transition from the growth stage to the fully developed stage is known as flashover **(Figure 14.13, p. 480)**. Under laboratory conditions or when a fire is fuel-controlled, flashover occurs during the growth stage. However, at a real fire scene, it may be difficult to identify what stage a fire is in, so firefighters should assume that flashover may occur at any time the conditions are right for it to occur. Because flashover can be unpredictable, a detailed description of it is addressed later in this chapter under Rapid Fire Development.

Flashover does not occur in every compartment fire. Instead, the fire may become ventilation-controlled, which limits the heat release rate or causes the fire to enter the decay stage. Pyrolisis is continuing at this stage and is increasing the fuel content of the smoke.

Most fires that develop beyond the incipient stage become ventilation-controlled. Even when doors and windows are open, there is often insufficient air to allow the fire to continue to develop based on the available fuel. When windows are intact and doors are closed, the fire will move into a ventilation-controlled state even more quickly. While this transformation reduces the heat release rate, fuel will continue to pyrolize, creating fuel-rich smoke.

Fully Developed Stage

The fully developed stage occurs when all combustible materials in the compartment are burning. During this stage:

- The burning fuels in the compartment release the maximum amount of heat possible for the available fuel and oxygen, producing large volumes of fire gases.

- The fire is ventilation-controlled because the heat release is dependent on the compartment openings. These openings provide oxygen, which supports the ongoing combustion and releases products of combustion. Increases in the available air supply will result in higher heat release.

- Flammable products of combustion are likely to flow from the compartment of origin into adjacent compartments or out through openings to the building's exterior. Flames will extend out of the compartment openings because there is insufficient oxygen for complete combustion in the compartment.

NOTE: If there are no openings in the compartment, it is unlikely that the fire will reach a fully developed stage due to limited ventilation.

Figure 14.13 Flashover is the rapid transition of a fire from the decay or growth phase to the fully developed stage.

Decay Stage

A compartment fire will decay as the fuel is consumed or if the oxygen concentration falls to the point that flaming combustion is diminished. Both of these situations can result in the combustion reaction coming to a stop. However, decay due to reduced oxygen concentration can follow a considerably different path if the ventilation of the compartment changes before combustion ceases and temperature in the compartment lowers.

Consumption of Fuel

As the fire consumes the available fuel in the compartment and the heat release rate begins to decline, it enters the decay stage. If there is adequate ventilation, the fire becomes fuel-controlled. The heat release rate will drop, but the temperature in the compartment may remain high for some time. During this stage, the flammable products of combustion can accumulate within the compartment or adjacent spaces.

Limited Ventilation

When a compartment fire enters the decay stage due to a lack of oxygen, the rate of heat release also declines. However, the continuing combustion reaction (based on available fuel and the limited oxygen available to the fire) may maintain an extremely high temperature within the compartment. Temperature decreases, but pyrolysis can continue. Under these conditions, a large volume of flammable products of combustion can accumulate within the compartment.

Traditional fire fighting tactics often assume that fires are fuel-controlled. New fire science suggests that fires involving new construction and/or modern furnishings are likely to be ventilation-controlled and require different tactics.

Modern buildings are likely to be wrapped in air-tight insulation **(Figure 14.14)**. Modern insulation is energy efficient but allows for no air transfer from the interior to the exterior of a structure other than through windows and doors. Fires in these insulated buildings consume the available oxygen in the structure quickly, giving firefighters a false sense that the fire has self-extinguished or entered decay.

When firefighters create an opening in the structure or if a portion of the structure fails, oxygen enters the structure. The fire now has a new source of oxygen and will rapidly re-enter the growth stage **(Figure 14.15, p. 482)**. Firefighters in a part of the structure that they thought was uninvolved may find themselves suddenly engulfed if ventilation tactics are not properly coordinated. Research is showing that the entire structure should be considered the fire compartment. ISOs need to consider this additional stage of decay when operations occur during early stages of fire growth or when buildings have not self-ventilated.

Figure 14.14 Modern construction often features exterior insulation in addition to in-wall insulation. Exterior insulation effectively wraps the building in air-tight "plastic."

Rapid Fire Development

Over the years, the fire service has coined words and phrases to describe various fire events that result in rapid fire development. Among these events are:

- Flashover
- Backdraft
- Smoke explosion

Rapid fire development has been responsible for numerous firefighter deaths and injuries. To protect yourself and your crew, you must be able to recognize the indicators of rapid fire development, know the conditions created by each

New Oxygen =
Near Decay to
Rapid Development

New Oxygen =
Increased Heat
Release Rate

Fresh
Air

Figure 14.15 New sources of oxygen increase the heat release rate and may cause transition of decayed fires from decay phase to the growth or fully developed phase.

Flashover — Stage of a fire at which all surfaces and objects within a space have been heated to their ignition temperature, and flame breaks out almost at once over the surface of all objects in the space.

of these situations, and determine the best action to take before they occur. In this section, rapid fire development conditions are described along with their indicators.

Flashover

When **flashover** occurs, the combustible materials in the compartment and fuel gases ignite almost simultaneously, resulting in full-room involvement **(Figure 14.16)**. Flashover typically occurs during the growth stage of a fire but may occur in the fully developed stage.

Flashover conditions are defined in a variety of ways. However, during flashover, the environment of the room or structure is changing from a two-layer condition (hot on top, cooler on the bottom) to a single well-mixed hot gas condition from floor to ceiling that is untenable even for fully protected firefighters.

The transition period between preflashover fire conditions (growth stage in a fuel-limited case) to postflashover (fully developed stage) can occur rapidly. During flashover, the volume of the fire can increase from approximately ¼ to ½ of the room's upper volume to filling the entire volume of the room and potentially extending out of any openings in the room. When flashover occurs, burning gases push out of openings in the compartment (such as a door leading to another room) at a substantial velocity.

There are four common elements of flashover:

- **Transition in fire development** — Flashover represents a transition from the growth stage to the fully developed stage.

- **Rapidity** — Although it is not an instantaneous event, flashover happens rapidly, often in a matter of seconds, to spread complete fire involvement within the compartment.

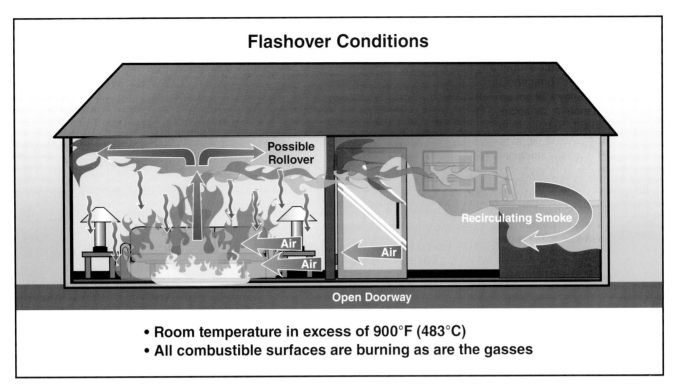

Figure 14.16 Flashover conditions result in full room involvement as the fuel gases ignite all at once.

- **Compartment** — There must be an enclosed space, such as a single room or enclosure.

- **Ignition of all exposed surfaces** — Virtually all combustible surfaces in the enclosed space become ignited.

Two interrelated factors determine whether a fire within a compartment will progress to flashover. First, there must be sufficient fuel and the heat release rate must be sufficient for flashover conditions to develop. For example, ignition of discarded paper in a small metal wastebasket may not have sufficient heat energy to develop flashover conditions in a large room lined with gypsum drywall. On the other hand, ignition of a couch with polyurethane foam cushions placed in the same room is quite likely to result in flashover.

Ventilation is the second factor. Regardless of the type, quantity, or configuration of fuel, heat release is dependent on oxygen. A developing fire must have sufficient oxygen to reach flashover, and a sealed room may not provide enough. Heat release is limited by the available air supply. If there is insufficient natural ventilation, the fire may enter the growth stage but not reach the peak heat release rate to transition through flashover to a fully developed fire.

Survival rates for firefighters are low in a flashover. While no exact temperature is associated with flashover, it typically occurs at 1,100°F (approximately 590°C) ceiling temperature. The ISO should assess for potential flashover conditions from the exterior of the structure, including but not limited to the following:

- **Building indicators** — Flashover can occur in any building; interior configuration, fuel load, thermal properties, and ventilation will determine how rapidly it can occur. The ISO should pay particular attention to windows, doors, cracks, vents, and gable ends as indications of imminent flashover potential.

Rollover — Condition in which the unburned fire gases that have accumulated at the top of a compartment ignite and flames propagate through the hot-gas layer or across the ceiling. These superheated gases are pushed, under pressure, away from the fire area and into uninvolved areas where they mix with oxygen. When their flammable range is reached and additional oxygen is supplied by opening doors and/or applying fog streams, they ignite and a fire front develops, expanding very rapidly in a rolling action across the ceiling.

Backdraft — Instantaneous explosion or rapid burning of superheated gases that occurs when oxygen is introduced into an oxygen-depleted confined space. The stalled combustion resumes with explosive force; may occur because of inadequate or improper ventilation procedures

- **Smoke indicators** — Rapidly increasing volume, turbulence, darkening color, optical density, and lowering of the hot gas level

- **Air flow indicators** — High velocity and turbulence, bi-directional movement with smoke exiting at the top of doorway and fresh air moving in at the bottom, or pulsing air movement

- **Heat indicators** — Rapidly increasing temperature in the compartment, pyrolysis of contents or fuel packages located away from the fire, darkened windows, or hot surfaces

- **Flame indicators** — Isolated flames in the hot gas layers or near the ceiling

Rollover is a possible and significant indicator of flashover. Rollover describes a condition where the unburned fire gases that have accumulated at the top of a compartment ignite and flames propagate through the hot gas layer or across the ceiling.

Rollover may occur during the growth stage as the hot gas layer forms at the ceiling of the compartment. Flames may be observed in the layer when the combustible gases reach their ignition temperature. While the flames add to the total heat generated in the compartment, this condition is not flashover. Rollover will generally precede flashover, but it may not always result in flashover. Rollover contributes to flashover conditions because the burning gases at the upper levels of the room generate tremendous amounts of radiant heat that transfers to the fuel packages in the room. The new fuels begin pyrolysis and release the additional gases necessary for flashover.

Backdraft

A ventilation-controlled compartment fire can produce a large volume of flammable smoke and other gases due to incomplete combustion. While the heat release rate from a ventilation-controlled fire is limited, elevated temperatures are usually present within the compartment. An increase in low-level ventilation (such as opening a door or window) prior to upper level ventilation can result in an explosively rapid combustion of the flammable gases, called a **backdraft** (**Figure 14.17**). Backdraft occurs in the decay stage, in a space containing a high concentration of heated flammable gases that lack sufficient oxygen for flaming combustion.

When potential backdraft conditions exist in a compartment, the introduction of a new source of oxygen will return the fire to a fully involved state rapidly (often explosively). A backdraft can occur with the creation of a horizontal or vertical opening. All that is required is the mixing of hot, fuel-rich smoke with air. Backdraft conditions can develop within a room, a void space, or an entire building. Anytime a compartment or space contains hot combustion products, personnel must consider the potential for backdraft before creating any openings into the compartment. Backdraft indicators include:

- **Building indicators** — Fire confined to a single compartment or void space, building contents have a high heat release rate.

- **Smoke indicators** — Optically dense smoke, light colored or black becoming dense gray-yellow, although the smoke color alone is not a reliable indicator. Neutral plane rising and lowering similar to a pulsing or breathing movement.

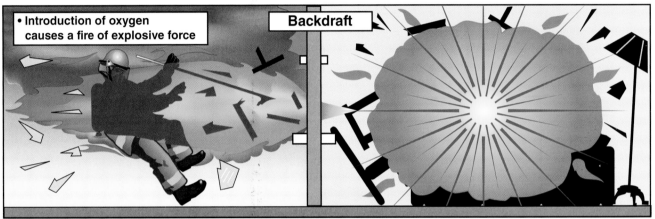

Figure 14.17 To avoid backdrafts, firefighters must make thorough observations of the fire behavior at the scene and then coordinate their ventilation operations.

- **Air flow indicators** — High velocity, turbulent smoke discharge, sometimes appearing to pulse or breathe.

- **Heat indicators** — High heat, smoke-stained windows **(Figure 14.18, p. 486)**.

- **Flame indicators** — Little or no visible flame.

The effects of a backdraft can vary considerably depending on a number of factors, including:

- Volume of smoke

- Degree of confinement

- Pressure

- Speed with which fuel and air are mixed

- Location where ignition occurs

Do not assume that a backdraft will always occur immediately after an opening is made into the building or involved compartment. If the hot, flammable products of combustion and air mix slowly, a backdraft is unlikely to occur. The mixing of hot flammable products of combustion with air due to gravity, air current, pressure differential, and wind effects sometimes delays the occurrence of a backdraft until after air is fully introduced.

Figure 14.18 Smoked stained windows like those on the second story of these houses are indicators of high heat in the structure and the presence of unburned fuel gases in the compartment. *Courtesy of Ron Jeffers.*

You must watch the smoke for indicators of potential rapid fire development, including the air current changing direction, neutral plane lifting, or smoke rushing out. To some degree, the violence of a backdraft can be dependent on the extent to which the fuel/air mixture is confined in the compartment. The more confined, the more violent the backdraft will be.

Smoke Explosion

A **smoke explosion** may occur before or after the decay stage. It occurs as unburned fuel gases come in contact with an ignition source. When smoke travels from the fire, it can cool and accumulate in other areas and mix with air. The smoke within its flammable range contacts an ignition source and results in an explosively rapid combustion. Smoke explosions are violent because they involve premixed fuel and oxygen. This process is similar to ignition of propane and air within its flammable range. The smoke is generally cool, less than 1,112°F (600°C), and located in void spaces connected to the fire or in uninvolved areas remote to the fire.

Fire Behavior and Fire Fighting Operations

Fire is controlled and extinguished by limiting or interrupting one or more of the essential elements in the combustion process (fuel, oxygen, heat, or chemical reaction). Firefighters influence fire behavior in a number of ways:

- Temperature reduction
- Fuel removal
- Oxygen exclusion
- Chemical flame inhibition
- Ventilation and fire behavior

Smoke Explosion — Form of fire gas ignition; the ignition of accumulated flammable products of combustion and air that are within their flammable range.

Temperature Reduction

Cooling with water is one of the most common methods of fire control and extinguishment. To extinguish a fire by reducing its temperature, enough water must be applied to the burning fuel to absorb the heat being generated by combustion. Water application in sufficient quantities reduces the temperature of a fuel to a point where it does not produce sufficient vapor to burn.

Cooling can extinguish solid fuels and liquid fuels with high flash points. Cooling low flashpoint flammable liquids with water cannot sufficiently reduce vapor production to extinguish fires. The use of water for cooling is also the most effective method available for the extinguishment of smoldering fires.

In addition to cooling solid and liquid fuels, water can also be used to control burning gases and reduce the temperature of hot products of combustion in the upper layer. This process slows the pyrolysis process of combustible materials, reduces radiant heat flux from the upper layer, and reduces the potential for flashover.

Water absorbs significant heat as its temperature is raised, but it has its greatest effect when it is vaporized into steam. When water is converted to steam at 212°F (100°C), it expands approximately 1,700 times. **(Figure 14.19)** Because of this expansion rate, firefighters should avoid creating too much steam. Excess steam production can make it difficult to see, increase the chances for steam burns, and disrupt the thermal balance. Firefighters can control steam production by:

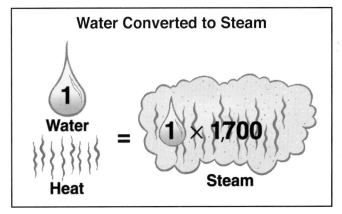

Figure 14.19 Water expands dramatically when it converts to steam, absorbing a large amount of heat in the process.

- Using good nozzle technique

- Applying the appropriate amount of water

- Applying water using the most effective form (fog, straight, or solid stream based upon existing conditions)

Fuel Removal

Removing the fuel source effectively extinguishes any fire. The simplest method of fuel removal is to allow a fire to burn until all fuel is consumed. While this practice is not always the most desirable extinguishment method, it is sometimes appropriate. For example, fires involving pesticides or flammable liquid spills may create greater environmental harm if they are extinguished with water, creating substantial runoff and contaminating soil or bodies of water. The best solution may be to allow the fire to burn, minimizing groundwater pollution. A fuel source may also be removed as follows:

- Stopping the flow of a liquid fuel

- Closing valves to stop the emission of gaseous fuels

- Moving solid fuels out of the path of the fire

Oxygen Exclusion

Reducing the oxygen available to the combustion process reduces a fire's growth and may extinguish it over time. In its simplest form, this method is used to extinguish stove top fires when a cover is placed on a pan of burning grease.

Flooding an area with an inert gas, such as carbon dioxide, displaces the oxygen and disrupts the combustion process. Oxygen can also be separated from some fuels by blanketing them with foam **(Figure 14.20)**. Of course, neither of these methods works on those rare fuels that are self-oxidizing.

While not generally used for extinguishment in structure fires, limiting the fire's air supply can be a highly effective fire control action. The simplest example of this method is when a building occupant closes the door to the fire room before leaving the building. This practice, sometimes referred to as **door control**, limits the air supply to the fire and can sometimes prevent flashover **(Figure 14.21)**.

Door Control — Fire fighting tactic intended to reduce available oxygen to a fire and create a controlled flow path in a structure for tactical ventilation, firefighter survivability, and occupant survivability.

Figure 14.20 Blanketing foam prevents oxygen from mixing with fuel gases which in turn inhibits the combustion process.

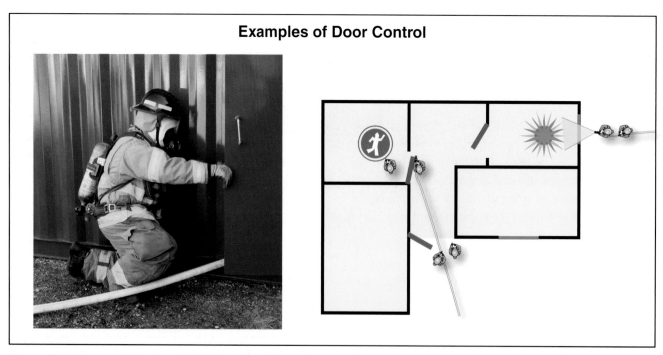

Examples of Door Control

Figure 14.21 Door control allows firefighters to create and control a flow path for air in the structure. Door control can create protected areas and assist with coordinated tactical ventilation.

Chemical Flame Inhibition

Extinguishing agents, such as some dry chemicals, halogenated agents (Halons), and Halon-replacement agents, interrupt the combustion reaction and stop flame production. This method of extinguishment is effective on gas and liquid fuels because they must flame to burn. These agents do not easily extinguish nonflaming fires because there is no chemical chain reaction to inhibit. The high agent concentrations and extended periods necessary to extinguish smoldering fires make these agents impractical in these cases.

Ventilation

In compartment fires, fire control is only one approach to provide a safer environment for firefighters and building occupants. Controlling the movement of smoke and air is also an important strategy.

Unplanned ventilation may occur before or after fire suppression operations start. Firefighters should expect unplanned ventilation that will significantly influence fire behavior in ventilation-controlled fires. Unplanned ventilation can result from the wind outside the structure. The wind can increase the pressure inside the structure, drive smoke and flames into unburned portions of the structure and onto advancing firefighters, and upset tactical ventilation efforts. You must be aware of the wind direction and velocity and use it to your advantage to assist in tactical ventilation **(Figure 14.22)**.

Unplanned Ventilation — Any ventilation that occurs outside of planned tactics such as ventilation from failed structural components, wind conditions, or firefighters acting outside of assigned tactics.

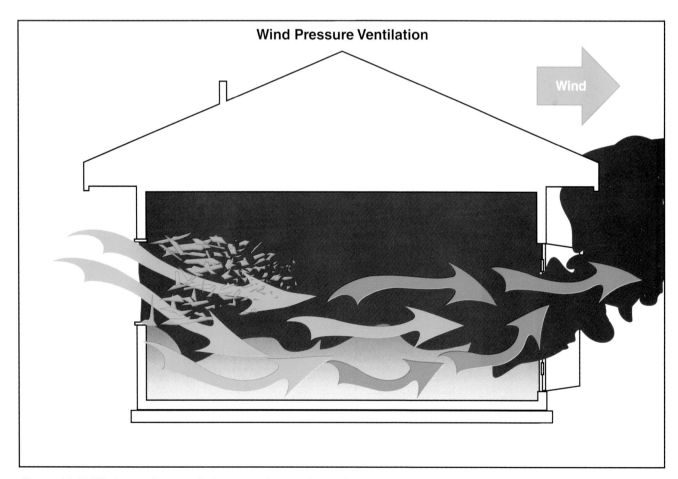

Figure 14.22 Wind can affect ventilation operations and may also create a pressure differential between the interior and exterior pressures which causes windows to fail.

Wind is an important factor, but unplanned ventilation is often the result of the following:

- Occupant action
- Fire effects on the building such as window glazing
- Firefighter freelancing such as unauthorized breaking of windows or opening doors

Tactical ventilation is the planned, systematic, and coordinated introduction of air and removal of hot gases and smoke from a building. It must be coordinated with fire suppression operations to prevent unwanted consequences for the hoseline crews **(Figure 14.23)**. The influences of ventilation on fire behavior are dependent on a variety of factors. Increased ventilation to a ventilation-controlled fire will quickly result in an increase in the heat release rate. Controlling ventilation can be as simple as keeping an exterior door closed until a charged line is in place or as complex as performing vertical ventilation. However, even with coordinated tactical ventilation, there will be an increase in the combustion rate when the fire is ventilation-controlled.

Figure 14.23 Tactical ventilation should always be coordinated with fire suppression operations to control the fire flow path and protect interior firefighters and victims. *Courtesy of Bob Esposito.*

Fire Behavior Indicators

Responsibility for size-up and risk assessment is not limited to fire officers. Everyone on the fireground needs to develop and maintain a high level of situational awareness. One element of situational awareness is recognition of key fire behavior indicators **(Figure 14.24)**. This practice includes not only recognizing what the fire is doing at the moment, but anticipating how fire

Figure 14.24 Incident safety officers should learn to recognize fire behavior indicators and what they may reveal about fire hazards at a scene and appropriate suppression operations.

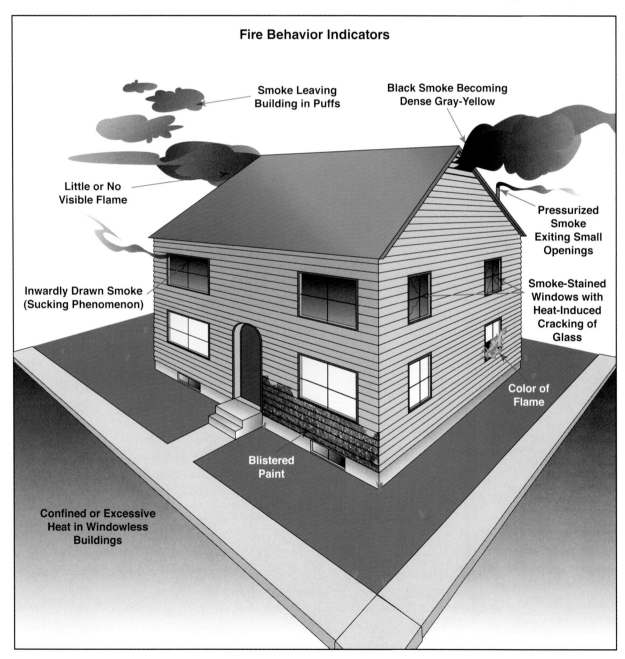

Fire Behavior Indicators

Smoke Leaving Building in Puffs

Black Smoke Becoming Dense Gray-Yellow

Little or No Visible Flame

Pressurized Smoke Exiting Small Openings

Inwardly Drawn Smoke (Sucking Phenomenon)

Smoke-Stained Windows with Heat-Induced Cracking of Glass

Color of Flame

Blistered Paint

Confined or Excessive Heat in Windowless Buildings

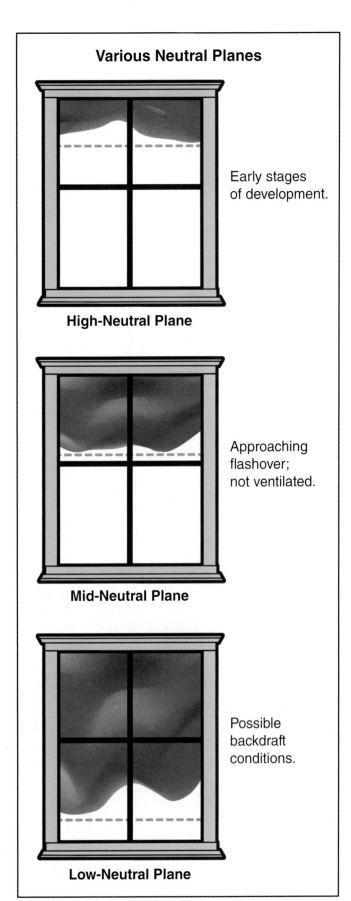

Various Neutral Planes

High-Neutral Plane

Early stages of development.

Mid-Neutral Plane

Approaching flashover; not ventilated.

Low-Neutral Plane

Possible backdraft conditions.

Figure 14.25 Observing the neutral plane behind windows can give the ISO some indication of interior conditions at a structure fire.

control actions and tactical ventilation will influence the fire's behavior. This section provides a simple overview of key fire behavior indicators. However, developing the ability to *read a fire* requires both training and experience.

Fire behavior indicators can be divided into the following five major categories:

- Building features
- Smoke
- Air flow
- Heat
- Flame

Smoke Volume

Smoke volume is the quantity of smoke visible. Small buildings will fill up with smoke sooner than larger buildings. However, a large building pushing smoke from openings is a sign of a large fire. The color or velocity may not indicate the true size and intensity of the fire in large buildings. Smoke must fill the building, and as it travels, it will lose its black color and become volume pushed. Lots of black smoke from a small house can be burnt food displaying a large quantity of smoke from the front door on arrival. Volume-pushed smoke will usually flow neither smooth nor turbulent. It floats out of openings, rising slowly.

Direction of Smoke Flow

The location of smoke may be an indicator of the location of the fire or a false indicator caused by movement of smoke through a structure so the color and velocity or pressure can indicate if smoke has traveled distances from the origin.

The neutral plane lowers as a fire develops. ISOs must carefully observe the level of the neutral plane through windows, doorways, and ventilation openings in order to communicate changing conditions to other personnel. Levels of the neutral plane are as follows (**Figure 14.25**):

- **High neutral plane** — May indicate that the fire is in the early stages of development. Watch the danger of high ceilings; they can hide the dangers of a fire that is in later stages. A high neutral plane can also indicate a fire above your level.

- **Mid-level neutral plane** — Could indicate that the compartment has not ventilated yet and that flashover is approaching.

- **Very low-level neutral plane** — May indicate that the fire is reaching backdraft conditions. This occurrence could also mean a fire is below you.

There are three ways to describe how smoke moves: floating or hanging, volume pushed, and heat pushed. The heat within the smoke will dictate speed.

Floating or hanging (lost its heat) smoke. Floating smoke is the same temperature as the air around it and is often found in air-conditioned buildings or fires that are sprinkler-controlled. Smoke particles that have passed through cracks in walls and been cooled and filtered also appear to float or hang.

Floating or hanging smoke will move according to air currents and indicates a small, early stage fire, mostly containing moisture from the first stage of pyrolysis. It could also mean a deep-seated fire in a large building, but the smoke is cooling off as it travels.

Volume-pushed smoke conditions. Once the area fills up with smoke, the speed with which it exits is a significant indicator. Fast exiting smoke indicates a large fire and/or a high rate of fire spread. Slower smoke exits in slow rolls that are not turbulent or active.

When smoke fills the compartment, it becomes pressurized. If the fire is under-ventilated, pressurization can reduce flame action. The confined smoke can be seen forcing out of cracks around windows, doors, and eves. The color and volume can indicate room location and contents or structure fire **(Figure 14.26)**. The area that smoke comes from will indicate passage for smoke, which means passage for fire.

Heat pushed. Indicated by speed which can be turbulent (bubbling, boiling, or active) or laminar (smooth straight). Fast, turbulent, or active smoke means there is a serious working fire and/or an imminent flashover. Turbulent black smoke has lots of particles and, indicative of vent-controlled smoke, has heat. It pushes from openings, rolling up a structure's sides as more smoke pushes out into it. Laminar/straight line smoke that is thin and fast-moving is heat-pushed, not under ventilated, and is exiting from openings near active flaming fire.

Figure 14.26 Smoke color and location are possible indicators of the location of the fire, its intensity, and possibly the fuel being consumed. *Courtesy of Bob Esposito.*

Smoke Color

Visible products of combustion. Tar, soot, and carbon are the most common heated particles found in smoke, giving it the black color. Moisture and heated gases give the smoke its white color.

Figure 14.27 Light white smoke indicates moisture being released from solids as the solids pyrolize.

Light white. Light white smoke indicates that pyrolysis (chemical change by heat) is occurring in areas adjacent to the main body of fire. The light white color indicates moisture and gases are being released from the product **(Figure 14.27)**. White smoke has lost particles because the particles have cooled from travel, water, and the addition of cold air. In the early stages of a fire, white wispy smoke is moisture coming off objects. A deep-seated fire where the smoke has been filtered or cooled from travel will also be white. On cold days when the temperature is below freezing, smoke turns white and turbulent immediately on leaving the structure. When smoke is forced from a structure through cracks, it filters large particles and will be white.

White smoke explosion. When a product is heated at a consistent temperature, it can pyrolyze and release types of flammable gases. When they accumulate in the right mixture, they become explosive when they come in contact with an ignition source.

Brown smoke. Brown smoke is common in mid-stage heating as moisture mixes with gases and carbon as pyrolysis increases **(Figure 14.28)**. It is also common in mid- to late-stage heating to see the caramel color brown smoke. Brown smoke is an indication of unfinished wood burning. Caramel colored smoke usually indicates clean wood burning, such as a fire involving structural wood members.

Gray smoke. Gray smoke indicates a combination of mixing smoke colors. It can indicate mid-stage heating with white, brown, or black, or it can occur

Figure 14.28 Brown smoke indicates that the heat release rate has risen, combustion has begun and carbon has begun to mix with released moisture.

when different smoke areas combine. It may also indicate changes in smoke production as the fire's heat increases from mid-stage to high.

Black smoke. Black smoke contains high quantities of carbon particles and is an indicator of the amount of ventilation available at the seat of fire. The thicker the smoke, the less clean burning and the less oxygen available as smoldering fires produce massive amounts of black smoke **(Figure 14.29)**. In the past, hydrocarbon fires were considered the source of black smoke. Now, fires involving synthetics, plastic, resins, polymers and products made from hydrocarbon derivatives will give off large quantities of black smoke. This black smoke contains unburned fuels and is a good indicator of carbon monoxide and many other flammable gases.

Unusual color smoke. Flammable metals and chemicals will give off uncharacteristic colors of smoke as they burn. Any unusual color smoke should give the IC an indication that different extinguishing agents may be needed.

Figure 14.29 Black smoke contains high quantities of unburned carbon. The thicker the smoke, the less oxygen is available to maintain the combustion process. Black smoke is, itself, a source of fuel.

Smoke Density

The darker and more turbulent the smoke is, the closer you are to a rapid fire event. Indicative of a large fire or under-ventilated fire are lots of suspended particles of tar, carbon, ash, and soot. Thick black smoke has lots of heat; thick white smoke has traveled and lost particles but still may have plenty of heat and fuel to burn. The denser the smoke, the lower the visibility, and the more likely that heat buildup indicates a pending flashover. Fast-moving black smoke can create fast-moving fires with rapid fire spread (black fire).

WARNING!
Smoke is a combustible byproduct of a fire and will burn rapidly when exposed to enough heat.

Thick white smoke. Thick white smoke is smoke that was black but has lost the solid particulates that made it black. This color loss can happen when smoke has been cooled or has travelled a long distance inside a structure while losing heat. Its consistency is fluffy as compared to a steam cloud, which is more opaque and mostly consists of condensation or water mist.

Thin black smoke. Thin black smoke is the direct result of heat from a flame. This smoke is black but transparent enough to see through. Thin black, fast-moving active smoke is an indication the fire is nearby. Thin black smoke with smooth lines exiting high in an opening and going straight up usually indicate open flames nearby with good ventilation.

Thick black smoke. The late stages of pyrolysis produce large amounts of carbon as unburned product, which creates thick black smoke. This production indicates the presence of flammable gases in the smoke, creating conditions for rapid ignition or flashover. The term *black fire* refers to dark black, thick, turbulent smoke (fuel) that is ready to ignite. It is called a black fire because it has the equivalent heat level to a flame; however, it does not have the needed oxygen to present visible flames. Vent point ignition is a possibility. This area would not be survivable by an occupant if the smoke filled the room from floor to ceiling. This thick black smoke can act like flame, cause pyrolysis, and can even char. Black fire is hot and can be seen traveling quickly out openings in hallways and other channels. Once the ventilation plane is unable to feed the large growing fire, it will become ventilation-controlled. Smoke will fill the area and become a backdraft or smoke explosion hazard. When black fire is present, applying water to cool the ceiling area is encouraged in an effort to reduce the potential for a flashover.

Flow Path

Flow path is the movement of fresh air toward the base of a fire and the movement of smoke and heated gases out of a structure; understanding this phenomenon can help in the ventilation of a fire. Flow path indicators include:

- **Velocity and direction** — Slow, smooth movement of air toward a fire indicates that it is in the early stages and still fuel-controlled. The velocity and the turbulence of the air entrained into the fire compartment will

Flow Path — Composed of at least one inlet opening, one exhaust opening, and the connecting volume between the openings. The direction of the flow is determined by difference in pressure; heat and smoke in a high pressure area will flow toward areas of lower pressure.

Figure 14.30 Ventilation-controlled fires will sometimes pulse smoke out of openings in a closed structure. *Courtesy of Dick Giles.*

increase during the transition to flashover. A sudden rush of fresh air into a compartment can create a backdraft. The direction of air flow can indicate the location of the seat or base of the fire.

- **Pulsations** — Fuel-rich and oxygen-deficient conditions result in smoke pulsing out of openings in a closed structure **(Figure 14.30)**. Opening the structure improperly or at the wrong location can rapidly add fresh oxygen to the compartment, resulting in a backdraft or move the fire to an undesired location. With these conditions, ventilation operations should be limited to above the fire and attack should not be initiated until ventilation has been accomplished.

- **Noise** — Whistling noise created by the movement of the air into the structure indicates that a backdraft condition may be imminent.

Heat

Heat is a form of energy transferred from one body to another as a result of a temperature difference. Smoke carries heat and cools as it moves away from a fire. Indications of increases in heat levels include the following:

- **Blackened or cracked glass** — Blackened, smoke-stained windows are an indicator of fire in the room or nearby as hot smoke condenses on a cooler window. Cracked glass indicates heat differentiation between the two sides of a pane. Double-paned windows resist failure due to heat; however, the interior pane may be cracked due to heat **(Figure 14.31, p. 498)**. Caution should be taken when opening a structure with these indicators.

- **Blistered paint** — Indicates both extreme temperature and location of the neutral plane. It may also indicate fire behind the wall.

- **Sudden heat buildup** — Gives a late indicator of flashover. When operating inside a structure, personnel must be aware of a rapid increase in temperature and act immediately to apply water or exit the structure.

Figure 14.31 Interior panes of windows may fail before the exterior pane fails, indicating a rise in heat inside the structure. *Courtesy of Yates and Associates.*

Flame

Flame color is usually an indicator of the oxygen supply and the extent of fuel-oxygen pre-mixing, which determines the rate of combustion. The direction of flame growth can be a good indicator of where sufficient oxygen is available in an area. In a structure fire, flames will typically extend beyond the room of origin if not quickly suppressed **(Figure 14.32)**. Fire growth requires sufficient oxygen, and flames will naturally seek out the path of least resistance toward the available oxygen. This fire spread can be into another room inside the structure or out an exterior window or doorway. The coordination of suppression efforts with ventilation is critical in preventing unwanted flame spread and growth. Efficient suppression activities will dictate smoke and flame movement until full extinguishment is achieved.

Building Construction Hazards

Building construction and construction materials have a profound effect on fire behavior and development. ISOs should be familiar with hazards associated with construction classifications. They must also take into account the materials used in construction and the age of construction when monitoring the scene and identifying hazards.

Hazards Associated with Construction Classifications

Both the *International Building Code® (IBC®)* and the National Fire Protection Association® (NFPA®) classify buildings in five types of construction (Type I through Type V). The types are then further divided into subcategories, de-

Figure 14.32 Fire will seek new sources of oxygen and will extend beyond the room of origin if not quickly suppressed. *Courtesy of Bob Esposito.*

pending on the code and construction type. Each construction type is defined by the construction materials and their performance under fire conditions. Every structure is composed of the following building elements:

- Structural frame
- Floor construction
- Roof construction

Besides the five classifications of construction, unclassified construction types also exist. They are comprised of the manufactured buildings that are completely assembled in a factory or on-site from modules.

Type I Construction Hazards

Type I, **fire resistive**, construction provides the highest level of protection from fire development and spread as well as collapse. All structural members are composed of only noncombustible or limited combustible materials with a high **fire-resistance rating**. Fire resistance is required to be 3 to 4 hours depending on the component (wall, floor, ceiling, or roof). Type I construction can be expected to remain structurally stable during a fire and is considered to be most collapse resistant. Reinforced concrete and precast concrete along with protected steel frame construction meet the criteria for **Type I construction (Figure 14.33, p. 500)**.

Type I structures are often incorrectly referred to as being fireproof. Even though the structure will not burn, it may degrade from the effects of fire. Although the use of Type I construction provides structural stability should a fire occur, the addition of combustible materials in the form of contents, furniture, wall and window coverings, stock, and merchandise can generate sufficient heat over time to compromise the structural integrity of the building.

Type I construction buildings may contain a number of conditions that can affect their behavior during a fire, including the following:

- Compartments can retain heat, contributing to the potential for rapid fire development.

> **Fire Resistive** — Ability of a structure or a material to provide a predetermined degree of fire resistance; usually according to building and fire prevention codes and given in hour ratings.

> **Fire-Resistance Rating** — Rating assigned to a material or assembly after standardized testing by an independent testing organization; identifies the amount of time a material or assembly will resist a typical fire, as measured on a standard time-temperature curve.

> **Type I Construction** — Construction type in which structural members, including walls, columns, beam, floors, and roofs, are made of noncombustible or limited combustible materials and have a specified degree of fire resistance.

Figure 14.33 Type I constructed buildings with reinforced concrete walls may still have combustible roofs. *Courtesy of Ron Moore, McKinney (TX) Fire Department.*

- Unauthorized penetrations of fire barriers can permit the extension of fire into unaffected compartments.

- Roofs may be difficult to ventilate due to construction material and design.

- Windows may be solid, causing them to be impossible to open for ventilation.

Type II Construction Hazards

Type II Construction — Construction type that is similar to Type I except that the degree of fire resistance is lower.

Buildings that are classified as Type II, noncombustible or limited combustible, construction are composed of materials that will not contribute to fire development or spread. **Type II construction** consists of noncombustible materials that do not meet the stricter requirements of those materials used in the Type I building classification. Steel components used in Type II do not need to be protected or fire rated for the same lengths of time as Type I **(Figure 14.34)**. Structures with metal framing members, metal cladding, or concrete-block construction of the walls with metal deck roofs supported by unprotected open-web steel joists are the most common form of this construction type. Fire resistance rating is generally half that of Type I or 1 to 2 hours depending on the component. The lower fire resistive rating of lighter weight materials used in this construction makes these buildings more prone to collapse.

Type II construction is normally used when fire risk is expected to be low or when fire suppression and detection systems are designed to meet the fuel load of the contents. You must remember that the term *noncombustible* does not always reflect the true nature of the structure. Lower fire resistance rates are permitted for roof systems and flooring. Unprotected metal twists and expands under heat. Large spans can push load bearing walls outward, resulting in roof failure. Additionally, combustible features may be included on the exterior of Type II structures, including balconies or facades for aesthetic purposes.

Figure 14.34 Exposed steel components in Type II construction may have a lower fire resistance rating than steel members in Type I construction. *Courtesy of Ron Moore, McKinney (TX) Fire Department.*

Type III Construction Hazards

Type III ordinary construction is commonly found in churches, schools, mercantile buildings, and residential structures. This construction type requires that exterior walls and structural members be constructed of noncombustible materials. Interior walls, columns, beams, floors, and roofs are completely or partially constructed of wood.

Type III construction is often considered an older mode of construction; however, buildings are still routinely built to Type III construction standards. The ISO should consult preincident survey information on new construction to verify which construction type was used rather than judging based upon the age of the structure.

Type III construction buildings may contain a number of conditions that can affect their reaction during a fire, including the following:

- Voids exist inside the wooden channels created by roof and truss systems and between wall studs that will allow for the spread of a fire unless fire stops are installed in the void.

- Old existing Type III structures may have undergone renovations that have contributed to greater fire risk due to the creation of large hidden voids above ceilings and below floors, which may create multiple concealed voids **(Figure 14.35, p. 502)**.

- When Type III construction is renovated, replacement materials may be of a different quality or material than the original construction type. The replacement material may react differently under fire conditions, leading to premature collapse or structural failure. This reaction may result in reducing the load-carrying capacity of the supporting structural member.

- The original use or occupancy of the structure may have changed to require a greater load-carrying capacity than the original design.

Type III Construction — Construction type in which exterior walls and structural members are made of noncombustible or limited combustible materials, but interior structural members, including walls, columns, beams, floors, and roofs, are completely or partially constructed of wood.

Figure 14.35 Older Type III constructed buildings may have undergone renovations that introduce hidden voids above ceilings or below floors.

Type IV Construction — Heavy timber construction in which interior and exterior walls and their associated structural members are made of noncombustible or limited combustible material; interior structural framing consists of heavy timber with minimum dimensions larger than those used in Type III construction.

Type IV Construction Hazards

Type IV construction, heavy timber, is characterized by the use of large-dimensioned lumber. Dimensions vary depending on the particular building code being used. As a general rule, these structural members will be greater than 8 inches (203.2 mm) in dimension with a fire resistance rating of 2 hours. The dimensions of all structural elements, including columns, beams, joists, and girders, must adhere to minimum dimension sizing. Any other materials used in construction and not composed of wood must have a fire resistance rating of at least 1 hour.

Type IV structures are stable and resistant to collapse due to the sheer mass of their structural members. When involved in a fire, the heavy timber structural elements form an insulating shell derived from the timbers' own char that reduces heat penetration to the inside of the beam. Type IV construction buildings may contain some conditions that can affect their behavior during a fire, including the following:

Figure 14.36 Type IV construction typically features very few concealed spaces that contribute to fire spread.

- The high concentration of wood can contribute to the intensity of a fire once it starts.

- Structural timbers exposed to fire can lose structural integrity, causing attached masonry walls to collapse.

- Exterior walls are constructed of noncombustible materials. Interior building elements, such as floors, walls, and roofs, are constructed of solid or laminated wood with no concealed spaces **(Figure 14.36)**. This lack of voids or concealed spaces helps to prevent fire travel.

Modern Type IV construction materials may include small-dimensioned lumber that is glued together to form a laminated structural element. These elements are strong and commonly found in churches, barns, auditoriums, and other large facilities with vaulted or curved ceilings. When exposed to fire, these beams heat may melt the glue in the laminate and cause them to fail in much the same way as plywood.

Type V Construction Hazards

Type V construction is commonly known as *wood frame* or *stick frame*. The exterior bearing walls are composed entirely of wood. Occasionally, a veneer of brick or stone may be constructed over the wood framing. The veneer offers the appearance of a Type III construction while providing little additional fire protection to the structure. A single-family residence is perhaps the most common example of this type of construction.

Type V construction consists of framing materials that include wood 2 x 4 or 2 x 6 inch studs. Most structures built in cold climates mandate 6-inch (152 mm) exterior wall cavities for increased insulation. The outside of the framing members is covered with exterior siding attached using nails, screws, or glue. Siding may be composed of any one of a number of covering materials, including:

Type V Construction — Construction type in which exterior walls, bearing walls, floors, roofs, and supports are made completely or partially of wood or other approved materials of smaller dimensions than those used in Type IV construction.

- Aluminum siding
- Shake shingles
- Wood clapboards
- Sheet metal
- Cement
- Plastic (vinyl) siding
- Planks
- Plywood
- Composite wood (chipboard, particle board, fiberboard)
- Styrofoam (which needs extra bracing) or stucco
- Veneers (brick or stone)
- Stucco (spread over a screen lattice that is attached to the framing studs)

Figure 14.37 Wooden I-beams are constructed of wood composite or plywood. The thinner beams form the bottom and top of each truss.

Type V construction has evolved in recent years to include the use of prefabricated wood truss systems in place of the solid floor joist. The truss system creates a large, open void area between the floors of a structure rather than the closed channel system found with solid wood floor joists. When wood I-beams are used, they are usually constructed of thin plywood or wood composite attached to 2 x 4 inch or thinner beams that form the top and bottom of the truss **(Figure 14.37)**. These wood I-beams may have numerous holes cut in them to allow for electric, communication, and utility lines to be extended through them. Under fire conditions, plywood I-beams fail and burn much more rapidly than solid lumber.

Engineered Construction — structures comprised primarily of composite materials such as laminate beams or oriented strand board (OSB) and lightweight steel or wood components. Structural components are often installed prefabricated and may be secured with adhesives.

Balloon-Frame Construction — Type of structural framing used in some single-story and multistory wood frame buildings; studs are continuous from the foundation to the roof, and there may be no fire stops between the studs.

Manufactured Home — Dwelling that is the assembly of four major components: the chassis and the floor, wall, and roof systems; although they are constructed of steel, wood, plywood, aluminum, gypsum wallboard, and other materials, they are basically frame construction. Characterized by small compartment sizes, low ceilings, and very lightweight construction throughout.

Lightweight construction, **engineered construction**, and **balloon-framed construction** also create unique fire spread considerations. Balloon frame may be prevalent in older homes. The studs in these structures extend two stories, which allows fire to extend vertically from the first story, past the second story, and into the attic.

Factory-Built Homes

Unclassified construction types include factory-built homes (also referred to as *manufactured, prefabricated,* and *industrialized* housing). Factory-built home is a generic term used to describe structures that are partially or completely built in a factory and shipped to the location they are to be installed on.

Factory-built homes do not conform to the model building codes. However, NFPA® 501, *Standard on Manufactured Housing,* addresses criteria for manufactured homes. However the U.S. Department of Housing and Urban Development (HUD) regulates their manufacture. Detailed requirements are included in Title 24 — Housing and Urban Development, Chapter XX — Office Of Assistant Secretary For Housing — Federal Housing Commissioner, Part 3280 — Manufactured Home Construction And Safety Standards. Like the model building codes, this federal standard describes the fire resistance requirements of materials used in the construction of these buildings.

Manufactured Homes. **Manufactured homes** are the most common type of factory-built homes, almost completely prefabricated prior to delivery, and the least expensive. The HUD code preempts all local building codes and is more stringent than model building codes. Because the HUD code is based on performance standards, it tends to encourage construction innovations. Manufactured homes usually have a permanent steel undercarriage and are delivered on wheels towed by a transport vehicle. They normally range from one-section single-wide homes to three-section triple-wide homes.

A manufactured (mobile) home is one type of factory-built structure that is popular in North America. While manufactured homes take many forms, a characteristic of mobile homes is the existence of an axle assembly under the frame. Current estimates indicate that manufactured homes make up 25 percent of all housing sales in the U.S.

Manufactured homes are not required to conform to the model building codes, although their construction type is similar to Type V construction. The age of the construction will make a difference in the fire resistance of the unit. Manufactured homes built before 1976 have less fire resistance than those of current construction. The major disadvantage of some of the manufactured homes is the fact that lightweight building materials used in them are susceptible to early failure in a fire. The heat produced by burning contents will cause the materials to rapidly ignite or melt. The contents have the same fuel loads as those found in conventional structures. At the same time, the use of lightweight materials makes forced entry much easier since walls can be quickly breached. In addition, some manufactured homes have open crawl spaces beneath them, providing an additional source for oxygen during a fire.

NFPA® analysis of fires in residential occupancies indicates a steady decline in fires in manufactured homes since 1980. The analysis compares manufactured homes built before the HUD standard was enacted in 1976 (referred to as *prestandard*) and those constructed after 1976 (*poststandard*). Reasons for the reduction in fire loss and fatalities can be contributed to requirements for:

- Factory-installed smoke alarms
- Use of flame retardant materials in interior finishes
- Use of flame retardant materials around heating and cooking equipment
- Installation of safer heating and cooking equipment
- Installation of gypsum board rather than wood paneling in interior finishes

Modular Homes. Modular homes, **modular buildings**, or sectional homes must comply with the same local building codes as site-built homes **(Figure 14.38)**. Only about 6 percent of all factory-built housing starts are modular homes. Modular sections can be stacked vertically and connected horizontally in a variety of ways. The modular section is transported to the site and then attached to a permanent foundation, which may include a full basement.

Modular Building — Building assembled at the factory in two or more all inclusive sections. All utilities and millwork are also installed at the factory, and connected when the building is delivered to a site.

Figure 14.38 Modular homes arrive at the construction site in constructed pieces and are joined on-site.

Panelized Homes. **Panelized homes** are assembled on-site from constructed panels made of foam insulation sandwiched between sheets of plywood. The panels arrive at the site already assembled. The individual panels are normally 8 feet (2.44 m) wide by up to 40 feet (12.19 m) long. The bottom edges of the wall panels are recessed to fit over the foundation sill. Each panel includes wiring chases. Because the panels are self-supporting, framing members are unnecessary. **(Figure 14.39, p. 506)**

Precut Homes. Precut homes come in a variety of styles, including pole houses, post-and-beam construction, log homes, A-frames, and geodesic domes. The precut home consists of individual parts that are custom cut and must be assembled on-site.

Hybrid Modular Homes. One of the most recent developments in factory-built homes, the **hybrid modular structure** includes elements of both the modular design and the panelized design. Modular core units, such as bathrooms or mechanical rooms, are constructed in the factory, moved to the site, and assembled. Preconstructed panels are then added to the modules to complete the structure.

Panelized Home — Home assembled on site consisting of constructed panels made of foam insulation sandwiched between sheets of plywood. The panels are assembled onsite and require no framing members.

Hybrid Modular Structure — Structure consisting of the elements of both modular design and panelized construction. Core modular units are assembled first and panels are added to complete the structure.

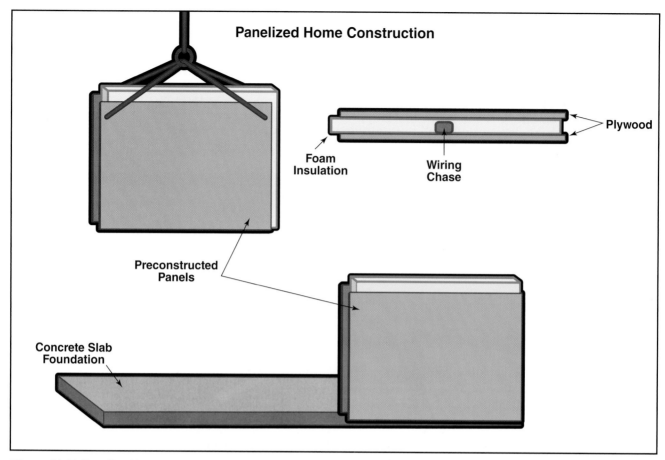

Panelized Home Construction

Plywood

Foam Insulation

Wiring Chase

Preconstructed Panels

Concrete Slab Foundation

Figure 14.39 Panelized homes are assembled on-site from panels shipped to the site from the manufacturer.

Building Materials' Effect on Fire Behavior

New construction materials and methods have increased the risk to fire operations. Fires burn hotter, have a shorter time to flashover, and increase the likelihood of early failure of structural components. The ISO must have adequate fire operations experience and a keen knowledge of building construction to effectively monitor conditions. The ISO should forecast the situation and communicate clearly with the IC on the stability of the structure.

Recent FEMA Sponsored Fire Behavior Studies

The U.S. Department of Homeland Security/Federal Emergency Management Agency (DHS/FEMA) funded a series of fire behavior studies relating to:

- Structural stability of engineered lumber involved in fire

- Legacy and contemporary residential construction

- Engineered floor systems and basement fires

Agencies and organizations involved in conducting, analyzing, and documenting these studies included:

- Underwriters Laboratories Inc. (UL)

- National Institute of Standards and Technology (NIST)

- Chicago Fire Department

- International Association of Fire Chiefs (IAFC)
- International Association of Fire Fighters (IAFF)
- Michigan State University

The results of these studies will pay double dividends. First, they can assist the Incident Commander with risk/benefit assessments during structural fires in both legacy and contemporary construction buildings. Secondly, they provide recommendations for changes to building codes that will influence future construction. The following sections incorporate information from these studies where indicated and describe critical results from the studies and their impact on decision-making during structural fire fighting operations.

Age of Construction

You should know the general construction types and materials used in your response area. Building construction materials will vary based upon geography, climate, and local codes. For example, houses in the southwestern United States may be commonly made with stucco siding over 2 x 4 inch (50.8 mm x 101.6 mm) frames and clay tiled roofs. Additionally, the age of structures and the time period communities were developed and settled will also have an influence on the type of materials used in building construction.

In residential and commercial construction, areas developed by the same contractor will generally possess the same construction materials, designs, and characteristics. Fire company surveys of new construction are essential to understanding how the completed structure will perform during a fire. Many residential neighborhoods may have a consistent construction design based on the time they were developed with the following characteristics:

- **Pre-20th Century** — mostly *mortise and tenon*, also called *post and beam* or *brace frame.*

- **Early 20th Century (1900 to 1950)** — mostly balloon frame construction

- **Post World War II (1950 and newer)** — mostly **platform frame construction**

- **1960s Construction** — use of Romex® wiring containing one strand of copper and one of aluminum became prevalent; the use of two dissimilar metals in wiring resulted in electrical fires in receptacles and switch boxes

- **1980s and 1990s Construction** — almost 1 million residential roof structures were constructed utilizing fire retardant plywood sheathing; these roofs disintegrate rapidly and only had a maximum 10-year lifespan. Although most of these roofs have been replaced, some may still be found.

- **2000 to the Present** — structures, especially private residences, are more frequently constructed using engineered materials and systems. Engineered materials allow for more open floor plans and wider variety in room arrangement, but these materials also fail more quickly when exposed to heat. These construction components may be referred to as engineered systems, integrated hybrid systems, or composite engineered systems.

Platform Frame Construction — A construction method in which a floor assembly creates an individual platform that rests on the foundation. Wall assemblies the height of one story are placed on this platform and a second platform rests on top of the wall unit. Each platform creates fire stops at each floor level restricting the spread of fire within the wall cavity.

While there is a general consistency in construction types based on the time period during which the area was developed, this is not always true. In some urban areas, older homes are being torn down and replaced by new construction. New construction that meets current building code requirements, architectural design, and building styles may include condominiums, townhouses, and multi-story "McMansions." In many cases, building lots that formerly contained one residence now contain two or more with reduced building separations. Fire company surveys of new construction are essential to understanding how the completed structure will perform during a fire.

If you know the time period in which your immediate response area was developed, you will be able to determine the general construction types and building code requirements. In older communities, some structures may not have been built to any code requirements while additions made to them were required to meet the codes in effect at the time of the addition. You should consult your fire prevention division or building department to determine the requirements for some of the buildings you are responsible for protecting **(Figure 14.40)**.

A recent FEMA-sponsored UL study compared legacy (older) residential construction to more contemporary residential construction. Two houses were constructed inside UL's large fire facility:

Variety of Residences in a Jurisdiction

Figure 14.40 You should be familiar with the variety of residential structures in your jurisdiction, their age, and construction features.

- A one-story, 1,200 square foot (110 square m) structure containing three bedrooms, one bathroom, and four other rooms similar to the smaller homes of decades ago.

- A two-story, 3,200 square foot (290 square m) structure containing four bedrooms, 2.5 bathrooms, and six other rooms. This house had a more open floor plan similar to more modern homes.

A total of fifteen ventilation experiments were conducted, varying the number and locations of ventilation openings. Tactical considerations that resulted from these experiments include:

- The normal stages of fire development change when fires become ventilation-limited. In modern fire environments, it is common to experience a decay period prior to flashover.

- Firefighters need to understand that forcible entry is a form of ventilation. The act of gaining entry into a structure on fire introduces air into the fire environment.

- Once fires become ventilation-limited, the amount of smoke forced out of structural gaps or openings is reduced or stopped.

- Adding air to fire without applying water within an appropriate amount of time increases the size of the fire while reducing safety. Greater coordination between ventilation and fire attack must occur.

- Opening the front door of a structure can allow air to rush or tunnel into the structure.

- During Vent Enter Search (VES) operations, doors should be closed following entry to reduce open venting and increase occupant and firefighter tenability.

- Each new ventilation opening creates another flow path to and from the fire, which is especially dangerous in a ventilation limited fire.

- Even with multiple ventilation openings, the fires remained ventilation-limited with each fire responding just as fast or faster to the additional air that was provided. As a result, temperatures inside the structures remained higher than if everything was sealed. Rapid fire progression was highly likely, and the need to coordinate ventilation and fire attack was critical.

- Closing doors between the occupants/firefighters and the fire kept temperature and oxygen concentrations within the structure tenable for both parties. Should firefighters become separated from one another, they should enter a room with a door and close it to provide a level of protection until they can be rescued or escape.

- Fire fighting personnel must understand and consider the potential impact of a window failing or being left open could have on the flashover time for the fire.

- Applying water from the exterior did not push the fire along the flow paths nor did it create temperature spikes in rooms adjacent to the fire room. It did push some steam along the flow paths.

- Fires grew until the level of oxygen available within the structures (drawn from surrounding and more remote rooms) fell below sustainable combustion levels. Surrounding rooms had no fire in them, even if the fire room became fully involved and had ventilated the structure.

Fire growth theories are generally based on models developed and tested in controlled environments in testing laboratories. ISOs should use the theories of fire behavior as a baseline to evaluate and predict actual fire behavior and to compare to their experiences and perceptions.

Engineered Materials

Engineered materials are frequently used in modern construction to reduce costs and accelerate the construction process. Engineered materials may include any of the following (**Figure 14.41, p. 510**):

- **Laminate beams or trusses** — structural members created from layers of composite plywood or OSB; these beams will ignite more easily and fail more quickly than wood members.

Laminate Beams — Structural members created from several layers of plywood or oriented strand board (OSB).

Engineered Materials

Figure 14.41 Engineered materials are used in a variety of construction applications that used to be constructed with wood.

Oriented Strand Board (OSB) — Wooden structural panel formed by gluing and compressing wood strands together under pressure. This material has replaced plywood and planking in the majority of construction applications. Roof decks, walls, and subfloors are all commonly made of OSB.

- **Oriented strand board (OSB)** — a type of plywood often used in floors, walls, and attics; ignites and propagates fire more quickly than wood.

- **Glues and adhesives** — some engineered truss systems may be factory-assembled with industrial adhesive rather than metal hardware; the systems arrive fully constructed on-site, which speeds the assembly of roof systems. The adhesives fail quickly, leading to roof collapses.

- **Wrapped or spray foam insulation** — Modern insulation is hydrocarbon-based (plastic) and is applied to effectively seal modern structures; this insulation prevents any unwanted airflow into or out of the structure, which may lead to ventilation-controlled fires.

- **Vinyl Siding** — Solid siding made of a variety of plastic, hydrocarbon materials. These materials may contribute to trapping heat in the structure and/or may make ventilation more difficult. Siding also adds a hydrocarbon fuel to the exterior fuel load on the structure. Vinyl siding may also be installed over older siding, such as asbestos shingles.

Lightweight Trusses

It is estimated that more than 60 percent of roof systems are constructed using a truss system. Composite and **lightweight wood truss** systems can contribute to increased structural fuel loads, create concealed spaces, and contribute to early collapse. When exposed to high temperatures in a compartment fire, lightweight steel trusses can also rapidly fail. Truss systems are designed to meet the minimum engineering requirements of the building code and are tested under controlled conditions in a laboratory setting. Because actual fires are unpredictable and uncontrolled, the failure time of truss systems cannot be predicted. In addition, lightweight and composite wood truss systems can deteriorate from prolonged exposure to moisture in the environment, a condition that may not be readily apparent during visual inspections.

Lightweight Wood Truss — Structural supports constructed of 2 x 3-inch or 2 x 4-inch members that are connected by gusset plates.

ISOs must learn about trusses and their performance under fire conditions. According to NIOSH, fire fighting tactics must be altered to meet the fire characteristics of lightweight construction, including:

- Know how to identify roof and floor truss construction

- Immediately report the presence of truss construction and fire involvement to the IC

- Use a thermal imager as part of the size-up process to help locate fires in concealed spaces

- Use extreme caution and follow SOP/Gs when operating on or under truss systems

- Open ceilings and other concealed spaces immediately whenever a fire is suspected of being in a truss system. Guidelines include:

  — Using extreme caution because opening concealed spaces can result in backdraft conditions

  — Having a charged hoseline available

  — Positioning between the nearest exit and the concealed space to be opened

  — Remaining aware of the location of other firefighters in the area

At the emergency incident, use the following procedures to protect firefighters:

- Ensure that the IC conducts an initial size-up and risk assessment of the incident scene before beginning interior fire fighting operations **(Figure 14.42)**.

- Evacuate firefighters performing operations under or above trusses as soon as it is determined that the trusses are exposed to fire, and move to a defensive mode.

- Use defensive overhauling procedures after extinguishing a fire in a building containing truss construction.

- Use outside master streams to soak smoldering trusses and prevent rekindles.

- Report any damaged sagging floors or roofs to command.

Source: National Institute for Occupational Safety and Health (NIOSH). "Preventing Injuries and Deaths of Fire Fighters Due to Truss System Failures," NIOSH Publication No. 2005-123.

Figure 14.42 The ISO should ensure that the IC performs a 360-degree size-up and risk assessment before interior fire fighting operations.

Bowstring Truss—
Lightweight truss design
noted by the bow shape, or
curve, of the top chord.

Bowstring Trusses

Before 1960, the **bowstring truss** roof design was one of the most common design types for large commercial and industrial structures. The bowstring truss roof was commonly used in facilities such as automobile dealerships, bowling alleys, grocery stores, and industrial complexes wherever large open floor spaces with limited interior supports were needed.

Bowstring truss roofs can be identified by the roof's arched or curved outline. The curved top chord members were made either by sawing straight lumber into curved shapes or laminating multiple smaller pieces bent over a jig to the desired shape. Bottom chord members were typically constructed with large, straight lumber members joined with either wood- or metal-bolted splice plates, located near mid-span, to achieve the required length. The top and bottom chord members were fastened at the truss ends with U-shaped steel heels, or end shoes, bolted to both chord members.

Some construction features, such as parapets, obstruct the ability to easily identify bowstring truss systems. Preincident surveys should provide information on hidden construction features and should be consulted during size-up and operations. Aerial mapping or photographs can also help identify bowstring truss structures.

The principles of bowstring truss construction are similar to other types of truss construction. Web members are used to form a series of triangles that transfer tension from the bottom chord and compression from the top chord of the truss onto the load bearing walls (**Figure 14.43**). One difference with

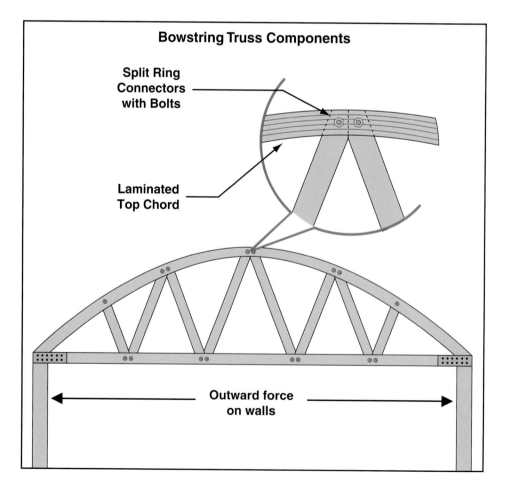

Figure 14.43 Bowstring trusses apply outward pressure to exterior walls, which could contribute to collapse under fire conditions.

Bowstring Truss Components

Split Ring Connectors with Bolts

Laminated Top Chord

Outward force on walls

the bowstring truss is that the compressional forces within the top chord act to force the load-bearing walls outward as well as downward. Another difference is that the space between trusses is greater than that found between other types of trusses. Because of this design, when one truss fails, the entire roof structure may fail. Additionally, this failure may occur with little or no warning.

Bowstring truss roof systems suffer from a little-known phenomenon related to inaccuracies in early industry-accepted truss design assumptions. All trusses constructed before the late 1960s have a common deficiency; the bottom chord members may have inadequate tensile strength to support code-prescribed roof loads. Tie rods or cables and anchor plates ("stars") installed for reinforcement on exterior walls are another indication that trusses or exterior walls are weakened **(Figure 14.44)**.

Floor Plans

The ISO must also be familiar with the interior arrangement of structures in your area. As mentioned in the fire behavior section, the interior arrangement of a compartment or structure influences fire spread and development. Understanding the structure's floor plan, wall and ceiling penetrations, and interior stairwell placement will help you predict fire and smoke spread, locate the seat of the fire, and make accurate ventilation decisions.

Void Spaces and Concealed Spaces

Many structures can have concealed vertical spaces that include pipe chases, HVAC ductwork, and vertical shafts that will allow fire spread to unaffected areas of the structure above the point of ignition. Concealed horizontal spaces are also a major concern in some parts of North America. Examples of these spaces are continuous attic or cockloft spaces that connect individual retail spaces in strip malls where fire stopping is not required.

Voids or concealed spaces are present in almost every type of building construction. Their ability to allow a fire to grow and spread undetected is significant to a building's risk of destruction by fire more than any other building construction related factor. These spaces are of particular concern when the materials used to construct them are combustible. For example, a renovated building may have a new roof assembly over the existing roof(s), which may conceal HVAC components. This roof assembly creates an additional undivided void space that is difficult to access. These roofs are also called **rain roofs** or *weather roofs* because they are built over existing roofs **(Figure 14.45, p. 514)**.

Rain roofs may be found on commercial buildings, schools, and residential structures. Generally, they are placed over older flat roofs for aesthetic purposes, to prevent leaks, and to channel moisture off the roof. They may be constructed from lightweight metal panels and trusses or wood and roofing materials to form a peak or a flat roof surface. The void created by the rain roof can conceal a fire and allow it to burn undetected. As the trusses are exposed to fire, they will weaken, increasing the potential for collapse of both the rain roof and the original roof. Ventilating a rain roof will not remove smoke from the structure until the original roof is penetrated. In addition, mechanical units placed under the rain roof place stresses on the existing roof and may cause the roof to collapse prematurely once exposed to fire from above or below.

Figure 14.44 "Stars" on the exterior of buildings often indicate installed reinforcements (tie rods and anchor plates) designed to reinforce weakened walls or bowstring trusses.

Rain Roof — Second roof constructed over an existing roof.

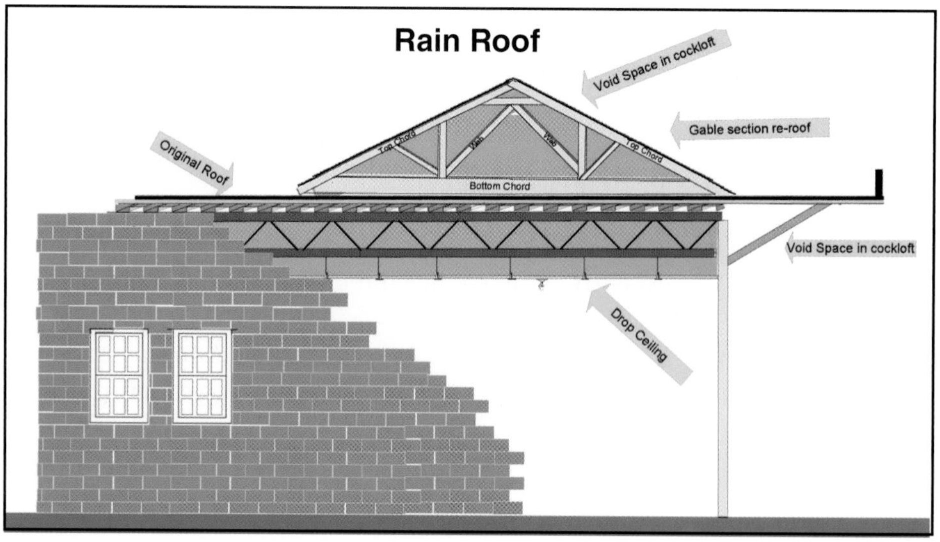

Figure 14.45 Rain roofs are built above flat roofs to route water off of the roof.

Lightweight Construction

Lightweight construction is a type of construction consisting of vertical and horizontal structural members formed by a system of wood and light gauge steel components that are lighter in weight than conventional solid wood components. These lightweight components include trusses, glue laminated beams, I-joists, structural composite lumber, structural insulated panels, and wood structural panel. They are replacing dimensional lumber in many building applications and are used to span wide areas without the need for vertical supports. Although many types of trusses exist, three typical truss construction methods are most commonly used:

- **Heavy timber roof and floor truss systems** — may require more water, higher gallons per minute

- **Lightweight wooden roof and floor truss systems** — less burn time, especially in modern engineered construction

- **Steel roof and floor truss systems** — steel framing, trusses will expand under heat; roofs soften and may begin to melt

Two recent FEMA-sponsored studies have analyzed the use of lightweight and engineered construction materials. The first study evaluated the use of wooden and engineered "I" beams in truss construction. The second study examined engineered floor systems and joists.

Structural Stability of Engineered Lumber Involved in Fire. The purpose of this study was to evaluate the structural performance of wood "I" beams and 2 X 4 inch wood trusses (lightweight wood construction) under fire conditions in comparison to older, legacy construction techniques using 2 X 10 inch floor joists and 2 X 6 inch roof supports. A total of nine fire tests were conducted, with seven tests on floor-ceiling assemblies and two tests on roof-ceiling assemblies. While the structural assemblies were designed to represent typical residential construction, the applied structural loads were made heavier than usually used in order to represent the weight of fully equipped fire fighting personnel.

Tactical considerations that resulted from this research study include:

- Protected and non-protected lightweight construction assemblies fail much faster than legacy construction assemblies.

- Legacy construction assemblies commonly fail over a small (local) area, while lightweight construction assemblies commonly fail over a larger (global) area.

- Sight, sound, and touch (sensory) indicators that firefighters use do not reliably indicate impending collapse.

- Data and images from thermal imagers do not reliably indicate impending collapse.

- Heated wood structural components (especially lightweight construction assemblies) weaken a structure before direct fire involvement.

- Modern roof sheathing is thinner than legacy construction roof sheathing, and it can fail locally well in advance of general structural collapse.

- Modern trusses are generally spaced 24 inches (610 mm) apart, and this spacing can contribute to early roof failure and provide large openings that firefighters can fall through **(Figure 14.46)**.

- Plastic continuous roof vents can melt, self-seal, and change the ventilation profile and fire conditions in the structure below.

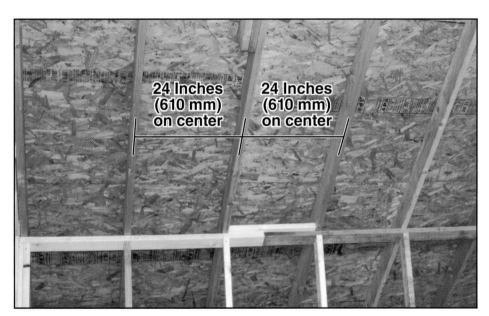

Figure 14.46 Modern trusses are installed far enough apart to contribute to early roof failure.

Engineered Floor Systems and Basement Fires. This study examined the effects of basement fires on a variety of engineered floor systems (floor joists). Examples of the joists included:

- Dimensional lumber

- Engineered I-joists **(Figure 14.47, p. 516)**

- Metal plate connected wood trusses **(Figure 14.48, p. 516)**

- Steel C-joists

- Castellated I-joists

- Hybrid trusses **(Figure 14.49, p. 516)**

Figure 14.47 Engineered joists may be present under floors/above basements.

Figure 14.48 Gusset plates may fail quickly under fire conditions as the wood around the nails that hold the plate in place pyrolizes and weakens.

Figure 14.49 Hybrid trusses combine different materials to create trusses of different sizes and strengths.

Experiments ranged from examining single floor joists in a laboratory setting to complete floor systems in an acquired structure. Other variables tested to determine their impact on structural stability and firefighter safety included a variety of applied loads, ventilation openings, fuel loads, span lengths, and methods of joist protection.

Tactical considerations that resulted from this study include:

- Collapse times for unprotected wood floor systems can vary depending on heat exposure and ventilation.

- Inspect the floor from below before operating on it, if possible. Personnel should be trained to recognize the collapse signs that relate to each type of floor system.

- Never rely solely on sounding the floor to determine its stability. Use other methods to improve safety.

- Thermal imagers might indicate the presence of a basement fire but are not useful in assessing the structural integrity of the floor system above the fire.

- Firefighters should not attack a basement fire from the stairway. This location places them in the flow path of hot gases exiting through the stairway.

- Temperatures at the bottom of basement stairs were often higher than those encountered at the top of the stairs.

- Ventilating a basement fire requires coordinated ventilation. Basement ventilation experiments create a flow path up the stairway and out the front door, increasing hot gas flow and temperatures to levels that could injure or kill fully protected firefighters.

- Firefighters can find it difficult to determine the amount of floor sag as they move through a structure, making it an unreliable indicator of potential floor collapse.

- The gas temperatures in a room above the fire are a poor indicator of fire conditions below and the structural integrity of a floor system.

- Firefighters should always have charged hoselines available when opening void areas to expose a wood floor system.

Changes to Building Loads and Forces

During fire suppression activities, water is a significant added load that can cause early collapse of roof structures. In 10 minutes, a master stream delivering 250 gallons per minute (1 000 L/min) can add approximately 10 tons (10 T) of weight to the structural components. A large defensive fire will have multiple master streams in place, which only compounds the added weight load form water to the structure. Additionally, a heavy master stream concentrated in a particular area may produce enough force to topple walls or parapets.

The ISO must assess the application of water based upon the use of master streams and the overall volume of water being added to the structure. All added water and added force from fire streams affects structural stability. Appropriate collapse zones should be established to forecast potential structural collapse.

Fire Suppression Systems

During the incident size-up, personnel should assess the operation of fire suppression systems at a location. Fire suppression systems can have water, foam, carbon dioxide, halon, or nitrogen. Firefighters must assess the type of system in operation and the location it is operating. This information can indicate the seat of the fire and target initial operations in the right location. Fire department standpipe systems should be charged as soon as possible to supplement the main water system and/or provide a delivery point of water for hoselines.

Access and Egress Challenges

Building construction features can be challenging to fire crews attempting to gain access or find an egress point. The size-up assessment should provide critical decision-making information about the access and egress points available. If appropriate egress points are unavailable, consideration should be given to a defensive operation. This assessment should also include consideration of the number and capabilities of equipment and resources available at a fire incident. Some incidents will require crew assignments specifically for ensuring interior crews have quick access and egress points. The ISO should independently assess the challenges of access and egress and ensure sufficient equipment and resource capabilities are available to fulfill this need. Some of the challenges include but are not limited to the following **(Figure 14.50)**:

- **Gates** – security gates can delay the response and entry of firefighters at the main street entrance. Preplanning with the facility is the best approach to ensuring quick access is feasible for crews.

- **Doors** – security doors, metal doors, metal locking mechanisms, or electronically controlled doors can be difficult to breach. Sometimes it may be easier to find another entry point than breaching heavily fortified doors.

- **Windows** – security bars can block the entry or escape of occupants and firefighters. Special metal cutters may be required to breach security bars.

- **Basements** – basements have the potential for being death traps for occupants and firefighters. Access is typically through the stairwell, with one other entry/exit point if not blocked.

The ISO should ensure a crew is assigned to soften access and egress points for fire crews when appropriate, especially at large structures when interior

---

Access and Egress Challenges

Figure 14.50 Any security features or access and egress challenges should be indicated on preincident surveys and updated when surveys are updated.

operations are still ongoing. All access and egress point openings need to be coordinated with interior fire suppression crews and ventilation operations to ensure operations are not inadvertently compromised.

Access

Access into a structure is typically through the main or front entrance. This entry point is usually the easiest for first-in crews to begin fire suppression activities. However, not all fire incidents are typical and routine. Alternate access points may be needed and depend on fire conditions and building construction features. Alternative points of access may need forcible entry with a crew specifically assigned for this purpose. Crews assigned to forcible entry need to have the equipment capabilities and personnel to overcome a variety of challenges, such as metal roll-up doors and security doors. The ISO should ensure the equipment and resources are sufficient to overcome access challenges and report this assessment to the IC.

Egress

Egress points from a structure are just as important as access points but may be more challenging to secure. All interior fire suppression crews should have an idea of various egress points prior to entering a structure. Alternative points of exit may have heavy metal doors and locking mechanisms or security bars that require significant effort to breach. Elevated operations on upper floors or roofs should have ladders in place for emergency egress. An exterior forcible entry crew should be assigned early in the incident and perform an independent assessment of the structure to provide quick egress for the interior operating crews if an emergency occurs. Alternate egress points should be communicated to all personnel operating on the scene. The ISO should ensure the egress points for interior crews are in the correct location and that all activities are achieved in a coordinated manner.

Green Construction

The use of alternate sources of fuel and power is a growing industry. Fire and emergency services personnel must stay informed on the changes in this industry and the special hazards they present. For example, the addition of solar panels and rooftop gardens limits or eliminates vertical ventilation as a tactical option. Fire and emergency services organizations must plan for this obstacle in the preincident planning stage and have alternate ventilation options established.

Preincident planning, site surveys, and incident size-ups must include an assessment of the presence of green technologies. Communication of the presence of a green technology must be communicated to all personnel operating at the scene.

Solar Panels

Fire and emergency services organizations should ensure personnel are trained on the identification of and hazards associated with solar power systems. They are becoming more common across the U.S., and they require special care during a fire event. Typically, solar panels will be found on rooftops or on top of parking shades. During the size-up of a structure fire or fire under or on a parking structure, personnel should determine if solar panels are present. If they are present, this information should be communicated to all personnel on the scene.

Thermal and photovoltaic (PV) are two types of solar power systems that fire and emergency personnel are most likely to encounter. These systems share many hazards, but are unique in that PV systems have battery shock hazards and a thermal system has a scalding hazard.

Some general fire suppression considerations include but are not limited to:

Lockout/Tagout Device — Device used to secure a machine's power switches, in order to prevent accidental re-start of the machine.

- Use a **lockout/tagout** device on all electrical shutoffs **(Figure 14.51)**

- Do not walk on or damage the solar panels

- Always consider the solar power system to be energized even if the panels are covered with salvage covers

- Treat the solar power system and panels as a Class C fire

- Remain alert for early roof collapse due to the extra weight of the panels

- Assume that vertical ventilation will not be possible due to solar panels affixed to roof structural components

- Include additional precautions against inhalation and electrical shock hazards

For more details on firefighter safety with solar systems, refer to the NFPA®'s report *Fire Fighter Safety and Emergency Response for Solar Power Systems*. In addition, Underwriter's Laboratory has information that can be found on its website.

Figure 14.51 Lockout/tagout devices can be applied to electrical shutoffs at a scene.

Roof gardens

Rooftop gardens can create hazardous conditions for interior fire fighting operations. Namely, the extra weight of these features can cause early roof collapse. Rooftop gardens also present special consideration for ventilation operations. Typical vertical ventilation will most likely not be possible. Additionally, because a rooftop garden is a vegetation-based covering, this feature adds potential fuel if the fire involves the roof structure.

Rooftop gardens are addressed in the International Code Council's (ICC) fire code, Section 317, *Rooftop Garden or Landscaped Roof Size* and International Building Code's, Chapter 15, *Roof Assemblies and Rooftop Structures*.

Construction, Renovation, and Demolition Hazards

For a variety of reasons, the risk of fire rises sharply when construction, renovation, or demolition is being performed in a structure. Contributing factors are the additional fuel loads and ignition sources (open flames from cutting torches and sparks from grinding or welding operations) that building contractors and their associated equipment bring **(Figure 14.52)**.

Some local fire codes mandate that standpipe systems must remain in operation during the demolition of multistory buildings. Unfortunately, contractors do not always adhere to these requirements. The result is that inoperative standpipes and sprinkler systems have become a contributing factor in fires in buildings under demolition.

Buildings under construction are subject to rapid fire spread when they are partially completed because many of the protective features, such as gypsum wallboard and automatic fire suppression systems, are not yet in place. The lack of doors or other barriers that would normally slow fire spread are also contributing factors to rapid fire growth.

Buildings that are being renovated, demolished, or are abandoned are also subject to faster-than-normal fire growth **(Figure 14.53, p. 522)**. Breached walls, open stairwells, missing doors, and deactivated fire suppression systems are potential contributors. The potential for a sudden building collapse during fires in these buildings is also a serious consideration. Arson is also a factor at construction or demolition sites because of easy access into the building.

Figure 14.52 Construction sites may have a high fuel load of exposed wood and other materials. *Courtesy of Ron Moore, McKinney (TX) Fire Department.*

Figure 14.53 Buildings that are being renovated or are abandoned are subject to faster than normal fire growth because the compartmentation of the building has been compromised.

Due to the cost of new construction, renovating old buildings is common in many areas. Hazardous situations may arise during renovation because occupants and their belongings may remain in one part of the building while work continues in another. Fire detection or alarm systems may be taken out of service or damaged during renovation. If good housekeeping is not maintained, accumulations of debris and construction materials can block exits. This debris may impede occupants trying to escape from the building in an emergency as well as making entry by firefighters more difficult.

Hotel Vendome Fire and Structural Collapse, 1972

In 1972, the Hotel Vendome in Boston, MA, caught fire. The fire quickly spread out of control, resulting in a firefighter response that used the vast majority of the resources in the surrounding area. During the incident, the structure collapsed catastrophically, resulting in many civilian casualties and the deaths of nine firefighters. An entire ladder truck was buried during the collapse.

The hotel was built in 1881 and later renovated a number of times. In 1890, a load-bearing wall was removed from the first and second story lobby area to create a larger entry space. The wall was replaced with cast-iron columns that were intended to carry the majority of building's load. From 1968-69, fires in the structure led the city to remove its license to function as a hotel. The building was undergoing renovations yet again in 1972 when it collapsed.

While the cause of the fire was never determined, the cause of the collapse was clear. The cast-iron columns in the lobby were insufficient to hold the building's load once exposure to heat weakened them. ISOs should pay attention to changes to older construction in preincident surveys. Renovations to structures can have a profound effect on how firefighters expect the fire to affect the building's materials.

Structural Collapse Indicators

Knowledge of building construction is important to help you recognize the potential for structural collapse. Unprotected structural members that have been exposed to high temperatures from fire and the increased weight from fire suppression activities can collapse with little or no warning. Knowing the construction material and how fire affects the materials will assist in the risk benefit analysis. This information is gathered as part of the preincident survey and on-scene size-up for building construction.

Figure 14.54 Wall collapse potential increases as the combustible wall materials are consumed. *Courtesy of Ed Prendergast.*

The stage of the fire can easily indicate the quantity of heat that the structure has been exposed to and the potential for structural collapse. Fires in the incipient stage will not have generated sufficient heat or flame to cause unprotected steel or wood frame construction to collapse. However, collapse potential increases in the growth stage as heat increases in the upper levels of the space and flame spreads to and consumes the combustible structural members **(Figure 14.54)**. In the decay stage and during post-suppression activities, collapse becomes likely due to the weakened state of structural members and the buildup of water.

Building contents, such things as stored materials, furniture, and machinery, also contribute to structural collapse. Like knowledge of the construction type, knowledge of the contents is gained through preincident surveys and inspections. The contents within a structure or stored in attics or on roofs may contribute to collapse in the following three ways:

- Adding to the fuel load in the building and generating higher temperatures and rapid combustion that will weaken the structure

- Adding weight to the weakened structural members, causing them to collapse more rapidly

- Retaining water, which increases their weight and applies more stress on structural members

While contents within a structure are visible during preincident surveys, storage in concealed spaces and attics of residences is not seen. Attic storage is often heavier than the ceiling joists have been designed to carry **(Figure 14.55, p. 524)**. When fire weakens the joists, storage weight increases the potential for ceiling joists to fail, putting firefighters at risk. Such storage is common in residential dwellings and has also been the cause of firefighter fatalities in industrial fires.

Finally, the quantity of water that is used to suppress the fire can have a direct effect on structural stability. Every gallon (4 liters) of water that is used to suppress the fire adds approximately 8 pounds (4 kilograms) of weight to floors that may already be weakened. The added weight may cause floors to pancake down or push walls out, resulting in a complete failure of the structure. As an estimate, 250 gpm (1,000 L/min) of water adds 1 ton (1 T) of weight per minute to the structure.

Figure 14.55 Attic storage adds to the fuel load and the collapse potential of the ceiling as joists weaken under fire conditions. The weight of items stored in an attic may also exceed the rated weight of the ceiling joists.

Besides the factors listed above, indicators of potential or imminent collapse include:

- Roof sagging, pulling away from parapet walls, or feeling spongy (soft) under foot **(Figure 14.56)**
- Floors sagging or feeling spongy (soft) under foot
- Chunks of ceiling tiles or plaster falling from above
- Movement in the roof, walls, or floors
- Noises caused by structural movement
- Little or no water runoff from the interior of the structure
- Cracks appearing in exterior walls with smoke or water appearing through the cracks
- Evidence of existing structural instability, such as the presence of tie rods and stars that hold walls together

- Loose bricks, blocks, or stones falling from buildings
- Deteriorated mortar between the masonry **(Figure 14.57)**
- Walls that appear to be leaning
- Structural members that appear to be distorted
- Fires beneath floors that support heavy machinery or other extreme weight loads
- Prolonged fire exposure to the structural members, especially trusses
- Structural members pulling away from walls
- Excessive weight of building contents

Figure 14.56 Roofs may sag as they weaken during a fire. *Courtesy of Jeff Fortney.*

Figure 14.57 Deteriorated mortar is an indication of a weakened wall that is more susceptible to collapse.

Heat release rates in modern structures or structures with modern furnishings may be high enough to cause steel joists or wooden trusses to fail in a short amount of time. However, time is only one indicator of structural collapse and often not the most reliable. Collapse of structures using lightweight construction can occur earlier in the incident and may not provide you with the warning indicators listed above. A thorough preincident survey and size-up of the incident scene will provide you with some indication of the presence of lightweight construction.

Utility Hazards

Assessing utility hazards at an incident is not a complex task, but does require attentiveness. Utilities include all electrical, gas, and water service to a location. These services can be located above or below ground. Main service disconnects are usually identifiable but not always easily found. Preincident planning can make this process simple if disconnects are identified and indicated on a site map. Additionally, any supplemental utility services, such as generator or fuel cell power sources, should also be identified during preincident planning.

Building Utility Component Assemblies

Building utilities will typically have similar components at the main shutoff point. Residential and commercial locations will have differing sized utility services and may not look the same. Not all locations will have municipal utility service, so each location must be assessed for actual utility service presence. The main utility components covered will be electrical, natural gas, and water services.

Electricity Component Assemblies

Electrical service can be above or below ground from the main feeder line. The electrical service will enter through a main service point where the main shutoff is located **(Figure 14.58)**. When necessary, the main shutoff should be used to isolate the power to the location and not the individual circuit breakers. Lockout/tagout devices should be utilized when operations require it.

In addition to the main power source, all locations should be assessed for alternate sources of power. These alternate sources include generators, solar power, and/or wind power, and they may automatically turn on when the main power is turned off. Personnel should ensure that all sources of power are isolated at the main disconnect as soon as possible.

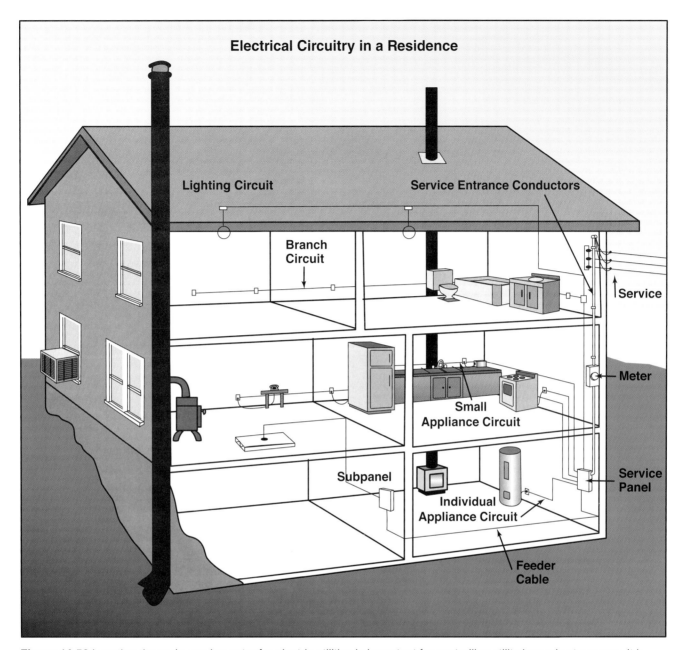

Figure 14.58 Locating the main service entry for electric utilities is important for controlling utility hazards at a scene. It is also useful to have a basic knowledge of structure circuitry.

Natural Gas Component Assemblies

Natural gas is not available in all locations, but should be identified when present. Residential gas service is usually located near the main electrical service point of entry. When turning off the main gas service, personnel can use a spanner wrench to manipulate the quarter-turn valve. Personnel should also ensure a secondary source of gas, such as propane, is not located on the property.

Water Systems Component Assemblies

Water can be supplied by a water company, a well system, an elevated storage tank system, or a combination of these. Personnel should determine if the water system needs to be isolated. During fire suppression activities, the water system should remain on to ensure water is available for the fire suppression system. However, after the fire has been extinguished, the water should be turned off if a water line break exists. In most cases, the water system is left on.

Common Utility Gases

Utility gas comes in two forms: natural gas and propane. Both forms are considered safe under normal conditions; however, when leaks or a transportation accident occurs, fire and emergency services personnel must work with the utility company to stabilize the incident. The ISO should be knowledgeable of the properties of these gases and the hazards associated with them. The ISO must monitor the scene for changing conditions or situations in which crews begin to operate in an unsafe location.

Natural Gas (Methane-Based)

Natural gas can be used in heating and cooling systems, for cooking, and in vehicles. It is transported via underground gas lines, railcar, or tanker trucks. Natural gas is used in industry, commercial, and residential properties. Natural gas is an odorless gas that is lighter than air. In order to detect the presence of natural gas, gas utilities use an additive called mercaptan to give it its distinctive rotten egg odor. Natural gas is a safe energy source when maintained within its storage system. When released, natural gas is flammable and can be explosive under the right conditions. Any fire department response to a suspected natural gas leak should include assistance from the gas utility. Gas utility employees have the necessary training, equipment, and resources to detect, isolate, and repair any natural gas leak. If natural gas is leaking from an underground line, fire crews should use a fog stream to disperse the concentration of gas at the site and reduce the chance of an explosion.

CAUTION
The ground may "scrub" the mercaptan odor from natural gas as it travels through the ground. As a result, odor alone is not always an accurate detector of gas leaks.

Propane

Liquid petroleum gas (LPG), commonly called propane, is stored in pressurized tanks on property where natural gas is unavailable. Propane, an odorless gas that is heavier than air, is transported by railcar and tanker truck. In order to detect the presence of propane, the propane industry uses an additive called ethyl mercaptan to give the gas a distinct odor. Like natural gas, propane is a safe energy source when maintained within its storage system. When released, propane is flammable and can be explosive under the right conditions. Any fire department response to a reported propane leak should include notification of the responsible propane company that services the specific location. Propane company employees have the necessary training, equipment and resources to detect, isolate, and repair any leaks.

Propane tanks exposed to direct flame contact pose an extreme risk to fire and emergency services personnel. When sufficiently heated, propane tanks will explode, sending shrapnel great distances. This occurrence is commonly referred to as a **boiling liquid expanding vapor explosion (BLEVE)** **(Figure 14.59)**. Fire suppression crews may set up water monitors that do not require constant attendance.

Pressurized Vessels

Pressurized vessels holding gases and liquids in industrial operations are common and include many different products. However, in the utility realm, pressurized vessels are used to produce steam and heat in the form of boiler units. OSHA defines a pressurized vessel as one which operates above 15 pounds per square inch gauge (psig) (approximately 200 kPa).

Emergencies involving pressure vessels require special care. Responders should not attempt to isolate operations of the pressure vessel system without specific training on proper procedures. Responders should obtain assistance from facility maintenance personnel to ensure unintended consequences do not result.

Common Electrical Grid Arrangements

Electrical service to an area can be serviced from more than one direction. The electrical grid is established similarly to a municipal water system. A single point in the system can be fed from two or more feeder lines. Fire and emergency personnel should rely on the electrical utility company to provide technical information about the specific power grid supply when necessary **(Figure 14.60, p. 530)**. Fire personnel should never come in contact with any down power lines, with or without power. Electrical utility personnel should move all lines.

Boiling Liquid Expanding Vapor Explosion (BLEVE) — Rapid vaporization of a liquid stored under pressure upon release to the atmosphere following major failure of its containing vessel. Failure is the result of over-pressurization caused by an external heat source, which causes the vessel to explode into two or more pieces when the temperature of the liquid is well above its boiling point at normal atmospheric pressure.

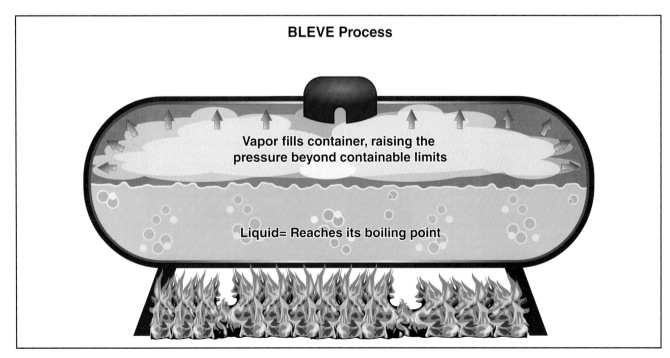

BLEVE Process

Vapor fills container, raising the pressure beyond containable limits

Liquid= Reaches its boiling point

Figure 14.59 There is a danger of BLEVE whenever pressurized containers are exposed to heat during an incident, even if the contents of the container are not flammable.

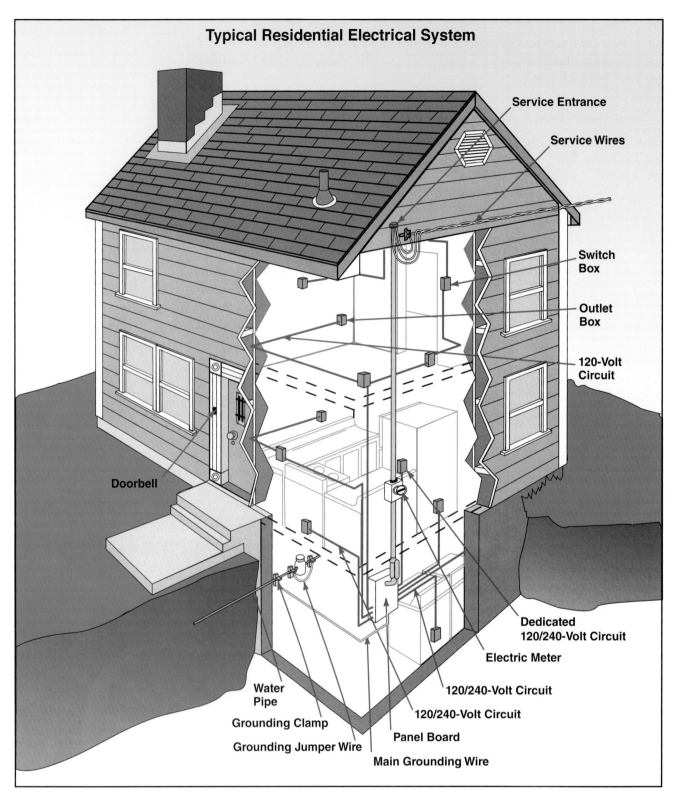

Figure 14.60 The utility company can provide the exact specifications of a structure's electrical system; however, some basic knowledge is often useful when identifying hazards at a scene.

Assistance from Utility Companies or Agencies

Fire and emergency services organizations should establish and maintain positive relationships with all local utility companies. The dispatch SOP/Gs should outline utility company notification for any incident that may require a utility service to be secured. The ISO should ensure an escort is provided to the utility company technician to ensure accountability and communications are maintained. The escort can then report directly to the IC when the utility service has been secured.

Wildland and Vegetation Fire Development

The boundary between wildland areas and residential growth has become known as a wildland urban interface (WUI). This interface has continued to expand over the years with catastrophic fires destroying neighborhoods and communities. Fire and emergency services organizations must assess their community risk with a WUI. The risk management plan should identify the WUI areas within the community, the departmental response, and resources needed to mitigate a fire event. The risk management plan should also identify potential wildland spread, starting from nearby wildland areas and affecting the local the community. Wildland fire behavior is a specialized field of study. All fire fighting personnel with the potential for wildland response should seek formal training resulting in National Wildfire Coordinating Group (NWCG) *red card* certification. Some agencies will require personnel to be *red card* certified before being assigned fire fighting duties in a wildland fire event. This certification request will include all command personnel as well as fire-fighting personnel. For more detailed information on wildland training or the red card certification, refer to the National Wildland Coordinating Group.

10 Standard Fire Fighting Orders[1,2]

1. Keep informed on fire weather conditions and forecasts.
2. Know what your fire is doing at all times.
3. Base all actions on current and expected behavior of the fire.
4. Identify escape routes and safety zones and make them known.
5. Post lookouts when there is possible danger.
6. Be alert. Keep calm. Think clearly. Act decisively.
7. Maintain prompt communications with your forces, your supervisor, and adjoining forces.
8. Give clear instructions and ensure that they are understood.
9. Maintain control of your forces at all times.
10. Fight fire aggressively, having provided for safety first.

18 Watch Out Situations[1,2]

The 18 watch out situations were developed to provide more specific situations to monitor. Remaining alert to these situations should reduce risks to firefighters from wildland fires.

1. Fire not scouted and sized up.
2. In country not seen in daylight.
3. Safety zones and escape routes not identified.
4. Unfamiliar with weather and local factors influencing fire behavior.

5. Uninformed on strategy, tactics, and hazards.

6. Instructions and assignments not clear.

7. No communication link with crewmembers/supervisors.

8. Constructing line without safe anchor point.

9. Building fireline downhill with fire below.

10. Attempting frontal assault on fire.

11. Unburned fuel between you and the fire.

12. Cannot see main fire, not in contact with anyone who can.

13. On a hillside where rolling material can ignite fuel below.

14. Weather is getting hotter and drier.

15. Wind increases and/or changes direction.

16. Getting frequent spot fires across the file line.

17. Terrain and fuels make escape to safety zones difficult.

18. Taking a nap near the fire line.

Types of Wildland Fuels

Wildland fuels have been referred to as ground or aerial fuels, or more recently as horizontal or vertical fuels. Each type of fuel presents unique fire behavior hazards that must be assessed. Ground fuels are generally low growing or downed vegetation. Light ground fuel fires can be easily extinguished, but heavy ground fuel fires can require extensive fire suppression activities. Aerial fuels are generally trees. Fire can grow and spread rapidly through the upper portions of trees in what are known as *crowning fires*. Horizontal and vertical wildland fuels are described with regards to their primary growth direction. Horizontal fires will move along the ground, whereas vertical fires have upward growth potential.

Firefighters must recognize the fuel type in a wildland fire. Firefighters must be able to predict the fire behavior and growth potential. Early recognition of these factors along with weather, topography, resource needs, and the establishment of a safety zone are essential. The ISO will assess these factors independently and ensure that fire fighting crews are operating in a safe location.

Topography Effects

Topography can significantly influence fire behavior. Fire fighting crews must assess topographical features and predict what effect it will have on fire growth. Topographical features can be used to their advantage when determining fire suppression activities and for identifying escape routes and safe zones. Some basic terms associated with topography include:

- **Aspect** — indicates the side (north, south, east, or west) of a hill or mountain.

- **Slope** — indicates the steepness of a portion of the hill or mountain. The steeper the slope, the faster the fire spread uphill **(Figure 14.61)**.

- **Terrain** — used to generally define the landscape of an area.

- **Box or narrow canyons** — these terrain features are especially dangerous. Fires in these areas can spread quickly, create increased up-slope winds, and lead to blow-ups.

- **Wide canyons** — can provide an avenue for shifting wind patterns.

- **Ridges and saddles** — terrain features that describe the formation on the top of a hill or mountain.

- **Elevation** — as elevation increases, natural fuel load will decrease.

- **Barriers** — landscape or man-made features that can provide natural fire breaks.

Figure 14.61 Wildfires spread more quickly uphill than downhill – the steeper the slope, the faster the fire will spread. *Courtesy of the California Office of Emergency Services.*

Weather and Wind Effects

Weather and wind play a significant role in wildland fire behavior. In hot and dry conditions, vegetation will have little moisture content and ignite easily, which will cause rapid fire growth even with low winds **(Figure 14.62, p. 534)**. Hot and dry conditions can also affect the efficiency of fire fighting crews. Personnel must be cognizant of heat-related illness and dehydration within their crew. Crews may have to carry extra water and implement work/rest cycles to combat the effects of the heat. High winds can push a wildland fire quickly, referred to as *wind driven fires*. Winds can also be erratic and/or shift directions without warning. Fire crews must be knowledgeable in how changing weather conditions can rapidly change the strength and direction of the wind.

Weather and wind conditions should be assessed prior to initiating wildland fire suppression activities. Fire crews must be able to assess these conditions and determine the proper approach to a wildland fire and the predicted growth direction and speed. If the weather and/or wind conditions are too severe, fire suppression activities may have to be suspended.

Figure 14.62 Extremely dry conditions and/or high winds increase the speed with which wildfires spread.

Predicting Wildland Fire Growth

Wildland fire growth can be predicted with relative accuracy. Overall, fire personnel will assess the location of the fire, the topography of the area, the weather conditions, the amount of fuel available, and the fuel types involved. Additionally, personnel must assess the fire's behavior. Several indicators of fire behavior include the length of the flame, any blow-ups, and any flaring.

Flame Length

Flame length will provide some indication on how much fuel and the type of fuel involved in a wildland fire. A taller or longer flame length will indicate a more vertical vegetation and higher fuel load, such as trees. Contrastingly, ground fuels or low growth vegetation will have limited flame length potential, such as grass and shrubbery.

Blowups

A **blowup** is a rapid fire growth that can be extremely dangerous. A seemingly tranquil wildland fire can become a raging inferno in a matter of seconds. Weather, wind, fuel, and topography play a part in the blowup potential. Fire crews must continually assess this potential and predict its occurrence. Crews should be evacuated from a potential blowup area well in advance of this event.

Flaring

Flaring is a short-lived, high intensity fire in a small area. Fire crews must be alert when flaring occurs, but do not typically have to alter their incident action plan. Flaring can cause *spot fires* and be a good indicator of the potential for a blowup. Flaring can provide an indication of the moisture content of the fuels. As a result, flaring should not be ignored.

Blowup — Sudden, dangerously rapid increase in fireline intensity at a wildland fire; caused by any one or more of several factors, such as strong or erratic wind, steep uphill slopes, large open areas, and easily ignited fuels. Blowup is sufficient to preclude direct attack or to change the incident action plan; often accompanied by violent convection and may have other characteristics of a firestorm.

Flaring — Short-lived, high intensity fire in a small area at a wildland fire.

Vehicle Incident and Apparatus Placement Hazards

Fire and emergency services personnel have continued to incur injuries and fatalities while operating on or near roadways. Fire and emergency services organizations must establish SOP/Gs for guidelines on how to properly protect a scene and the personnel operating at the scene. NFPA® 1500 Section 8.7, *Standard on Fire Department Occupational Safety and Health Program,* provides criteria for traffic incidents. This standard can be adapted for any incident on or near a roadway for proper scene protection.

Vehicle Incident Hazards

Vehicle construction materials and design features are incident considerations that will alter how personnel perform their duties at collisions and/or fire events. All vehicle incident events require a scene assessment to determine which of the following hazards exists, but also any changing conditions that may affect the safety of responders or occupants. The use of protective clothing and equipment must be considered depending on the type and complexity of the incident and comply with minimum best practice standards.

Traffic

Traffic-related incidents require planning. SOP/Gs should outline proper scene control with signage, retroreflective cones, and apparatus placement. Additionally, it is crucial to have a traffic incident preplan with law enforcement. Scene operations between law enforcement and fire and emergency services personnel must be coordinated in advance to help avoid disagreements in traffic incident scene safety between them.

Utilizing the MUTCD and TIMS from the U.S. Department of Transportation is an excellent tool in coordinating a traffic incident preplan. NFPA® 1500 also provides traffic safety guidelines that are specific to fire department response to traffic incidents. For example, the first-arriving company should position its apparatus upstream of the incident as one component of a safe work zone. Advanced warning devices are intended to slow traffic well before the traffic arrives at the safe work zone. The position of advanced warning devices should take into account several factors, such as weather, day/night, topography, and roadway speed **(Figure 14.63, p. 536)**. Personnel can then safely assess the incident scene and determine the next course of action. The ISO should assess the apparatus placement and safe work zone to determine if any changes are needed. Incidents can change and become larger or smaller. Apparatus placement and the safe working zone should change with the incident to ensure only the needed space is utilized. Any traffic reduction or diversion creates additional hazards that should be considered. This is a crucial assessment for the ISO. The ISO should communicate with the IC on this condition and report any recommendations to improve traffic flow without compromising scene safety. Local SOP/Gs and district surveys may provide additional guidance about creating safe work areas and diverting traffic on roadways within the jurisdiction.

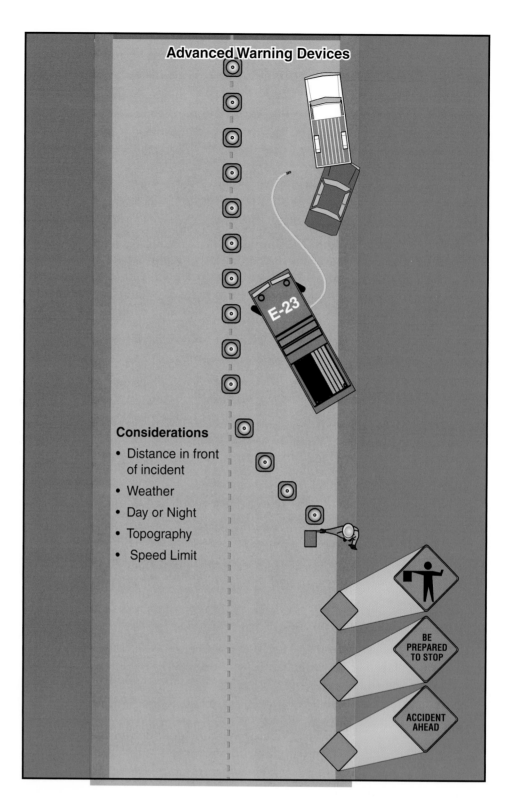

Advanced Warning Devices

Considerations
- Distance in front of incident
- Weather
- Day or Night
- Topography
- Speed Limit

E-23

BE PREPARED TO STOP

ACCIDENT AHEAD

Figure 14.63 Certain considerations should be accounted for when placing advanced warning devices.

Flammable and Combustible Liquids

Any fluid leaking from a vehicle creates a hazard. Fire is the most significant hazard, but fluids create a potential fall hazard. Inhalation and skin burns are also hazards that should be considered. All leaking fluids should be isolated and protected to prevent a fire and/or injury. A vapor suppressant can be applied to gasoline or diesel to reduce the risk of fire. An absorbent material can be applied to any leaking liquid to reduce the risk of falls, but also to isolate the spill area. Any extrication operation should have at least one protective precharged hoseline readily available in the event of a fire.

Combustible Metals

Exotic, or Class D metals, such as magnesium, titanium, and lithium used in vehicles, are difficult to extinguish when on fire. Direct water application to a burning exotic metal can create a spectacular reaction, at times with explosive results **(Figure 14.64)**. It can also endanger personnel operating nearby. Combustible metals are categorized differently and have differing extinguishment recommendations. If the correct extinguishing agent is unavailable for a specific combustible metal, the best course of action is to let it burn itself out.

Figure 14.64 Applying water to combustible metals generally makes an incident more hazardous and is more likely to spread the fire than extinguish it.

Extrication Hazards

Vehicle extrication has become technically advanced. New vehicle technology requires familiarity of unique vehicle design features before conducting extrication or cutting into vehicle components. New electrical systems and alternative fuel systems need to be identified and precautions taken before initiating extrication procedures. There are, however, some common hazards that should be assessed and controlled when present:

- **Automotive fluid leaks** — flammable and combustible fluids must be controlled or isolated during extrication activities.

- **Vehicle stabilization** — this can include a variety of vehicle positions, such as vehicle on its side or top **(Figure 14.65, p. 538)**, vehicle suspended off a bridge or other object, or vehicle on a steep embankment or cliff.

- **Sharp objects** — broken glass and metal edges create a hazard for responders and victims.

- **Airbags** — airbags can be dangerous to personnel. During extrication activities, personnel should never be located within striking distance of a non-deployed airbag. Extrication tactics must consider airbags and the associated components because of their explosive discharge capability. Airbags can be located throughout a vehicle and care must be taken to identify hidden components, such as in the door post, before cutting or spreading tools are used **(Figure 14.66)**.

- **Bumpers** — Bumpers have shock absorbing capability. However, newer bumpers are light-weight plastic and Styrofoam-based and will not support a load. Under fire conditions, bumpers can become airborne projectiles.

Figure 14.65 Vehicle stabilization, regardless of the vehicle's orientation, is a necessary safety step before extrication operations can begin.

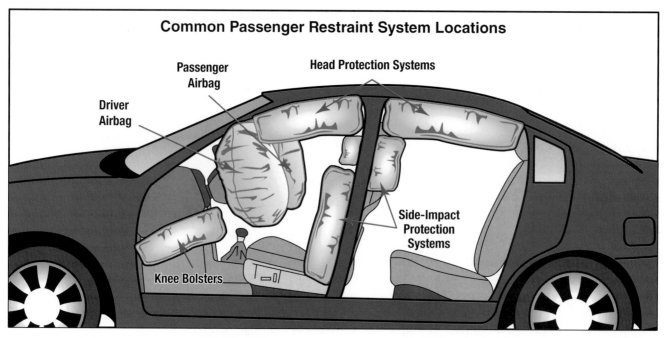

Figure 14.66 ISOs should know the common location of airbags on passenger vehicles. Undeployed airbags present a hazard to responders performing extrication operations.

Electrical Systems

Hybrid vehicles have a variety of battery systems with different voltage and current capacities. The ISO should ensure that the hybrid vehicle high-voltage system is isolated according to manufacturer recommendations **(Figure 14.67)**. Supplemental restraint systems may have stored energy capacity for various periods of time after the battery system has been isolated. Fire and emergency service organizations should obtain computer software or other printed material outlining the presence and general location of battery components and wiring. Specifically, the location of the main batteries and any color-coded wiring should be identified. Orange wiring was universally used in hybrid vehicles to identify high voltage; however, newer models will have multiple color-coding in the wiring system.

Hybrid or electric vehicles are virtually silent. Firefighters should ensure these vehicles are placed in park and turned off, even if they cannot hear the vehicle running.

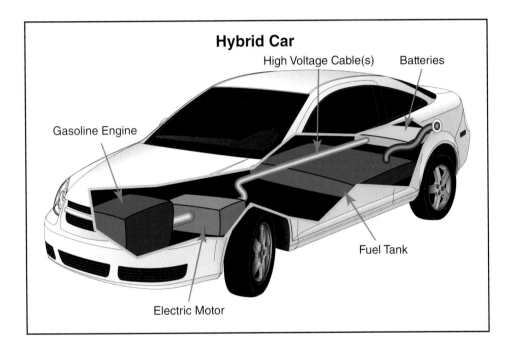

Hybrid Car

High Voltage Cable(s)   Batteries

Gasoline Engine

Fuel Tank

Electric Motor

Figure 14.67 The electrical systems in hybrid and electric vehicles should be isolated as a safety precaution at vehicle incidents where hybrid or electric cars are involved.

Alternative Fuels

Alternative fuel vehicles are gaining popularity but are not common place in the U.S. so far. Alternative fuel-powered vehicles use hydrogen, liquid natural gas (LNG), or liquid petroleum gas (LPG). These fuels are stored as compressed gases in tanks that may be visible to responders. Other possible but rarely found fuels are alcohol-based racing fuel and vegetable oil. During the incident size-up, personnel should determine the type of fuel used in a vehicle. Consideration of these fuels must be taken into account when extrication or fire suppression activities are required.

Apparatus Placement Hazards

Apparatus placement at emergency incidents is dictated by the specific circumstances of the incident and the surrounding environment. However, company officers and apparatus driver/operators must be trained in the general guidelines for safe and effective apparatus placement. These guidelines may be in the department's SOP/Gs manual or in the incident management plan. The HSO must participate in the development of these policies and plans to ensure a safe working environment.

Proximity to Exposures

If the fire has the potential to threaten exposures, the apparatus should be positioned so the fire streams can be deployed to protect those exposures. In some cases, it will be necessary to sacrifice the original fire building in order to save severely threatened exposures. This practice is a strategic decision that the IC makes.

When considering exposures, personnel should remember that we bring our own potential exposure with us: the apparatus itself. Avoid positioning the apparatus in a location that subjects it to high levels of radiant heat, falling embers, or others products of combustion. Any position that requires wetting the apparatus to prevent damage is not a good position.

Backing Procedures

Backing fire apparatus can be a hazardous action because of the vehicle's size and the mirrors do not provide a full view around the apparatus. While conducting emergency operations or during routine driving, fire apparatus must often be backed into or out of position. In addition, apparatus may be backed into the station. Backing accidents generally account for a significant percentage of all damage repair costs. Although most injuries sustained in these collisions are minor, fatalities have occurred during backing accidents. Proper backing techniques can eliminate these accidents **(Figure 14.68)**.

All jurisdictions should develop a policy for backing apparatus. Always follow SOP/Gs and local ordinances for backing procedures. Fire service best practices for backing apparatus include the following:

- If possible, position the apparatus so that backing will be unnecessary.
- Walk all the way around the apparatus to clear any obstructions.
- Ensure that all equipment is secured and compartment doors are closed.
- Require the use of one or more spotters.
- Preposition lights to illuminate the area where the spotter will stand (approximately 8 to 10 feet [2.5 to 3 m] behind the apparatus)
- Back the apparatus at a slow speed and use caution to not outpace the spotter(s).
- Use hand signals that are agreed upon and understood by the spotter and driver/operator.
- Use portable radios, if feasible.
- Use backup cameras in addition to the mirrors, if the apparatus is so equipped.
- Sound two short blasts of the vehicle's horn immediately before backing the apparatus.
- Avoid mounting equipment on the apparatus that may interfere with the driver's rear visibility.

All apparatus should be equipped with a backup warning alarm. Driver/operators should continue to exercise caution, though, because members

Figure 14.68 Spotters and proper backing techniques should be used at all incidents. *Courtesy of Ron Jeffers.*

may not be able to hear the backup alarm when operating at the scene of an emergency.

Some apparatus are equipped with backup cameras that also act as recorders. These devices provide a limited view of the area behind the apparatus. The in-cab monitors are somewhat limited by screen size as well as environmental factors. To safely back the fire apparatus, driver/operators should use all means at their disposal, including scanning between their direct field of vision, video screens, and spotters.

> **CAUTION**
> The driver/operator must not rely solely on backup cameras to provide a full and accurate view of the scene. Spotters are still required.

Wind Direction

Attempt to position the apparatus upwind of an incident whenever possible **(Figure 14.69, p. 542)**. This positioning may negate the need for the driver/operator to wear SCBA while operating the vehicle and reduce the possibility of the apparatus becoming an exposure if fire conditions worsen.

Terrain

Try to park apparatus on hard surfaces whenever practical. This practice will eliminate the chance of getting stuck in an unpaved area. In cold weather climates, a buildup of ice and snow before or during an incident should be considered relevant to apparatus safety. When operating at an incident involving hazardous or flammable liquids, an uphill position eliminates the chance of a hazardous liquid flowing underneath the apparatus. Similarly, at vehicle

Figure 14.69 Apparatus should be positioned upwind of an incident if possible. At the above incident, the smoke is moving away from the photographer who was standing near the apparatus.

fires, an uphill position will protect the apparatus from burning fuel that may leak from the vehicle. One exception to the uphill rule involves wildland fires. Apparatus and personnel should be downhill of the main body of fire as wildland fires move uphill faster than on flat terrain or downhill.

Placement to Divert Traffic at Nonvehicular Incidents

For incident control to be achieved efficiently and safely, driver/operators must position apparatus so that its use is maximized. Proper positioning of the apparatus provides a safety barrier that protects the scene, victims, and emergency personnel. Proper positioning also provides a protected work area. When positioning apparatus, driver/operators must allow for adequate parking of additional fire department apparatus. Driver/operators must allow enough distance to prevent a moving vehicle from striking and forcing fire apparatus into the work area. Where possible, driver/operators should position apparatus at a 45-degree angle into the curb. This practice helps to direct motorists around the scene. At intersections or where the incident may be near the middle of the street, two or more sides of the incident may need to be protected. All exposed sides should be blocked if possible.

During pump operation, the pump panel should be positioned at curbside if that position protects the pump panel operator from oncoming traffic. If it does not, the apparatus should be positioned so that the pump panel operator is in a downstream position with the apparatus protecting him or her from traffic. When laying hose and positioning at a water source, the driver/operator must take the necessary steps to warn motorists of these operations. The IC and or ISO must perform a continuous risk assessment of the scene to ensure the safest working environment possible for firefighters.

Control Zone Hazards

For safety considerations, the driver/operator must not position the apparatus under overhead power lines, too close to a potential structural collapse/fire spread, or in the access or egress path of other apparatus. The HSO should establish a policy that requires the driver/operator to chock the apparatus wheels when the vehicle is parked at the incident scene.

Driver/operator training must also address weight limitations of roadbeds, bridges, or parking structures and incident traffic. Equipment carried in the cab area must be secured as well. Most importantly, the driver/operator must ensure that all persons on the apparatus are seated and belted. Visual warning devices must be turned off while returning to quarters.

Should the company receive an alarm while en route from an incident, the officer must take the necessary steps to ensure that the firefighters can safely and properly dress for the type of incident. This situation may require the driver/operator to stop and pull off the road to allow all members to put on the proper protective equipment needed, then be seated and belted.

Chapter Summary

Incident hazard recognition is a critical skill for the ISO. The ISO must have the experience and training to recognize a multitude of hazards in an all-hazards environment, including structural fires, wildland fires, and vehicle incidents. The ISO should also be familiar with building construction features that can affect fire behavior and fire fighting tactics. ISOs should continue to seek out training opportunities to further their knowledge and maintain a well-rounded ability to protect other responders.

Review Questions

1. What types of environmental and physiological hazards could a responder face at an emergency incident? (pp. 462 -466)

2. What factors affect compartmental fire development? (pp. 467-474)

3. How can the incident safety officer use knowledge of the four fire development stages to assess conditions at a structure fire? (pp. 474-481)

4. What are the conditions that result in rapid fire development? (pp. 481-486)

5. How can firefighters influence fire behavior? (pp. 486-491)

6. What indicators can help the incident safety officer "read a fire"? (pp. 491-498)

7. What hazards are associated with building construction classifications? (pp. 498-505)

8. How can fire behavior be affected by a building's construction materials? (pp. 506-518)

9. What challenges may fire personnel face when attempting to gain access or find egress points in a structure? (pp. 518-519)

10. What hazards does green construction present to firefighters at an emergency scene? (pp. 519-521)

11. What hazards are possible when construction, renovation, or demolition are being performed in a structure? (pp. 521-522)

12. What are some structural collapse indicators? (pp. 523-526)

13. What should the incident safety officer look for when assessing utility hazards? (pp. 526-531)

14. How can the incident safety officer assess and predict wildland and vegetation fire development? (pp. 531-534)

15. What types of hazards are present at vehicle incidents? (pp. 535-539)

16. What procedures should be followed when placing apparatus at an emergency scene? (pp. 539-543)

Chapter 14 End Notes

1. Quoted from the United States Fire and Aviation Management website, www.fs.fed.us

2. Quoted from the United States National Park Service website at www.nps.gov

Refer to Appendix B: Learning Activity Answers in the back of this manual for suggested responses.

Purpose

Each type of incident will have hazards that must be identified during size-up and throughout the incident operation. The ISO's key responsibility is to recognize incident hazards and make corrective recommendations to prevent injuries to responders.

Directions

1. Review the Rhoads Building Scenario, first presented in **Learning Activity 13-1**. For convenience, the scenario has been reprinted below.

2. As you read the scenario, focus on *hazard identification*. Make sure that you consider:

   • Environmental and Physiological Hazards

   • Structure Fire Development Hazards

   • Building Construction Hazards

   • Utility Hazards

   • Apparatus Placement Hazards

   NOTE: You will have to make some educated guesses about some of the hazards presented in the scenario. For instance, you may not know the specific type of building construction, but you do know that it is an older apartment building, which suggests the building may be Type III construction.

3. Make a list or table of hazards as you identify them.

Rhoads Building Scenario

9:26 a.m. – The St. Florian Fire Department receives a call reporting the collapse of a five-story apartment structure known as the Rhoads Building on the west side of town. For the past week, the area has been receiving heavy snowfalls, averaging accumulations of 2 inches (50 mm) a day. The snow has created dangerous conditions all over town, but particularly to the west where many of the streets are narrow and full of dead-ends and potholes.

Built in 1943, the Rhoads Building is a condemned structure that's well known for sheltering numerous squatters and homeless people. The structure sits on a large weedy lot bordered by four narrow streets, and without address markings it's difficult to tell which side of the building is the front entrance.

The caller has reported that the heavy snow was the apparent reason for the collapse. Also, a 55-gallon barrel had been seen inside the structure and was apparently being used to contain a fire. Not only did the caller witness the building's collapse, but he also witnessed a fire begin to build at the center of the structure where the barrel tipped over.

LEARNING ACTIVITIES

14-1 (cont.)
Practice identifying hazards at an emergency operation.

Refer to Appendix B: Learning Activity Answers in the back of this manual for suggested responses.

9:39 a.m. – The fire department arrives at the collapsed structure with a total of nine personnel:

- One Engine Company of three responders
- One Ladder Company of four responders
- A battalion chief serving as Incident Commander
- You are serving as Incident Safety Officer.

Upon arrival, you and the IC observe that a good portion of the Rhoads Building has "pancake"-collapsed under the weight of the snow. You also observe that the reported fire has broken through the center of the building, the flames reaching heights of up to 50 feet (15 m) and producing thick, black columns of smoke. There are no victims immediately visible in the rubble. The IC assigns the Ladder Company to position the aerial apparatus along the southwest corner of the structure's Alpha side. The IC also orders you to assist the Ladder Company in backing up the aerial apparatus. Meanwhile, the IC takes two personnel from the Engine company to the building's Charlie and Delta sides to continue size-up. The Engine Company's driver-operator parks the pumping apparatus on the Alpha side's southeast corner and awaits orders.

9:47 a.m. – While attempting to record personnel positions for accountability, you hear a command from the IC on your radio, but the communication is too garbled to understand. You ask for a repeat of the command but receive no response. The Engine company driver-operator offers to walk around back to retrieve the IC, but you tell him to assist as spotter for the repositioning of the aerial apparatus, which is having a hard time in the snowy, constricted street, especially with so many power lines crossing overhead.

9:49 a.m. – The IC returns to the Alpha side of the structure alone, having ordered the two Engine company responders to stay around back, make entry, and search for survivors. He reports that victims may be trapped at the rear of the structure and orders you to make a call for Mutual Aid from a neighboring county department. Meanwhile, the Ladder company has successfully repositioned the apparatus and is awaiting further orders. The IC directs the Ladder company to begin an indirect attack on the fire from the Bravo side using an elevated master stream.

9:51 a.m. – You make the call for Mutual Aid and receive a response that one additional Ladder company of four firefighters will be responding. You then notify the IC that the incident is large enough to require a written incident action plan, but the IC informs you there is no time for a written plan. He orders all commands to be verbally communicated. You decide the IC is wrong and that it would be best to proceed without the IC's permission and develop a written tactical worksheet to keep the incident focused and organized. The IC informs you he is going back around to the rear of the building – which he is now referring to as "the Alpha side" – to assist the two responders in their search. He directs you to monitor the progress of the Ladder Company's indirect attack on the fire.

Refer to Appendix B: Learning Activity Answers in the back of this manual for suggested responses.

9:53 a.m. –While developing your tactical worksheet, you note that because the building is in such disrepair, the front entrance is not obvious and confusion has set in over which side is Alpha. You also document the earlier problem with the radio communication. After taking a few more notes on observed safety hazards, you join the Ladder company and assist in the attack operations. The fire inside the structure appears to intensify.

10:17 a.m. – During the fire attack, you hear a muddled transmission on your radio and realize the IC is communicating actively with Mutual Aid, who has just arrived at the rear of the Rhoads Building on the opposite street. You walk to the rear of the structure and see that the IC has already allocated two respective teams of Mutual Aid – the first assisting with victim search, the second standing by as RIC for the search operation. At this point you realize that more than ten responders are now on scene and that you do not have accurate accountability.

Incident Responsibilities

Key Terms

NFPA® Job Performance Requirements

This chapter provides information that addresses the following job performance requirements of NFPA® 1521, *Standard for Fire Department Safety Officer Professional Qualifications (2015).*

5.2.1	5.2.9	5.2.14	5.4.1	5.5.3
5.2.2	5.2.10	5.3.1	5.4.2	5.5.4
5.2.3	5.2.11	5.3.2	5.4.3	
5.2.6	5.2.12	5.3.3	5.5.1	
5.2.7	5.2.13	5.3.5	5.5.2	

Learning Objectives

After reading this chapter, students will be able to:

1. Describe the role of the incident safety officer in communicating scene hazards. (5.2.1, 5.2.3, 5.2.13, 5.3.2, 5.3.5, 5.4.2, 5.5.2)

2. Explain the processes for creating an incident safety plan and safety briefing. (5.2.3, 5.2.13, 5.3.3, 5.4.2, 5.4.3, 5.5.2, 5.5.3)

3. Determine procedures for managing the transfer of incident safety officer duties. (5.2.3)

4. Explain considerations for identifying and requesting technical specialists or assistant safety officers. (5.1.1, 5.2.10, 5.4.1, 5.4.2, 5.5.1, 5.5.2)

5. Describe procedures for establishing operational zones. (5.2.7, 5.2.11, 5.2.13, 5.3.3, 5.4.2, 5.5.2, 5.5.4)

6. Determine ways to monitor communications at an incident scene. (5.2.6, 5.2.9)

7. Explain procedures for establishing rapid intervention crews (RICs). (5.3.1, 5.3.2)

8. Determine procedures for establishing rehabilitation areas at an incident scene. (5.2.14)

9. Describe factors that would lead the incident safety officer to stop, alter, or suspend operations. (5.2.2, 5.2.4, 5.2.5, 5.3.3)

10. Explain considerations for monitoring incident-related stress. (5.2.12)

11. Learning Activity 15-1: Prepare an incident safety plan for an emergency operation. (5.2.3, 5.4.2, 5.4.3, 5.5.2, 5.5.3)

Chapter 15
Incident Responsibilities

Case History

In order to remain current with the national transition to digital communications, a fire department upgraded all of its handheld radios to digital radios. The old radios were analogue, 800 MHz trunked radios. The newly purchased radios were digital, narrow-band 700 MHz trunked radios. In emergency settings, they discovered that the new radios introduced operational complications that responders had not experienced before. They were used to signal degradation (signal gradually fading away) over greater distances when using the analogue radios. The new digital radios, however, simply stopped working when out of range of the signal tower, a phenomenon known as the "digital cliff." The problem was especially noticeable in large occupancies, such as high rises, big box stores, schools, and warehouses where concrete and steel hamper signal propagation at the 700-800MHz wavelengths.

ISOs in the department had to change their communication monitoring as a result of the change in equipment. They began to monitor for highly localized losses of radio communications, such as a particular part of a structure. In addition, they were trained on methods to establish alternative communication solutions, such as the deployment of portable repeaters, if possible, or the transition to tactics that allow more visual or voice communication.

The incident safety officer (ISO) plays an integral role in ensuring operations at incidents and training events are safe and in compliance with departmental SOP/Gs and legal mandates. The assignment of the ISO is the responsibility of the Incident Commander (IC). The IC is the ISO until this assignment is delegated. A combination of departmental SOP/Gs, incident size, complexity, type of operation, and/or length of operation will determine the responsibilities that the IC delegates to the ISO at the scene.

The IC should forecast resource and Incident Command System (ICS) needs early in the development of the incident. Delegating the ISO function early in the incident allows the IC to focus on the overall incident operation and the development of effective strategy and tactics; the ISO focuses on potential safety issues and communicates recommendations to the IC. To adequately fill these responsibilities, the ISO should have experience, training, and knowledge in a variety of operational settings to assess hazards and provide corrective recommendations if personnel safety is at risk.

Communicating Scene Hazards

All personnel have the responsibility to recognize and communicate scene hazards through the proper channels to the IC. Personnel and tactical-level supervisors provide the first line of defense in recognizing and mitigating hazards. Simple hazards, such as tripping hazards, can be addressed without communication to the IC. However, larger hazards, such as downed power lines, need to be communicated to the IC. The ISO should monitor simple and complex hazards to ensure appropriate corrective action is taken. The ISO should be viewed as the last line of defense in incident operations in preventing an injury or fatality.

The ISO should determine incident scene hazards by assessing or performing a reconnaissance of the overall operational setting and environment. Some hazards will require immediate corrective action, while others will need to be communicated to the IC for consideration in the incident action plan (IAP) and the strategy and tactics decision-making process.

Incident Hazards

Incident hazards should be assessed from an operational and environmental perspective. Operational hazards are typically viewed as expected and imminent. Expected hazards are those that are common and predictable based on the incident type. Departmental SOP/Gs and training should provide for hazard recognition and correction in the development of the incident strategy and at the task level.

Imminent threats are those that must be corrected immediately. In these situations, personnel are at risk of immediate injury or death. The ISO has the responsibility and authority to stop, alter, or suspend operations in these situations. The environment should also be assessed as a potential hazard. The ISO should evaluate what impact the environment can have on the operation or personnel.

Incident Reconnaissance

The ISO should perform a 360-degree reconnaissance of a scene similar to the size-up that the IC or assigned firefighters perform. The ISO is looking for any initial hazards at the scene, such as hazardous energy sources or possible structural collapse indicators. All of these initial hazards should be communicated to the IC so that the hazards can be considered when developing the IAP for the incident.

The ISO should continue reconnaissance throughout the incident **(Figure 15.1)**. Staying within the cold zone and no closer than the warm zone, the ISO's role is to continually monitor operational activities, environmental conditions, fire development, and structural integrity. As part of reconnaissance, communications to the IC and other responders should remain open so that any updated information is conveyed in a timely fashion.

Expected Incident Hazards

All incidents will have hazards that are inherent to the operational situation. Expected hazards should have preexisting preventive measures outlined in SOP/Gs and addressed in regular training. Some common incident type hazards and their preventive measures include but are not limited to the following:

- **Fire incidents** — smoke, fire, falling debris, equipment use, and noise hazards are reduced with full structural fire protective clothing and equipment, and rehabilitation. The weather should also be assessed for its impact on fire conditions and personnel.

Figure 15.1 ISOs should perform reconnaissance before operations begin and continue to monitor the scene and firefighter activities throughout the incident. *Courtesy of Ron Jeffers.*

- **Emergency medical incidents** — have the potential for exposure to bodily fluids, communicable disease, needle sticks, combative patients, lifting and moving patients, and traffic hazards. These exposures are mitigated with the use of body substance isolation clothing and equipment, training on proper ergonomics, and traffic management systems.

- **Hazardous materials incidents** — have the potential for chemical, biological, radiological, and nuclear exposure and indirect contamination from victims to unprotected responders. The weather should also be assessed for its impact on the release and reactivity of materials and on personnel. Mitigation is achieved with hazard identification, hazard control zones, proper protective clothing and equipment, medical surveillance and rehabilitation, and decontamination.

- **Technical rescue incidents** — have the potential for personnel operating in or with a confined space, trench, high-angle, building collapse, atmospheric, flash-fire, sharp objects, machinery, and water hazards. Mitigation is achieved with proper protective clothing and equipment, air monitoring and ventilation, and stabilization equipment.

- **Atypically stressful incidents** — emotional and psychological stress hazards can be mitigated with regular personnel rotations, work/rest cycles, and postincident support.

- **Disasters** — natural and man-made disasters are a special consideration in that they could involve all of the above listed incidents and hazards **(Figure 15.2)**. Protective measures could include any of the preventive measures listed depending on the type and extent of the disaster.

- **Violence** — incidents involving violence will require close coordination and communication with law enforcement through a unified command. Department SOP/Gs should address proper staging, communications, coordination of operations, and overall scene safety. Violent incidents should be evaluated for explosive or chemical devices and secondary devices that target bystanders and/or responders. Violent events can occur on a small or large scale; therefore, personnel should be alert to the potential of these devices.

- **Weapons of Mass Destruction (WMD)** — WMDs include any chemical, biological, radiological, nuclear, and/or explosive device (CBRNE). Depending on the device and substance used, there may be indications of the presence of a life-threatening hazard. Departmental SOP/Gs should address the training of personnel, proper selection and use of protective clothing and equipment, and scene operations to ensure the highest level of safety possible.

Weapon of Mass Destruction (WMD) — Any weapon or device that is intended or has the capability to cause death or serious bodily injury to a significant number of people through the release, dissemination, or impact of toxic or poisonous chemicals or their precursors, a disease organism, or radiation or radioactivity; may include chemical, biological, radiological, nuclear, or explosive (CBRNE) type weapons.

CAUTION

Flammable gas incidents can transition into rapidly expanding incidents, leading to the higher potential for injury.

Managing incident hazards can typically be achieved within the established ICS. However, special consideration should be given to those incidents that require technical specialists when a hazard is unexpected or of a unique nature (chemicals, biologics, and explosives). The ISO should independently assess the incident, the strategy and tactics employed, and the hazards present to ensure the IC has appropriately addressed personnel safety.

Figure 15.2 Flooding and other natural disasters present unique hazards that may require specialized personnel or a number of assistant safety officers. *Courtesy of Chris Mickal, District Chief, New Orleans (LA) FD Photo Unit.*

Identifying Imminent Threats

Imminent threats are those that require immediate action to prevent a significant injury or fatality. The ISO has the authority to immediately stop, alter, or suspend an operation until corrective actions are taken. The ISO should communicate with the IC before and/or after the corrective action depending on the situation. Either way, the IC must be informed, as these situations generally require a review and/or revision of the IAP. Some imminent threats may include but are not limited to:

- **Structural collapse** — the potential for structural collapse should be forecasted early in a fire incident so personnel and equipment are relocated. The ISO will play an integral role in evaluating structures under fire conditions to ensure the strategy and tactics employed meet the risk/benefit assessment.

- **Flashover, backdraft, or smoke explosion** — the potential for flashover, backdraft, and/or smoke explosion should be monitored **(Figure 15.3, p. 556)**. Any indication of a flashover, backdraft, or smoke explosion must be communicated to the interior crew so they may immediately withdraw from the structure. The ISO should monitor the timing of tactics to forecast incident hostile fire behavior.

- **Electrical hazards** — electrical hazards should be assessed for all overhead and ground level operations **(Figure 15.4, p. 556)**. Downed power lines should be identified and the area isolated until the arrival of the utility company. All ladder operations must ensure proper clearance from any power line. Solar systems are always energized if the solar panels are exposed to light. Even if the system is disconnected, the system will still have electrical energy.

- **Weather** — strong storms producing lightning, tornados, hurricanes, and large hail can stop, alter, or suspend operations or delay response to incidents. The ISO should assist in determining current and forecasted weather to ensure personnel safety.

Figure 15.3 Observed lowering of the neutral plane through windows may be an indication of developing backdraft conditions. *Courtesy of Dan Madrzykowksi, NIST.*

Figure 15.4 Electrical hazards could be both on the ground, such as a downed power line, or overhead, such as this overheated transformer. *Courtesy of Chris Mickal, District Chief, New Orleans (LA) FD Photo Unit.*

Environmental Hazards

In addition to identifying expected and imminent hazards in the operational setting, the ISO should assess the environment for potential impact on operations. This assessment should include weather conditions, terrain, temperature extremes (heat/cold), time of day, and topography **(Figure 15.5)**. The ISO should ensure the IC has considered the environment in developing the IAP. This consideration should include the provision for the protection of personnel, apparatus and personnel placement, and the quick movement of apparatus and personnel if needed.

Prioritizing Scene Hazards

Scene hazards can be prioritized based on the severity of the hazard and risk posed to responders. The prioritization should be viewed from an all-hazards perspective to ensure all reasonable preventive measures are addressed during an incident. The IC will complete the initial prioritization during the initial incident size-up and decision on strategy and tactics. Life safety is the first priority. The prioritization of scene hazards can be set using the risk management principles, risk/benefit analysis, and risk management framework outlined in Chapter 13, Risk Management Principles.

Figure 15.5 Fire fighting in extreme cold or hot temperatures both have safety considerations that must be addressed during fire fighting operations. *Courtesy of Ron Jeffers.*

Forecasting

Forecasting is the ability to reasonably predict the future well in advance of the change. Forecasting is important in the all-hazards environment in which fire and emergency services personnel operate. For example, new construction methods have been shown to lead to early structural failure and collapse. The ISO should be able to forecast this event with his/her knowledge of building construction, building contents and fire load, and burn time. Interior operations should be halted and all personnel removed from the structure well in advance of the structure failing and collapsing **(Figure 15.6)**. Forecasting predictions should be communicated to the IC with enough time for changes in the strategy to be considered, ordered, and implemented.

Figure 15.6 In the event of imminent structural collapse, all interior crews should be notified of the hazard and retreat from the structure immediately.

Access and Egress Suitability

Chapter 14, Incident Hazard Recognition, covered the challenges associated with access and egress. During incident operations, the ISO should evaluate the effectiveness of the forcible entry crew's progress with achieving access and egress. In addition, the ISO should assess if the access and egress points are suitable to the operation. This process will require an assessment of the incident operations with regards to strategy and tactics and ventilation method used. Gaining access and providing egress points should not compromise the strategy and tactics employed. However, forcible entry crews should have points prepared so those personnel in need of emergency exit can do so without delay. The suitability of the access and egress points should be relatively close to those individuals who may need it, but may depend on suitability of use. For example, a window exit may be the closest exit point for interior crews to exit a structure, but may not be suitable due to its remote location, height, or the inability of ground crews to safely operate in that location.

Establishing access and egress at the scene should account for the flow path or possible flow path of the fire. If an access area is in the current flow path, the area must be made safe before allowing access. Access and egress points that are safe should remain so throughout the incident. The ISO should ensure that coordinated tactics control the flow path of the fire and maintain safe access and egress.

Incident Action Plan (IAP)

Tactical Worksheet — document that the IC may use on the fireground to track units and record field notes during an incident; could evolve into a written IAP if an incident escalates in size or complexity.

The IAP is based on information gathered during the incident size-up, and it may be written or verbal. The majority of emergency incident operations will be managed with a verbal IAP that is dynamic to the changing incident conditions. The IC may also use a **tactical worksheet** to track units and make field notes about the incident. The verbal IAP with the tactical worksheet may evolve into a written IAP as the incident grows in size and/or complexity.

Verbal IAP

The IC will communicate the incident objectives of the IAP to units and individuals operating at the scene who are tasked with a specific work assignment. This communication is done in person or over designated radio frequencies. All incident personnel must function within the scope of the IAP. Incident personnel should direct their actions toward achieving the incident objectives, strategies, and tactics specified in the plan. When all members understand their positions, roles, and functions in the ICS, the system can safely, effectively, and efficiently use resources to accomplish the plan.

All verbal instructions should be communicated to the ISO. The ISO should ensure that all SOP/Gs are followed, such as the establishment of an accountability system or rapid intervention in the verbal orders. If the IC's instructions do not follow established procedures, the ISO should discuss this issue with the IC and recommend changes to assignments.

Assigned Incident Tasks

The IC should brief the ISO on all assigned incident tasks. The ISO can then independently verify incident operations are proceeding as designed. This monitoring should not be viewed as a "policing the scene" function, but one of verifying continuity of operations and accountability of personnel. All personnel should be working towards the common goal of the IAP. Personnel operating outside the established IAP or **freelancing** are a danger to themselves and all other personnel on scene. A properly implemented ICS structure with clear incident objectives should be sufficient to address this concern.

Freelancing — To operate independently of the Incident Commander's command and control.

NIMS IAP Planning Process

As the incident grows or has the potential for involving multiple units or agencies for an extended period, the IAP may need to be in written form. A written IAP should be forecasted early in the incident operations. By forecasting this need, the IC can expand the ICS structure to include a formalized planning process in which the written IAP is developed **(Figure 15.7)**. Following the NIMS *Planning "P"* is an effective and standardized approach for developing the IAP and for all command and general staff personnel to understand their responsibilities in this process. Standardized ICS forms are available to record the various elements of the plan.

The IC develops and implements the initial written IAP with assistance from the Operations Section Chief when needed. As the incident grows in size and complexity, a formalized planning process will be needed. The *Planning "P"*, according to NIMS, takes the initial phases of Incident Command and develops a formal planning process with specific command and general staff responsibilities. In the *Planning "P"*, the ISO will develop a written general safety message and the *Incident Action Plan Safety Analysis* (ICS form 215A). The ISO will be required to attend several meetings in the *Planning "P"* process and should ensure safety is addressed with a risk/benefit analysis in all aspects of the IAP planning process.

IAPs usually contain the following elements:

- **Tactical worksheet** — basis for the development of an IAP
- **Incident briefing** — serves as an initial action worksheet (ICS 201 Form)
- **Incident objectives** — objectives should be SMART: Specific, Measurable, Action-oriented, Realistic, and Time frame (ICS 202 Form)
- **Organization** — description of the ICS table of organization, including the units and agencies that are involved (ICS 203 Form)
- **Assignments** — specific unit tactical assignments divided by branch and division (ICS 204 Form)

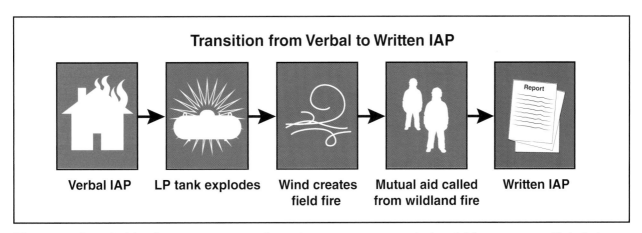

Transition from Verbal to Written IAP

| Verbal IAP | LP tank explodes | Wind creates field fire | Mutual aid called from wildland fire | Written IAP |

Figure 15.7 As an incident becomes more complex and more resources are deployed, it becomes more likely that a written IAP will be needed to document scene operations.

- **Support materials** — includes site plans, access or traffic plans, locations of support activities (staging, rehabilitation, logistics, and others), and similar resources
- **Safety message** — information concerning personnel safety at the incident; may also be part of the incident safety plan that the incident safety officer develops (ICS 208 or 208H Form)

The written IAP is maintained at the Incident Command Post and updated or revised as warranted or at the end of the specified time interval (NIMS *Planning "P"*). At the end of the incident, the plan is used as part of the postincident analysis and critique.

Situation Status Information

The IC, or if assigned, the planning section maintains the situation status information. The ISO should monitor the overall incident for current situation status and if the incident stabilization effort is succeeding. Communication of the situation will generally be achieved from the tactical-level supervisors to the operations section chief and onto the IC. The ISO should monitor the effectiveness of this communication and ensure the operational strategy and tactics remain appropriate to the situation. If a discrepancy exists, then the ISO should communicate this issue to the IC.

Resource Status Information

The IC – or if assigned, the planning section – maintains the resource status information. After a briefing from the IC, the ISO should evaluate the resources assigned on scene, in staging, in rehab, and those that have been requested. The ISO should ensure the resource needs are appropriate to the situation. If resource needs are determined to be insufficient, the ISO should communicate recommendations to the IC.

Safety Communications

The IC must control incident scene communications. Irrelevant radio traffic can create confusion, negatively impact operations, and be a significant safety issue. The IC should have a command presence on the radio in which he/she is commanding the operation by communicating assignments and/or asking for update reports. By creating a positive and efficient command presence on the radio, irrelevant radio traffic can be reduced.

For the ISO, safety communications are critical messages that are broadcast over the radio to or from the IC and intended for all personnel to hear. For example, the presence and location of a downed power line should be communicated over the radio to the IC. Operations personnel will hear this message and be alert to the hazard. The IC will be responsible for eliminating the hazard by requesting assistance from the utility company.

Some radio systems will support the use of a specific safety channel or talk group for limited communications between the safety officer, assistant safety officers, technical safety officers, and the IC. This channel or talk group may also be a secondary MAYDAY communication link.

Recommending Mitigation Actions

As the ISO monitors incident operations, hazard mitigation actions may be needed. If the threat is not imminent, the ISO should communicate the message and make recommendations to the IC. Mitigation actions communicated to the IC will include situations where the hazard is not a simple correction. Some considerations that may require mitigation actions include but are not limited to:

- Protective clothing and equipment use or modification
- Collapse zone establishment or modification
- Hazard control zone establishment or modification
- Traffic control establishment or modification
- Apparatus placement modification **(Figure 15.8)**

Receiving Incident Information and Orders from the IC

The IC has overall incident responsibility. The assignment of an ISO may be a predetermined assignment or one that is completed at the scene. Either way, the IC must formally assign someone to the ISO function when it is deemed necessary. The IC will provide an incident briefing to the ISO, which is usually face-to-face. The IC will then provide the ISO with orders on specific needs. The ISO should have clear instructions to perform an independent incident assessment and provide hazard mitigation recommendations to the IC.

Communicating Hazards to Responders

Communicating scene hazards to responders should be achieved in a consistent manner and according to SOP/G. Simple hazards that can be quickly mitigated can be communicated face-to-face. However, hazards that are more global, or those affecting more than one operational crew, should be communicated to the IC via radio for all responders to hear. SOP/Gs should outline the process for communication of a hazard, the isolation of an area (downed power line), and who should answer the IC that the communication was heard, understood, and action is being taken by a crew.

Figure 15.8 When apparatus have to be repositioned at a scene, all safety procedures should be followed, including the use of a spotter.

Documenting Communications

The ISO should be provided some method of documenting scene communications. On large complex incidents, the ISO should have writing material to make notes and ensure clear communications with the IC. Notes can be taken during the incident briefing or when the ISO is stationed at the Incident Command Post. As stated earlier, ICS forms may be required for certain incidents. In this situation, the ISO should have access to a laptop or other electronic device for documenting communications during the NIMS *Planning "P"* process or when completing ICS forms. The ISO should know what forms are needed (discussed below) and the proper completion process.

Writing on forms may not be possible when the ISO is performing a 360-degree incident assessment. In this situation, critical communications with the IC should be done via the radio so it is recorded. The dispatch center typically captures the recording of radio communications. Types of recording equipment will vary between jurisdictions. Departments should ensure an SOP/G outlines the process for saving specific incident communications for later review. Recordings are typically time-stamped and can be used for future reference on when something occurred or was said. They can also be used during the postincident analysis.

Creating an Incident Safety Plan and Safety Briefing

An incident safety plan and safety briefing are completed during complex incidents when the IAP is written. The ISO is responsible for completing both. The incident safety plan requires a detailed analysis of the incident and a plan for ensuring safe operations. The ISO may need to consult with technical and/or weather experts during the analysis. The **incident safety plan** should provide reasonable mitigation strategies for the incident planning process. **Learning Activity 15-1** provides an opportunity to practice creating an incident safety plan.

The safety briefing is a summary of the safety highlights and high priority concerns that personnel should be aware of. The safety briefing is also summarized on ICS form 201, *Incident Briefing*, as the safety message.

Initial Data to Gather for the Incident Safety Plan

Preparing for the incident planning process, the ISO should examine multiple points of information. The incident safety plan should include information about the impact of the weather, material identification, geographical data, location site and building plans, and general incident information. In gathering this data, the ISO may need to work with the planning section or technical experts.

Weather Condition Information

The ISO should monitor weather conditions for potential adverse effects on the incident operations, fire behavior, and personnel safety. At times, the ISO may need to consult with a weather expert to obtain needed forecast information. Dispatch communications centers can also assist with providing weather updates. This information may be important during extended operations, wildland fires, or during significant weather events. If weather forecasting is needed during an incident, the IC can assign an official *weather observer* under

Incident Safety Plan — Written document at complex incidents which outlines hazards identified during preincident surveys and size-up. It also defines planned mitigation strategies for those hazards.

the situation unit leader in the planning section. Weather information will be included on ICS Form 209, *Incident Status Summary*. When requested, the weather observer will prepare an incident weather forecast on ICS form 222.

Safety Data Sheets (SDS)

Safety data sheets (SDS) are formally known as material safety data sheets (MSDSs). OSHA's Hazard Communication Standard, 29 CFR 1910.1200, regulates the production of SDSs by manufacturers or distributors. SDSs provide specific chemical data that includes:

- Section 1: Identification
- Section 2: Hazard(s) Identification
- Section 3: Composition/Information on Ingredients
- Section 4: First Aid Measures
- Section 5: Fire Fighting Measures
- Section 6: Accident Release Measures
- Section 7: Handling and Storage
- Section 8: Exposure Controls/Personal Protection
- Section 9: Physical and Chemical Properties
- Section 10: Stability and Reactivity
- Section 11: Toxicological Information
- Section 12: Ecological Information (non-mandatory)
- Section 13: Disposal Considerations (non-mandatory)
- Section 14: Transport Information (non-mandatory)
- Section 15: Regulatory Information (non-mandatory)
- Section 16: Other Information

This information can be critical during incident operations. The ISO should ensure the IC requests and obtains this information. The IC may also need to assign technical experts under the hazardous material branch supervisor in the operations section or the situation unit leader in the planning section.

Topographical and Street Maps

Both topographical and street maps provide important preincident information. Topographical information is critical during wildland fire operations, but may be needed for other incidents as well. Evaluating topography is needed to identify previous burn areas, high and low points, routes of access and egress, and dangerous slopes. Street maps can be useful when landmarks or street signs have been destroyed. However, aerial photography may be needed to supplement the printed map(s). Aerial photography may also show site plan details that are obscured from the street, such as which floors of a building are at street level or where additional entrances to a structure are located.

The ISO should ensure that the IC requests topographical information and that the information is obtained. A fire behavior specialist can assist in assessing how the topography will affect the fire and suppression activities.

Safety Data Sheet (SDS) — Form provided by chemical manufacturers, distributors, and importers; contains information about chemical composition, physical and chemical properties, health and safety hazards, emergency response procedures, and waste disposal procedures. *Also known as* Material Safety Data Sheet (MSDS).

Preincident Plans

Chapter 6, Operational Risk Management, discussed developing preincident plans. These plans should provide information on hazards that affect operations, location specific risks, site safety plan information, and any recommended control measures. During an incident, the ISO should ensure these preincident plans are readily available for command and general staff personnel. Preincident plans provide important site characteristics that are needed during the IAP development and planning process.

Blueprints and Building Drawings

Blueprints and building drawings should be a part of the preincident planning process, especially with target hazard locations. However, in situations where these documents are unavailable prior to an incident, the IC should request assistance from facility maintenance personnel or those individuals with access to these drawings. The ISO should ensure this action is done. The ISO can also independently evaluate these drawings to ensure operations and the IAP address any safety concerns.

Initial Information about the Incident

The initial information gathered about an incident is critical to establishing a safe and effective IAP. The initial information will come from the dispatch information, preincident plans, and scene size-up. The IC should brief the ISO on this information and the employed IAP. The ISO should evaluate this information to ensure risks and hazards are identified and mitigated to ensure personnel safety is maximized.

NIMS Documentation for the Incident Safety Plan

The ISO has several responsibilities with NIMS documentation. NIMS documentation on ICS forms will be required for events where the IAP is written. These ICS forms are typically not required when the IAP is verbal. Those personnel with the potential to serve as the ISO should seek specific training on and become proficient at completing the following ICS forms:

- ICS form 208, *Safety Message/Plan*
- ICS form 214, *Activity Log*
- ICS form 215A, *IAP Safety Analysis*
- ICS form 225, *Incident Personnel Performance Rating*

NOTE: NFPA® 1521, *Standard for Fire Department Safety Officer Professional Qualifications,* only requires that the ISO complete ICS form 215A.

The ISO should also be knowledgeable of his/her responsibility for reviewing and/or providing information on the following ICS forms:

- ICS form 201, *Incident Briefing*
- ICS form 206, *Medical Plan*
- ICS form 215, *Operational Planning Worksheet*

The safety analysis is one of the primary ICS form responsibilities for the ISO. This worksheet provides the opportunity to document risks and hazards in different areas of operation and what corrective measures have been taken.

Recommendations for Control and Exclusion Zones

Control and exclusion zones are established to isolate three main areas of incident operations. The exclusion zone is a part or parts of the hot zone as determined by the IC (**Figure 15.9**). The ISO should evaluate the established zones to ensure operations, supporting operations, decontamination, and corridors for entry and exit are appropriate to the situation. This ISO should provide recommendations of improving the zones when needed.

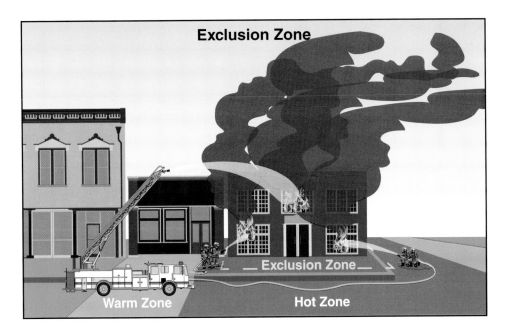

Figure 15.9 When an exclusion zone is established at a scene, it may be a separate area within the hot zone into which no personnel are allowed under any circumstances.

Protective Clothing and Equipment Requirements for the Incident

Personal protective clothing and equipment should be selected based on the incident type. Specific types of personal protective clothing and equipment are now designed for structural fire fighting, wildland fire fighting, aircraft rescue and fire fighting, technical rescue, and hazardous materials. NFPA® provides for specific design criteria for each of these incident types so personnel are protected against the risks and hazards associated with each. The ISO should monitor the selection and use of personal protective clothing and equipment for each incident type to ensure it meets SOP/Gs and legal mandates.

Technical Rescue Protective Clothing and Equipment Considerations

Technical rescue includes several types of situations. However, the personal protective clothing and equipment are similar. NFPA® 1951, *Standard on Protective Ensembles for Technical Rescue Incidents*, addresses the protection of personnel in common technical rescue incidents. The exception to this case is water rescue. Those departments performing water rescues and dive team operations should refer to NFPA® 1952, *Standard on Surface Water Operations Protective Clothing and Equipment*, and NFPA® 1953, *Standard on Protective Ensembles for Contaminated Water Diving*.

Hazardous Materials Protective Clothing and Equipment Considerations

Hazardous materials protective clothing and equipment was discussed in detail in Chapter 13, Risk Management Principles. For hazardous materials incidents, the ISO should evaluate the level of suit protection to ensure compliance with information listed on the SDS. The ISO should also evaluate all support positions to ensure indirect contamination does not occur. The ISO may need to consult with technical experts in some situations to ensure personnel are properly protected.

NFPA® Safety Alert Issued for SCBA Facepiece Lenses!

On July 2, 2012, the National Fire Protection Association® issued the following safety alert:

Safety Alert

Exposure to high temperature environments, which firefighters can encounter during fires they are attempting to extinguish, can result in the thermal degradation or melting of a Self-Contained Breathing Apparatus (SCBA) facepiece lens, resulting in elimination of the protection meant for the user's respiratory system and exposing the user to products of combustion and superheated air

This alert was based on data gathered by the National Institute for Occupational Safety and Health (NIOSH) while investigating firefighter line of duty deaths between 2002 and 2011. The investigations into three fatalities indicated that firefighters encountered thermal conditions that exceeded the level of protection the facepiece lenses were designed to withstand. At the same time, it was determined that the facepiece lens offered the lowest level of thermal protection of any part of the personal protective ensemble. The degradation of the lens resulted in the inhalation of products of combustion and thermal injuries to the firefighter's respiratory system.

The NFPA® has incorporated new test methods and performance requirements into the 2013 edition of NFPA® 1981, *Standard on Open-Circuit Self-Contained Breathing Apparatus (SCBA) for Emergency Services*. The NFPA® made the following recommendations:

- SCBA facepieces should be inspected before and after each use in accordance with NFPA® 1852, *Selection Care and Maintenance of Open-Circuit Self-Contained Breathing Apparatus*.

- SCBA facepieces that exhibit evidence of exposure to intense heat, such as cracking, crazing, bubbling, discoloration, deformation, or gaps between the lens and frame, must be removed from service and repaired or replaced.

- Fire department training programs must contain information on the limitations of respiratory protection, the effects on the facepiece of prolonged or repeated exposures to intense heat, and how to respond to problems that may occur when the facepiece is exposed to intense heat.

- When firefighters and fire officers are evaluating structure fires, they must consider the potential for facepiece failure during an interior fire attack. Situational awareness and an understanding of fire behavior are essential to preventing facepiece failure.

- When interior conditions deteriorate, firefighters must be able to recognize the change in conditions and withdraw or seek a safe refuge.

In response to this safety alert, NFPA® has included lens radiant heat testing to the latest edition of NFPA® 1981, *Standard on Open-Circuit Self-Contained Breathing Apparatus (SCBA) for Emergency Services*. The test is designed to measure the inhalation and exhalation performance of the facepiece assembly while under radiant heat. The facepiece must maintain air pressure specified in the standard under radiant heat conditions typical for a structure fire for 24 minutes. This new testing requirement is intended to provide manufacturers with a benchmark for creating SCBA facepieces that are more resistant to heat and less likely to fail unexpectedly.

Common Strategies and Tactics

Each incident type will have common strategies and tactics that are considered in the IAP for that incident. Departmental SOP/Gs should outline these common strategies and tactics, so personnel can perform their duties in a consistent and expected manner. SOP/Gs should not be restrictive in this sense, but create a methodical decision-making process to achieve an effective and safe incident stabilization process.

Technical Rescue Strategies and Tactics

Technical rescue strategies and tactics will be based on the location and status of victims and the extent of the hazard(s) present. Initial response personnel should identify the last known location of the victim(s), known hazards, and any protective measures in use by the victim(s). The IC will need to determine what specialized equipment will be needed and request sufficient resources to conduct a technical rescue operation. The ISO of a technical rescue incident should be trained to the level of the operations employed or have a technical expert (technical safety officer - TSO) assigned to assist with assessing the scene. Strategies and tactics will involve teams of personnel performing specific tasks. The ISO and/or TSO should evaluate all rope rescue systems, communications systems, and safety systems prior to entry into the hazard zone **(Figure 15.10)**.

Hazardous Materials Strategies and Tactics

Hazardous materials strategies and tactics will be based on the type of hazard present. Victim location and status is also a consideration; however, some hazards will prevent immediate action until the proper level of suit protection is available. As with technical rescues, the ISO should be trained to the level of the operations employed or have a technical expert assigned to assist with assessing the scene. Strategies and tactics will involve teams of personnel performing specific tasks. During a hazardous materials incident, as with all other incidents, the rescue of victims is a primary consideration when the personal protective equipment and clothing provide adequate short-term protection from the material present. When the rescue of victims is not possible, the primary mission will be to control the material's release point.

Figure 5.10 The ISO or an assisting TSO at a rescue operation should check all rigging, rope systems, and knots before allowing the rescue to proceed.

Corrective and Preventative Actions for the Incident

As risks and hazards are identified for each incident type, a process of mitigation should also be identified. Mitigation strategies should start in the preincident planning stage and be outlined in the SOP/Gs. Mitigation actions will continue during the incident as hazards are identified. An evaluation of different incidents during the postincident analysis can lead to further mitigation strategies.

Fireground Hazard Mitigation Strategies

Fireground hazards mitigated in the preincident phase include:

- Providing ICS training **(Figure 15.11)**

- Training of personnel on fireground strategies

- Purchasing and providing availability of protective clothing and equipment

- Developing preincident plans

- Establishing member assistance programs (MAPs) and psychological support systems

- Establishing an effective plan review and annual inspection program

  Fireground hazards mitigated during the incident include:

- Eliminating slips, trips, and fall potential **(Figure 15.12)**

- Establishing operational and collapse zones

- Establishing rehab

Figure 5.11 All firefighters should be well-trained in ICS and the various command positions in the structure before ever being assigned duties at an emergency incident.

Figure 5.12 Disorganized hose lays are one of many possible tripping hazards at an incident scene. *Courtesy of Ron Jeffers.*

Technical Rescue Hazard Mitigation Strategies

Technical rescue hazard mitigation will include some of the same strategies as those employed above. The ISO should have the technical knowledge to identify appropriate mitigation steps to ensure personnel safety. The ISO should reference NFPA® 1006, *Standard for Technical Rescuer Professional Qualifications,* for system safety checks for the multitude of technical rescue type of incidents. A primary consideration for the ISO at a technical rescue incident is to ensure enough technically trained personnel are present to complete any required critical tasks of the event.

Hazardous Materials Hazard Mitigation Strategies

Some specific hazard mitigation will depend on the material(s) present and the extent of the release. As with technical rescue incidents, hazardous materials incidents should be evaluated to ensure enough technical personnel are present to complete any required critical tasks of the event. The ISO should reference NFPA® 472, *Standard for Competence of Responders to Hazardous Materials/Weapons of Mass Destruction Incidents,* for specific reference of operations at hazardous materials incidents. Some additional hazard mitigation strategies will include:

- **Personal protection clothing and equipment** — the suit level protection should meet the level of the hazard.

- **Medical assessment and rehabilitation** — personnel operating in suit level protection may do so under extreme conditions. Personnel should receive a medical assessment and hydration prior to entering a hazardous materials incident. Personnel should subsequently receive rehabilitation and medical surveillance assessment immediately after decontamination.

- **Decontamination** — decontamination must meet the level of hazard present. A decontamination corridor should be communicated to the entry team to expedite the exit process. A decontamination team, set up with all needed equipment, must be in place prior to the entry team making entry into the hazard zone **(Figure 15.13)**.

Figure 15.13 Decontamination areas should be present at all hazardous materials incidents and match the level of the hazards present. All responders, equipment, and victims leaving the contaminated zones should exit through decontamination corridors without exception.

- **Air monitoring** — air monitoring will help identify which hazards may exist. Some monitoring equipment is specialized to one type of hazard, such as a Geiger counter for radiological contamination; however, some air monitors can detect several types of hazards.

- **Computer software support** — the use of computer programs can assist in emergency planning and in determining airborne contamination areas that may require evacuation.

CAMEO (Computer-Aided Management of Emergency Operations)

CAMEO (Computer-Aided Management of Emergency Operations) was developed in partnership with the U.S. Environment Protection Agency (EPA) and the National Oceanic and Atmospheric Administration (NOAA). The software is designed to assist the IC in managing emergency operations, especially operations involving hazardous materials. CAMEO includes four interrelated programs of CAMEOfm, CAMEO Chemical, ALOHA® (Areal Locations of Hazardous Atmospheres), and MARPLOT® (Mapping Applications for Response, Planning, and Local Operational Tasks). More information on these computer software programs is available on the EPA's website.

Recommendations for Assistant Incident Safety Officers

The ISO should evaluate each incident for the potential of needed assistance. Within the ICS structure, the IC assigns assistant incident safety officers (AISOs) to the ISO. Depending upon the type of incident, AISOs may be referred to by different titles and have varying functions as follows **(Figure 15.14)**:

- Technical Safety Officer (TSO) - technical rescue or haz mat incidents

- Line Safety Officer - wildland fires

- Assistant Safety Officers - large scale NIMS-ICS incidents

AISOs can help evaluate large and/or complex incident scenes for safety concerns and communicate them to the ISO. AISOs may also be technical experts who provide advice to the ISO. The IC and the ISO should make the determination of the need of AISOs.

Safety Briefing

Safety briefings should be conducted prior to starting technical rescue or hazardous materials operations. These operations are slower in forming and require specially trained personnel with specialize equipment. This process does not mean that initial scene size-up, rescue, and basic scene operations are suspended. The ISO conducts the safety briefing to ensure that all personnel know the IAP and the following **(Figure 15.15)**:

- Expected hazards

- Protective clothing and equipment requirements

- Established zones

- Decon procedures

- Emergency procedures
- Air monitoring
- Medical surveillance
- Chain of command

Figure 15.15 A safety briefing should provide all of the safety and hazard information about an incident scene and planned incident operations.

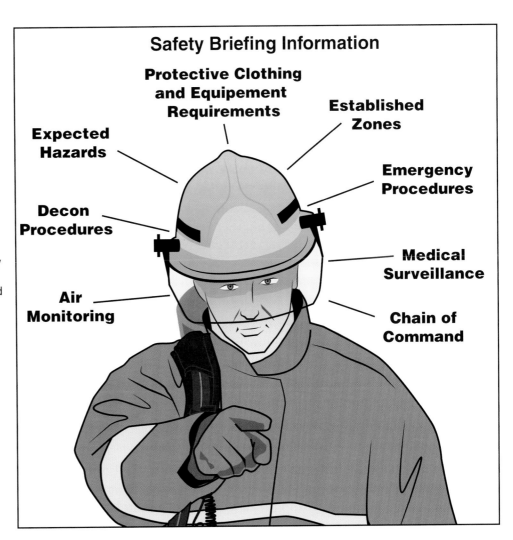

Safety Briefing Information

Protective Clothing and Equipement Requirements

Expected Hazards

Established Zones

Emergency Procedures

Decon Procedures

Medical Surveillance

Air Monitoring

Chain of Command

Advisors to the ISO

TSO

Line Safety Officer

AISO

Technical Rescue & Haz Mat Incidents

Wildland Fires

Structural fires and large scale incidents

Figure 15.14 ISOs should recognize when they need additional assistance to ensure safety at a scene and seek out the proper assisting personnel and advisors. *Right hand photo courtesy of Ron Jeffers.*

Transferring Duties

At times, it will be necessary for the ISO to transfer duties to another ISO. Transfer consideration will be given to work/rest cycles, knowledge and/ or expertise needed, or the use of multiple operational periods. In each of these transfer of duty situations, the ISO needs to provide a briefing to the incoming ISO. The briefing should include the current IAP, hazards identified and mitigated, and any outstanding issues that still need to be addressed. Face-to-face communication is the most preferable method in transferring ISO duties.

In a few situations, the ISO or IC will see the need to transfer the safety function to another member. These situations rarely occur, but may be necessary during technical operations where a specific expertise is needed to ensure personnel safety. Consideration of the need of this expertise may occur during technical rescue and hazardous materials incidents.

Transferring Incident Information

The outgoing ISO should provide all documentation to the incoming ISO. This documentation should include the IAP, ICS forms, reports or plans for the next operational period, and accountability tracking of all personnel. The transfer should be a seamless transition of assignment responsibility so the incoming ISO can continue. This transition should be done face-to-face if possible.

Documentation

On incidents with a verbal IAP, documentation will be limited and may only include the accountability of personnel and any field notes. On incidents with a written IAP, documentation will be more detailed. The written IAP and all pertinent ICS forms should be passed along. This information should include any safety messages or analysis that has been communicated. In addition, all accountability and field note reports need to be transferred with the ISO duties. The communication and documentation should provide a clear picture of the current status of the incident and any forecasting that has been done.

Reports and Plans for Next Operational Period

During the planning process, the ISO will participate in all meetings leading up to a new IAP. This process will include attending the strategy meeting, tactics meeting, planning meeting, and operational briefing. As stated previously, the ISO will prepare the following forms during the planning process:

- ICS form 208, *Safety Message/Plan*
- ICS form 215A, *IAP Safety Analysis*

The ISO will evaluate the information from the strategy and tactics meetings to prepare these forms. The outgoing ISO will brief the incoming ISO on all reports and plans to be implemented in the next operational period.

Resource Accountability and Tracking

Resource accountability and tracking is the IC's responsibility until the responsibility is delegated to the Resources Unit in the Planning Section. The ISO should ensure that the IC has implemented a process, so resources are

Figure 15.16 The ISO should ensure that other command staff have established and are following an accountability system.

accounted for and tracked as long as they are assigned to the incident **(Figure 15.16)**. At any given point, a unit and all associated personnel should be identified by their assignment and location. The ISO needs to communicate any deficiency in this component to the IC, so that a personnel accountability role call can be accomplished. Additionally, if a transfer of ISO duties occurs during an incident, the outgoing ISO should provide the incoming ISO a summary of the number of units assigned, those available for assignment, and those that need to be requested.

Communicating Planned Incident Changes

During an incident, changes to the IAP may be needed. Planned changes in the IAP are typically associated with changes to the incident's complexity. The greater the complexity, the greater the potential for changes in the IAP. Any change in a verbal or written IAP must be communicated to all personnel operating on scene. The ISO should monitor this communication and ensure all operational crews are complying with the directed changes. Any failure of implementation of a change in the IAP by any crew or member can put personnel at significant risk. If the ISO recognizes any failure to implement a change in the IAP, the failure should be immediately communicated to the IC for corrective measures.

Maintaining Incident Continuity

Changes in ISO responsibility should be communicated to all personnel on the scene. Personnel can get accustomed to hearing the voice of the ISO and can get confused if a different voice begins broadcasting ISO information. The IC needs to inform personnel of changes in order to limit confusion about who is the functioning ISO. Good communications help maintain the incident continuity and situational awareness during times of change.

Identifying and Requesting Technical Specialists or Assistant Safety Officers

ISOs need to recognize when an incident is beyond their ability to manage as the sole safety officer. This situation can occur when the size and/or complexity of the incident continues to grow. It may also involve extended operations where specific operational periods are implemented. Another significant consideration ISOs must assess is the type of hazard and if it is out of their scope of expertise. This situation will typically occur during technical rescue and/or hazardous materials incidents. The safety of personnel is paramount to deciding when to add AISOs or call in technical specialists. The ISO needs to provide the IC with an honest assessment of the incident along with recommendations if/when assistance is needed to improve safety oversight.

NOTE: The ISO and any assigned AISOs must also meet the requirements of NFPA® 1021, Fire Officer Level 1.

Incident Strategic Considerations

After the ISO receives a briefing from the IC, the ISO should conduct an evaluation of the incident strategies. In this evaluation, the ISO should consider the size and complexity of the incident, the expected duration, types of hazards, and any likely risks that may be present. This evaluation process will guide the ISO in making any needed recommendations for technical specialists and/or AISOs. Recommendations to add personnel under the supervision of the ISO should come early in the decision-making process. Incidents can change rapidly, which can overwhelm the ISO prior to assistance arriving.

Size and Complexity

On simple incidents, the ISO will survey the incident by performing a 360-degree walk-around assessment. This first-hand assessment is critical to ensuring the IAP is implemented and personnel are operating in a safe manner. On larger incidents, the 360-degree walk-around may not be possible. In these situations, the ISO needs to recommend to the IC adding AISOs.

The complexity of the incident can also lead to a recommendation of AISOs or technical specialists. Some departments may refer to technical specialists as technical safety officers or TSOs. When technician-level operations are employed, the ISO should either be trained to that level or have a TSO assisting with mitigating the risks and hazards of the incident.

Changes to Incident Command Structure

The ICS can expand or contract based upon incident needs, such as when TSOs or AISOs are needed. Technical rescue and hazardous materials incidents often require additional assistance. Hazardous materials incidents can vary widely as to the type of hazard present, and not all ISOs will have the needed expertise for each hazard. Requesting expertise with specific knowledge of a specific hazard is important for ensuring operational control measures are safe and appropriate.

As an incident involving multiple safety officers progresses, the ISO will become stationary at or near the command post while the TSOs or AISOs become tactical-level safety officers. During these times, the ISO will ensure the

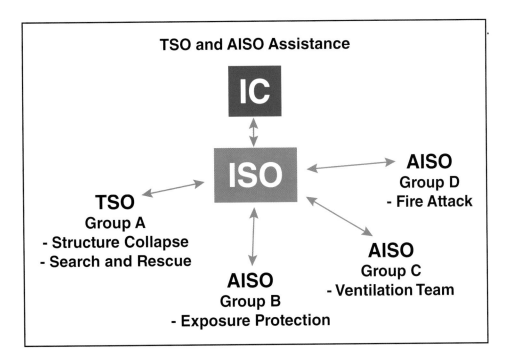

TSO and AISO Assistance

IC

ISO

AISO
Group D
- Fire Attack

TSO
Group A
- Structure Collapse
- Search and Rescue

AISO
Group B
- Exposure Protection

AISO
Group C
- Ventilation Team

Figure 15.17 TSOs and AISOs will monitor specific groups, activities, or hazards, and relay safety information through the ISO to the IC.

overall incident safety concerns are addressed with the IC. The TSOs or AISOs will ensure tactical-level safety concerns are monitored and recommendations made when needed at the tactical level. **(Figure 15.17)**

Incident Duration

The longer an incident lasts, the greater the need for work/rest cycles. This action includes the ISO. Departmental SOP/Gs should provide some general guidelines on when crew rotations should begin to occur. The ISO should monitor and forecast the need for crew rotations and make recommendations to the IC as needed. Some personnel rotations can occur at the change of an operational period. However, some rotations may need to occur at more frequent time periods due to exertion, fatigue, and weather conditions.

Types of Hazards at the Incident

An ISO will typically not be an expert in every type of incident response. Technical rescue, hazardous materials, target hazard fires, multicasualty emergency medical response, downed aircraft, and terrorism have numerous hazards that must be considered to ensure personnel safety. These hazards can be specialized and technical. It is during incidents where the ISO does not have the needed expertise that recommendations should be made to request technical specialists or AISOs.

Likely Risks at the Incident

Risk was defined in Chapter 5, Organizational Risk Management, as the likelihood of suffering harm from or being exposed to a hazard. The ISO should assess each incident to determine what risk exists with each type of hazard present. Some likely risks may include but are not limited to:

- Burns
- Electrical shock
- Strains, sprains, and fractures

- Dehydration
- Cardiac illness/injury
- Respiratory injury
- Psychological illness

Technical Rescue Incident Considerations

Technical rescue encompasses numerous incident types. Each type of technical rescue will have strategic and tactical considerations to address specific rescue and/or recovery operations. The IC and the ISO must be knowledgeable in technical rescue techniques to ensure personnel safety. An experienced technician-level rescuer should assist in developing the IAP and the strategies and tactics to meet the demands of the incident. This rescuer may also be assigned technical safety officer responsibilities for oversight of safety throughout the incident. The IAP must conform to the techniques employed in these technical operations. The NFPA® 1006 should be referenced for specific information on each type of technical rescue incident.

Likely Resource Needs for the Rescue

Technical rescue SOP/Gs should outline the critical tasks for each type of technical rescue that a fire and emergency services organization provides. Some tasks will be limited to the technician-level members, while other tasks may be assigned to operations-level members **(Figure 15.18)**. The ISO should ensure the proper number of technician-level personnel is assigned to the scene to complete the needed operation. Adequate support from operations-level personnel should also be verified before operations commence.

Stabilization Strategies for the Rescue

Stabilization strategies are needed for trench rescue, some vehicle and machinery rescues, and for structural collapse incidents **(Figure 15.19)**. During the incident size-up, a determination should be made for the resources needed to accomplish the initial rescue and/or recovery effort. Forecasting should also be done if the initial rescue and/or recovery effort does not achieve all tactical objectives. The ISO should assist with forecasting the contingency need(s) and make recommendations to the IC before each need arises.

Hazardous Materials Incident Considerations

Hazardous materials incidents can encompass CBRNE materials or weapons of mass destruction. Some indication of the presence of a hazardous material may be easily detected for some incidents, while at other incidents, hazardous materials may not be located until well into a response effort. Hazardous materials incidents may last for extended periods of time and may tax resources assigned to the incident. Weather will play a significant role in the complexity of the incident as well as the terrain and topography of the location. The IC and ISO must assess the incident on a case-by-case basis and request the appropriate resources needed to mitigate the hazard.

Search & Rescue Task Levels

Operations

Technician

Figure 15.18 Search and rescue specialists are trained to two levels of skill: operations or technicians. Operations level serves more often in support functions while technicians perform advanced rescue techniques.

Figure 15.19 Trench rescue operations generally begin with stabilizing the trench to prevent its collapse.

Available Preincident Information

If a hazardous materials incident occurs at a business or industrial location, preincident plans may be a source of reference. Additionally, Emergency Planning and Community Right-to-Know Act (EPCRA - Tier II), site safety plans, and safety data sheets should be requested from facility personnel. Preincident plans can provide the site and floor plans along with specific information needed in the development of an IAP. Preincident plans can also be valuable for entry teams to review prior to entry into the hazard area. The plans can facilitate efficient operations, which, in turn, can improve safety. The ISO should review the preincident plan during the assessment of the IAP and in the development of a safety message.

Hazardous Materials Incident Level

After the initial size-up has determined an incident's scope, the level of the incident can be determined in accordance with the local emergency response plan. The NFPA® 472 incident-level model identifies three levels of response, graduating from Level I (least severe) to Level III (most severe).

Level I. This type of incident is within the capabilities of the fire or emergency services organization or other first responders. A Level I incident is the least serious and the easiest to handle. It may pose a serious threat to life or property, although this is not usually the case. Evacuation, if required, is limited to the immediate area of the incident. The following are examples of Level I incidents:

- Small amount of gasoline or diesel fuel spilled from a vehicle
- Leak from domestic natural gas line on the consumer side of the meter
- Broken containers of consumer commodities, such as paint, thinners, bleach, swimming pool chemicals, and fertilizers (owner or proprietor is responsible for cleanup and disposal)

Level II. This type of incident is beyond the capabilities of the first responders on the scene and may be beyond the capabilities of the first response agency/organization having jurisdiction. Level II incidents require the services of a formal haz mat response team. A properly trained and equipped response team could be expected to perform the following tasks:

- Use chemical protective clothing (CPC).
- Dike and confine within the contaminated areas.
- Perform plugging and patching activities.
- Sample and test unknown substances **(Figure 15.20)**.
- Perform various levels of decontamination.

    The following are examples of Level II incidents:

- Spill or leak requiring limited-scale evacuation
- Any major accident, spillage, or overflow of flammable liquids
- Spill or leak of unfamiliar or unknown chemicals
- Accident involving extremely hazardous substances

- Rupture of an underground pipeline
- Fire that is posing a boiling liquid expanding vapor explosion (BLEVE) threat in a storage tank

Level III. This type of incident requires resources from state/provincial agencies, federal agencies, and/or private industry in addition to unified command. A Level III incident is the most serious of all hazardous material incidents. A large-scale evacuation may be required. Most likely, the incident will not be concluded by any one agency. Successful handling of the incident requires a collective effort from several of the following resources/procedures:

- Specialists from industry and governmental agencies
- Sophisticated sampling and monitoring equipment
- Specialized leak and spill control techniques
- Decontamination on a large scale

The following are examples of Level III incidents:

- Incidents that require an evacuation extending across jurisdictional boundaries
- Incidents beyond the capabilities of the local hazardous material response team
- Incidents that activate (in part or in whole) the federal response plan

Qualifications of TSOs for Haz Mat Incidents

NFPA® 472 states that hazardous materials safety officers must be trained up to and including the technician level of competence. If the ISO does not have this level of competence, he or she must assign a hazardous materials safety officer from the hazardous materials branch of the operation to function as the TSO at the incident.

Figure 15.20 Hazardous materials response teams should have the equipment and training to safely sample and test unknown substances.

Likely Resource Needs for the Operation

Department SOP/Gs should identify the critical tasks that are assigned to hazardous materials technical-level members. The SOP/G should also identify which tasks can be assigned to operations-level members. The type of hazards present will be a leading determination in identifying critical tasking, but some incidents will have some common assignments. For example, the entry team will be a technician-level assignment, while the medical monitoring will be assigned to operations-level members. The ISO should verify the assignments of each member on the scene to ensure they are operating within their scope of practice.

Stabilization Strategies for the Operation

Stabilization strategies do not always go as planned during hazardous materials incidents. Contingency plans and forecasting of alternatives should begin early in the IAP development and implementation phase. A "what's next" consideration should be evaluated with possible solutions.

Stabilization — Stage of an incident when the immediate problem or emergency has been controlled, contained, or extinguished.

This evaluation may include consultation with technical specialists on a specific type of hazard. Consultation may also be needed with CHEMTREC or CANUTEC, the manufacturer of the material, or the shipper responsible for its transportation.

Establishing Operational Zones

There are numerous reasons for establishing control zones at an emergency incident scene including:

- Controlling the perimeter facilitates the use of a personnel accountability system
- Accounting for occupants or victims
- Establishing preplanned operational tasks for each zone that take into account the level of threat or hazard present
- Keeping the scene free of curious spectators

NOTE: Departmental SOP/Gs should outline a guide for determining the zone size and shape and which tasks are performed within each zone.

The ISO should evaluate operational zones to ensure each zone perimeter is appropriately established. The ISO should also ensure personnel are properly attired for the task being performed within a specific zone. Operational zones can share common features; however, some incidents will have unique characteristics that will need to be evaluated for specific threats and hazards. Operational zones can also expand and contract throughout an incident. Regular monitoring of these zones is crucial for personnel safety. Some specific incident operations are highlighted in this section due to regulatory standards that must be met **(Figure 15.21)**.

Control and Exclusion Zones

Establishing **control zones** is an incident control strategy that the IC sets to ensure personnel safety and accountability. Establishing the three traditional operating *control zones – hot, warm, and cold* – is the most common and effective way to initially control the perimeter of an incident scene. Control zones should be established as soon as possible when resources are available for this assignment.

The traditional three-tiered zone terminology is now accompanied by terms such as an *exclusion zone*, a *no-entry zone*, a *threat zone*, a *traffic control zone*, and a *home ignition zone*. Some of these terms may be used interchangeably; however, having specific definitions for each helps to clearly define the zone along with the threat and/or hazard present. Including these specific and individual terms with the traditional control zones allows fire and emergency services organizations to more clearly identify threats and hazards and set an expectation of where task-level operations will occur. These specifically identified zones can improve the overall safety of personnel and allow the ISO to more definitively evaluate the IAP for appropriate strategies and tactics. The sections that follow describe the reason for control and exclusion zones and describes the various types.

Control Zones — System of barriers surrounding designated areas at emergency scenes, intended to limit the number of persons exposed to a hazard and to facilitate its mitigation. A major incident has three zones: Restricted (Hot) Zone, Limited Access (Warm) Zone, and Support (Cold) Zone.

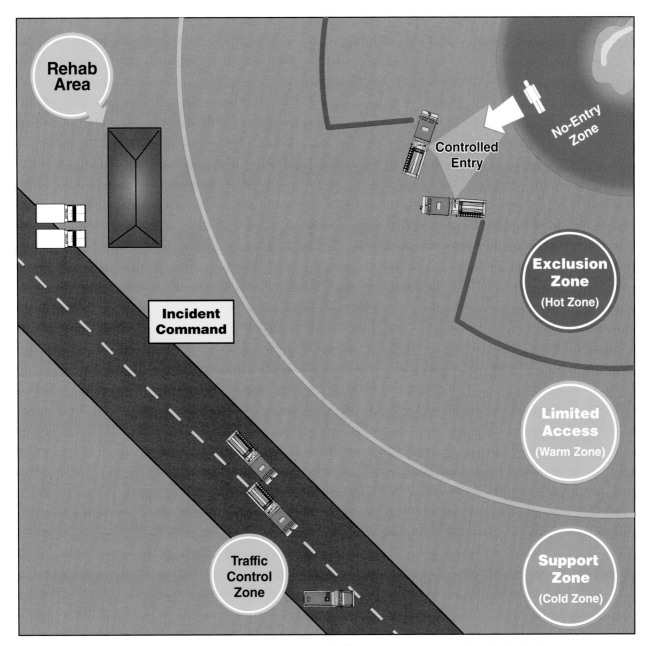

Figure 15.21 Operational zones can be established for any incident scene and are not just limited to hazardous materials incidents.

Operational Zones

When considering the establishment of control zones at hazardous material incidents, several aspects of the incident and the environment must be evaluated **(Figure 15.22, p. 582)**. The incident hazards must be assessed based on unique characteristics of each potential material - solid, liquid, or gas. Operational zones will vary depending on which material(s) is/are involved. Environmental aspects must also be considered with regards to the weather, terrain, and topography. Each factor can influence the incident operations and the reaction of materials. A generally accepted approach to hazardous materials incident is from the up-hill, up-wind direction. This approach is a prime reason for assessing environmental aspects.

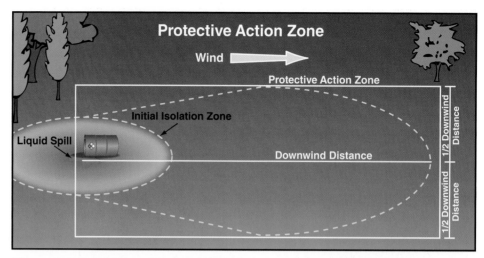

Figure 15.22 Wind direction is an environmental factor that should be considered when mapping operational zones at an incident scene, especially incidents involving release of hazardous gases into the air.

Threats/Hazards Requiring Control and Exclusion Zones

Control zones should be established for every incident or training exercise. The size and shape of the control zone will depend on the type of threat and/ or hazard present and the need to identify specific operational tasks within an area. Control zones may be a simple area surrounding where an operation is being conducted, such as an emergency medical patient treatment area **(Figure 15.23)**. Other control zones may be large, encompassing city blocks or miles, such as a disaster destruction area. Other specific threats and/or hazards will be present with:

- **Fire suppression activities** — fire suppression hazards include direct fire and heat exposure, toxic atmospheres, falling debris or structural collapse, and traffic.

- **Emergency medical scenes** — typical emergency medical scenes do not require three control zones unless a specific hazard has been identified with a patient. Simple measures by the crew on scene are generally sufficient in maintaining personnel safety.

- **High-energy sources** — consideration of electrical safety at incidents and training exercises should be a part of the scene size-up. Mitigation or elimination of electrical hazards should be a high priority during the IAP. Lock-out/tag-out measures may be required for some operations and should be verified by the ISO.

- **Roadway operations** — any roadway operation (collision, fire, or spill) should include a traffic control zone with a traffic management system. Some departments use circular assessment techniques to look for hazards. This same circular pattern can be used around specific scene operations, as hazards can be different with each operation area.

- **Violence** — violent situations can create several zone identifications. The hot zone can include a specific exclusion, no-entry, or threat zone for fire and emergency services personnel due to the threat of further violence. This area can also be considered the threat zone that may have an active shooter, secondary explosive device(s), or an intentionally targeted violent act, such as terrorism.

Figure 15.23 A control zone could be as small as marking the area surrounding the entry point in a confined space rescue operation.

- **Disasters** — wide-spread destruction can create safety, traffic, and control issues. Interagency coordination of isolating large areas will be needed. Interaction between fire and emergency services personnel and the public will occur during the initial response phase. The establishment of effective control zones early in a disaster will promote greater overall incident control and coordination of effort.

- **Wildland** — the area immediately surrounding a residence is called the *home ignition zone*. This zone presents the likelihood of a structure succumbing to the radiant heat of a wildland fire.

Some departments employ the use of tactical medical personnel, specially trained to assist law enforcement in high-risk warrant operations, active shooters, or other potentially armed conflicts. Departmental SOP/Gs need to address these specific operations and coordination of effort with the law enforcement agencies in which cooperative agreements exist.

Hot Zone

The **hot zone** is where trained personnel are working to resolve the problem at the scene. Only personnel who are directly involved in disposing of the problem are allowed to enter this zone, which limits crowds and confusion at the most critical area of the scene. The size of the zone may vary greatly, depending upon the nature and extent of the problem. Personnel requirements include **(Figure 15.24, p. 584)**:

- Trained appropriately to manage the situation

Hot Zone — Potentially hazardous area immediately surrounding the incident site; requires appropriate protective clothing and equipment and other safety precautions for entry. Typically limited to technician-level personnel.

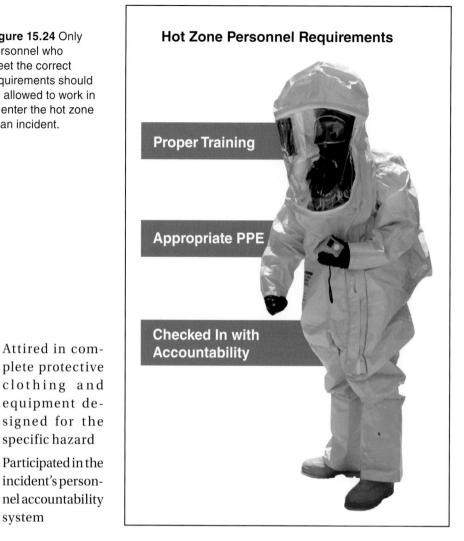

Figure 15.24 Only personnel who meet the correct requirements should be allowed to work in or enter the hot zone at an incident.

Hot Zone Personnel Requirements

Proper Training

Appropriate PPE

Checked In with Accountability

- Attired in complete protective clothing and equipment designed for the specific hazard
- Participated in the incident's personnel accountability system

Warm Zone — Area between the hot and cold zones that usually contains the decontamination corridor at haz mat incidents; typically requires a lesser degree of personal protective equipment than the Hot Zone.

Cold Zone — Safe area outside of the warm zone where equipment and personnel are not expected to become contaminated and special protective clothing is not required; the Incident Command Post and other support functions are typically located in this zone.

Warm Zone (Hazard Reduction Zone)

The **warm zone** is immediately outside the hot zone. Personnel in the warm zone directly support personnel working in the hot zone. It is limited to personnel who are operating hydraulic tool power plants and providing emergency lighting and fire protection. These personnel are in full protective clothing and equipment and are ready to enter the hot zone if needed. In hazardous materials incidents, this zone is where a decontamination station is normally assembled.

Cold Zone (Support Zone)

The **cold zone** immediately surrounds the hot and warm zones and may include the Incident Command Post (ICP), locations of rapid intervention crews (RICs), the location of the public information officer (PIO), rehabilitation area, and staging areas for personnel and portable equipment. The outer boundary of this area is the control line for the general public (crowd-control line). Examples include:

- Backup personnel available to enter warm or hot zones
- Witnesses and family members of victims
- News media accompanied by the PIO or organization representative

Exclusion Zone

Exclusion zones are areas identified, typically in the hot zone, where operational tasks should not be performed and/or operational personnel should avoid. An exclusion zone does not necessarily represent a specific threat or hazard, but is identified for safety reasons. An exclusion zone can include a potential explosive area, an area with an active shooter, a potential structural collapse zone, and/or an area with a high energy discharge potential.

No-Entry Zone

Some operational zones may be deemed too dangerous for personnel to be assigned under any conditions. These **no-entry zones** need to be communicated to all personnel on the scene. No level of personal protective clothing or equipment will be sufficient in adequately protecting personnel from an identified imminent hazard in this area. The no-entry zone and exclusion zone terms are commonly used interchangeably. The ISO should regularly monitor no-entry zones to ensure personnel do not encroach upon the area.

NOTE: No-entry zones may also be established to preserve evidence for investigation after the hazard has been mitigated.

Threat Zone

Threat zones indicate areas, usually within the hot zone or exclusion zone, where there is an active shooter and/or explosion potential. The threat zone is specific to a known or reasonably anticipated threat and may extend for some distance. Explosive threats can include intentional man-made devices or those materials exposed to fire conditions (chemicals, flammable or combustible materials).

Traffic Control Zone

Traffic control zones should be established for any incident on or near a roadway. Personnel should coordinate a traffic management system with local law enforcement to ensure responder and civilian safety. A traffic control zone may have hot, warm, and cold zones within it depending on the type of hazard present **(Figure 15.25, p. 586)**. Traffic control zones should be coordinated with local law enforcement to ensure an appropriate safe working zone while maintaining as much traffic flow as reasonably possible.

When a hazardous materials incident occurs on or near a roadway, roadblocks and the rerouting of traffic may be necessary. The ISO should evaluate the traffic management plan and recommend improvements as needed. In these situations, it may be necessary to involve the public information officer to ensure public notification is achieved in a timely and coordinated manner.

Home Ignition Zone

Home ignition zones identify the area surrounding a home in a wildland fire **(Figure 15.26, p. 586)**. This zone allows firefighters to identify the potential threat and determine whether the home can be reasonably protected from an encroaching wildland fire. A home ignition zone is a term used to identify fire potential and is not specifically associated with a control zone unless it is located within an active fire situation.

Figure 15.25 Control zones around vehicle incidents should establish a boundary within which extrication operations can be completed safely. *Courtesy of Chris Mickal, District Chief, New Orleans (LA) FD Photo Unit.*

Figure 15.26 Home ignition zones establish areas that wildland firefighters should try to preserve. In this case, firefighters are creating a trench around this building in an attempt to create a fire barrier.

Control and Exclusion Zones at Technical Rescue Incidents

The first arriving unit to the scene should establish control zones at technical rescue incidents. The IC should size up the incident and begin the process of identifying the last known location of the victim(s), the likely hazards present, and what led up to the emergency situation. It may take some time to assemble the needed equipment and personnel resources to affect a rescue or recovery. During this initial incident phase, first-arriving crews should be isolating the area, marking victim(s) location(s) if possible, and isolating any utility hazards that may be present.

Since technical rescue covers numerous types of specialized rescue, each incident type should be evaluated on a case-by-case basis. For example, the approach to a trench rescue will involve different control zone considerations than a high-angle or confined-space rescue. If the ISO is not specifically trained to the level of the technical operation, a technical specialist or AISO should be assigned to oversee the task-level operation.

Control Zone Schematics for Hazardous Materials Operations

Control zones during hazardous materials incidents may need to be mapped out for responder safety and/or cordoned to provide physical barriers at the scene. These schematics define the various zones and travel pathways at hazardous materials incidents.

Zone Marking Schemes

A three-ringed circular zone perimeter can be used with the hot, warm, and cold zones. The hot zone is the inner most area that is considered the contamination area. No-entry zones may be included in the hot zone. The warm zone is in between the hot and cold zones and contains decontamination corridors. The cold zone is the outer most ring where rehabilitation, the command post, and staging of resources occurs.

Additional zone boundaries should be identified as needed for the threats and hazards present after the IC has completed a good scene assessment. The zones can be cordoned off with rope or fire line tape tied to signs, utility poles, parking meters, or any other objects readily available **(Figure 15.27)**. NFPA® 1500, *Standard on Fire Department Occupational Safety and Health Program*, recommends control zones be identified with colored tape or flags as follows:

- No-entry zone: red/white chevron
- Hot zone: red
- Warm zone: yellow
- Cold zone: green

Figure 15.27 Different colors of cordon tape or rope can be used to identify the boundaries of different control zones.

It may be impractical to string colored tape around an incident area. Flags can be an effective alternative for identifying perimeters and corridors. NFPA® 1500 also suggests the use of fences, flashing beacons, and streets as alternatives.

There is no specific distance or area that should be cordoned off for each zone or from the total incident scene. Zone boundaries should be established by considering the:

- Amount of area needed by emergency personnel to work
- Degree of hazard presented by elements involved in the incident
- Wind and weather conditions
- General topography of the area based on hazmat research
- Recommended zones based on hazmat research

Most incidents do not require this type of cordoned area. Bystanders typically respect the immediate area of operation for fire and emergency services personnel; however, simple direction to move bystanders from an area may be needed. More detailed crowd and traffic control can be coordinated with local law enforcement.

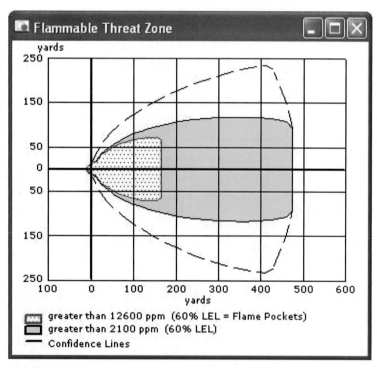

Figure 15.28 Computer software can be used to create maps of the likely movements of smoke, fire, or hazardous materials based upon environmental factors. *Courtesy of ALOHA® software, U.S. Environmental Protection Agency.*

Air Current Markings

Cone-shaped or irregular shaped zones should be identified when air currents directly affect the contamination area. The use of computer software programs, such as the ALOHA® suite stated above as a mitigation strategy, can create maps outlining hazardous atmospheres and their likely movement with the influence from the environment **(Figure 15.28)**.

Responder Proximity

Control zones help establish scene control strategies to ensure responder and civilian safety. The IC will evaluate the incident for threats and hazards and ensure responders are staged in the cold zone before being specifically assigned a task. The ISO should independently assess the use of control zones and ensure personnel task assignments are appropriate in each zone. Departmental SOP/Gs should outline acceptable operational tasks in each control zone and provide training for personnel in these policies.

Travel Pathways

Travel pathways, or corridors, should be established through the control zones. This pathway should provide the shortest and safest route between each zone. Personnel in suit-level protection can easily become overheated and exhausted while working in the hot zone. The established pathway, or corridor, will align the entry and exit points and allow for rapid decontamination of crews. Tactical-level supervisors should monitor the effectiveness of these pathways and recommend improvements when needed. The ISO should monitor the overall use as well and communicate recommendations when needed.

Collapse Zones

Collapse zones are established when there is evidence that a structure or portion of a structure may collapse. Strategy will shift from offensive to defensive, and apparatus, personnel, and master streams must be relocated to a point of safety outside the designated collapse zone. The collapse zone is generally a space 1 ½ times the height of the structure and extending the full length of the structure **(Figure 15.29)**.

Collapse zones, sometimes referred to as safety zones, should also be established around structures that have large glass partition walls. These walls can be weakened or broken by internal fires or earthquake damage, presenting a hazard of flying glass around the structure or some distance from the structure if there is a wind current. While high-rise buildings are typically of Type I construction and not prone to collapse, consideration should be given to falling debris and glass.

Collapse zones should be established when there is an indication that the structure has been weakened by prolonged exposure to fire or heat, when a defensive strategy has been adopted, or when interior operations cannot be justified **(Figure 15.30)**. The size of the collapse zone must take into consideration the type of building construction, other exposures, and the safest location for apparatus and

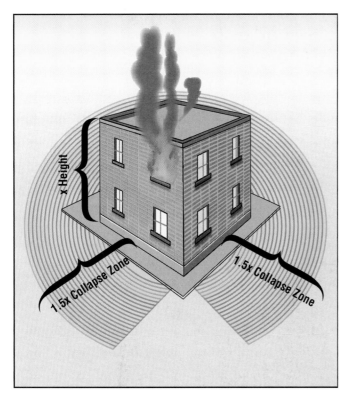

Figure 15.29 Collapse zones should be the equivalent of 1 ½ times the height of the building.

Figure 15.30 When a structure shows signs of collapse, establish a collapse zone and recommend a transition to a defensive strategy. *Courtesy of Ron Moore, McKinney (TX) Fire Department.*

personnel. Church steeples, water tanks, chimneys, and false facades that extend above the top of the structure must be viewed as a potential collapse hazard, even if the structure is not. It should also be noted that most collapses usually involve brick or masonry block and may be structural components or veneer. At the same time, remember that structural collapses are not limited to the actual emergency and can occur well after the fire is extinguished. Fire inspectors must ensure the structural stability of the site before entering.

Because the collapse zone is the full length of all of the effected walls, the safest location for defensive operations is at the corner of the building. In this 90-degree area, master streams and apparatus can be located as long as they are far enough away that flying debris will not strike them.

Helicopter Landing Zones

The Federal Aviation Administration (FAA) and organizational policy regulate helicopter landing zones at established heliports or unimproved temporary landing sites. All medical and military service providers must comply with regulations when landing on or off airport property. Fire and emergency services organizations need to be knowledgeable of the requirements of establishing temporary landing zone sites. Coordination may be needed between several agencies in order to effectively secure a temporary landing site. For example, shutting down a roadway will require traffic and crowd control with the assistance of law enforcement. Additionally, holding a temporary landing site for several minutes after lift-off (in case of an emergency with the aircraft) should be coordinated between all involved agencies.

Preplanning with potential helicopter service providers is essential to ensuring safe air and ground operations. Ground crews need training on proper lighting, hazard identification and mitigation, and communications **(Figure 15.31)**. The ground crew will identify a temporary landing zone, but the flight crew will approve it. The temporary landing zone size ultimately

Figure 15.31 Ground crews should be well-trained on safe operations on or around helicopter landing zones.

depends on the size of the helicopter and day/night operations. A good rule to follow is for the landing zone site to be two times the size of the rotor diameter. The flight crew will have the ultimate say of whether to land. The ground crew should have alternate sites pre-identified if the initial location is not approved.

Communications between ground and flight crews should be prearranged. The goal is for ground and flight crews to be able to communicate without the need for relaying information. Some radio systems can be programmed with radio channels or talk groups to facilitate direct communications. When this type of system is not possible, radio frequencies should be identified and readily available. Hand signals are a last resort means of communicating with the flight crew and may be needed in rare situations. Ground crew members should follow standard FAA hand signals as outlined in FAA AC 91-32B, *Safety In and Around Helicopters*.

Locations Identified During Preincident Planning

As stated, preincident planning should be done with each helicopter service provider – military and civilian. This working group should identify generally acceptable landing zone sites along with unacceptable sites. Sites with paved surfaces are preferred over dirt or soft surfaces. Flat surfaces are preferred over slopes, but no slope should exceed five percent. Locations identified as acceptable should be identified on hardcopy maps or in a computerized mapping system in the mobile data terminals on apparatus.

Departmental SOP/Gs should be established that complement helicopter service provider operational needs. Departments with the potential for supporting landing zone operations should ensure crews have the needed marking devices and training to ensure personnel safety. All personnel should be trained on these procedures to ensure consistent operations.

Safe Landing Zone Locations

Landing zone size will depend on the size of the helicopter and local helicopter service provider policies. Some considerations for safe landing zones are as follows:

- Generally, a 100 ft. x 100 ft. (30m x 30m) area is recommended as a minimum landing zone site. Military and civilian helicopter policies may differ, so coordination with both groups should be considered to ensure safe operations.

- Night operations may require a larger landing zone area.

- Desert locations or those with dusty environments may cause difficulty for some helicopters while others are designed to handle these conditions.

Preplanning is needed to identify generally acceptable landing locations with each service provider and type of helicopter according to the above considerations. Coordination of landing sites on the highway, schoolyards, parking lots, or other large open areas will also be needed. The primary concern is the safety of the flight operation and all persons near the landing zone.

Landing Zone Hazards

There are several landing zone hazards that personnel should recognize and communicate to the flight crew (**Figure 15.32**):

- **Helicopter rotor and tail blades** — ground crew members should never approach a helicopter without flight crew approval. Approach only from the front or sides and as directed by the flight crew. No person should ever walk in the 180-degree arc that encompasses the rear of the helicopter.

- **Multiple helicopter operations** — all flight crews must be informed if multiple helicopters have been requested to a site. Communications between helicopters is essential to safe operations.

- **Weather** — the flight crew will know the overall weather conditions; however, the landing zone manager should communicate ground level winds to the flight crew. Personnel should state wind speeds and direction (where they are from). An in-to-the-wind approach is desirable and ground crews should ensure this approach path is feasible.

- **Darkness** — identifying hazards at night is more difficult for the ground and flight crews. Greater landing zone size is recommended at night.

- **Debris** — the ground crew should walk the landing zone area and secure any trash or debris that can easily become airborne. Flying debris can be hazardous to the helicopter and ground personnel.

- **Obstacles** — the landing zone manager should identify and communicate all utility poles, overhead wires, or other tall objects that are near the landing zone for the flight crew.

- **Dust and dirt** — the ground crew should dampen the landing zone if it is dusty. This option should be communicated to the flight crew for preference.

- **Lighting** — only approved lighting should be used at the landing zone. This action may require preplanning with local helicopter services. Flares are not recommended for landing zones.

- **Slope** — a general description of the slope of the ground should be given to the flight crew. Typically, the slope should not exceed five percent.

- **People/vehicles** — all people and vehicles should be clear of the landing zone. The flight crew typically does not need a person to guide a landing. Preplanning is vital to ensuring safety landing zone operations.

After the landing zone is identified and hazards mitigated, the landing zone manager should communicate with the flight crew. Predetermined radio channels or talk groups should be programmed into portable and/or mobile radios so ground crews can communicate directly with the flight crew.

Flagstaff Medical Center Helicopter Collision[1]

In June of 2008, two helicopters approaching for landing at Flagstaff Medical Center (FMC) in Flagstaff, AZ, collided in midair. The dispatch centers, the pilots of the two helicopters, and FMC were communicating arrival times, landing clearances, and takeoffs. Both pilots reported their arrival times to their respective dispatch centers. The dispatch centers

(Continues on page 594.)

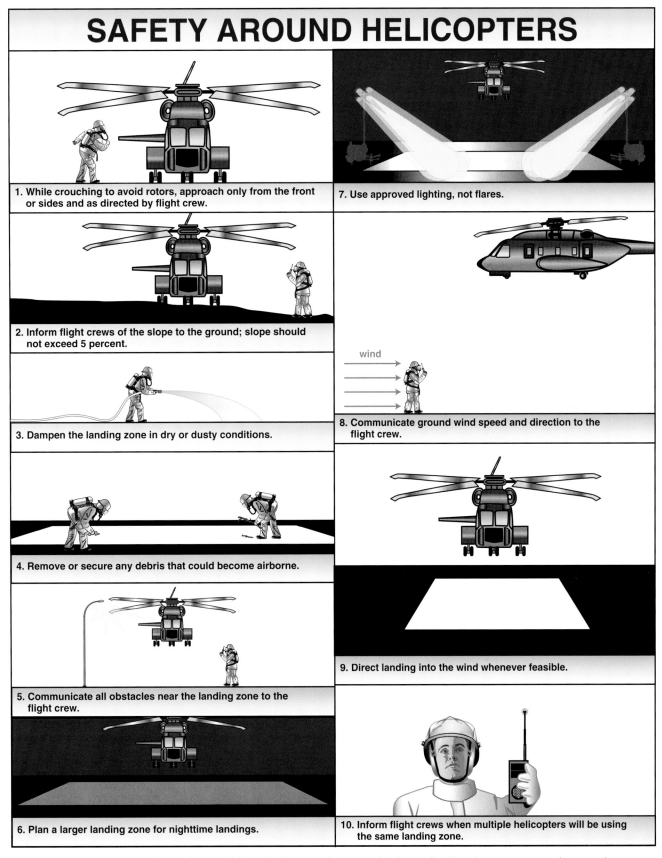

SAFETY AROUND HELICOPTERS

1. While crouching to avoid rotors, approach only from the front or sides and as directed by flight crew.

2. Inform flight crews of the slope to the ground; slope should not exceed 5 percent.

3. Dampen the landing zone in dry or dusty conditions.

4. Remove or secure any debris that could become airborne.

5. Communicate all obstacles near the landing zone to the flight crew.

6. Plan a larger landing zone for nighttime landings.

7. Use approved lighting, not flares.

8. Communicate ground wind speed and direction to the flight crew.

wind

9. Direct landing into the wind whenever feasible.

10. Inform flight crews when multiple helicopters will be using the same landing zone.

Figure 15.32 Landing zone hazards are mitigated using good communications, situational awareness, and responder training.

Flagstaff Medical Center Helicopter Collision[1] *(Continued from page 592.)*

communicated with one another and with FMC to gain clearance for the aircraft to land. Because they were likely to land at nearly the same time, the pilots should have been in communication with one another but were not. They were in communication with different FMC medical teams who were not in contact with one another. As far as either pilot knew, he had clearance to land and there would be no impediments or complications.

Both aircraft arrived at the same time. The last they had heard from their dispatch centers was that there was a wide enough window between their arrivals for each to safely land. Upon arrival, they were not communicating with one another and both tried to land at the same time, resulting in a midair collision. Six occupants on the two aircraft were killed, and a seventh was critically wounded and later died.

When working large incidents with multiple helicopters arriving and taking off, ISOs must establish clear communication guidelines to prevent accidents similar to the one at FMC. Pilots, dispatch centers, and responders on the ground should maintain constant contact. Pilots should be in contact with one another. In addition, pilots and dispatchers should have a central point of contact who can coordinate all the aspects of helicopter operations on the ground.

Monitoring Communications

Radio communications are the foundation of incident scene operations, and they allow for the sharing of information that begins with the dispatch information. The scene size-up, initial assignments, and initial IAP will be communicated via the radio. Quality communications can lead to a coordinated operational effort while poor communications can lead to chaos and confusion. The ISO should monitor radio communications to ensure communications are clear, promote accountability, and lead to a coordinated incident stabilization effort.

Monitoring Personnel Accountability

Departmental SOP/Gs should mandate that all members use an accountability system. The IC implements and maintains personnel accountability. Tracking personnel with an accountability system should be performed per SOP/Gs. Accountability systems vary across the country. Tags, rings, cards, and computer software programs can be used to facilitate the tracking of personnel. The ISO is responsible for verifying the implementation and use of an accountability system at all incidents and training exercises.

Staffing Relevant Positions and Functions

As previously discussed, the ICS is a flexible system that can expand and contract to meet the needs of the incident. When an event expands, it will become necessary to fill command and general staff positions to assist in maintaining an appropriate span of control. Other than the IC position, the ISO position should be the first delegated position within the command and general staff positions.

Identifying Possible Accountability Deficiencies

All personnel must be accounted for on incidents and training events. Unaccounted for personnel or freelancing can be a significant safety issue. While the IC has the overall responsibility for personnel accountability, the ISO has the responsibility for verifying the implementation and use of an accountability system **(Figure 15.33)**. Any deficiencies noted by the ISO should be addressed in the form of recommendations to the IC.

Correcting Accountability Deficiencies

Correcting accountability deficiencies is critical to ensuring personnel safety. If personnel are unaccounted for, a radio **personnel accountability report (PAR)** can usually correct any deficiency. If the accountability system at the command post has not been implemented or is not being used as designed, the ISO must provide the IC with a recommendation of correction. Designating a staff aide or deputy IC may be needed to help correct accountability deficiencies.

Missed, Unclear, or Incomplete Communications

Radio communications can be missed, unclear, or incomplete. Several factors can influence the quality of radio transmissions, such as stress, exertion, background noise, multiple communications, or static. The IC should listen for the these signs of poor radio communications quality and provide a calming reassurance with a command presence on the radio while verifying any missed, unclear, or incomplete transmissions. The ISO should also monitor the radio for these signs and make any needed recommendations to the IC.

> **Personnel Accountability Report (PAR)** — Roll call of all units (crews, teams, groups, companies, sectors) assigned to an incident. The supervisor of each unit reports the status of the personnel within the unit at that time, usually by radio. A PAR may be required by standard operating procedures at specific intervals during an incident, or may be requested at any time by the Incident Commander or the incident safety officer.

Monitoring Radio Transmissions

The ISO is responsible for monitoring all radio transmissions during an incident and ensuring that barriers or obstacles to receiving clear communication are overcome. The ISO should make some field notes about the quality of the radio transmissions during an incident and include recommendations in the postincident analysis report.

Identifying Transmission Barriers

Newer radio systems effectively prevent bleed-over transmissions and transmissions by more than one person at a time. Older radio systems will still encounter these transmission issues. Other barriers to radio use occur when unnecessary communications overwhelm the communication system. This is a common issue for many departments that can potentially prevent the IC from communicating with crews in an IDLH atmosphere. This is a significant safety concern the ISO must address

Figure 15.33 The IC or ISO may appoint an accountability officer. All personnel at the scene have to check in with this officer before entering the hot zone or exclusion zone.

with a recommendation to the IC. Feedback on new and old radio systems can occur when two radios are too close or when voice amplifiers are too loud or close to the microphone.

Correcting Transmission Barriers

Correcting radio transmission issues should begin in the preincident preparation phase. Personnel should train on radio communications to ensure transmissions are clear and concise. Personnel should be trained on when communications are appropriate and inappropriate. Some communications can and should be done face-to-face instead of over the radio. Issues that have occurred in the past should be incorporated and addressed in a training program.

Controlling radio transmissions on the incident scene is the IC's responsibility. A strong command presence on the radio by the IC will typically mitigate any overuse of the radio. The ISO can make other correction recommendations with the tactical-level supervisors face-to-face **(Figure 15.34)**.

Figure 15.34 The IC should be in control of radio communications at the scene. The ISO should remain in radio contact with the IC, but speak to firefighters face-to-face whenever possible to avoid confusing radio traffic.

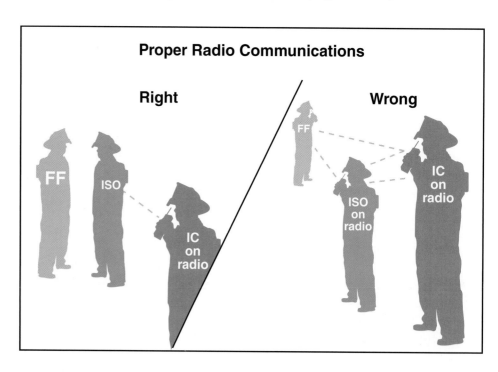

Establishing Rapid Intervention Crews (RICs)

A rapid intervention crew (RIC) is required for any incident or training exercise where a crew enters an IDLH atmosphere as defined in NFPA® 1500. NFPA® 1500 defines two incident phases with regards to RICs. First, during the early stages of the incident, the assignment of an *initial rapid intervention crew* (IRIC) of two members must be staged outside and remain in contact with the interior crew. This complement of two members interior and two members exterior of the IDLH also complies with OSHA 29 CFR 1910.134, *Respiratory Protection* regulation (two-in/two-out rule). Second, after the initial stages of work by the first arriving company, a dedicated RIC shall be assigned with four members. The change in terminology from IRIC to RIC occurs when more than one fire company is operating at the incident.

The IRIC or RIC shall be fully equipped with personal protective clothing and equipment that is consistent with that of the interior crew(s) **(Figure 15.35)**. SOP/Gs should outline the requirement of IRIC/RIC, training of members who can potentially be assigned to this function, and the performance of IRIC/RIC responsibilities. Fire and emergency service organizations should evaluate the following standards for specific RIC deployment and training criteria:

- NFPA®1500, *Standard on Fire Department Occupational Safety and Health Program*

- NFPA® 1561, *Standard on Emergency Services Incident Management System and Command Safety*

- NFPA® 1710, *Standard for the Organization and Deployment of Fire Suppression Operations, Emergency Medical Operations, and Special Operations to the Public by Career Fire Departments*

- NFPA® 1720, *Standard for the Organization and Deployment of Fire Suppression Operations, Emergency Medical Operations, and Special Operations to the Public by Volunteer Fire Departments*

- NFPA® 1407, *Standard for Training Fire Service Rapid Intervention Crews*

Figure 15.35 RICs should be fully equipped with necessary tools and equipment; wearing full personal protective clothing and equipment; and ready to enter the structure on short notice.

Assigning RICs

The IC is responsible for ensuring an IRIC or RIC is assigned to any incident where crews enter an IDLH atmosphere. In the ICS structure, IRIC/RIC report to the IC or, if assigned, the operations section chief. NFPA® 1500 states that additional consideration should be given to complex incidents in which RIC becomes a tactical-level management component of the ICS structure.

According to NFPA® 1500, an IRIC can have one member staged ready for rescue deployment while the second member performs other duties – as long as they are non-critical to the overall safety of the operation and personnel. IRIC/RIC typically stage at the point of entry of the interior crew with all needed equipment ready to deploy in the event of missing, lost, or trapped firefighter(s). The IRIC/RIC should monitor the movement, location, actions, and radio communications of those personnel within the IDLH in the event an interior member/crew declares a MAYDAY emergency.

NFPA® 1500 includes a provision for the IC to assign multiple RICs when the size and/complexity of the incident dictate this need. This situation will typically arise in commercial or industrial settings where multiple points of entry are separated by some distance. NFPA® 1500 recommends the IC consider assigning a RIC at each point of entry when deployment from one location will not be suffice in performing a rescue **(Figure 15.36)**. Further consideration for assigning RICs can be left to each tactical-level management component in a geographical area of the incident. The ISO should independently evaluate the incident and the assignment of RIC(s) and make recommendations to the IC if a deficiency is noted.

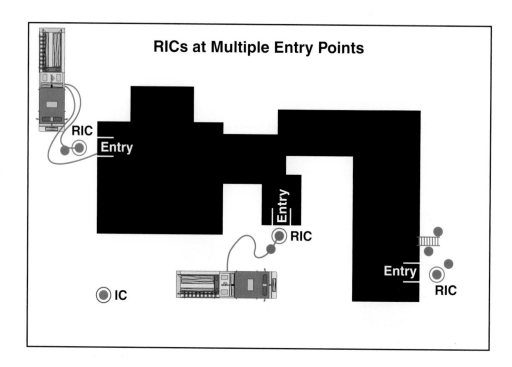

Figure 15.36 RICs should be established at all points of entry surrounding a structure during an incident.

Increasing RIC Capabilities

RIC members should have specific training in performing a downed firefighter rescue that is outlined in NFPA® 1407. At a minimum, a RIC should have full personal protective clothing and equipment to operate in an IDLH atmosphere that is consistent with that being used by the interior crew. Additionally, RIC should have any rescue tools that may be needed to affect a rescue for a particular incident. Some common equipment that may be used by RICs include but may not limited to **(Figure 15.37)**:

• Universal air connection for SCBAs

• Spare facepiece

• Spare SCBA cylinder

• Portable radio with a dedicated channel or talk group

• Rope

Figure 15.37 RICs should have rescue tools with them and spare SCBA to help downed firefighters if needed.

- Charged hoseline
- Forcible entry tools
- Flashlights
- Thermal imager
- Harness, if an elevated rescue or mechanical advantage system is needed

The capabilities of RIC should be evaluated to ensure an adequate number of personnel are available with the proper training and equipment to support the RIC function. Most incidents can be handled with the first-alarm assignment resources; however, ICs and ISOs should not get complacent in managing the incident with this initial allotment of resources. Requesting additional resources, or the upgrading of an assignment, should be supported within the organizational SOP/Gs. A RIC activation must be planned for in the IAP and in the decision-making process of the IC. The number of personnel needed to perform a rescue of a downed firefighter can include several crew rotations. Research has shown that rescuing a downed firefighter(s) is difficult and may occur in stages. Just locating a downed firefighter may take crews more than one attempt. During a rescue, the IC must ensure a constant assignment of RIC outside the IDLH. This requirement may include having multiple rotations of crews prepared to fulfill the RIC function until the rescue operation is complete or the incident is stabilized.

The ISO should evaluate the potential need for multiple RICs and recommend resource needs to the IC. Mutual and/or automatic aid assistance may be needed to fulfill this resource need. Interoperability of radio communications and SCBA components should be preplanned before an incident occurs in which this assistance is requested.

Communicating Hazards to RICs

The RIC should quickly assess the incident for potential hazards. The IC or the ISO should brief the RIC(s) on the assessment of the incident, the identified hazards, and those hazards identified in the preincident plan. Alternate points of access and egress should be identified and communicated to the RIC. Additionally, a RIC should monitor radio traffic during the incident for any specific hazard communication from the interior crews, the ISO, and/or the IC.

Hoarding: Collyer's Mansions

Hoarding is the practice of never removing items from a residence after the items become obsolete or broken. Hoarding may also be a psychological disorder in which the owner of a home places inappropriately high value on valueless objects, such as broken appliances or out-of-date magazines.

Homes where hoarders live are often referred to in the fire service as Collyer's Mansions, named after two brothers who lived together in New York City. Upon their death, their hoarding obsession became a fascination to the public when the reports of the contents of their home were made known. Firefighters often use this term to describe a hoarder's residence.

Hoarders tend to be suspicious of uniformed personnel, which makes identifying hoarders' residences during district surveys difficult. When firefighters working in a structure see evidence of hoarding, the information must be relayed immediately to the IC. The ISO may recommend that RIC capabilities be increased because the high volume of contents in the residence will make rescue of a downed firefighter more difficult. In addition, the ISO may recommend firefighters work only outside the building or evacuate the structure because of excessive fuel loads and high volumes of combustible materials that cannot be identified. There may also be a structural collapse risk because of the weight of the hoarded materials.

Establishing Rehabilitation Areas

Rehabilitation areas should be established in accordance with the recommendations of NFPA® 1584, *Standard on the Rehabilitation Process for Members During Emergency Operations and Training Exercises*. Fire and emergency services personnel can be exposed to a great amount of stress and exertion during incident response and training. Providing a process of rest, rehydration, nourishment, and body temperature regulation improves the overall health and wellbeing of members. Providing rehabilitation services to members should be a standardized process that ensures work/rest cycles and medical evaluation. This process should include recommendations for when members can continue working at an incident, be released to finish their assigned duty shift, or receive further medical care. It is the organization's responsibility to support rehab operations with SOP/Gs, training, and funding.

Identifying the Rehabilitation Needs

Rehabilitation of some type should always be mandatory. The level of rehabilitation should be consistent with the size and scope of the incident, and the needs of members operating at the incident. The department's SOP/Gs should provide general guidelines for identifying rehabilitation needs at incidents or training exercises. Further consideration should be given to but not limited to:

- Level of exertion
- Likelihood of fatigue
- Duration of the incident or training exercise
- Environmental factors and heat/cold stress potential
- Work/rest cycle needs
- Psychological needs

While on the scene, the rehabilitation area is the best opportunity for the ISO or other assigned personnel to assess firefighters for stress indicators. Over time, normal levels of stress can cause detrimental health effects, such as sleep deprivation, fatigue, depression, or illness.

Firefighters not only deal with the day-to-day stresses of life; they also wake up to alarms and move from a state of rest to an immediate state of action. These rapid transitions add to normal levels of stress as do the fire suppression activities that follow. Long-term stress can also be a contributing factor to cardiovascular disease.

Firefighters who are sleep deprived, overstressed, or otherwise exhausted should not be allowed back into operational duty without sufficient rest. **Incident-related stress** combined with cumulative stress can be contributing factors when a firefighter suffers sudden cardiac arrest while on a scene.

ISOs should ensure that the rehabilitation manager checks firefighters in and out of the rehab area and that they are medically cleared to leave the scene when the incident is terminated. The physical and psychological effects of the incident (increased body temperature, exertion or overexertion, mental and physical fatigue, and dehydration) continue to affect firefighters after incidents are terminated. As a result, research is showing that sudden cardiac arrest can also occur after a firefighter has returned to the station or has returned home. The effects of stress do not miraculously disappear simply because the incident is terminated. Any firefighters showing signs of distress should remain in rehab until the symptoms subside, receive medical treatment before leaving the scene, or be sent to a medical treatment facility for additional care.

Incident-Related Stress — Physical and psychological stress related to emergency response; could be associated with especially traumatic events involving fatality or serious injury; may also stem from the normal demands of emergency response over time.

Identifying Rehabilitation Locations

Locating the rehab function within close proximity to on-scene medical support is a logical approach. Trained medical personnel, along with medical supplies, and transportation are then located in one area. Medical personnel can monitor personnel in rehab for core body temperature, blood pressure and rate, hydration, and other vital signs. They can provide immediate assistance and transportation if a firefighter shows symptoms of heat stress, cardiovascular problems, or other ailments. If the emergency incident is too far from a medical facility by ground transport, then an emergency helipad can be established at or near the on-scene medical facility.

Setting Up Rehab Areas

Rehabilitation should be set up close to the incident scene but far enough away to permit personnel to remove all personal protective clothing and equipment. The rehab area needs to be in the cold zone and provides relief from the environment. The IC is responsible for establishing rehab and assigning the rehab manager responsibilities.

Rehab Area Requirements

NFPA® 1584 recommends the following considerations of a rehab area:

- Be clear of any vehicle exhaust
- Be clear of any personal protective clothing and equipment
- Have limited noise interference
- Sheltering for hot/cold environments
- Have active and passive cooling measures available
- Have fluid replenishment
- Have nourishment replenishment as needed
- Medical surveillance
- Personnel accountability and documentation

Medical Surveillance

Medical surveillance needs to be incorporated into the rehab area. On some incidents, such as hazardous materials response, firefighters should receive a premedical screening before entering warm and hot zones of the incident. **Premedical surveillance** should include evaluating baseline vitals and hydrating personnel prior to conducting hot zone activities. The rehab area should include **postmedical surveillance** operations for firefighters who are checking in during operations or after operations are terminated.

Personnel entering postmedical surveillance and rehab should be given time to remove their protective clothing and equipment, rehydrate, and use the restroom before being medically evaluated – unless a medical emergency exists. Medical personnel should be readily available to evaluate all members that report to rehab **(Figure 15.38)**. Medical personnel should be given the authority to keep personnel in rehab or recommend ambulance transport to a medical facility when needed. Postmedical surveillance should include vital sign assessment, body temperature, and the evaluation of symptoms of dehydration, heat/cold stress, cardiovascular illness, stroke, or other ailment.

Rehab Officer Responsibilities

The Responder Rehabilitation Manager reports to the Medical Unit Leader in the Logistics Section of the ICS structure. The person given this assignment is responsible for the following:

- Locating the rehab area
- Securing medical personnel to monitor firefighters
- Obtaining the needed resources for rehydration and replenishment
- Maintaining documentation on all personnel that report to rehab

Medical Surveillance — Rehabilitation function during an incident intended to monitor responders' vital signs and incident-stress levels.

Premedical Surveillance — Evaluation of responders' baseline vital signs before clearance to enter the hot zone; also includes hydration before beginning work at the scene.

Postmedical Surveillance — Evaluation of responders' vital signs, body temperature, and symptoms of dehydration, heat/cold stress, cardiovascular illness, stroke, or other ailment before leaving a scene to return to duty or cycling off a work shift.

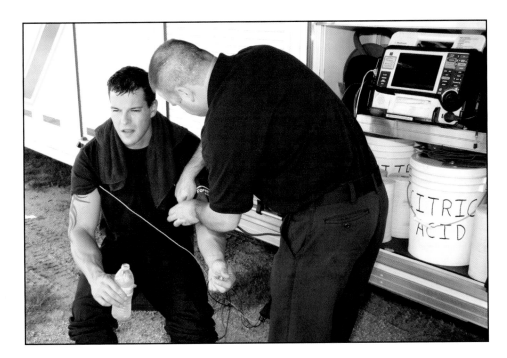

Figure 15.38 Medical personnel should be available to evaluate firefighters when they enter and leave rehab.

The Rehab Manager will make any need requests through the proper chain of command established for a particular incident. Departmental SOP/Gs should outline what documentation is gathered and retained regarding medical surveillance of personnel.

Ensuring the Use of Rehab

Ensuring the use of rehab starts with the organization's administration. Support from the department's leaders is critical to having an effective rehab operation. This support should filter down the organization to all members and reinforce a positive safety culture. Additionally, departments should promote a process of communicating rehab needs as personnel monitor their own health and that of fellow crewmembers. Finally, the ISO should assess the use of rehab at incidents and training exercises and provide recommendations if deficiencies exist. The ISO should also include an assessment of rehab in the postincident analysis so future rehab use is improved.

Stopping, Altering, or Suspending Operations

Within the ICS structure and according to NFPA® 1521, the ISO has the authority to stop, alter, or suspend operations when an imminent threat or hazard places personnel at significant risk of injury or death. Departmental SOP/Gs should formalize this authority along with procedural guidelines to follow when these imminent threats do occur. These situations do not typically occur on a regular basis. Anytime the ISO exercises this authority, communications with the IC must occur either before or just after the order is given. This action will most likely be followed by a reassessment of the incident along with a revision to the IAP. Forecasting the incident is critical to avoiding the situation where the ISO must stop, alter, or suspend operations. Any incident where the ISO exercises this authority, a postincident analysis and critique should occur. This analysis and critique will help identify what led to this action and ways to improve in the future.

Recognizing Unacceptable Levels of Risk

Chapter 13 details the Risk Management Principles that should be applied to each incident and training operation. The risk/benefit analysis will help guide the development of the IAP while placing member safety at the forefront of consideration. Unacceptable levels of risk should be identified during the risk/benefit analysis to ensure appropriate strategy and tactical decision-making. The ISO should evaluate the following to ensure the level of risk is acceptable:

- **Strategy** — the ISO should evaluate the incident strategy that the IC chooses to ensure its appropriateness in stabilizing the incident. For example, an inappropriate strategy may be evident when an offensive strategy is used on a defensive fire, or when defensive operations begin with crews still operating on the interior of a structure.

- **Tactics** — the ISO should evaluate the tactics that crews use. Miscommunication, misunderstanding, or freelancing can lead to inappropriate tactics, placing personnel at risk. For example, opposing hose streams or a hose stream being directed into a ventilation hole can create significant risk to personnel.

- **Weather** — weather can create unsafe conditions that place personnel at unacceptable risk. At times, personnel may be required to seek shelter until the weather improves to a safe level.

- **Culture** — personnel who exhibit risky behavior or are overly aggressive in their actions place themselves and others at great risk **(Figure 15.39)**.

Monitoring Incident Hazards

The incident should be constantly monitored for changing conditions. Personnel must ensure the strategy and tactics employed at an incident remain safe and appropriate. Incident operations should be monitored for their positive and negative effects. The goal of an operation is for incident stabilization; however, operations can also create new hazards. The ISO will play an integral role in monitoring the incident for hazards and communicating the changing conditions to the IC, especially when new hazards are created due to operations.

Determining Scene Conditions

The goal of determining scene conditions is to evaluate all aspects of the incident, the location, the operations, and the influence from the environment. All three aspects will interrelate as personnel work to stabilize the incident and identify factors that may have an effect on the situations. For instance, a structure fire should be evaluated to determine the following:

- Fire behavior in relation to the location (or specific site characteristics) **(Figure 15.40)**

- How fire suppression operations are changing the fire behavior

- Any environmental factors (heat, wind, storms, and terrain) influencing fire behavior

All personnel should constantly analyze scene conditions. The process of incident stabilization can alter conditions for the better or worse. This wide variety of potential changes must be monitored to ensure the employed strategy and tactics do not place personnel in an unacceptable risk situation.

Figure 15.39 Firefighters who freelance at scenes or engage in risky behavior place themselves and others at risk. *Courtesy of Bob Esposito.*

Figure 15.40 Large amounts of smoke coming from beneath the eaves could indicate large involvement in the attic space or an extensive fire in the first floor. *Courtesy of Bob Esposito.*

The role of the ISO in determining scene conditions is to initially assess the situation and the IAP to ensure proper strategy and tactics are being employed. Some common scene conditions the ISO should assess include but are not limited to:

- **Scene safety** — the overall scene should be assessed for imminent threats and hazards that have placed personnel at risk **(Figure 15.41)**.

- **Fire behavior** — fire conditions should be assessed for location, extent, fire load potential, and the effectiveness of suppression activities. Imminent hazards of flashover, backdraft, and smoke explosion should be eliminated if interior operations are to be utilized.

- **Structural collapse potential** — all incidents where the stability of a structure is questioned should be evaluated. If the structure cannot be adequately stabilized, personnel should be restricted from operating in that area.

- **Emergency medical scenes** — an ISO will typically only be assigned during vehicle extrication, mass casualty, or violent events where medical services are the primary tactical objective. The ISO should be alert for atypical stress indicators, especially on mass casualty incidents.

- **Hazardous materials** — as described in Chapter 13, Risk Management Principles, hazardous materials can be from chemical, biological, radiological, nuclear agents/materials, and/or explosives (CBRNE). Some hazardous materials produce immediately identifiable signs and symptoms, while other materials may not be so readily detectable. Determining the presence of hazardous materials is important to personnel safety, but may not always occur in a timely manner. The ISO may have AISOs or technical specialists to assist with evaluating the scene conditions.

- **Technical rescue incidents** — these specialized incidents involve numerous technical rescue situation types that need to be assessed for risks and hazards. The ISO may have AISOs, TSOs, or technical specialists to assist with evaluating the scene conditions.

- **Multiagency or multijurisdictional incidents** — these incidents will involve multiple emergency response disciplines that must be coordinated. The ISO may have AISOs or technical specialists to assist with evaluating the scene conditions.

- **Violence** — every incident scene should be assessed for the potential for violence and devices designed for a maximum destructive effect. Coordination with law enforcement is critical to the operation and for the safety of personnel.

- **Traffic** — any roadway or near-roadway operation should be evaluated to ensure a traffic management system is implemented with the cooperation and coordination of law enforcement.

- **Weather** — the weather conditions should be evaluated to determine its influence on the incident and personnel safety and health. Rehabilitation and sheltering should be considered when developing the IAP.

- **Topography and terrain** — the topography and terrain should be evaluated for their influence on the incident and the placement of apparatus and personnel.

Figure 15.41 All safety risks – location of power lines, apparatus placement risks, working from aerial devices – should be assessed as part of the safety plan for the incident. *Courtesy of Ron Jeffers.*

Monitoring Scene Conditions

Monitoring scene conditions throughout the incident is just as important as conducting the initial scene size-up. Conditions will change as incident stabilization efforts progress. The ISO should provide a critical assessment with the big picture perspective of the operation to the IC. This assessment can be accomplished by surveying the scene, listening to radio communications, and talking with personnel as they leave the hazard zone **(Figure 15.42, p. 608)**. All of the factors in determining the scene conditions should be reevaluated for changes, including scene conditions and personnel actions. This evalu-

Figure 15.42 The ISO should gather information from responders when they leave the hot zone as one part of monitoring the scene conditions. *Courtesy of Ron Jeffers.*

ative process ensures personnel are operating in accordance with SOP/Gs and any regulatory mandates. All personnel, especially crew leaders and tactical-level management supervisors, should conduct audits of conditions. However, according to NFPA® 1521, the ISO has a formal responsibility for auditing personnel actions and communicating recommendations to the IC if deficiencies are noted.

Recognizing Operational Activities That Introduce Imminent Threats

The process of stabilizing an incident can introduce unintended conditions or consequences that place personnel at risk. These imminent threats or hazards need to be identified so corrective measures can be incorporated into the IAP. Some of these activities include:

- Applying large volumes of water can add significant weight to a structure and precipitate collapse.
- Performing vehicle extrication, which may weaken the stability of the vehicle.
- Performing a back-burn on a wildfire that generates greater fire spread instead of slowing the advancement of the fire by removing fuel ahead of it.

These are just a few of the examples of how operational activities can create new hazards that must be recognized and communicated to the IC so the IAP can be adjusted to meet these conditions.

IAP Considerations

The IAP is the game plan for all personnel to function within. The primary considerations in developing the IAP are the incident priorities and risk/benefit analysis. The commonly accepted incident priorities continue to be life safety, incident stabilization, property conservation, and societal restoration. These priorities help organize a consistent decision-making process for the IC. The risk/benefit analysis (see Chapter 13, Risk Management Principles) will help the IC in determining the appropriate level or risk when deciding on the strategy for the incident. Once the incident priorities and acceptable level of risk are determined, the incident objectives will be established in terms of the specific strategy and tactics.

IAP Monitoring

The IAP should be monitored to ensure the risk/benefit analysis remains current. If it appears that tactics are not achieving the incident objectives, then the plan must be revised. In some situations, it may be necessary to shift from an offensive, interior attack strategy to a defensive, exterior strategy. When this shift is made, a new IAP must be developed and communicated to all personnel and units. The transitional phase from an offensive to a defensive strategy is a brief period of time for personnel to adjust their position and tactics to comply with the new IAP **(Figure 15.43)**. When changes such as this occur, communications between operational crews and their division/group supervisor are needed to ensure that the message is received and understood, and for accountability purposes.

Offensive to Defensive Attack

Figure 15.43 When changes are made to tactics in the IAP, a transitional attack from offensive to defensive attack mode allows personnel to adjust to new assignments. *Courtesy of Bob Espositio.*

Adjustments to the IAP

As stated, adjustments to the IAP will be needed when it is determined the IAP is no longer effective in stabilizing an incident or is possibly placing personnel in an unacceptable risky situation. The IC should receive status updates on the changing conditions in order to make effective decisions about the strategy and tactics. The ISO should monitor these communications and the changing conditions and make recommendations to the IC if deficiencies exist.

Suspending or Terminating Operations

Fire and emergency services personnel want to stabilize an incident expeditiously; however, at times, it will be necessary to suspend or terminate operations. The main consideration in these situations is responder safety. Some of the considerations are listed above in the Recognizing Unacceptable Levels of Risk section. Some specific operations that should be suspended or terminated include but are not limited to:

● **Aerial ladder operations** — during lightning, high winds, and icing conditions **(Figure 15.44)**

● **Hazardous materials operations** — with extreme heat or direct fire impingement on a vessel or container

● **Wildland operations** — during high winds, inaccessible terrain, or when a blowup occurs

● **All response activity** — during extreme weather, such as tornadoes, hurricanes, volcanoes, or lightning storms

While the IC has the overall incident responsibility, the ISO holds the authority and responsibility to suspend or terminate operations when a significant, imminent hazard places personnel at risk of injury or death. Any action by the ISO to suspend or terminate an operation must be communicated to the IC as soon as possible. This type of action will typically require an alteration to the IAP, including the possibility of sheltering personnel until conditions improve.

Figure 15.44 During icing conditions, any aerial device operations should be halted and any firefighters operating on the device should be recalled from those assignments and reassigned. *Courtesy of Chicago (IL) Fire Department.*

Altering Operations

Alterations to operations can be subtle or significant. Subtle alterations, such as changing the hose stream applications can be handled at the task level and likely do not involve more than one crew. Significant alterations will involve all personnel and changes to the IAP. These alterations are the result of changing incident conditions that force a reevaluation of and an adjustment to the IAP.

Incident status reports should be communicated to the IC regularly within the proper ICS channels. The ISO should monitor these communications and ensure the IC is incorporating recommendations into the IAP.

The ISO has the authority to alter operations when the risk to personnel is too great. The ISO is required to communicate this action to the IC at the earliest possible time. The communication from the ISO should include any recommendations to alter the IAP when needed.

Monitoring Incident-Related Stress

Stress has always been a part of the emergency responder's life due to the high level of uncertainty, limited control over the work environment, and the psychological effect of repeated emergency calls. Add major events that exceed the normal level of stress and the ability of the body to cope, and critical stress develops. For this reason, a stress management plan must be part of the organization's member physical fitness and wellness program.

Several stress-related psychological reactions and disorders can occur in relation to a critical incident. Fire and emergency services organizations are encouraged to develop partnerships with professional psychological service providers for their **critical incident stress management (CISM)** program. The program should be comprehensive and confidential. Departments should ensure a positive culture and training program exists so that acute and chronic stress reactions and disorders can be recognized and proper care recommended. Professional support partners can assist departments and their members in this process.

Critical Incident Stress Management (CISM) — Comprehensive crisis intervention system composed of 7 elements: pre-crisis preparation, a disaster or large scale incident, defusing one-on-one crisis intervention/counseling, family/organizational crisis intervention, and follow-up/referral mechanisms.

National Fallen Fire Fighters (NFFF) Protocol for Exposure to Occupational Stress

Stress management is an evolving field of study. The National Fallen Firefighters Foundation (NFFF) has begun the process of phasing in best practice recommendations on behavioral health based on recent mental health research. The NFFF program uses different terms but is compliant with NFPA® 1500.

The NFFF program has a recommended process for firefighters to determine their level of occupational stress and move through various levels of professional care to manage the stress. The program starts immediately following incidents with After Action Reports (AAR) designed to identify firefighters who may be experiencing high stress levels. ISOs or other officers identify individuals who need to be approached about their experience. Firefighters may also self-report. NFFF's *Curbside Manner* training instructs ISOs and company officers about procedures at the scene for identifying responders with stress-related difficulties.

After individuals in need are identified, there is a cooling-off period before approaching responders who may be in need or reported a need. After the cooling-off period, firefighters complete a brief screening process. NFFF, with the help of mental health professionals, has developed a Trauma Screening Questionnaire (TSQ) of ten questions designed to quantify a firefighter's experience of stress. Based upon this screening, a

Critical Incident Stress (CIS) — Physical, mental, or emotional tension caused when persons have been exposed to a traumatic event where they have experienced, witnessed, or been confronted with an event or events that involve actual death, threatened death, serious injury, or threat of physical integrity of self or others.

Atypical Stressful Event — term used in National Fire Protection Association® (NFPA®) standards to describe incidents that have a likelihood of causing critical incident stress.

Potentially Traumatic Event (PTE) — term developed by the National Fallen Firefighters Foundation (NFFF) in their programs to describe incidents that have the potential for critical incident stress.

Critical Incident Stress (CIS)

A critical incident is generally referred to as an event that is out of the normal or routine and one that causes abnormal physiological and psychological reactions. **Critical incident stress (CIS)** can occur with a single incident or from cumulative events over time. Each responder will react to stress in an individualized manner. Adverse stress reactions can occur over a short- or long-term basis after a critical incident(s). Personnel must be able to function at a high level during operations; however, this ability to function can be diminished when stress remains unmanaged.

Atypical Stressful Events

Atypical stressful event is the term used in NFPA® standards to describe critical incident stress. As knowledge of incident stress management evolves, the NFFF has developed widely accepted stress management programs that use the term **potentially traumatic event (PTE)**. The ISO should be familiar with both terms as descriptors for incident stress.

Personnel often experience atypical stress after incidents involving the following situations:

• Mass casualties

• Fatalities involving children

• Serious injuries or fatalities involving members of the organization, both on and off duty

• Suicides

• Serious injuries or fatalities involving close friends, relatives, or colleagues

• Violence directed toward firefighters or other emergency responders

• Deaths of civilians as a result of emergency operations

• Excessive media attention generated after incidents

Notification of Intervention

Departmental SOP/Gs should provide guidelines for all personnel to recognize the signs and symptoms of critical incident stress. Notification of the need for intervention can occur in several areas of an incident operation. Personnel and crews, as well as division and group supervisors, should monitor each other for stress. Beyond the tactical-level operations, rehabilitation members should be monitoring personnel for signs and symptoms of physiological and psychological stress. Rehab can be an effective time to monitor responders for their initial stress reaction to an incident. All members should monitor for stress and the need for intervention, according to NFPA® 1521. However, the ISO has a formal responsibility to monitor personnel for signs and symptoms of critical incident stress and inform the IC of the need for intervention. When the need for intervention is recognized at any of these levels, communication should flow through the proper channels to the IC.

Signs and Symptoms of Incident-Related Stress

Personnel should be monitored during and after incidents for atypical stress reaction(s). All members operating at an incident should be aware of the potential for atypical stress. The ISO is responsible for monitoring personnel and making recommendations to the IC when atypical stress is a possibility. A process of recognizing and managing stress should be included in the department's SOP/Gs, training, and professional referral process.

When the body undergoes normal levels of stress, it responds with increases in heart rate and blood pressure, oxygen consumption, muscle tension and strength, and dilation of the pupils. Excessive stress, however, results in further emotional and cognitive responses. Symptoms associated with excessive stress include, but are not limited to:

- Difficulty concentrating or staying focused
- Temporary loss of short-term memory
- Obsessive thoughts
- Loss of mental flexibility
- Tendency to withdraw or become isolated
- Feelings of invulnerability
- Fantasy or wishful thinking experiences
- Abuse of alcohol and drugs

Incident-Related Stress Assistance

In order to address the symptoms listed above, fire and emergency service organizations should consider establishing a critical incident stress management plan. The plan should consist of emergency services personnel, healthcare professionals, and clergy who have specialized training in dealing with critical incident stress. These individuals can provide the necessary support for those members experiencing excessive stress or the effects of cumulative stress. The plan should include training/support for emergency personnel about the causes and results of critical incident stress, cumulative stress, stress reduction methods, and sources of professional assistance (**Figure 15.45, p. 614**).

Peer Support

Peer support members are formally trained emergency service providers who assist with delivering the department's critical incident stress management plan. Only formally trained personnel should participate as facilitators in the stress management process. Peer support members provide a valuable service

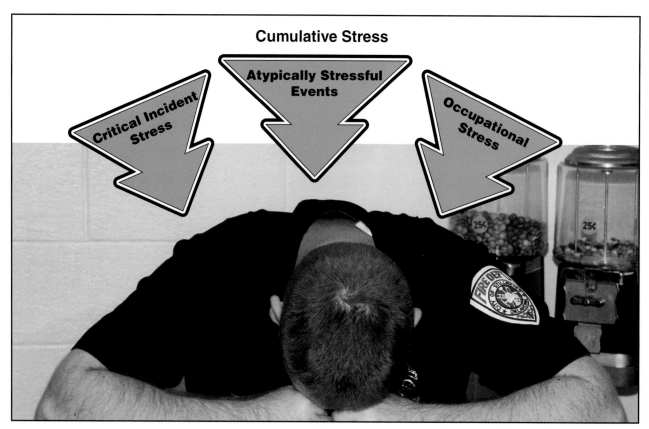

Figure 15.45 Stress is cumulative and comes from occupational duties, "routine" emergency calls, and atypically stressful events. Seeking counseling for individuals showing signs of cumulative stress is a good way to lengthen their firefighting careers and protect their health.

Defusing — Informal discussion with incident responders conducted after the incident has been terminated, either at the scene or after the units have returned to quarters. During the discussion commanders address possible chemical and medical exposure information, identify damaged equipment and apparatus that require immediate attention, identify unsafe operating procedures, assign information gathering responsibilities to prepare for the postincident analysis, and reinforce the positive aspects of the incident.

Debriefing — A gathering of information from all personnel that were involved in incident operations; in terms of incident-related stress, helps personnel process the scope of an event after a few days have passed.

and bring a level of credibility with the fire and emergency services field of professionals. Peer support should be utilized within its scope of training and not be confused with professional support and care.

Long-Term Professional Support

Some personnel may need psychological support beyond the peer support level. The stress management program should include guidelines for providing professional support to department members. This support can be a part of the member assistance program or a specifically targeted support program. Either way, the professional support network must be confidential for any member seeking assistance.

Defusing and Debriefing

The use of **defusing** and **debriefing** may be a part of a department's stress management plan. Defusing and debriefing are terms defined in NFPA® 1521 as elements of a stress management program. The terms are defined here, but this does not indicate they are mandatory components of a stress management program.

Defusing occurs the same day as the critical incident and before members are relieved of duty. The defusing process is brief and includes the sharing of information within small groups of responders **(Figure 15.46)**. The defusing process includes three phases that allow trained personnel to assess, triage,

Figure 15.46 Diffusing is usually a brief process and involves discussing an incident with small groups of responders. Diffusing is a good time for firefighters to self-report any issues they are going through that they have not been able to manage. *Courtesy of Steve Baker.*

and mitigate acute stress symptoms. Formal stress management meetings or debriefings may follow in the coming days after a defusing.

The debriefing process, if used, occurs within a few days of the incident and is intended to help personnel process the scope of the event. Only trained personnel in CISM techniques should provide or assist with the debriefing process. The debriefing process does not replace the need for professional support when personnel have been exposed to an atypically stressful event. Professional services must be confidential and may be associated with the member assistance program of the organization.

The ISO should be knowledgeable of the fact that stress reactions and stress management are beyond the scope of this manual. The ISO must be aware that these situations can and will arise, and ensure a process is available to assist personnel when needed. This assistance and support can be short- and/or long-term depending on the individual and the scope of the incident.

What This Means to You

Critical incident stress has a cumulative effect over the course of a firefighter's career. Though it is possible that a particularly challenging incident could result in detrimental health or psychological problems for an otherwise healthy firefighter, it is more likely that the incident that triggers a problem is the last of many such incidents that have been troubling that firefighter for a long time.

A series of events occurred in a metro fire department that illustrate the effects of cumulative stress. Firefighters responded to a motor vehicle accident (MVA) in which a teenager was trapped in one of the wrecked vehicles and needed immediate extrication or was likely to die.

The firefighters were successful in extricating the young man and getting him to a local hospital. No mistakes were made, and everyone performed admirably and according to all procedures. There was a feeling of optimism that the firefighters had saved the young man's life. They learned later that he died in the hospital shortly after arrival.

After hearing the news about the teenager, one of the firefighter paramedics who was at the scene tendered his resignation. The firefighter had 16 years of dedicated service and a successful career. He gave little explanation as to why he resigned, but it was assumed he made his decision based upon the vehicle incident that took the boy's life.

According to departmental records, two previous captains had minor issues with the firefighter who resigned. He was described as having a negative attitude and being "touchy" or irritable.

Before the firefighter's resignation could be processed, the department administration enrolled him in a counseling program. During counseling, the firefighter expressed that the stresses of the job were having a profoundly negative effect on his personal life and the people around him. He stated that the accident with the teenager "put him over the edge." Even with counseling, he did not change his mind about wanting to leave the fire service. At that point, it was too late for him and he needed to move on.

As the ISO who worked the scene, what might you have been able to do to initiate the professional help this firefighter needed to come to terms with his profession and the things he had seen? There are many methods available, even something as simple as taking the time at the end of an incident such as the one described to have a private conversation with each responder. You could also ask the rehab staff if they felt that anyone was showing unusual stress indicators. In some departments, you may also have the authority to set up a number of peer group meetings for the firefighters at the scene so that they can share their experiences.

Chapter Summary

Incident response and operations have inherent hazards that can place personnel at risk of injury or death. A good risk management process should identify these hazards, provide mitigation steps, and ensure operations follow an effective IAP. All personnel have a responsibility for recognizing scene hazards and communicating them through the proper channels so mitigation efforts can be included in the IAP. The ISO provides additional scene safety support. The ISO must have a broad range of knowledge, training, and experience in recognizing scene hazards, but should also recognize when technical expertise is needed. Ultimately, the ISO ensures all personnel, including the IC, are following SOP/Gs and functioning in a safe manner. Rarely will the ISO need to stop, alter, or suspend an operation; however, this authority is the final line of defense for ensuring the safety of personnel.

Review Questions

1. What factors should the incident safety officer take into consideration when assessing incident hazards and evaluating access and egress suitability? (pp. 552-558)

2. What is the incident safety officer's role in establishing an incident action plan (IAP)? (pp. 558-560)

3. How can the incident safety officer successfully control safety communications at an incident scene? (pp. 560-562)

4. What information should the incident safety officer include in incident safety plans and safety briefings? (pp. 562-571)

5. What procedures should the incident safety officer follow when transferring duties to another ISO? (pp. 572-573)

6. What factors should the incident safety officer consider when identifying and requesting technical specialists or assistant safety officers? (pp. 574-580)

7. How are operational zones established at an emergency incident? (pp. 580-594)

8. What are the incident safety officer's responsibilities in regards to monitoring communications at an incident? (pp. 594-596)

9. What role does the incident safety officer perform in the establishment of and communication with rapid intervention crews (RICs)? (pp. 596-600)

10. What procedures should the incident safety officer follow when establishing rehabilitation areas at an incident scene? (pp. 600-603)

11. What factors should comprise the decision to stop, alter, or suspend operations at an emergency scene? (pp. 603-611)

12. What information should the incident safety officer consider when monitoring incident-related stress? (pp. 611-616)

Chapter 15 End Notes

1. U.S. National Transportation Safety Board (NTSB) Accident Number: DEN08MA116B

Refer to Appendix B: Learning Activity Answers in the back of this manual for suggested responses.

Purpose

The ISO is responsible for creating an incident safety plan during complex incidents when the incident action plan is written. The incident safety plan requires a detailed analysis of the incident and a plan for ensuring safe operations and should provide reasonable mitigation strategies for the incident planning process.

Directions

1. Review the Rhoads Building Scenario, first presented in **Learning Activity 13-1**.

2. Read the additional information for the scenario provided below.

3. As you read both items, focus on the information you need in order to prepare an *incident safety plan*. Make sure you consider:

   • General incident information

   • Impact of the weather

   • Material identification

   • Geographical data

   • Location site/building plans/preincident plans

   • Hazards

   • Mitigation and prevention

   NOTE: You will have to make some educated guesses about some of the information presented in the scenario. For instance, you may not know the specific type of building construction, but you do know that it is an older apartment building, which suggests the building may be Type III construction.

4. Record the information relevant to the bullet points in step 3.

5. Refer to your list or table of identified hazards from **Learning Activity 14-1**.

6. Based on this combined information, provide a brief description of the incident safety plan that might be developed to identify hazards and offer mitigation strategies for this incident.

   NOTE: It might be helpful to download a copy of ICS form 208 (Safety Message/Plan) from the FEMA website and follow the format provided in the form.

Rhoads Building Scenario, Cont.

10:18 a.m. – You contact the IC and tell him that an incident safety plan needs to be prepared. He agrees and requests dispatch to attempt to locate maintenance personnel or call-out for the Rhoads Building. Dispatch advises that they have already contacted the call-out on record for the building and that the property manager is on her way to the scene.

Refer to Appendix B: Learning Activity Answers in the back of this manual for suggested responses.

10:19 a.m. – You ask dispatch to assist with weather updates, as more snow could hamper rescue and fire suppression efforts. The IC quickly briefs you on the scene size-up and the control and exclusion zones. You agree with his assessment and remind him that in order to prepare an appropriate incident safety plan quickly, you need him to request preincident plans, building blueprints, and SDS information from the property manager when she arrives. He delegates that responsibility to you.

10:21 a.m. – The fire appears to be contained and nearly extinguished. Personnel assigned to search the building have found no victims so far. You are looking over street maps of the area when the building manager arrives. You find out there is no preincident plan in place for the building and no Safety Data Sheets, as the building has no permanent tenants. However, she does have blueprints of the building and interior photos taken in the last year on her tablet device. She explains that the building has been condemned for many years and that while preparing for demolition, significant asbestos was discovered. There are no active utilities currently working in the building. You provide this information to the IC and provide him with a verbal incident safety plan.

Accident Investigation and Postincident Analysis

Chapter Contents

Key Terms

NFPA® Job Performance Requirements

This chapter provides information that addresses the following job performance requirements of NFPA® 1521, *Standard for Fire Department Safety Officer Professional Qualifications (2015)*.

5.1.2

5.6.1

5.7.1

5.7.2

Accident Investigation and Postincident Analysis

Learning Objectives

After reading this chapter, students will be able to:

1. Describe the incident safety officer's responsibilities in the accident investigation process. (5.1.2, 5.6.1)

2. Explain the incident safety officer's role in the postincident analysis process. (5.7.1, 5.7.2)

3. Learning Activity 16-1: Assist in the investigation process at the scene of an emergency incident. (5.1.2, 5.6.1, 5.7.2)

Chapter 16
Accident Investigation and Postincident Analysis

Case History

A fire department was dispatched for a possible structure fire in a one-story commercial brick building after a passerby reported fire visible inside the structure with light smoke showing. The building was occupied by both a restaurant and a drycleaner. It had been some time since this particular department had responded to a fire call, and the firefighters were eager for the response. The first fire personnel on scene was a deputy chief who arrived within 2 minutes of the initial alarm, assumed command, performed a size-up, and communicated a working fire from the drycleaner occupied part of the building.

When the department's safety officer arrived, he notified the IC that he was the incident safety officer for the incident and performed a 360 of the structure to identify any possible hazards. Without waiting to hear if the ISO had discovered any hazards, the IC began giving orders to his crews to begin interior attack.

Before the ISO could complete his reconnaissance, the truck company had already forced entry into the structure. The engine company was entering with a 1½-inch line. Smoke conditions had worsened.

In their eagerness to get to the fire, the firefighters had made a number of safety oversights. Accountability procedures were not in place, so the ISO had no reliable information on how many firefighters were inside. The fire was inside the drycleaners, and the ISO could not determine if the IC had looked up the proper preincident information to identify the building's contents. In addition, only about half of the firefighters working near the smoke had donned SCBA. Had the incident escalated, the lack of risk management could have gotten firefighters injured or killed.

The ISO included all of this information in field notes while observing the scene. He then later ensured that all of the SOP/G deviations were included in a written postincident analysis. Based upon his analysis, refresher training on scene size-up was instituted in the department and SOP/Gs were reviewed to ensure that they did, in fact, provide accurate information.

The incident safety officer (ISO) begins the fact-gathering process when an accident occurs during an incident, training, or other activity to which the ISO was assigned. The ISO is responsible for investigating incidents that result or could result in hazardous conditions, injuries, illnesses, exposures, and fatalities involving fire department members. Investigations must be documented, so that the health safety officer (HSO) can analyze the information to determine the root cause of the accident. The ISO provides the HSO with a written accident report on any safety and health issues identified during an incident. This process follows the same guidelines of a postincident report.

To reduce the potential for accidents to occur or to reduce the severity of accidents, each organization must develop and implement an accident investigation policy and procedure. The policy should define accidents, establish the authority for investigating each type of accident, and establish a procedure for accident investigation. The ISO, the HSO, and the organization's safety and health committee will have the ultimate authority for accident analysis.

While the ISO focuses on reports of injuries or fatalities, instances and accidents where there was the potential for an injury are of equal importance. Reporting and keeping records of these occurrences is a proactive way for the ISO to make recommendations for change, preventing a firefighter injury or death. The sections that follow describe the ISO's role in investigating accidents and the postincident analysis (PIA) that takes place afterward in an attempt to prevent any further incidents involving department personnel.

16 Firefighter Life Safety Initiatives 9

The *16 Firefighter Life Safety Initiatives* were discussed in Chapter 1, Health Safety Officer Responsibilities. Initiative 9 is pertinent to the ISO's understanding of accident investigation and postincident analysis:

9. Thoroughly investigate all firefighter fatalities, injuries, and near misses.

ISO Accident Investigation Responsibilities

Members should follow established SOP/Gs for reporting accidents and injuries using a standard reporting procedure. Once an accident has been reported, it must be investigated. Beginning with the report of the incident, the ISO will assist with the gathering of information pertinent to the investigation. Learning Activity 16-1 provides a scenario designed to help you identify your responsibilities during an accident investigation.

NOTE: In the event that the ISO lacks proper training, a trained investigator should be consulted.

Accidents and near-misses are generally investigated even in the absence of injury. Apparatus and equipment failures need to be reported so that the ISO can report to the HSO to account for aging or malfunctioning equipment when assessing equipment specifications. Vehicle incidents can range from a traffic accident involving department vehicles, apparatus, and apparatus equipment failures to property damage as a result of improper backing or brake failures. Any of these occurrences may result in a firefighter injury or fatality.

In addition to written reports, investigations may include photographs or video footage of the accident or incident. During the investigation phase of the incident, the ISO collects information from many sources, such as the following:

- Dispatch records
- Apparatus data on transmission and rpm speeds
- GPS, mobile terminal data, and automatic vehicle locator (AVL) data
- Interviews with all participants

- Emergency incident reports
- Incident action plan (IAP)
- Incident safety plan
- Police reports/accident reconstruction team
- Other witnesses
- Weather conditions/reports
- Maintenance records
- Photographs and videotapes of the scene or incident **(Figure 16.1)**
- Video surveillance footage from surrounding occupancies
- Site diagrams
- Physical property involved in the incident **(Figure 16.2, p. 626)**
- Chain of custody documentation **(Figure 16.3, p. 626)**
- Laboratory analysis of evidence relating to the incident **(Figure 16.4, p. 627)**
- Testimony from experts
- Incident safety officer report
- Training records

This information provides the ISO with a fairly accurate description of the incident. A written report is then compiled on the incident relating to health and safety issues. The finalized report may include diagrams as an explanatory tool for understanding an accident or incident. Computer software programs are available to make this process easier.

Recognizing Conflicts of Interest

The ISO must be able to recognize any conflicts of interest that exist with personnel involved in the investigation process, including the ISO's own role. If a conflict is not eliminated, the findings of an investigation and any recom-

Figure 16.1 Reviewing photographs of the scene provides important information about an accident.

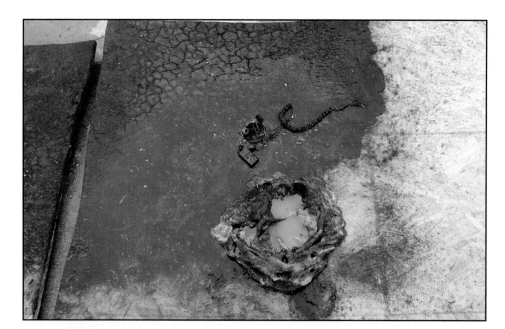

Figure 16.2 The remains of incendiary devices may be important physical evidence in an investigation. *Courtesy of Neal Moore, Stillwater (OK) Fire Department.*

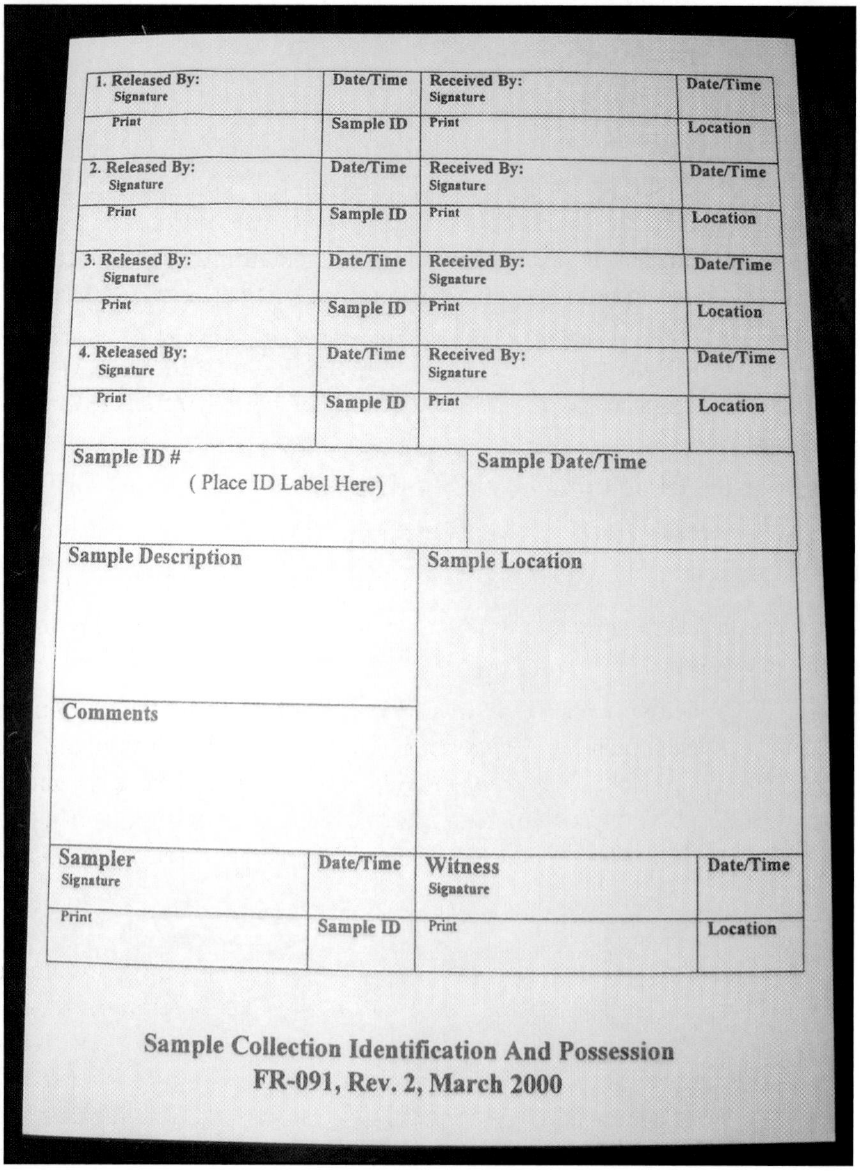

1. Released By: Signature	Date/Time	Received By: Signature	Date/Time
Print	Sample ID	Print	Location
2. Released By: Signature	Date/Time	Received By: Signature	Date/Time
Print	Sample ID	Print	Location
3. Released By: Signature	Date/Time	Received By: Signature	Date/Time
Print	Sample ID	Print	Location
4. Released By: Signature	Date/Time	Received By: Signature	Date/Time
Print	Sample ID	Print	Location

Sample ID # (Place ID Label Here)		Sample Date/Time
Sample Description		**Sample Location**
Comments		
Sampler Signature	Date/Time	Witness Signature	Date/Time
Print	Sample ID	Print	Location

Sample Collection Identification And Possession
FR-091, Rev. 2, March 2000

Figure 16.3 Chain of custody should be documented every time each piece of evidence changes hands during an investigation.

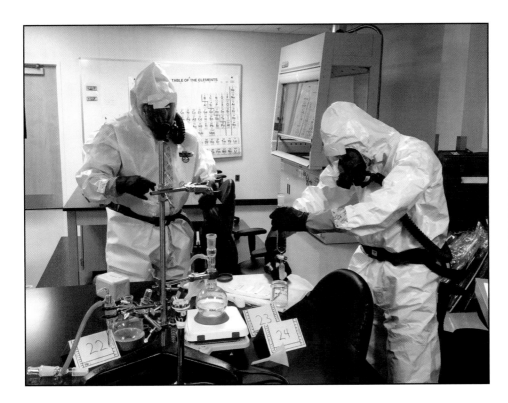

Figure 16.4 Laboratory analysis of physical evidence may be necessary, especially when the incident or accident included hazardous materials. *Courtesy of B. White.*

mendations made as a result of it may come into question. To maintain the credibility of the investigation, the ISO should ensure all real and perceived conflicts are removed as soon as they are noticed.

Departments should have an SOP/G that defines the procedural adjustments that should be made to the investigation process to eliminate the perception of conflict or bias. If the ISO must remove oneself from an investigation because of a conflict, the SOP/G should address which personnel will assume the ISO's responsibilities in the fact-finding process. A conflict of interest may exist when the ISO:

- Is or was a part of the involved fire company.
- Is related to the individual(s) being investigated.
- Is open to have his or her role in the incident questioned.
- Has been involved with a previous disciplinary action with anyone under investigation.

Investigations should be conducted as objectively as possible. Department personnel and the public could question the integrity of an investigation if they feel that it was performed unfairly and/or with a perceived bias toward any of the parties involved in the incident. Even if a conflict of interest is identified, the ISO can still perform duties at the incident, such as secure the scene.

Identifying Evidence

As ISOs conduct scene examinations, they should constantly be looking for any **physical evidence** that will assist in the determination of the cause of the accident. As part of the investigative process, materials identified as potential evidence should be secured and protected from further damage until they can be documented and collected for preservation and further analysis **(Figure 16.5, p. 628)**. No evidence shall be removed in any fashion from the

Physical Evidence —
Tangible or real objects that are related to the incident.

Figure 16.5 When surveying a scene for evidence during an investigation, the ISO should take precautions to preserve all identified evidence to prevent contamination or spoliation.

scene. Furthermore, all tools, handlines, ladders, apparatus, supply lines, and other relevant items of importance should remain in place. ISOs should follow the procedures established by their departments regarding the collection of physical evidence.

When ISOs arrive at an incident scene, they may not necessarily be able to identify what may later be determined to be evidence. Upon arrival, everything at the scene should be considered potential evidence. Through investigation, gathering of data, and developing and testing a hypothesis, relevant items of evidence will be identified. As a result, ISOs should try to minimize disturbing the scene as much as possible. Some observations and items will be readily apparent as evidence, while others will only be discovered through the investigative process.

Preserving Evidence

The ISO should understand the process of preserving evidence, but may not have preservation authority at the scene. SOP/Gs should address incident scene preservation and the securing of evidence. The ISO will begin collecting evidence immediately upon arrival at the scene, so an emphasis must be placed on ensuring that potential evidence is not destroyed, disposed of, or compromised by other personnel or outside conditions. Investigations may involve external agencies, such as law enforcement, NIOSH, and/or OSHA, and scene preservation of all evidence must be protected. This assistance may include having a police department crime scene investigation (CSI) photographer or evidence collection technician photograph the scene before any possible evidence is collected. The gathering of information should be expedited and accomplished as soon as possible after the event. Scene control and preservation should continue until all documentation and photographs are obtained.

Collecting Evidence

The first responders at the scene are not in a position to decide if the potential evidence they identify at the scene will have any value to an incident or accident investigation. As a result, ISOs should preserve, collect, and document all possible evidence according to local policies. ISOs who lack proper evidence collection training should either seek training or allow trained investigators to collect physical evidence.

The ISO can take photographs to capture how the scene looked shortly after the incident and the location of items in relation to each other **(Figure 16.6)**. These photographs will provide a visual reference of the scene long after the incident occurred and the area has been cleaned up. The ISO could also gather information on the incident from the following:

- Witness statements
- Interviews with first responders
- IAP forms
- ICS information

Figure 16.6 Taking photographs shortly after an accident occurred captures how the scene looked.

- Timeline information from the incident
- Collected communications

When an item of evidence is tagged and assigned an identification number, this number should be recorded in the investigation notes and on the scene diagram **(Figure 16.7)**. An ISO should also generate an evidence log sheet that lists each item collected. The log will become an essential portion of the documentation of the chain of custody of evidence collected during the investigation.

Figure 16.7 Collected evidence should be tagged to track it properly throughout the investigation.

Identifying and Interviewing Witnesses

During the investigation, an ISO may need to interview the following witnesses:

- Those who discovered the accident
- Those who reported the accident
- Those who observed the accident
- Anyone who has information about the preincident condition of the premises, such as the owner or occupant
- Residents of neighboring properties
- First-arriving first responders
- First responders who resolved the incident, such as extinguishing the fire
- First responders who were present at the incident for other reasons
- Anyone else identified as having relevant information

During the interviews, the ISO should look for pertinent information that consists of who, what, when, where, why, and how. These are the six basic questions that should be asked of every witness. Additional areas of inquiry that may elicit useful information include:

- Unusual circumstances before, during, or after the incident
- Location(s), size, and appearance of the fire at the time of discovery and during suppression
- Nature and extent of suppression efforts
- Type of material that was seen burning
- History of recent repairs or remodeling
- Use of the building
- Where or how the accident occurred
- Size of the fire when the witness first saw it
- Location of witnesses in relation to the incident
- Witness names and contact information for future follow-up

Information gathered during the interviews should be accurately documented and preserved. Documentation can be collected as notes, audio or video recordings, or written statements. Interviews should be conducted in a non-accusatory manner, preferably away from the incident scene. A variety of resources are available to assist the ISO in this process, including NFPA® 921, *Guide for Fire and Explosion Investigations,* Chapter 13, Sources of Information, and the IFSTA **Fire Investigator** manual, both of which contain information on conducting interviews.

Interviewing Personnel Involved

Department personnel involved in an incident must be interviewed. While interviews should be conducted as early in the investigation as possible, consideration of the situation must be taken into account. Interviews may be delayed when personnel are being medically treated or when the emotional and psychological well-being of the personnel involved is a concern. Interviews should be conducted with individuals and not as a group. The ISO should ensure the department has an established SOP/G and/or collective bargaining agreement outlining interview participation and when that will occur.

Conversations between witnesses should be limited when appropriate. An individual's account of an event can change with the passage of time and when conversations between witnesses occur. Written witness statements should be included in the early stages of the investigation. All interviews and documents should address and capture the relevant factors of what occurred and clarify any confusing or conflicting information. Department policy should address when, and if, audio or video recordings are used during interviews. At a minimum, signed written statements should be obtained and filed in the report.

Documenting Personal Observations and Actions

Good documentation is essential in any investigation because most scenes are altered or destroyed during or after an investigation. Documentation can include:

- Sketches
- Diagrams

- Drawings
- Maps
- Photography

A simple sketch is the minimum drawing that needs to be developed as part of every investigation **(Figure 16.8)**. A more detailed sketch may be necessary, depending on the complexities of the incident. The sketch provides a graphical representation of the scene that is proportional but not necessarily to scale.

For many investigations, the simple sketch completed at the incident will only be the beginning of what is needed. It may become necessary to develop a formal set of drawings, diagrams, or maps that present detailed information related to the incident. Detailed diagrams of specific areas or systems involved in an incident may be needed to provide necessary details for the investigation.

Photographs provide exact representations of the key components of an incident. Photographs show the

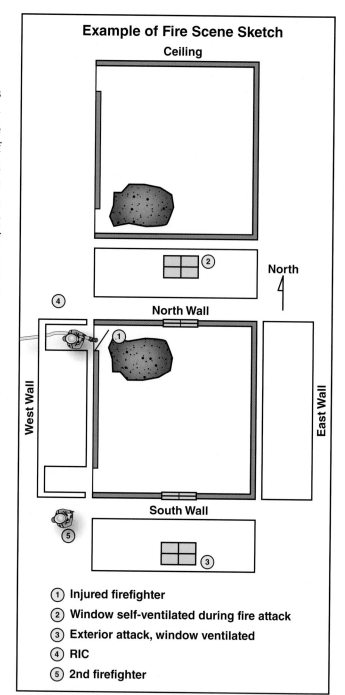

Figure 16.8 A simple fire scene sketch that shows the basic layout and location of relevant personnel and events is a minimum requirement for an investigation.

scene as it was found and depict the investigative process at the scene throughout the debris removal, reconstruction of the area of origin, and identification and collection of evidence stages of the investigation. When the investigation is completed and the scene is cleaned, reconstructed, or demolished, the photographs taken during the scene examination may be all that remains.

Maintaining Chain of Custody

During an investigation, the ISO often starts the **chain of custody** of any documents and evidence collected. The ISO may also conduct interviews that become evidence. The chain of custody tracks an item of evidence from the time it is found until its **final disposition**. Maintaining the chain of custody of evidence is essential to ensure that evidence remains accurate for later analysis and maintains its evidentiary value.

Once an item is considered evidence, it should be properly secured, and its handling and transfer of custody should be documented from the time it comes into a first responder's possession until it reaches its final disposition. Each person who has possession of an item of evidence must be able to attest to the fact that the item was not subject to tampering or **contamination** while it was in his or her custody. If an item was altered while in a laboratory technician's possession, the technician must document what was done to it and provide results of the testing. Anytime the custody of an item changes, the following information should be obtained:

- Name and contact information of the current and prior custodian(s)
- Date and time that the item was transferred and its new location
- Description of any modification, handling, testing, or other alteration that occurred while the item was in the custody of the current custodian
- Condition of the item or its packaging when it was transferred to the new custodian

Chain-of-custody issues extend beyond the physical evidence collected at a fire scene. All incident-related evidence, including documents of evidentiary value and any other items that support the findings of the investigation, is subject to chain-of-custody rules. Chain of custody, however, depends on the case and policies of the jurisdiction involved.

Chain of Custody — Continuous changes of possession of physical evidence that must be established in court to admit such material into evidence. In order for physical evidence to be admissible in court, there must be an evidence log of accountability that documents each change of possession from the evidence's discovery until it is presented in court.

Final Disposition — Point in the chain of custody where a piece of evidence is determined to no longer have value as evidence; options at this point may include permanent storage, return to the owner, or authorized destruction.

Contamination — General term referring to anything that can taint physical evidence during an investigation.

Identifying the Cause of the Accident

The ISO has the responsibility of gathering the investigative information that will aid the HSO in determining the root cause(s) of the accident **(Figure 16.9)**. The analysis of information may be a simple task for most ISOs when the volume of information is relatively small. As the complexity of an investigation

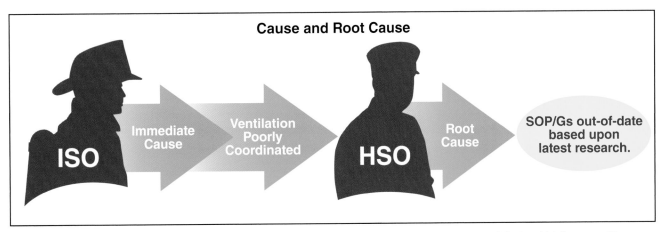

Figure 16.9 It is the ISO's responsibility to identify the immediate cause of an accident. The HSO should follow up with an investigation identifying the root cause.

increases, so does the task of sorting through the information and making decisions regarding its relevance. Once all the information collected is organized, the ISO can assist the HSO in developing a plan for corrective actions. The ISO's report to the HSO should not include the names of any personnel or units. Based on the data gathered during an investigation, the ISO should have an understanding of the potential scenarios that are being evaluated.

The data must be organized to be manageable, and a formal analysis process must be followed for the results to be meaningful. A systematic approach allows the ISO to obtain a better overview of the available data, identify relevant information, and use that information to make informed decisions related to the investigation. The ISO should also determine if any further information is needed to prove or rule out the scenarios that are being evaluated.

Preparing Documentation

Documentation may be completed electronically or on hard copy. Reports on accidents, incidents, events, and activities should be completed in narrative form following departmental SOP/Gs. These reports require sections that include descriptions, recommendations and objectives for action plans, contributing information, findings, and outcomes.

Providing Information to the HSO

The HSO will confirm the facts provided by the ISO and conduct any follow-up interviews that are needed. When gathering additional information, the HSO will focus on the human performance aspect, the choice of equipment used, the performance and use of the equipment, and environmental factors that may have influenced the outcome of an accident.

In this process, the HSO will work with the ISO (if assigned), the IC, company officers, and any other members who are witnesses to the occurrence **(Table 16.1)**. Written statements, interviews, photographs or hand-written diagrams of the scene, and a review of the sequence of events will be a part of the process. In addition, the HSO may work with law enforcement, OSHA investigators, risk management personnel, or the fire department physician during the process. Refer to Chapter 9, Root Cause Analysis: Accident Investigation and Postincident Analysis for more information on this topic.

Table 16.1 ISO vs. HSO Duties		
ISO Duties	**HSO Duties**	**Outside Assistance**
Collect evidence	Evaluate human performance	Law enforcement
Document the accident	Evaluate equipment	OSHA investigators
Interview witnesses	Conduct follow-up interviews	Risk management personnel
Take scene photographs	Confirm the facts of the report	Fire department physician
Interview firefighters	Analyze environmental factors	
Identify immediate cause of the accident	Identify the root cause of the accident	

ISO Postincident Analysis (PIA) Responsibilities

The PIA is a review of incidents to assess actions and decisions taken to stabilize an incident. Properly developed and written, the PIA determines the strengths and weaknesses of the organization's response to the emergency. A SOP/G should define criteria for the PIA and the responsibilities of personnel in providing information and participating in the process.

The PIA provides an opportunity for participants to objectively review the operation in a constructive manner. It provides a training tool as well as the basis for future planning for emergency responses. It also motivates change in policies and procedures that may be outdated or ineffectual in meeting the current needs of the response area.

According to NFPA® 1500, *Standard on Fire Department Occupational Safety and Health Program,* and NFPA® 1521, *Standard for Fire Department Safety Officer Professional Qualitfications,* ISOs are responsible for collecting safety-related information for a PIA. They gather data from witnesses, participants, reports, incident action and safety plans, and communication logs and tapes. They then analyze the data, reconstruct the incident, and provide recommendations to the organization's HSO and chief/manager. The primary concerns for this portion of the analysis are to find answers to the following:

- If SOP/Gs were followed or deviated
- If hazards were properly identified and mitigated
- If procedures need to be reviewed or changed based upon the incident

The HSO also evaluates the use of personal protective equipment, the personnel accountability system, rehabilitation operations, hazardous conditions, and any other issues that pertain to personnel safety at the incident. A written report containing recommendations is created and forwarded to each organization's chief or manager. Personnel safety must be a major responsibility within each element of the ICS structure and should get considerable attention before, during, and after any emergency incident. The HSO and ISO are responsible for ensuring all safety and health concerns are included in the PIA.

Keeping Field Notes

Field notes provide a written record of an ISO's observations and findings during an incident. Good field notes are accurate, complete, concise, and written in the format that the department requires. These notes assist in recalling observations at the scene that will be used to develop the final postincident report and may be used to provide background information if an ISO is called to testify in a criminal or civil trial. In most cases, the ISO writes the field notes while at the scene or when the investigation continues beyond the scene **(Figure 16.10, p. 636)**.

Whatever format is used, ISOs must develop enough information so that a report can be prepared and the investigative findings are accurately and effectively supported. While developing their notes, ISOs should adhere to the following guidelines:

- Include the date and only the information that is pertinent to the investigation.
- Avoid the inclusion of irrelevant personal comments or opinions.

Field Notes — Written record of an incident safety officer, or other officer's, observations during an incident; often used as the basis for a postincident analysis (PIA) report.

Figure 16.10 Field notes taken during an incident are important documents to preserve and review in case an accident occurs. *Courtesy of Ron Jeffers.*

- Record only facts and actual observations related to the accident.

- Do not mix information from different incidents in field notes – compile a separate set of notes for each incident.

- Keep field notes in a notebook where the pages are spiral bound and the notes are kept together.

- Be complete – an ISO may not get the chance to obtain the information again.

- Remember that field notes may be discoverable as part of the legal process or under the Freedom of Information Act (FOIA).

- Use a systematic and consistent method that enables an ISO to recall and interpret them at a later date.

Creating a Postincident Analysis (PIA)

A PIA is a formal document that will be analyzed to establish departmental needs, changes to SOP/Gs, and other recommendations. The PIA needs to be a finalized document based upon collected data from the incident. The ISO's field notes combined with other documentation from the incident are key to creating a PIA that can become part of organizational records.

A verbal PIA is common at less complex incidents and takes the form of an immediate debriefing. The informal debriefing is normally held at the company level, although multiple units may be involved. A company officer or IC leads the debriefing immediately after incident termination **(Figure 16.11)**. Weather permitting, the debriefing may be held at the incident scene. Being on scene permits crew members to walk through the site, point out physical barriers, describe actions, and observe conditions that may not have been evident to them during the incident.

If weather or fireground conditions are too hazardous to permit an on-scene debriefing, then it can be held upon return to quarters. In either case, the debriefing should be held as soon as possible. Informal debriefings are a learning exercise for all crew members. They can be especially helpful for newly hired personnel or recent transfers to the company as a means of helping them learn their duties and become part of the team. Informal debriefing should be documented in compliance with departmental SOP/Gs.

A written PIA is a detailed review and analysis of large-scale or tactically-challenging incidents. These incidents normally involve a large-scale response and/or assistance from other outside agencies. Incidents requiring a written PIA may include:

- Natural disasters
- Terrorist attacks
- Mass casualty incidents
- Greater alarm fires or major fires
- Incidents resulting in multiple injuries or deaths
- Building collapse
- Hazardous material incidents
- Confined space/trench rescue
- Transportation disasters
- Large-scale wildland fires

Deviations from SOP/Gs

The PIA is an opportunity to review of all relevant SOP/Gs associated with an operation. In addition, it provides an assessment on the performance of IC, decisions made, communications, and strategy and tactics employed. This assessment can be a useful training tool for those members who function as ICs. The review should determine if SOP/Gs were followed or if a deviation occurred. If a deviation occurred, the reason should be determined.

Figure 16.11 A debriefing immediately following an incident may be a sufficient postincident analysis at incidents of low complexity where a written PIA is not required.

The PIA is not intended to find specific individuals at fault for the result of incidents. The final written report on the completed PIA will instead describe any needed changes to the department policy and procedures manual. This process should involve a careful consideration of existing SOP/Gs versus the recommended revisions. Any ISO recommendations will be reviewed during the HSO's analysis.

Recommendations for Change

Recommendations made in a PIA should address critical needs to improve the safety and health of personnel during incident operations. The PIA should also include training for operational procedural deviations or changes, resource management or maintenance improvements, management deficiencies, and dispatch protocols. The complexity and special circumstances of each incident must be taken into consideration on a case-by-case basis. The ISO should recognize that not all incident circumstances can, or need, to be addressed in the department policy and procedures manual. Some operational flexibility is needed to accomplish incident stabilization in a dynamic all-hazards environment. With this in mind, the ISO should understand that unsafe acts with no consequences may be perceived as acceptable, which reinforces the unsafe act and may lead personnel to taking additional risk that result in an accident. This practice may create drift from policy in subsequent emergency operations.

When analyzing an accident report, attempts should be made to find answers to a number of basic questions. Some of these questions are as follows:

- Who was involved?
- What was involved?
- What were the circumstances?

The analysis may provide a number of potential recommendations, including the following:

- More personnel
- Additional or better equipment
- More training
- Additional funding
- Realignment of resources
- Mutual aid agreements
- Purchase or creation of new training programs
- Shifting of the risk to the private sector
- Changes in building codes, traffic laws, or building design

Postincident Critique

Postincident Critique — Meeting to discuss strategy and tactics, problems, SOP/G changes, or training changes derived from a postincident analysis report; usually led by a chief officer some time after a major incident.

A chief officer who was not involved in the incident usually facilitates a **postincident critique** from the written PIA **(Figure 16.12)**. All participants, or their representatives, meet to discuss the strategy and tactics used, problems encountered during the incident, and any SOP/Gs or training changes that should be made to address any deficiencies. The ISO may want to speak individually with responders on a one-on-one basis to get a clearer picture of the incident and eliminate group thinking.

Two types of reports are made on the PIA:

- Results of the analysis, focusing on the specific incident and the recommended changes or additional training

- Effectiveness of the PIA policy and recommendations for any changes to it

Both reports contain the same general information parts: executive summary, statement of events, strength and weaknesses, and recommendations for changes. The organization's chief or emergency services manager and the appropriate members of the administrative staff need to receive copies of the report. Further distribution is at their discretion or as defined in local protocols.

Participating in Debriefing

After creating formal PIA reports, the ISO may be asked to participate in a formal debriefing process following an incident. During this debriefing, the ISO will present his or her portions of the PIA. The IC from the incident will supervise the event and has the final authority for any actions taken as a result of the PIA.

Reporting Observations, Concerns, and Recommendations

The PIA is not intended to place blame or punish personnel for perceived infractions of policies or procedures. It should be used to improve the effectiveness and efficiency of responders and to increase scene safety and improve operations. Two primary areas of analysis are the application and effectiveness of the operational strategy and tactics and personnel safety.

Figure 16.12 A postincident critique is usually held sometime after an incident's termination when a third party not involved in the incident has had an opportunity to review the incident and make recommendations based upon personnel performance and operations.

Operations often include unsafe acts, unsafe conditions, or both. The point of the PIA is to document and analyze the actions at the scene to identify unsafe acts or conditions. Unsafe acts may result from the following:

- Inadequate training and supervision

- Improper attitudes of the individual(s) involved

- Well-intentioned attempts to save time by cutting corners

- Careless attitudes that reflect the low morale of those individuals involved

Unsafe conditions are common at most emergency incident scenes and during emergency responses. SOP/Gs should be designed to reduce the risks to fire and emergency responders in these situations. The procedures may prove inadequate if the circumstances were beyond those anticipated in the SOP/Gs. Unsafe conditions also exist during training exercises and daily nonemergency activities.

Listening to Feedback

The final step in a PIA or an accident investigation is to make corrective action recommendations and the appropriate implementation procedures based on the facts of the situation. Corrective actions should guide the organization and membership toward improvements in policy and practice as they relate to people, the department, and the apparatus and equipment used.

The PIA process should ensure that the analysis is used consistently and the results are applied to correct deficiencies or celebrate successes. Developing the analysis procedures is similar to developing any policy or procedure. Consider these actions in the development process:

- Seek full participation and input from each organization's membership
- Define goals
- State the purpose clearly
- Assign authority for making the analysis
- List types of data to be collected
- List and provide materials for the analysis
- Explain how the analysis will be used
- Establish methods for record keeping
- Establish implementing, monitoring, evaluating, and revising procedures

Once PIA procedures are developed, they should be tested to ensure that they meet the desired goals. Testing may occur as part of a training exercise or following an actual incident. When testing is complete and the PIA procedures are determined to be accurate and effective, they must be implemented, continuously monitored, evaluated for strengths and weaknesses, and revised as needed.

Chapter Summary

While fire departments have SOP/Gs in place to protect their personnel from possible injuries and fatalities, accidents often occur as a result of unsafe acts and/or unsafe conditions. The ISO's responsibility is to assist with the gathering of information pertinent to an investigation. The ISO begins the fact-finding process by identifying, collecting, and preserving potential evidence as well as interviewing witnesses and personnel at the scene. The ISO will also collect safety-related data to assist with the creation of the postincident analysis.

Review Questions

1. From what sources can the incident safety officer collect information during the investigation phase of an incident? (pp. 624-625)

2. When can a conflict of interest exist for the incident safety officer during an investigation? (pp. 625-627)

3. What processes should the incident safety officer follow when identifying, preserving, and collecting evidence? (pp. 627-632)

4. How should the incident safety officer maintain chain of custody during an investigation? (p. 633)

5. What are the responsibilities of the incident safety officer in the final phases of an accident investigation? (pp. 633-634)

6. Why is the postincident analysis an important part of investigation procedures? (p. 635)

7. Why are field notes important to the postincident analysis process? (pp. 635-636)

8. What is involved in the creation of a postincident analysis? (pp. 636-639)

9. What is the incident safety officer's role in the debriefing process? (pp. 639-640)

16-1

Assist in the investigation process at the scene of an emergency incident.

Refer to Appendix B: Learning Activity Answers in the back of this manual for suggested responses.

Purpose

After the initial report of an accident, the investigation process begins. The ISO's role in this process is to assist in gathering information relevant to the investigation. The ISO begins the fact-finding process by identifying and collecting vital material from various sources, as well as identifying, collecting, and preserving potential evidence. In addition, the ISO must be able to recognize potential conflicts of interest that might exist in the investigation process.

Directions

NOTE: This learning activity builds on work performed and information found in **Learning Activities 13-1, 14-1, and 15-1**.

1. Based on the evidence provided in the Rhoads Building Scenario, make a list of *sources* where you could obtain information for the investigation phase of the incident. Be as thorough as possible when building your list, and be sure no source is left unidentified.

   NOTE: Though the scenario does not specifically mention some information sources (such as police reports), you should still draw conclusions as to which sources you would need in order to continue the investigation.

2. Identify any potential *conflicts of interest* that may exist. If a conflict exists, write a brief description of what the conflict is and how the investigation process should proceed.

3. Make a list of any *physical evidence* that might be significant for the investigation. Once the evidence is identified, write a brief summary of how the evidence should be secured and protected.

4. Include in the summary any *additional evidence* that you, as ISO at the scene, would need to obtain (such as witness statements).

Appendices

Appendix A

Chapter and Page Correlation to NFPA® 1521, Standard for Fire Department Safety Officer Professional Qualifications, 2015 Edition Requirements

NFPA® 1521 Requirments	Chapter References	Page References
4.1.1	1	13-20
4.1.2	9	312-314, 335-339
4.2.1	3, 5	78-92, 108, 109, 157-172, 179-192
4.2.2	3, 5	108, 109, 183-189
4.2.3	3, 5, 8	62-71, 173-186, 288-304
4.2.4	2, 6	30-34, 38, 39, 44, 46-49, 55, 56, 210-219
4.2.5	4	132-136
4.3.1	2, 4	30-56, 116-126, 144-151
4.3.2	2, 12	30-56, 393-399
4.4.1	8	283-287, 304
4.4.2	3, 8, 12	71-92, 288-304, 399
4.4.3	3, 4	83, 87-92, 127-132
4.5.1	3, 5, 7	82, 83, 157-172, 254-258, 278, 279
4.5.2	8	288-304
4.5.3	7	268-276, 278, 279
4.5.4	2, 7	30-56, 258-264, 278, 279
4.6.1	3, 9	78-82, 87-90, 311-318, 324-333, 335-339
4.6.2	2. 3, 4, 9	30-56, 78-82, 87-90, 137-39, 328-333, 335-339
4.6.3	2, 9	30-34, 39, 44-56, 318-324, 335-339
4.6.4	3, 9	78-82, 86, 91, 324-327, 332, 333, 335-339
4.7.1	2, 3, 9	30-44, 46-49, 55, 56, 92-109, 111, 328-333, 335-339
4.7.2	2, 3	30-34, 44-56, 62-78
4.7.3	3	62-71
4.7.4	9, 12	328-333, 335-339, 400, 401

NFPA® 1521 Requirments	Chapter References	Page References
4.8.1	2, 3, 5, 11	30-43, 55, 56, 86, 162-721, 191, 192, 362-371, 388
4.8.2	2, 3, 5, 11	30-43, 55, 56, 86, 162-172, 191, 192, 362-366, 369-371, 388
4.8.3	11	371-376
4.8.4	11	366-369, 374-376
4.8.5	11	366-369, 375, 376
4.8.6	2, 11	30-39, 44, 46-49, 55, 56, 376-386, 388
4.9.1	2, 3, 4	30-39, 44-56, 86, 87, 139-141
4.9.2	2, 3, 10	30-39, 44-56, 86, 87, 343-357
4.10.1	2, 3, 4, 7	30-34, 44, 46-49, 55, 56, 69-71, 141-143, 227-254, 278, 279
4.10.2	2, 3, 4, 7	30-34, 44-56, 69-71, 141-143, 227-254
4.11.1	1, 12	20-23, 403, 405
4.11.2	6	198-210, 221
4.11.3	3, 12	92-109, 401-403, 405
4.11.4	2, 8	30-34, 44, 49, 52, 55, 56, 287
4.11.5	6	204-209, 221
4.12.1	2, 7	30-34, 38, 39, 44, 49, 55, 56, 264-268, 278, 279
4.12.2	2, 7, 8	30-34, 38, 39, 44, 49, 55, 56, 264-268, 301
5.1.1	15	574
5.1.2	16	625-627, 642
5.2.1	13, 15	410-417, 424-448, 449-453, 552-562
5.2.2	13, 15	410-423, 455-457, 603-611
5.2.3	13, 15	442-448, 552-573, 618, 619
5.2.4	13, 14, 15	417, 422, 423, 442-448, 455-457, 461-547, 603-611
5.2.5	13, 15	417, 452, 453, 455-457, 604-608
5.2.6	13, 15	414, 417, 452, 453, 455-457, 594, 595
5.2.7	13, 14, 15	455-457, 461-547, 580-591
5.2.8	13, 14	455-457, 535-543, 545-547
5.2.9	13, 15	412-414, 417, 452, 453, 455-457, 595, 596
5.2.10	13, 15	410-423, 455-457, 574-580
5.2.11	15	590-594
5.2.12	15	611-616

NFPA® 1521 Requirments	Chapter References	Page References
5.2.13	14, 15	526-531, 545-547, 552-571, 580-594
5.2.14	15	600-603
5.3.1	15	596-600
5.3.2	14, 15	466-526, 545-547, 552-558, 600
5.3.3	14, 15	498-526, 545-547, 562-571, 589, 590, 603-611
5.3.4	14	466-498, 545-547
5.3.5	14, 15	531-534, 545-547, 552-558
5.3.6	13, 14	417, 424-428, 442-448, 518, 519, 545-547
5.4.1	15	576, 577
5.4.2	13, 15	410-421, 455-457, 552-571, 576, 577, 580-590, 618, 619
5.4.3	15	562-571, 618, 619
5.5.1	15	576-580
5.5.2	13, 15	410-421, 455-457, 552-571, 576-590, 618, 619
5.5.3	15	562-571, 618, 619
5.5.4	15	580-590
5.6.1	16	624-634, 642
5.7.1	13, 16	413, 635-639
5.7.2	13, 16	413, 639, 640, 642

Appendix B
Learning Activities Answers

Chapter 2

Learning Activity 2-1: Determine compliance with applicable safety and health laws, codes, regulations, and standards.

Answers will vary. A compliance checklist or inspection form should have been developed based on the two chosen departmental areas of focus. Checklists should be in your own words but can be drawn in part from provided examples. Checklists should also reference specific laws, codes, regulations, and standards for which each department area would be seeking compliance.

Items the checklist(s) should include (minimum requirements):

- Inspection date

- Name of inspector

- Name of department or jurisdiction

- Criteria to consider for each element of the inspection

- A citation of sources for more detailed explanations of the criteria
  (e.g., local statutes, SOP/Gs, OSHA regulations, NFPA® standards and chapters being referenced)

Chapter 3

Learning Activity 3-1: Create a departmental records and data management system.

Answers will vary. A comprehensive electronic file folder structure – using either text or visuals – should have been developed that is specific to your jurisdiction's needs. See the sample below as an example of a departmental file folder structure.

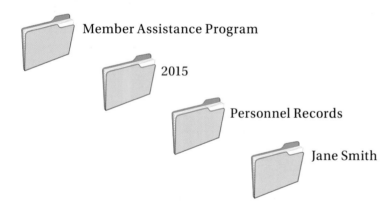

Member Assistance Program

2015

Personnel Records

Jane Smith

Chapter 4

Learning Activity 4-1: Create a standard operating procedure or guideline based on departmental documents or materials.

Answers will vary. However, the activity should have accomplished at least some of the following:

- The situation or problems presented in the chosen document have been effectively analyzed.
- Findings have been transcribed into a draft SOP/G using the general process outlined in Chapter 4.
- Any and all laws, codes, regulations, or standards pertinent to the situation(s) have been included, referenced, and/or consulted in the draft SOP/G.
- Safety and health aspects of the situation have been focused on in the draft SOP/G.

Chapter 5

Learning Activity 5-1: Identify risks inherent in a motor vehicle collision (emergency).

Answers will vary. The following hazards and risks should have been addressed:

- Fertilizer bags combined with smoking engine may lead to possible fire/explosion
- Cold weather may lead to frostbite, hypothermia
- Busy city street has high probability of additional collisions
- Light snowfall may create additional unsafe road conditions
- Time of day (dusk), reduced visibility may also lead to additional collisions
- Victim behavior (frantic parent, hysterical child) may lead to unsafe behavior

Expected Incident Rate (IR) and Expected Severity (S) will vary according to judgment.

Table 5.1 Hazards and Risks				
Hazard	**Risk(s)**	**Expected Incident Risk**	**Expected Severity**	**Risk**
Cold temperature, possible ice formation	Other cars colliding with the accident	6	4	24

Learning Activity 5-2: Identify risks inherent in a live-fire training evolution (nonemergency).

Answers will vary. The following hazards and risks should have been addressed:

- High winds may lead to out-of-control fires
- Inadequate instructor/student ratio may lead to miscommunication or confusion
- Acquired apartment building presents unforeseen structural issues (e.g., stair or wall collapse) leading to possible injuries
- Interior darkness may lead to falls or confusion
- Potential improper ladder placement may lead to injuries
- Potential improper use of hoses may lead to inadequate water supply or injuries
- Potential PPE and SCBA issues may lead to injuries

Expected Incident Rate (IR) and Expected Severity (S) will vary according to judgment.

Table 5.2 Hazards and Risks				
Hazard	**Risk(s)**	**Expected Incident Risk**	**Expected Severity**	**Risk**
High temperatures	Heat exhaustion, dehydration	6	3	18

Chapter 6

Learning Activity 6-1: Gather information for a preincident plan for a public building.

Answers will vary. You will not be able to develop a full preincident plan for the chosen structure in your community; however, you should have been able to gather some of the following types of information:

- Safety concerns for firefighters and occupants

- Building construction type and material to determine resistance to fire spread

- Building services, including utility shut-offs, high-voltage equipment, generators, elevators, and HVAC

- Building access and egress, including lock box location

- Building age

- Building area and height

- Contents to estimate fire load

- Building use to determine life safety and fire load

- Exposures

- Collapse zone

- Location and capacity of available water supply

- Location of fire control and protection system control valves and connections

- Hazardous materials or processes, including flammable/combustible liquids and gases

- Location of Safety Data Sheets (SDS) as revised in the Globally Harmonized System (GHS) of Classification and Labeling of Chemicals

- Occupancy load at all hours

- Names and telephone numbers of contact or responsible persons for owner/occupant

- Estimated quantity of water required to extinguish a fire in the structure or a portion of it (fire flow)

- Emergency evacuation plan

- Additional unique features

Chapter 7

Learning Activity 7-1: Identify safety and health programs based on departmental needs.

Scenario 1:

Answers will vary. Safety and wellness problems in the scenario include the consumption of foods high in fat and sodium and tobacco use. The **Health Maintenance Program** should be the targeted program and should specifically include comprehensive Medical Surveillance, Physical Fitness, Wellness, and Member Assistance programs. Descriptions of the overall program will vary but should include any legal mandates, guidelines, or other sources that could provide the necessary framework for the program (e.g., NFPA® standards, federal guidelines, etc.). Examples of resources that would address the specific problems outlined in the scenario:

- NFPA® 1500, *Standard on Fire Department Occupational Safety and Health Program*
- NFPA® 1582, *Standard on Comprehensive Occupational Medical Program for Fire Departments*
- NFPA® 1583, *Standard on Health-Related Fitness Programs for Fire Fighters*
- The IAFF, IAFC, and American Council on Exercise peer fitness training program (as part of the Fire Service Joint Labor Management Wellness-Fitness Initiative).

Scenario 2:

Answers will vary. Safety and wellness problems presented in the scenario include a failure to use appropriate PPE and a lack of SOP/Gs regarding tool/equipment use. The **Accident Prevention Program** should be the targeted program. Examples of resources that would inform the Accident Prevention Program include:

- The *Crew Resource Management* (CRM) program

Scenario 3:

Answers will vary. Safety and wellness problems presented in the scenario include diesel exhaust exposure resulting from apparatus running outside the bay, open facility doors, and the lack of a ventilation system. The **Safety Audit Program** should be the targeted program. Examples of resources that would inform the Safety Audit Program include:

- Other fire and emergency services organizations
- The National Institute for Occupational Safety and Health (NIOSH) *Health Hazard Evaluation* program
- The American Chemical Society Committee on Chemical Safety, *Safety Audit/Inspection Manual*
- The Center for Public Safety Excellence, Commission on Fire Accreditation International (CFAI), *Fire & Emergency Service Self-Assessment Manual* (for template information)

Scenario 4:

Answers may vary. Safety and wellness problems presented in the scenario include failure to use appropriate PPE to prevent exposure to bloodborne pathogens and a lack of SOP/Gs for documentation if an exposure does occur. The **Infection Control Program** should be the targeted program. Examples of resources that would inform the Infection Control Program include:

- U.S. OSHA's Title 29 CFR 1910.1030 *Bloodborne Pathogens*
- NFPA® 1581, *Standard on Fire Department Infection Control Program*
- The Ryan White HIV/AIDS Treatment Extension Act of 2009, Part G – Notification of Possible Exposure to Infectious Diseases

Scenario 5:

Answers may vary. Safety and wellness problems presented in the scenario include a lack of appropriate SOP/Gs for backing apparatus. The **Emergency Vehicle Safety Program** should be the targeted program. Examples of resources that would inform the Emergency Vehicle Safety Program include:

- NFPA® 1002, *Standard for Fire Apparatus Driver/Operator Professional Qualifications*
- NFPA® 1451, *Standard for a Fire Service Vehicle Operations Training Program*
- NFPA® 1911, *Standard for the Inspection, Maintenance, Testing, and Retirement of In-Service Automotive Fire Apparatus*

- NFPA® 1912, *Standard for Fire Apparatus Refurbishing*
- U.S. DOT, *Manual on Uniform Traffic Control Devices* (MUTCD)
- *Manual of Uniform Traffic Control Devices for Canada* (MUTCDC)
- U.S. DOT, *Traffic Incident Management Handbook* (TIMS)
- USFA FA-336, *Emergency Vehicle Safety Initiative*
- USFA FA-330, *Traffic Incident Management Systems*
- IAFC, *Guide to IAFC Model Policies and Procedures for Emergency Vehicle Safety*
- IAFF, *Best Practices for Emergency Vehicle and Roadway Operations Safety in the Emergency Services*
- National Fire Service Incident Management System Consortium, *Model Procedures Guide for Highway Incidents*
- NFPA® 1091, *Standard for Traffic Control Incident Management Professional Qualifications*

Chapter 8

Learning Activity 8-1: Develop safety and health information for various training topics.

Answers will vary. However, the memorandum should have accomplished the following:

- Identifies the problem
- Presents research and provides evidence
- Gives a list of action items that address safety issues

See the Sleep Awareness Memo to the right for an example.

MEMORANDUM
Anytown Fire Department

To: All Fire Department Personnel
From: HSO Jones
Date: 2/17/2014
Re: Safety Briefing - Sleep Awareness

AWARENESS AND IMPORTANCE OF SLEEP

Learning Objectives:
1. Understand the importance of sleep and rest
2. Realize that alertness decreases with sustained wakefulness
3. Understand the consequences of prolonged wakefulness

As firefighters stay awake, their alertness decreases and may influence risk of accidents and injuries. Two important studies illustrate the relationship between performance levels and continued wakefulness against the equivalent effects of alcohol consumption.[1-2] After 17 hours of being awake, performance levels are equivalent to those with 0.05 percent Blood Alcohol Concentration (BAC). At 24 hours, performance levels decrease to an equivalent 0.10 BAC. This would be considered illegally intoxicated in most states in the U.S. Driving while sleep deprived may lead to an increased risk of errors.[3]

Traffic errors, injuries, and accidents increase with individuals when they are not fully rested. This is a result of poor alertness.

These studies illustrate the importance of obtaining sleep and rest. Sleep is needed to restore cognitive functions and alertness, which are essential in the fire service. Rest, on the other hand, is needed to reduce fatigue. The following suggestions can help firefighters prevent adverse effects of wakefulness and sleep deprivation:

- Always obtain full sleep. If sleep is interrupted by an emergency, naps may be used to offset some of the consequences of sleep loss
- Always obtain full sleep and recovery during non-working days
- Limit time employed working a second job; never let secondary employment hinder sleep recovery
- Encourage an environment to promote healthy sleeping: individualized sleep quarters, lighting and alerting enhanced system, sound reducing windows and doors, and customized temperature control

For more information regarding the studies, read the following journal articles:

1. Dawson, D., and K. Reid. 1997. "Fatigue, Alcohol and Performance Impairment," Nature 388:235-537.
2. Williamson, A. M., and A. Feyer. 2000. "Moderate Sleep Deprivation Produces Impairments in Cognitive and Motor Performance Equivalent to Legally Prescribed Levels of Alcohol Intoxication," Occupational and Environmental Medicine 57:649-655.
3. Philip, Pierre. 2005. "Sleepiness of Occupational Drivers," Industrial Health 43:30-33.

Chapter 9

Learning Activity 9-1: Conduct a postincident analysis of a MVA incident where two responding firefighters were injured.

Answers will vary. The review memorandum based on your full postincident analysis of the MVA should at least include:

- A list of possible root causes for each firefighter injury
- Any additional documentation required for your investigation such as departmental SOP/Gs
- A request to conduct interviews with those involved in the accidents
- A notation of and reasoning for any possible conflicts of interest.

Chapter 10

Learning Activity 10-1: Conduct a mock health and safety inspection for a fire department facility.

Answers will vary widely but should include information on:

- Carbon monoxide and smoke detectors
- Air quality testing
- Proper separation of living and working areas
- Noise level testing
- Quick access fire pole safety
- Operational readiness
- Health hazards
- Physical hazards
- Ergonomics
- Necessary resources and equipment
- Safety precautions

Chapter 11

Learning Activity 11-1: Review department specs regarding structural fire fighting boots.

Answers will vary. At a minimum, answers should include a:

- Summary of your department's/manufacturer's specifications on structural fire fighting boots
- Summary of your findings based on the physical inspection of your department's boots
- Determination of whether the currently used boots meet departmental specs and requirements set forth in NFPA® 1971
- Brief discussion of any new relevant technology or products that could impact your department's footwear needs or requirements

Chapter 12

Learning Activity 12-1: Write a memorandum recommending changes to PPE specifications.

Answers will vary. At a minimum, the memorandum should include:

- The number and type of injuries sustained by firefighters due to slick conditions
- Types of structural fire fighting boots currently approved for use by your department

    NOTE: This information should include the tread depth and slip resistance findings based on the physical inspection you performed for **Learning Activity 11-1**.

- Rationale for changing the type of footwear currently used (this should include all pertinent research taken from national standards, vendor information, etc.)
- A recommendation to upgrade the type of footwear based on your research

Chapter 13

Learning Activity 13-1: Analyze fire department operations for adherence to risk management principles and practices.

Answers will vary but should include at least some of the following:

Pros
- Firefighters followed the IC's orders (with the exception of the ISO)
- The ISO notified the IC for the need of an incident action plan (IAP)
- The ISO took note of breakdown in communications
- The aerial apparatus was appropriately positioned away from the building's collapse zone
- Mutual Aid arrived in a timely manner

Cons
- Lack of a proper Incident Management System (IMS)
- Overall miscommunication (poor identification of the Alpha side, not all hazards communicated to all responders, unclear radio transmissions, etc.)
- An incomplete incident action plan (IAP) – IC did not write IAP
- ISO did not fill out appropriate safety plan based on the IAP, confused the safety plan with a tactical worksheet
- Failure in personnel accountability
- Rapid intervention crew (RIC) not in place in a timely manner
- Interior search and rescue occurring at the same time as an indirect master stream attack

Chapter 14

Learning Activity 14-1: Practice identifying hazards at an emergency operation.

Answers will vary but should include at least some of the following:

Environmental and Physiological Hazards
- Snow and ice
- Cold stress

Structure Fire Development Hazards
- Fuel type/load – possible trash buildup

Building Construction Hazards
- Unknown renovations possible
- If Type III, may have voids inside wooden channels that allow for fire spread
- Condemned building may have had illicit/illegal changes made to it
- Access/egress challenges

Utility Hazards
- Proximity of power lines
- Must find electricity component assemblies and main shutoff
- Possible alternate/illegal sources of power

Apparatus Placement Hazards
- Icy/slippery conditions
- Backing procedures

Chapter 15

Learning Activity 15-1: Prepare an incident safety plan for an emergency operation.

Answers will vary but should include at least some of the following:

General Incident Information
- Five-story condemned building
- Pancake collapse; possibly due to heavy snow
- Building often frequented by homeless residents
- Fire in the center of the structure; possibly from a 55-gallon barrel used as a fire receptacle
- Asbestos identified by building manager
- Narrow, poorly maintained streets
- No address markings

Impact of Weather

Potential Hazard: Additional snow and ice; slippery conditions

Hazard Mitigation: Contacted dispatch for weather updates; scene size-up and monitoring for additional hazards created by fire suppression efforts

Material Identification

Potential Hazard: Asbestos contamination

Hazard Mitigation: ISO should monitor the selection and use of personal protective clothing and equipment for each incident type to ensure it meets SOP/Gs and legal mandates.

Geographical Data

Potential Hazard: Narrow streets with dead-ends and potholes; No address visible

Hazard Mitigation: Review street maps for landmarks, means of egress, and locations for the safe deployment of apparatus.

Location Site/Building Plans/Preincident Plans

Potential Hazard: There is no preincident plan for this building; could be illegal modifications to the interior; Type III construction may have voids that allow fire spread; access and egress points may be hidden or blocked; possible trash buildup

Hazard Mitigation: Contact building manager or maintenance personnel for plans, blueprints, photos.

Each incident type will have common strategies and tactics that are considered for that incident. Departmental SOP/Gs should outline the common strategies and tactics, so personnel can perform their duties in a consistent and expected manner. The ISO should be trained to the level of the operations employed.

Chapter 16

Learning Activity 16-1: Assist in the investigation process at the scene of an emergency incident.

Answers will vary. However, you should have listed at least some of the following:

Sources for Information:

- Dispatch records
- Interviews with all participants
- Emergency incident reports
- Incident action plan (IAP)
- Incident safety plan
- Weather conditions/reports
- Photographs and videotapes of the scene or incident
- Site diagrams
- Physical property involved in the incident

- Chain of custody documentation
- Incident safety officer report

Conflicts of Interest:

- A conflict of interest exists for the ISO. The Incident Commander ordered the ISO to assist the Ladder Company in maneuvers, and the ISO assisted in fire attack operations. In addition, the ISO defied the IC's orders to communicate an incident action plan verbally.

Physical Evidence:

- Source or origin where the "pancake" collapse might have initially occurred
- The 55-gallon barrel inside the structure (possible origin of the fire)
- Possible ignition source(s) for the fire
- Any evidence of suspicious activity, if any

Additional Evidence:

- Blueprints of the Rhoades Building and interior photos on the building manager's tablet device (from **Learning Activity 15-1**)
- Witness statements
- Photographs of the fire's point of origin
- Interviews with first responders
- IAP forms
- ICS information
- Timeline information from the incident
- Collected communications
- Other pertinent documentation including sketches, diagrams, drawings, maps, and additional photographs

Appendix C
Safety Audit Template

MUNICIPAL FIRE SERVICE SAFETY AUDIT/SURVEY TOOL
Fire service injury prevention during fire, EMS and training operations

Instructions: This is a scored pro-active safety auditing tool designed for periodic use to reduce high risk behaviors and increase safe behaviors. "Yes" answers should be scored at (1) and "No" answers should be scored at (0). In the corrective action column, either a time frame for completing the correction *or* the actual date corrective action was completed should be noted. Check the "NA" column if this item is not applicable. Total and track audit scores over time to track up or down trends along with tracking the number of incidents, accidents and injuries sustained.

Fire ground operations require emergency response on short notice and a multitude of situations where heavy lifting is required. It is essential for municipal fire agencies to promote occupational safety and health among employees. The NFPA 1500, *Standard on Fire Department Occupational Safety and Health Program*, and Annex B, *Fire Service Occupational safety and Health Program Worksheet* cover this information for fire service operations.

The most common illnesses and injuries among firefighters are heart attacks and injuries related to motor vehicle accidents. Back injuries from heavy lifting and knee injuries from slips and falls must also be addressed in safety programs. The efficacy of on duty health and wellness programs such as *The Fire Service Joint Labor Management Wellness-Fitness Initiative* developed by the International Association of Fire Fighters and others is proven and can greatly reduce injury and illness workers' compensation claims.

Task/Job Part – Human Resources	Yes	No	Corrective action date	NA
Personnel policies applied in a consistent manner				
Fairness – all employees treated the same				
Progressive discipline in place with emphasis on worker integrity and accountability				
Sexual harassment prevention training completed				
Other				

Task/Job Part – Facilities, Logistics and Records	Yes	No	Corrective action date	NA
Completed all weekly equipment inspections, maintenance and checklists				
Completed all necessary records				
✓ Incident reports, injuries, illness, deaths				
✓ Training completed				
✓ Equipment, maintenance, service records				
✓ Safety meeting attendance				
✓ Blood-borne pathogen & occupational exposures				
✓ Inspections				
✓ Emergency response and other calls				

1

Task/Job Part – Facilities, Logistics and Records	Yes	No	Corrective action date	NA

Facility safety and design
   ✓ Sleeping areas separated from equipment areas and fire safe
   ✓ Air quality monitoring in equipment bays (CO detectors), ventilation adequate
   ✓ Facilities equipped with fire alarms and sprinklers (if newer)				

Other?				

Task/Job Part – Illness Prevention and Environmental Safety	Yes	No	Corrective action date	NA
Proper Vaccinations for Hepatitis A and Hepatitis B				
Proper work practices around hazardous wastes, blood borne pathogen exposure risks with proper clean up				
Use of respiratory protection, sun block and insect repellent if needed				

Task/Job Part – Training and Certifications	Yes	No	Corrective action date	NA
All training completed with passing scores in a timely manner in accordance with department policies				
Blood-Borne Pathogen/Universal Precautions training				
Hazardous materials awareness or HAZWOPER				
All licenses (EMT) required are current				
All certifications and CEUs current				
All written procedures and systems of operation reviewed during training operations at least once annually				
New procedures and equipment training before use				

Task/Job Part – Vehicle Operation and Code Responses	Yes	No	Corrective action date	NA
Fire apparatus in compliance with NFPA 1901 (*Standard for Automotive Fire Apparatus*)				
Proper emergency communications including frequent notification of vehicle location to other emergency responders				
All code responses in accordance with department policies and best practices for safe driving				
All drivers properly trained				
Code III responses no more than 10% above posted speed limits				
Code III response includes stopping at intersections before clearing intersection unless it is totally free of traffic				

2

Task/Job Part – Vehicle Operation and Code Responses	Yes	No	Corrective action date	NA
Proper vehicle egress and exiting procedures with three point contact and no jump-offs				
Any problems with code response or vehicle operations reviewed at monthly management or safety committee meetings				

Task/Job Part – Safe Fire Ground Operations	Yes	No	Corrective action date	NA
Entry and suppression policies followed				
Safe work practices, lifts, tool use, ergonomics				
Rescue crew back up standing by				
Use of technology to limit penetration; sensible life saving risk taking (heat sensing devices, use of portable deck guns on large structure fires)				
Proper work zone set up and traffic control on motor vehicle accident/fire responses on roadways				
Policies followed and all personnel properly trained for Haz Mat responses				
Management keeps workers on task with safety best practices				
All personnel held accountable for unsafe actions				

Task/Job Part – Use of Personal Protective Equipment (PPE)	Yes	No	Corrective action date	NA
Use of Universal Precautions PPE during first aid/BBP exposures				
Proper use of gloves during emergency response, training, and routine operations				
Proper use of bunkers & boots (this equipment should be OSHA approved, but also state of the art in terms of being light weight and as comfortable as possible heat-wise.				
Use of 8" steel toe and shank, zippered duty boot				
Proper use of wild land fire suits – designed for minimum heat retention during use, fire-resistant treated fabric				
Proper use of under hood, shielded helmet, radio equipped if possible, safety goggles under shield for eye protection				
All personnel radio equipped				
Use of eye protection as needed for routine maintenance				
SCBA & respiratory safety program, annual check up				
Proper use of hearing protection				
Proper PPE use during training and drills				
Any PPE problems reviewed at management or safety committee meetings				

3

Task/Job Part – Proper lifting technique & Equipment Design	Yes	No	Corrective action date	NA
Proper training on all lifting procedures, including ladders, smoke ejectors, saws, rescue equipment, and hose stretches				
Proper technique and position while lifting				
2 or more workers if load is more than 50# during all maintenance and training operations (e.g. smoke ejector fans, rescue equipment, hoses, and ladders)				
No lift above waist level or out of position whenever possible	Yes	No	Corrective action date	NA
Task/Job Part – Proper lifting technique & Equipment Design	Yes	No	Corrective action date	NA
Minimize heavy lifting during training (e.g. single raise on 24' ladder)				
When possible, apparatus fitted with pull-out equipment trays, heavy equipment stored at waist level, and hydraulic ladder pull-downs so ladders can be removed at below shoulder level				
Pre-connect hose lines on reels				
Proper patient lifting during EMS operations including at least 4 people on backboard lifts and gurneys when needed				
Other?				

Task/Job Part – Proper use of incident reporting forms & logs with proper recording	Yes	No	Corrective action date	NA
All worker injuries reported to supervisor and recorded				
All worker accidents involving property, chemicals reported and recorded				
All "near misses" reported to supervisors and recorded				
If a reporting program was in place, all hazards and potential hazards reported and recorded				
A workers compensation claim was filed if a) an injury involved lost time, b) medical care with costs, or c) the worker requested a claim be filed				

Task/Job Part – Workplace Wellness and Fitness	Yes	No	Corrective action date	NA
On duty exercise – physical fitness program; custom fitness program for each worker with personal trainer as needed				
Annual physical and job relevant agility testing				
Employee assistance program				
Injury rehab program				
Pre-employment physical, mental health test				

4

Task/Job Part – Communications and Culture of Respect and Caring	Yes	No	Corrective action date	NA
All employees understand they are a very important asset to the fire service and municipality ✓ Core fitness needed to perform the job safely maintained ✓ Mental health best practices such as Critical Incident Stress Management (CISM) ✓ Employees accountable for following safety ✓ policies and watching out for each other				
Proper communication during emergency response and on scene				

Task/Job Part – Communications and Culture of Respect and Caring	Yes	No	Corrective action date	NA
Implementation and maintenance of a non-punitive, candid reporting culture with open communication of safety and other concerns between management and employees				
Open communication and cooperation between management and union representation				
Proper inter-departmental communication to provide for optimal safe operations for the entire municipality				
Issue customized work out clothing and PPE (e.g. boots)				

Task/Job Part – Employee Integrity and Accountability	Yes	No	Corrective action date	NA
All staff expected to be honest and forthright in reporting complaints, mistakes, and actions that need corrective actions				
Pre-employment background check completed				
Fire ground operations reviewed as needed, with frank communication concerning problems and mistakes, and corrective actions taken				
All workers monitor safe practices and safety check ups among each other, with a culture of safety first				
All workers subject to consistent discipline for any unsafe behaviors that are not in compliance with safety policy				

TOTAL SCORE

Signature_____

Print Name _____

Date_____

5

Glossary

Glossary

A

Accident Review Board (ARB) — Committee of department personnel and stakeholders whose responsibility is to review vehicular accident investigations.

Advanced Life Support (ALS) — Advanced medical skills performed by trained medical personnel, such as the administration of medications, or airway management procedures to save a patient's life.

AISO — *see* Assistant Incident Safety Officer.

All-Hazard Concept — Coordinated approach to a wide variety of incidents; all responders use a similar, coordinated approach with a common set of authorities, protections, and resources.

ALS — *see* Advanced Life Support.

Ambient Conditions — Common, prevailing, and uncontrolled atmospheric weather conditions. The term may refer to the conditions inside or outside of the structure.

American National Standards Institute (ANSI) — Voluntary standards-setting organization that examines and certifies existing standards and creates new standards.

ANSI — *see* American National Standards Institute.

ARB — *see* Accident Review Board.

Assistant Incident Safety Officer (AISO) — Individual(s) who reports to the Incident Safety Officer and assist with monitoring hazards and safe operations for designated portions of the operation at large or complex incidents.

ASTM — *see* ASTM International.

ASTM International — Voluntary standards-setting organization that sets guidelines on characteristics and performance of materials, products, systems and services; for example the quality of concrete or the flammability of interior finishes. *Formerly known as* American Society for Testing and Materials (ASTM).

Atypical Stressful Event — Term used in National Fire Protection Association® (NFPA®) standards to describe incidents that have a likelihood of causing critical incident stress.

Automatic Aid — Written agreement between two or more agencies to automatically dispatch predetermined resources to any fire or other emergency reported in the geographic area covered by the agreement. These areas are generally located near jurisdictional boundaries or in jurisdictional "islands."

Automatic Vehicle Locator (AVL) — Computer system onboard an apparatus that uses GPS coordinates to deliver and log real-time location and driving information (speed, direction of travel) about the apparatus over wireless networks.

AVL — *see* Automatic Vehicle Locator.

B

Backdraft — Instantaneous explosion or rapid burning of superheated gases that occurs when oxygen is introduced into an oxygen-depleted confined space. The stalled combustion resumes with explosive force; may occur because of inadequate or improper ventilation procedures.

Balloon-Frame Construction — Type of structural framing used in some single-story and multistory wood frame buildings; studs are continuous from the foundation to the roof, and there may be no fire stops between the studs.

Bowstring Truss — Lightweight truss design noted by the bow shape, or curve, of the top chord.

Basic Life Support (BLS) — Emergency medical treatment administered without the use of adjunctive equipment; includes maintenance of airway, breathing, and circulation, as well as basic bandaging and splinting.

BLEVE — *see* Boiling Liquid Expanding Vapor Explosion.

Bloodborne Pathogens — Pathogenic microorganisms that are present in the human blood and can cause disease in humans. These pathogens include (but are not limited to) hepatitis B virus (HBV) and human immunodeficiency virus (HIV).

Blowup — Sudden, dangerously rapid increase in fireline intensity at a wildland fire; caused by any one or more of several factors, such as strong or erratic wind, steep uphill slopes, large open areas, and easily ignited fuels. Blowup is sufficient to preclude direct attack or to change the incident action plan; often accompanied by violent convection and may have other characteristics of a firestorm.

BLS — *see* Basic Life Support.

Boiling Liquid Expanding Vapor Explosion (BLEVE) — Rapid vaporization of a liquid stored under pressure upon release to the atmosphere following major failure of its containing vessel. Failure is the result of over-pressurization caused by an external heat source, which causes the vessel to explode into two or more pieces when the temperature of the liquid is well above its boiling point at normal atmospheric pressure.

Bowstring Truss — Lightweight truss design noted by the bow shape, or curve, of the top chord.

C

Canadian Centre for Occupational Health and Safety (CCOHS) — Canadian federal government agency that provides information and policy development regarding work-related injury, illness prevention initiatives, and occupational health and safety information.

Canadian Standards Association (CSA) — Develops worker safety standards, safety certification labeling, and other related services for Canada.

Candidate Physical Ability Test (CPAT) — Optional, nationally recognized physical fitness examination for firefighter candidates which is oriented toward firefighter job tasks with established benchmarks.

Capital Improvement Program (CIP) — 5 to 10 year program intended to identify large equipment purchases or project expenses, schedule their purchase, and identify the needed funding sources.

Case Law — Laws based on judicial interpretations and decisions rather than created by legislation.

CCOHS — *see* Canadian Centre for Occupational Health and Safety.

Ceiling Jet — Horizontal movement of a layer of hot gases and combustion by-products from the center point of the plume, when the vertical development of the rising plume is redirected by a horizontal surface such as a ceiling.

Center for Public Safety Excellence (CPSE) — Nonprofit organization that promotes quality improvement of fire and emergency services organizations.

Chain of Custody — Continuous changes of possession of physical evidence that must be established in court to admit such material into evidence. In order for physical evidence to be admissible in court, there must be an evidence log of accountability that documents each change of possession from the evidence's discovery until it is presented in court.

Chemical Protective Clothing (CPC) — Clothing designed to shield or isolate individuals from the chemical, physical, and biological hazards that may be encountered during operations involving hazardous materials.

CIP — *see* Capital Improvement Program.

CIS — *see* Critical Incident Stress.

CISM — *see* Critical Incident Stress Management.

Code — A collection of rules and regulations that has been enacted by law in a particular jurisdiction. Codes typically address a single subject area; examples include a mechanical, electrical, building, or fire code.

Cold Zone — Safe area outside of the warm zone where equipment and personnel are not expected to become contaminated and special protective clothing is not required; the Incident Command Post and other support functions are typically located in this zone.

Collapse Zone — Area beneath a wall in which the wall is likely to land if it loses structural integrity.

Command Staff — In a fully developed fireground organization, the Information Officer (PIO), Safety (ISO), and Liaison Officer, who report directly to the IC.

Communicable Disease — Disease that is capable of being transmitted from one person to another.

Compliance — Meeting the minimum standards set forth by applicable codes or regulations.

Control Measures — Specific actions taken to reduce risks through a reduction in either the frequency or severity of the risk.

Contamination — General term referring to anything that can taint physical evidence during an investigation.

Control Zones — System of barriers surrounding designated areas at emergency scenes, intended to limit the number of persons exposed to a hazard and to facilitate its mitigation. A major incident has three zones: Restricted (Hot) Zone, Limited Access (Warm) Zone, and Support (Cold) Zone.

Corrective Actions — Measures implemented to improve the workplace, reduce hazards, or correct any unsafe acts.

Cost/Benefit Analysis — Examination of the proposed expense of an effort and deciding if the overall benefit is worth the investment of money and/or time.

CPAT — *see* Candidate Physical Ability Test.

CPC — *see* Chemical Protective Clothing.

CPSE — *see* Center for Public Safety Excellence.

Cribbing — Lengths of solid wood or plastic, usually 4- X 4-inches (100 mm by 100 mm) or larger, used to stabilize vehicles and collapsed buildings during extrication incidents.

Critical Incident Stress (CIS) — Physical, mental, or emotional tension caused when persons have been exposed to a traumatic event where they have experienced, witnessed, or been confronted with an event or events that involve actual death, threatened death, serious injury, or threat of physical integrity of self or others.

Critical Incident Stress Management (CISM) — Comprehensive crisis intervention system composed of 7 elements: pre-crisis preparation, a disaster or large scale incident, defusing, critical incident stress debriefing, one-on-one crisis intervention/counseling, family/organizational crisis intervention, and follow-up/referral mechanisms.

Cross-Contamination — In terms of health safety, any spread of a harmful contaminant into an environment in which the contaminant should not normally be found.

CSA — *see* Canadian Standards Association.

Cultural Change — The modification over time of an organization's shared assumptions, beliefs, and values through leadership, innovation, discovery, or other means.

Culture — The shared assumptions, beliefs, and values of a group or organization.

D

Data Mining — The process of collecting, searching, and analyzing a large amount of data in a database or other record system in order to identify patterns or relationships within the data. *Also Known As* Knowledge Discovery.

Database — Computer software program that serves as an electronic filing cabinet; used to create forms, record and sort information, develop mailing lists, organize libraries, customize telephone and fax lists, and track presentation and program outcomes.

Debriefing — A gathering of information from all personnel that were involved in incident operations; in terms of incident-related stress, helps personnel process the scope of an event after a few days have passed.

Decontamination — Process of removing a hazardous foreign substance from a person, clothing, or area.

Defusing — Informal discussion with incident responders conducted after the incident has been terminated, either at the scene or after the units have returned to quarters. During the discussion commanders address possible chemical and medical exposure information, identify damaged equipment and apparatus that require immediate attention, identify unsafe operating procedures, assign information gathering responsibilities to prepare for the post-incident analysis, and reinforce the positive aspects of the incident.

District Survey — Evaluation of an entire response district to identify hazards on a broader scale than preincident planning; may also involve identifying standards of coverage needs for the district or jurisdiction.

Division — NIMS-ICS organizational level having responsibility for operations within a defined geographic area. It is composed of a number of individual units that are assigned to operate within a defined geographical area.

Documentation — Written notes, audio/videotapes, printed forms, sketches and/or photographs that form a detailed record of the scene, evidence recovered, and actions taken during the search of the crime scene.

Door Control — Fire fighting tactic intended to reduce available oxygen to a fire and create a controlled flow path in a structure for tactical ventilation, firefighter survivability, and occupant survivability.

DPPA — *see* Federal Driver's Privacy Protection Act.

Drysuit — Protective outwear worn during water-based rescue operations; provides an impermeable barrier between the wearer and the surrounding water. May be used in ice rescue or as protection from contaminants in water.

E

Emergency Management Institute (EMI) — Flagship training institution for public, volunteer, and private sector officials on emergency management including National Incident Management System (NIMS), the National Response Framework (NRF), National Disaster Recovery Framework (NDRF), and National Preparedness Goal (NPG).

Emergency Vehicle Operator's Course (EVOC) — Training that originated with the National Highway Traffic and Safety Administration in the U.S. The training certifies drivers of emergency vehicles; courses may vary depending upon response discipline and jurisdiction.

EMI — *see* Emergency Management Institute.

Employee Right-to-Know — Section of OSHA and other workers' rights laws that states that employees have a right to information about hazards that exist in their workplace; these rights extend to chemical hazards, changes to worker rights, exposure data for the facility, illness and injury reports associated with the facility, and the employee's medical records.

Engineered Construction — Structures comprised primarily of composite materials such as laminate beams or oriented strand board (OSB) and lightweight steel or wood components. Structural components are often installed prefabricated and may be secured with adhesives.

Engineering Controls — Barrier to a hazard that is built into the design of a building, apparatus or piece of equipment, for example fire doors, smoke evacuation systems, or sprinkler systems.

Ergonomic Risk Factors — Aspects of a job task that might cause biomechanical stress to a worker.

Ergonomics — Applied science of equipment and workplace design intended to maximize productivity by reducing operator fatigue and discomfort.

Evidence — Information collected and analyzed by an investigator.

EVOC — *see* Emergency Vehicle Operator's Course.

Exclusion Zones — Area usually within the hot zone which personnel should avoid regardless of their level of protective clothing and equipment.

Exposure — Contact with a hazardous material, causing biological damage, typically by swallowing, breathing, or touching (skin or eyes). Exposure may be short-term (acute exposure), of intermediate duration, or long-term (chronic exposure).

Exposure Control Program — Organizational program that provides resources, training, and equipment to firefighters in order to protect them from exposure to chemical and biological hazards in the workplace including hazardous materials, infectious diseases, and bloodborne pathogens.

F

Family Educational Rights and Privacy Act (FERPA) — U.S. Legislation that provides that an individual's school records are confidential and that information contained in those records may not be released without the individual's prior written consent.

Federal Driver's Privacy Protection Act (DPPA) — U.S. Federal law that establishes a limited list of reasons (law enforcement request, insurance underwriting, and others) under which a department of motor vehicles can distribute personal information. State laws based upon the federal statute may vary. Federal Emergency Management Agency (FEMA).

FERPA — *see* Family Educational Rights and Privacy Act.

Field Notes — Written record of an incident safety officer, or other officer's, observations during an incident; often used as the basis for a postincident analysis (PIA) report.

Final Disposition — Point in the chain of custody where a piece of evidence is determined to no longer have value as evidence; options at this point may include permanent storage, return to the owner, or authorized destruction.

Fire Department Physician — Physician designated by a fire department to treat members of the department.

Fire-Resistance Rating — Rating assigned to a material or assembly after standardized testing by an independent testing organization; identifies the amount of time a material or assembly will resist a typical fire, as measured on a standard time-temperature curve.

Fire Resistive — Ability of a structure or a material to provide a predetermined degree of fire resistance; usually according to building and fire prevention codes and given in hour ratings.

First Aid — Immediate medical care given to a patient until he or she can be transported to a medical facility.

Fitness-for-duty Evaluation — Health evaluation administered by a fire department physician to determine an individual's ability to perform fire service tasks; evaluations may be physiological or psychological in nature depending on need.

Flaring — Short-lived, high intensity fire in a small area at a wildland fire.

Flashover — Stage of a fire at which all surfaces and objects within a space have been heated to their ignition temperature, and flame breaks out almost at once over the surface of all objects in the space.

Flow Path — Composed of at least one inlet opening, one exhaust opening, and the connecting volume between the openings. The direction of the flow is determined by difference in pressure. Heat and smoke in a high pressure area will flow toward areas of lower pressure.

FOIA — *see* Freedom of Information Act.

Formative Evaluation — Evaluation of a new or revised program in order to form opinions about its effects and effectiveness as it is in the process of being developed and tested (piloted). Its purpose is to gather information to help improve the program while in progress.

Freedom of Information Act (FOIA) — Legislation used as a model for many state laws designed to make government information available to the public.

Freelancing — To operate independently of the Incident Commander's command and control.

Frequency — In terms of risk management, refers to the number of times a given risk has been the cause of an injury or illness.

Fuel-Controlled — A fire with adequate oxygen in which the heat release rate and growth rate are determined by the characteristics of the fuel, such as quantity and geometry. (NFPA® 921)

Fuel Load — The total quantity of combustible contents of a building, space, or fire area, including interior finish and trim, expressed in heat units of the equivalent weight in wood.

G

Gap Analysis — Comparison between standards/regulations/best practices and actual behaviors within the organization to determine where real world performance differs from best practice.

General Staff — Group of incident management personnel: the incident commander, operations section chief, planning section chief, logistics section chief, and finance/administrative section chief.

Geographic Information Systems (GIS) — Computer software application that relates physical features on the earth to a database to be used for mapping and analysis. The system captures, stores, analyzes, manages, and presents data that refers to or is linked to a location.

GIS — *see* Geographic Information Systems.

Global Positioning System (GPS) — System for determining position on the earth's surface by calculating the difference in time for the signal from a number of satellites to reach a receiver on the ground.

Goals-Based Evaluation — Summative assessment of whether or not a given program has met its intended goals.

GPS — *see* Global Positioning System.

Group — NIMS-ICS organizational subunit responsible for a number of individual units that are assigned to perform a particular specified function (such as ventilation, salvage, water supply, extrication, transportation, or EMS) at an incident.

Guide — Document that provides direction or guiding information; does not have the force of law but may provide the basis for what is reasonable in cases of negligence.

H

Hazard Communication Program — OSHA mandated safety program stating that an employer must clearly communicate any hazardous materials on-site using the appropriate hazardous communication signage, placards, labels, and internally generated documents.

Health and Fitness Coordinator (HFC) — Individual who, under the supervision of the fire department physician, is responsible for all physical fitness programs in the fire and emergency services organization.

Health Hazard Evaluation Program (HHE) — Program funded through the National Institute for Occupational Safety and Health (NIOSH) intended to learn whether workers are exposed to hazardous materials or harmful conditions in their workplace. Any private sector, federal, state, or local workplace (management or labor representative) or employee can request an HHE.

Health Insurance Portability and Accountability Act (HIPAA) — Congressional law established to help ensure the portability of insurance coverage as employees move from job to job. In addition to improving efficiency of the health care payment process, it also helps protect a patient's/client's privacy. The law also applies to information pertinent to juvenile firesetting situations.

Heat Release Rate (HRR) — Total amount of heat produced or released to the atmosphere from the convective-lift phase of a fire, per unit mass of fuel consumed per unit time, expressed in kilowatts or British Thermal Units (Btu).

HFC — *see* Health and Fitness Coordinator (HFC).

HHE — *see* Health Hazard Evaluation Program.

Hierarchy of Controls — Widely accepted system designed to mitigate and/or eliminate exposure to hazards (risks) in the workplace.

Hindsight Bias — Tendency during investigations to see events as more predictable than they actually were or to judge events differently based upon the outcome of the event rather than the behavior that transpired.

HIPAA — *see* Health Insurance Portability and Accountability Act.

Home Ignition Zones — Area surrounding a home during a wildfire which indicates that the home should be evaluated for protection from an encroaching wildfire.

Hot Zone — Potentially hazardous area immediately surrounding the incident site; requires appropriate protective clothing and equipment and other safety precautions for entry. Typically limited to technician-level personnel.

HRR — *see* Heat Release Rate.

Hybrid Modular Structure — Structure consisting of the elements of both modular design and panelized construction. Core modular units are assembled first and panels are added to complete the structure.

I

IAP — *see* Incident Action Plan.

IC — *see* Incident Commander.

ICP — *see* Incident Command Post.

ICS — *see* Incident Command System.

IDLH — *see* Immediately Dangerous to Life and Health.

Immediately Dangerous to Life and Health (IDLH) — Description of any atmosphere that poses an immediate hazard to life or produces immediate irreversible, debilitating effects on health; represents concentrations above which respiratory protection should be required. Expressed in parts per million (ppm) or milligrams per cubic meter (mg/m³); companion measurement to the permissible exposure limit (PEL).

Incident Action Plan (IAP) — Written or unwritten plan for the disposition of an incident; contains the overall strategic goals, tactical objectives, and support requirements for a given operational period during an incident. All incidents require an action plan.

Incident Command Post (ICP) — Location at which the Incident Commander and command staff direct, order, and control resources at an incident; may be co-located with the incident base.

Incident Command System (ICS) — Standardized approach to incident management that facilitates interaction between cooperating agencies; adaptable to incidents of any size or type.

Incident Commander (IC) — Person in charge of the incident command system and responsible for the management of all incident operations during an emergency.

Incident-Related Stress — Physical and psychological stress related to emergency response; could be associated with especially traumatic events involving fatality or serious injury; may also stem from the normal demands of emergency response over time.

Incident Safety Plan — Written document at complex incidents which outlines hazards identified during preincident surveys and size-up. It also defines planned mitigation strategies for those hazards.

Incumbent Physical Ability Test (IPAT) — Physical fitness test developed within an individual jurisdiction to assess fitness-for-duty of potential firefighter candidates.

Infection Control Officer — Designated individual from the fire or EMS division whose responsibilities include managing the infection control program and investigating exposures to infectious agents.

Infection Control Plan — Policies and procedures managed as part of an exposure control program to protect members from contracting infections in the workplace; includes training on the plan and supervision of the plan.

Infectious Agent — Biological agent that causes disease or illness to its host.

In-Service Training — Formal or informal training received while on the job; in the fire service, this training generally occurs in-house at the station rather than at formal training facilities.

IPAT — *see* Incumbent Physical Ability Test (IPAT).

Isolated Flames — Flames in the hot gas layer that indicate the gas layer is within its flammable range and has begun to ignite; often observed immediately before a flashover.

J

Job Performance Requirement (JPR) — Statement that describes a specific job task, lists the items necessary to complete the task, and defines measurable or observable outcomes and evaluation areas for the specific task.

Job Task Analysis — Process of evaluating firefighter job tasks and determining the best medical, physical fitness, safety, and health requirements and programs to help ensure that firefighters can perform those tasks safely and without injury.

JPR — *see* Job Performance Requirement.

L

Laminate Beams — Structural members created from several layers of plywood or oriented strand board (OSB).

Level A Protection — Highest level of skin, respiratory, and eye protection available, as specified by the U.S. Environmental Protection Agency (EPA); consists of positive-pressure self-contained breathing apparatus, totally encapsulating chemical-protective suit, inner and outer gloves, and chemical-resistant boots.

Level B Protection — Personal protective equipment that affords the highest level of respiratory protection, but a lesser level of skin protection; consists of positive-pressure self-contained breathing apparatus, hooded chemical-protective suit, inner and outer gloves, and chemical-resistant boots.

Level C Protection — Personal protective equipment that affords a lesser level of respiratory and skin protection than levels A or B; consists of full-face or half-mask APR, hooded chemical-resistant suit, inner and outer gloves, and chemical-resistant boots.

Level D Protection — Personal protective equipment that affords the lowest level of respiratory and skin protection; consists of coveralls, gloves, and chemical-resistant boots or shoes.

Liaison Officer — Point of contact for assisting or coordinating agencies; member of the command staff.

Light Duty Policy — Department policy that indicates certain assignments that may be given to firefighters who are recovering from injuries; the assignments should be evaluated to ensure that they will not interfere with injury rehabilitation.

Lightweight Wood Truss — Structural supports constructed of 2 x 3-inch or 2 x 4-inch members that are connected by gusset plates.

Line-of-Duty Death (LODD) — Firefighter or emergency responder death resulting from the performance of fire department duties.

Lockout/Tagout Device — Device used to secure a machine's power switches, in order to prevent accidental re-start of the machine.

LODD — *see* Line-of-Duty Death.

M

Manual on Uniform Traffic Control Devices (MUTCD) — Nationwide, U.S. standard that road managers use to install and maintain traffic control devices on public streets, highways, bikeways, and private roads that are open to public traffic.

Manufactured Home — Dwelling that is the assembly of four major components: the chassis and the floor, wall, and roof systems; although they are constructed of steel, wood, plywood, aluminum, gypsum wallboard, and other materials, they are basically frame construction. Characterized by small compartment sizes, low ceilings, and very lightweight construction throughout.

MAP — *see* Member Assistance Program.

MAYDAY — Internationally recognized distress signal.

Mean — Statistical term that refers to the "average" of a set of numerical values scores; calculated by adding all of the set of values and dividing by the total number of values.

Median — Statistical term that refers to the numerical value in a set of values that represents the middle value, or midpoint of the values when they are arranged or ranked in size (order) from high to low.

Medical Surveillance — Rehabilitation function during an incident intended to monitor responders' vital signs and incident-stress levels.

Medical Surveillance Program — Series of medical evaluations based upon medical fitness-for-duty requirements for firefighters which begin when the firefighter is hired and continue on a regular basis throughout the firefighter's career.

Member Assistance Program (MAP) — Program to help employees and their families with work or personal problems.

Mitigation — In terms of risk management, refers, generally, to the reduction of the probability, frequency, and s everity of risk.

Mode — Statistical term that refers to the numerical value that appears most frequently in a set of values.

Modular Building — Building assembled at the factory in two or more all inclusive sections. All utilities and millwork are also installed at the factory, and connected when the building is delivered to a site.

MSDs — *see* Musculoskeletal Disorders.

MSDS — *see* Safety Data Sheet.

Multigas Detector — Personal device that checks air quality against a wide range of harmful gases.

Musculoskeletal Disorders (MSDs) — **injuries** or disorders of the muscles, nerves, tendons, joints, cartilage, and supporting structures caused or increased by sudden exertion or prolonged exposure to repeated motions, force, vibration, or awkward posture.

MUTCD — *see Manual on Uniform Traffic Control Devices.*

Mutual Aid — Reciprocal assistance from one fire and emergency services agency to another during an emergency, based upon a prearranged agreement; generally made upon the request of the receiving agency.

N

National Fire Academy (NFA) — Division of the U.S. Fire Administration that provides training and certification to members of the fire and emergency services, public and private, across the U.S. Through its courses and programs, this federal agency works to enhance the ability of emergency service providers and allied professionals to deal more effectively with fire and related emergencies.

National Fire Data Center — Division of the USFA that manages the National Fire Incident Reporting System (NFIRS). Also coordinates and manages collection, analysis, and dissemination of data about fire and other emergency incidents.

National Fire Incident Reporting System (NFIRS) — National fire incident data collection system managed by the United States Fire Administration. Local fire departments forward incident data to a state coordinator. The coordinator collects statewide fire incident data and reports information to the USFA.

National Fire Protection Association® (NFPA®) — U.S. nonprofit educational and technical association devoted to protecting life and property from fire by developing fire protection standards and educating the public.

National Incident Management System (NIMS) — The U.S. mandated incident management system that defines the roles, responsibilities, and standard operating procedures used to manage emergency operations; creates a unified incident response structure for federal, state, and local governments.

National Institute For Occupational Safety And Health (NIOSH) — U.S. government agency that helps ensure workplace safety; investigates workplaces, recommends safety measures, and produces reports about on-the-job fire injuries. Operates as part of the Centers for Disease Control and Prevention, within the U.S. Department of Health and Human Services.

National Institute of Standards and Technology (NIST) — Non-regulatory U.S. agency whose mission is to advance measurement science, standards, and technology to promote innovation, enhance economic security, and improve quality of life; the fire-science division provides testing results on protective clothing and equipment and on fire behavior, spread, and rapid development.

National Response Framework (NRF) — Document that provides guidance on how communities, states, the U.S. federal government, and private-sector and nongovernmental partners conduct all-hazards emergency response.

NDT — *see* Nondestructive Testing.

Near-Miss — Occurrence that had a high likelihood to cause an injury or fatality, but the injury or fatality was avoided.

Neutral Plane — Level at a compartment opening where the difference in pressure exerted by expansion and buoyancy of hot smoke flowing out of the opening and the inward pressure of cooler, ambient temperature air flowing in through the opening is equal.

NFA — *see* National Fire Academy.

NFIRS — *see* National Fire Incident Reporting System.

NFPA® — *see* National Fire Protection Association®.

NIMS — *see* National Incident Management System.

NIOSH — *see* National Institute For Occupational Safety And Health.

NIST — *see* National Institute of Standards and Technology.

No-Entry Zones — Operational zone deemed too dangerous for personnel to enter under any conditions.

Nondestructive Testing (NDT) — Method of testing metal objects that does not subject them to stress-related damage.

Normalization of Deviation — State of a safety culture in which acting against SOP/Gs becomes normal behavior rather than an exception.

NRF — *see National Response Framework.*

O

Occupational Health and Safety Agency (OH&S) — Canadian federal agency that regulates workplace safety for some federal employees; regulation under the OH&S is typically delegated to a provincial agency.

Occupational Safety and Health Administration (OSHA) — U.S. federal agency that develops and enforces standards and regulations for occupational safety in the workplace.

Occupational Safety and Health Committee — Group of individuals appointed by the fire chief from all levels of the organization which are dedicated to resolving issues related to safety and health; conducts research, develops recommendations, and reviews matters pertaining to safety and health.

Occupational Safety and Health Program — Collectively, all departmental programs intended to reduce risks associated with emergency service as an occupation; should have clearly outlined components and identify the roles and responsibilities of the fire department and its members.

OH&S — *see* Occupational Health and Safety Agency.

Organizational Risk Management Plan — Portion of the overall risk management plan that focuses on safe work practices outside of the operational environment.

Oriented Strand Board (OSB) — Wooden structural panel formed by gluing and compressing wood strands together under pressure. This material has replaced plywood and planking in the majority of construction applications. Roof decks, walls, and subfloors are all commonly made of OSB.

OSB — *see* Oriented Strand Board.

OSHA — *see* Occupational Safety and Health Administration.

Outcomes-Based Evaluation — Summative assessment of what community or consumer benefit was gained or enhanced as a result of a particular program.

P

Panelized Home — Home assembled on site consisting of constructed panels made of foam insulation sandwiched between sheets of plywood. The panels are assembled onsite and require no framing members.

PAR — *see* Personnel Accountability Report.

Peer Fitness Trainer — Firefighter-certified fitness trainers who oversee fitness programs for firefighter recruits as directed by the Health and Fitness Coordinator (HFC).

Personal Flotation Devices (PFD) — Life jackets, vests, or other devices that provide buoyancy for the wearer. Devices must be United States Coast Guard approved Type III or V when used for rescue operations.

Personnel Accountability Report (PAR) — Roll call of all units (crews, teams, groups, companies, sectors) assigned to an incident. The supervisor of each unit reports the status of the personnel within the unit at that time, usually by radio. A PAR may be required by standard operating procedures at specific intervals during an incident, or may be requested at any time by the Incident Commander or the incident safety officer.

Personnel Accountability System — Method for identifying which emergency responders are working on an incident scene.

PFD — *see* Personal Flotation Devices.

Physical Evidence — Tangible or real objects that are related to the incident.

Physical Fitness Plan — Individualized or department-wide plan that firefighters can follow to maintain fitness-for-duty and improve their overall health and well-being.

Physical Performance Assessment — Series of exercises that are performed and evaluated before beginning a physical fitness plan in order to individualize the plan and establish a baseline for evaluating progress.

Physical Performance Requirements — Fitness level benchmarks based upon recommended industry standards which firefighters must meet to be considered fit-for-duty.

Physical Rehabilitation Program — Physical fitness training program designed for firefighters who do not meet or no longer meet the physical performance requirements associated with their job functions.

PIA — *see* Postincident Analysis.

PIO — *see* Public Information Officer.

Platform Frame Construction — A construction method in which a floor assembly creates an individual platform that rests on the foundation. Wall assemblies the height of one story are placed on this platform and a second platform rests on top of the wall unit. Each platform creates fire stops at each floor level restricting the spread of fire within the wall cavity.

Point of No Return — Point at which air in the SCBA will last only long enough to exit a hazardous atmosphere.

Postincident Analysis (PIA) — Overview and critique of an incident by members of all responding agencies, including dispatchers. Typically takes place within two weeks of the incident. In the training environment it may be used to evaluate student and instructor performance during a training evolution.

Postincident Critique — Meeting to discuss strategy and tactics, problems, SOP/G changes, or training changes derived from a postincident analysis report; usually led by a chief officer some time after a major incident.

Postmedical Surveillance — Evaluation of responders' vital signs, body temperature, and symptoms of dehydration, heat/cold stress, cardiovascular illness, stroke, or other ailment before leaving a scene to return to duty or cycling off a work shift.

Potentially Traumatic Event (PTE) — term developed by the National Fallen Firefighters Foundation (NFFF) in their programs to describe incidents that have the potential for critical incident stress.

Premedical Surveillance — Evaluation of responders' baseline vital signs before clearance to enter the hot zone; also includes hydration before beginning work at the scene.

Preincident Plan — Document, developed during preincident planning that contains the operational plan or set procedures for the safe and efficient handling of emergency situations at a given location, such as a specific building or occupancy.

Preincident Planning — Act of preparing to manage an incident at a particular location or a particular type of incident before an incident occurs.

Preincident Survey — Assessment of a facility or location made before an emergency occurs, in order to prepare for an appropriate emergency response.

Preservice Tests — Tests performed on fire pumps or aerial devices before they are placed into service; these tests consist of manufacturers' tests, certification tests, and acceptance tests.

Process-Based Evaluation — Formative assessment of how well a program functions after it has been implemented and is currently in progress; measures strengths, weaknesses, and efficiency.

PTE — *see* Potentially Traumatic Event.

Public Information Officer (PIO) — Member of the command staff responsible for interfacing with the media, public, or other agencies requiring information direct from the incident scene.

Public Records — Information, files, or other documents that a fire and emergency services organization must maintain and make available to the public upon request; federal, state/provincial, and local laws, codes, and regulations stipulate which records are or are not in the public domain.

Pyrolysis — Thermal or chemical decomposition of a solid material by heating, generally resulting in the lowered ignition temperature of the material; the pre-ignition combustion phase of burning during which heat energy is absorbed by the fuel, which in turn gives off flammable tars, pitches, and gases; often precedes combustion.

Pyrolize — Description of the process of a solid beginning to emit gases due to heat exposure.

Q

Qualitative Analysis — Examination of nonmeasurable data such as firefighters' opinions about or reactions to a certain program.

Quantitative Analysis — Means of assessment that uses numbers and statistical data to compare different materials and methods, is likely to be more sophisticated than qualitative methods, and involves formal testing; intended to discover quantifiable data.

R

Rain Roof — Second roof constructed over an existing roof.

Rapid Intervention Crew (RIC) — Two or more firefighters designated to perform firefighter rescue; they are stationed outside the hazard and must be standing by throughout the incident.

Records — Permanent accounts of past events or of actions taken by an individual, unit, or organization.

Records Management — Maintenance, review, and security of records including controlling access, ensuring that records are organized, current, and searchable, and that record keeping is compliant with applicable laws, codes, and regulations.

Records Management Liaison Officer (RMLO) — Organizational member responsible for processing requests for public records and maintaining the security of departmental or organizational records; serves as the central point of contact between the public and the organization with regards to release of records.

Regulations — Rules or directives of administrative agencies that have authorization to issue and enforce them.

Rehabilitation — Allowing firefighters or rescuers to rest, rehydrate, and recover during an incident; also refers to a station at an incident where personnel can rest, rehydrate, and recover.

Responder Rehabilitation Manager — Fire department or other responder personnel designated at an incident or training exercise to manage rehabilitation resources; duties may also include medical surveillance and ensuring that work shift schedules are followed.

Retroreflective Trim — Surfaces such as those used on road signs, emergency vehicle markings, or safety vests which are designed to reflect light along multiple planes at once, giving the surface the appearance of illumination.

RIC — *see* Rapid Intervention Crew.

Risk Avoidance — Method of controlling a risk in which an identified risk is completely removed as a possible hazard; often impractical in the fire and emergency services.

Risk Management Plan — Written plan that identifies and analyzes the exposure to hazards, selects appropriate risk management techniques to handle exposures, implements those techniques, and monitors the results.

Risk Transfer — Method of controlling risk in which the individual who should assume the risk instead transfers or shares the risk with others.

RMLO — *see* Records Management Liaison Officer.

Rollover — Condition in which the unburned fire gases that have accumulated at the top of a compartment ignite and flames propagate through the hot-gas layer or across the ceiling. These superheated gases are pushed, under pressure, away from the fire area and into uninvolved areas where they mix with oxygen. When their flammable range is reached and additional oxygen is supplied by opening doors and/or applying fog streams, they ignite and a fire front develops, expanding very rapidly in a rolling action across the ceiling.

Root Cause — The cultural and attitudinal reasons that led to the circumstances or behavior surrounding an accident, injury, fatality, illness, exposure, or near-miss.

Root Cause Analysis — Investigative tool used to go beyond the immediate facts to discover what cultural attitudes or behaviors contributed to an accident, injury, fatality, illness, exposure, or near-miss.

S

Safety Audit — Comprehensive compliance review of all organizational components that could contribute to firefighter safety including policies, procedures, practices, inspection reports, and firefighter behaviors.

Safety Data Sheet (SDS) — Form provided by chemical manufacturers, distributors, and importers; contains information about chemical composition, physical and chemical properties, health and safety hazards, emergency response procedures, and waste disposal procedures. *Also known as* Material Safety Data Sheet (MSDS).

Safety Officer — Member of the IMS command staff responsible to the incident commander for monitoring and assessing hazardous and unsafe conditions and developing measures for assessing personnel safety on an incident.

SDS — *see* Safety Data Sheet

Search Warrant — Written order, in the name of the People, State, Province, Territory, or Commonwealth, signed by a magistrate, that commands a peace officer to search for personal property or other evidence and return it to the magistrate.

Service Test — Series of tests performed on apparatus and equipment in order to ensure operational readiness of the unit; should be performed at least yearly, or whenever a piece of apparatus or equipment has undergone extensive repair.

Severity — In terms of risk management, refers to the degree of negative consequences that could result from any given risk.

Shoring — General term used for lengths of timber, screw jacks, hydraulic and pneumatic jacks, and other devices that can be used as temporary support for formwork or structural components or used to hold sheeting against trench walls. Individual supports are called shores, cross braces, and struts. Commonly used in conjunction with Cribbing.

Site Safety Plan — Facility plan that identifies potential hazards and risks to employees and the public at businesses that meet certain hazardous criteria such as hazardous waste storage facilities.

Smoke Explosion — Form of fire gas ignition; the ignition of accumulated flammable products of combustion and air that are within their flammable range.

Span of Control — Maximum number of subordinates that that one individual can effectively supervise; ranges from three to seven individuals or functions, with five generally established as optimum.

Stabilization — Stage of an incident when the immediate problem or emergency has been controlled, contained, or extinguished.

Standard — A set of principles, protocols, or procedures that explain how to do something or provide a set of minimum standards to be followed. Adhering to a standard is not required by law, although standards may be incorporated in codes, which are legally enforceable.

Standards Council of Canada — Federal Crown corporation in Canada that establishes a variety of standards for accepted work practices, technical requirements, and specific terminologies for products, services, and systems. Cooperates with the Canadian Standards Association (CSA) to approve their published standards.

Statute — Federal or state/provincial legislative act that becomes law; prescribes conduct, defines crimes, and promotes public good and welfare. *Also known as* Statutory Law.

Summative Evaluation — Evaluation of a program after all of its various components have been implemented and established; the evaluation is intended to measure achievement of intended goals and the effect of the program on the public (outcomes).

Surface-To-Mass Ratio — Ratio of the surface area of the fuel to the mass of the fuel.

T

Tactical Worksheet — Document that the IC may use on the fireground to track units and record field notes during an incident; could evolve into a written IAP if an incident escalates in size or complexity.

Technical Safety Officer (TSO) — Individual assigned to function as the safety officer at technical rescue or hazardous materials incidents; assigned at the request of an incident safety officer to ensure the proper level of experience based upon incident type and conditions.

Temporary Traffic Control Devices — Cones, flags, lighting, and other devices set up at a vehicle incident to temporarily divert traffic and create a safe work zone.

Thermal Imager — Electronic device that forms images using infrared radiation. *Also known as* Thermal Imaging Camera.

Thermal Layering (of Gases) — Outcome of combustion in a confined space in which gases tend to form into layers, according to temperature, with the hottest gases found at the ceiling and the coolest gases at floor level.

Threat Zone — Operational zone designation that indicates an active shooter or explosion hazard.

Titers — Measurement of a concentration of a substance in a solution; in the case of immunizations, a measurement of the concentration of certain antibodies in the blood stream to determine the need for new inoculations against diseases such as hepatitis or tetanus.

Traffic Control Zone — Operational zone established on or near a roadway for the rerouting of traffic and protection of civilians and responders; may include a hot, warm, and cold zone depending on the incident.

Traffic Preemption Device — Wireless system (coded emitter or GPS activated) on apparatus that can communicate with traffic signals to request right-of-way at intersections for emergency vehicles.

TSO — *see* Technical Safety Officer.

Type I Construction — Construction type in which structural members, including walls, columns, beam, floors, and roofs, are made of noncombustible or limited combustible materials and have a specified degree of fire resistance.

Type II Construction — Construction type that is similar to Type I except that the degree of fire resistance is lower.

Type III Construction — Construction type in which exterior walls and structural members are made of noncombustible or limited combustible materials, but interior structural members, including walls, columns, beams, floors, and roofs, are completely or partially constructed of wood.

Type IV Construction — Heavy timber construction in which interior and exterior walls and their associated structural members are made of noncombustible or limited combustible material; interior structural framing consists of heavy timber with minimum dimensions larger than those used in Type III construction.

Type V Construction — Construction type in which exterior walls, bearing walls, floors, roofs, and supports are made completely or partially of wood or other approved materials of smaller dimensions than those used in Type IV construction.

U

UL — *see* Underwriters' Laboratories, Inc.

Underwriters' Laboratories, Inc. (UL) — Independent fire research and testing laboratory that certifies equipment and materials, which can be approved only for the specific use for which it is tested.

Unity of Command — Organizational principle in which workers report to only one supervisor in order to eliminate conflicting orders.

Unplanned Ventilation — Any ventilation that occurs outside of planned tactics such as ventilation from failed structural components, wind conditions, or firefighters acting outside of assigned tactics.

U.S. Fire Administration (USFA) — U.S. agency whose aim is to reduce the nation's fire deaths. Promotes better fire prevention and control, supports existing programs of research, training, and education, and encourages new programs sponsored by state and local governments. Administers an extensive fire data and analysis program and co-administers a program concerned with firefighter health and safety. USFA is a division of the Federal Emergency Management Agency (FEMA), which itself is a division of the Department of Homeland Security (DHS). *Formerly known as* National Fire Prevention and Control Administration (NFPCA).

USFA — *see* U.S. Fire Administration.

V

Ventilation-Controlled — Fire with limited ventilation in which the heat release rate or growth is limited by the amount of oxygen available to the fire. (NFPA® 921)

W

Warm Zone — Area between the hot and cold zones that usually contains the decontamination corridor; typically requires a lesser degree of personal protective equipment than the Hot Zone.

Weapon of Mass Destruction (WMD) — Any weapon or device that is intended or has the capability to cause death or serious bodily injury to a significant number of people through the release, dissemination, or impact of toxic or poisonous chemicals or their precursors, a disease organism, or radiation or radioactivity; may include chemical, biological, radiological, nuclear, or explosive (CBRNE) type weapons.

Wellness Program — Ongoing program that provides information, education, and counselling to fire service members on topics such as good nutrition, tobacco cessation, injury prevention, and substance abuse.

Wetsuit — Protective outwear worn during water-based rescue operations; water permeable: allows water between the garment and the rescuer's skin to provide thermal insulation.

Index

Weapons and violence affecting operations, 205
Weather conditions
    affecting operations, 205
    flooding, 464
    hail, 464
    hazards, 462–464
    helicopter landing zones and, 592
    humidity, 463
    ice, 463, 610
    identifying imminent threats, 555
    for incident safety plan, 562–563
    lightning, 463
    rain, 463
    risk levels and, 604
    scene condition, determination of, 606
    snow, 463
    storms, 463–464
    suspending or terminating operations, 610
    visibility reducing situations, 464
    wildland fire behavior and, 533, 534
    wind. *See* Wind
Weather roof, 513–514
Wellness programs
    defined, 246
    health and fitness coordinator, 249
    health fitness instructor training program, 249
    injury and illness prevention, 250–253
    injury and illness rehabilitation, 253
    monetary cost of firefighter injuries and fatalities, 252
    NFPA® standard for, 48
    nutrition information, 247–249
    peer fitness trainers, 249
    program coordination, 227
    safety and health program, 227
    tobacco policy and cessation information, 250, 251
Wellness-Fitness Initiative (WFI), 52
Wetsuit, 441
WFI (Wellness-Fitness Initiative), 52
Whirlpool Corporation v. Marshall, 31–32
Wide canyon, topographical feature, 533
Wildland urban interface (WUI), 531–534
    control zones, 583
    defined, 531
    fire apparatus standards, 73, 367–368
    fire growth, predicting, 534
    National Wildfire Coordinating Group *red card*, 531
    risk management plan, 531
    suspending or terminating operations, 610
    topography effects, 532–533
    types of fuels, 532
    weather and wind effects, 533
Williams-Steiger Occupational Safety and Health Act, 35
Wind
    apparatus positioning and, 541, 542
    effect on fire and emergency services, 463
    wildland fire behavior and, 533, 534
    wind driven fires, 533
    wind pressure ventilation, 489, 490
Windows as access challenge, 518
Witness interviews, 630–631
WMD. *See* Weapon of mass destruction (WMD)
Wood frame construction, 503

Work Performance Evaluation (WPE), 238
Work practice safety, 257–258, 265
Work safety zone, 448, 450
Work shifts
    as environmental hazard during operations, 443
    extended shift hazards, 466
Worker's Compensation Board (WCB), 41
Workplace Safety and Health, 41
Workplace Safety and Insurance Board (WSIB), 41
WPE (Work Performance Evaluation), 238
WSIB (Workplace Safety and Insurance Board), 41
WUI. *See* Wildland urban interface (WUI)

X
X-rays, 434

Z
Zones. *See* Operational zones

Indexed by Nancy Kopper

NOTE:

NOTE: